GENERAL ELECTRICAL ENGINEERING

A COMPREHENSIVE INTRODUCTION FOR STUDENTS, APPRENTICES AND ALL CONNECTED WITH THE ELECTRICAL ENGINEERING INDUSTRY

Edited by

PHILIP KEMP, M.Sc. (Tech.), M.I.E.E., A.I.Mech.E.

Head of The School of Engineering,
The Polytechnic, Regent Street, London

ODHAMS PRESS LIMITED, LONG ACRE, LONDON, W.C.2

ENGINEERS TESTING SWITCHGEAR

Testing electrical equipment is one of the most highly skilled operations in electrical engineering. The dynamo in the foreground provides electricity for the Metrovick equipment (shown above) which is subjected to loads far in excess of those which it will receive under normal working conditions.

CONTENTS

ASSEMBLING ELECTRICAL EQUIPMENT

Fig. 1. Electric train control gear being assembled in a B.T.H. factory. Each unit comprises the wiring of several complicated circuits, and it is most important to have a sound knowledge of the theory of electricity in order to check the connections and make the necessary final adjustments.

CHAPTER 1

ELECTRICITY EXPLAINED

Electricity and Magnetism. Electron Theory. Direct Currents Explained. Electro-Magnetism. Fleming's Right-Hand Rule. Three-Wire Distribution System. Alternating Current Theory. E.M.F. and Current. Frequency. Electrical Degrees. Voltage and Current. Inductance. Capacitance. Resistance. Condensers in Series and Parallel. Reactance. Power Factor. Polyphase Systems. Three-Phase System.

In introducing the subject of electrical science it may be of advantage to consider first the principal effects which result from what is termed the "flow" of an electric current, and these effects may be set down in the following order :—

Heating. If the plug that is attached to the flexible lead of an electric radiator is fitted into a suitable socket at a supply point, an electric current from the supply point will flow along one of the wires of the lead, through the radiator element, and back along the other wire of the lead to the electric supply point. Due to the fact that the element is constructed of wire suitable for that particular purpose, the flow of current through the element causes it to become red hot, thus producing the heating effect. Closing a switch forming part of a lighting system will result in an electric current flowing along the wires and through the lamp, causing the filament to become incandescent. This results in the emission of light owing to the high temperature reached. There is no essential difference between an electric lamp and a tubular heating element.

Magnetic Effect. The flow of an electric current through a length of insulated wire wound in the form of a coil, gives rise to effects similar to those exhibited by permanent magnets (see Magnetism). This effect makes possible the design of electric generators and motors.

Chemical. This effect is due to the passage of electric currents through certain substances, important examples being silver and chromium plating, primary batteries and accumulators.

In a large number of modern domestic kitchens one finds an electric cooker, a

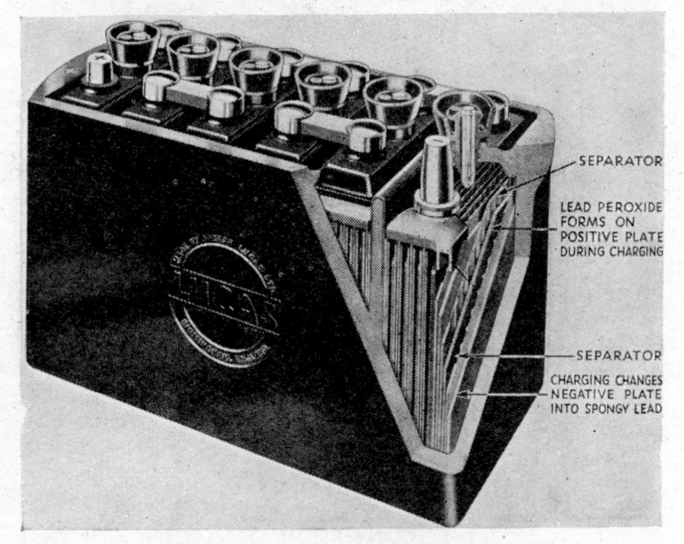

APPLICATION OF CHEMICAL EFFECT

Fig. 2. Practical application of the chemical (or electrolytic) effect produced by the flow of an electric current through certain chemical solutions is to be seen in the ordinary accumulator or secondary battery.

radiator and electric lighting, all these being examples of the application of the heating or thermal effect of electricity. It is interesting to note that there is no fundamental difference between their principles of operation. In Fig. 2 is seen a practical use of the chemical or electrolytic action of a flow of electrical current. Figs. 3A and 3B illustrate well contrasted examples of the magnetic effect. All these effects have one common feature, the apparatus to be used for producing any given effect must form part of what is known as the "electric circuit", and, as the conditions necessary to cause water to flow along a pipe are in many respects similar to those existing in an electric circuit, this simple analogy will be first considered.

A reasonably clear understanding of the conditions necessary to produce a flow of electric current, may be obtained by considering the flow of water round the pipe circuit shown in Fig. 4, which represents a simple layout for a garden fountain.

The above arrangement consists of a pond dug in the garden, into which two pipes are fitted. One, terminated with a rose spray, is just above the level of the top of the pond, the other, terminating in the bottom of the pond, being connected in some remote position to a pump, which is driven by some external means. When the pond has been filled with water, the pipe B will be filled back to the pump, water will not flow up pipe A until a difference of pressure exists between the end connected to the pump and the spray end; the pump end must be at a higher pressure. The difference in pressure is supplied by the pump when it is

CONVERSION OF ELECTRICAL POWER

Fig. 3a. Magnetic effect caused by the flow of an electric current is shown in this illustration of an electro-magnetic crane. Electro-magnetism is the important factor in the conversion of electrical power into mechanical power and is illustrated in this instance by the motor which propels the crane and also operates the lifting gear. (Another example is illustrated in Fig. 3b.)

MODERN INDUCTION MOTOR

Fig. 3b. Very high efficiency of conversion of electric to mechanical power is given by the modern induction motor. The illustration shows the salient features; by means of the magnetic effect caused by an electric current flowing through the stator, the rotor is set in motion. There is not necessarily any direct electrical connection to the rotor winding. The rotation of the rotor is made possible by the movements of the electro-magnetic fields which are set up in the stator.

operating, and is usually expressed in "pounds per square inch". The small holes in the rose spray offer opposition or resistance to the water, so that the greater the pressure supplied by the pump, the more powerful will be the streams of water issuing from the spray. The streams of water fall back again into the pond keeping the level of the water practically constant.

In effect, therefore, there is a continuous path or circuit for the water, consisting of the pump, pipes, pond and spray, so that, actually, water is being drawn in at the low pressure side of the pump, shown by a minus sign, from the pond, forced along pipe A from the high pressure side of the pump, shown with a plus sign, to the spray, and then returning to the pond in streams from the spray. The pipes also offer some resistance to the flow of water; therefore, the pump must supply additional pressure to overcome this resistance. The larger the size or bore of the pipes the less the resistance offered.

Considering the quantity of water which flows round the complete circuit, that could be expressed as so many "gallons", but, if the number of gallons that pass a certain point in the circuit in one second is measured that would be known as the "rate of flow" and is expressed in "gallons per second". Therefore, the pump must be capable of supplying enough pressure to maintain a definite rate of flow against all the resistance offered by the circuit.

ELECTRIC CIRCUIT

As stated previously, the conditions existing in the electric circuit are in many respects similar to those in the water circuit. Fig. 5A shows a simple electric circuit, which is represented diagrammatically in Fig. 5B.

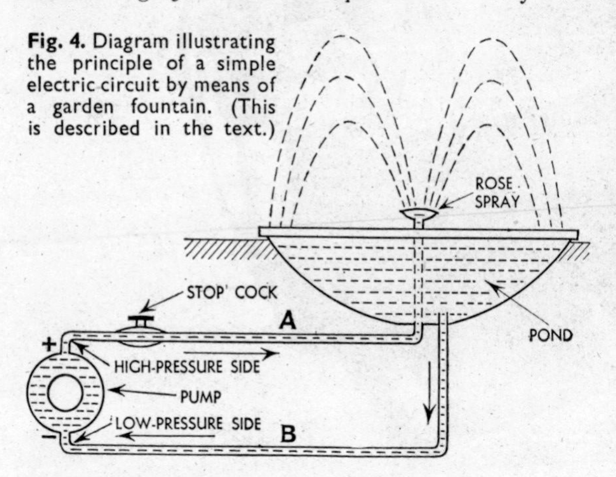

Fig. 4. Diagram illustrating the principle of a simple electric circuit by means of a garden fountain. (This is described in the text.)

A difference of pressure must be provided, but, in this case, it is a difference of electrical pressure, or "electromotive force", which is denoted by the abbreviation "e.m.f.", the unit of e.m.f. being the "volt". Generators of e.m.f. are usually primary cells or batteries, or electric generators. In Fig. 5B a four cell battery has been used.

The e.m.f. of a single cell of the type used is about two volts (see sections on Primary Cells and Accumulators, Chapter 2). With a battery of four cells the individual cells are joined together in the following way, the high pressure or positive terminal, marked with a plus sign, of the first cell is connected to the low pressure or negative terminal, marked with a minus sign, of the next cell, then the positive of the second to the negative of the third, and the positive of the third to the negative of the fourth. Therefore, between the positive of the fourth cell and the negative of the first cell the e.m.f. will be equal to the sum of the e.m.f's. of the individual cells, this method of connecting the cells being known as a series method.

Insulated copper wires are used for the path or circuit for the electric current, and, interposed in the circuit is the particular piece of apparatus to develop any one of the effects previously mentioned. In this case a wire-wound variable resistance or "rheostat" is used. whose value may be varied between minimum and maximum values by means of the sliding contact. If the resistance has no sliding contact it will have a fixed value, and is then known as a "resistor". The switch shown in the diagram is used to open and close the circuit and is, of course, analogous to the stop-cock in the water circuit.

If the switch is closed a current will flow round the circuit, in the direction shown by the arrows in the diagram, and the value of the current will depend upon the e.m.f. available and the resistance the complete circuit offers.

OHM'S LAW

The total resistance of the circuit is made up of the rheostat, the internal resistance of the cells (see Primary Cells), and the resistance of the conducting wires. The larger the cross sectional area of the wires, which is analogous to the bore of the water pipe, the less their resistance and the greater is the current. This may be expressed as follows:—

Current = e.m.f./total resistance.

In the water circuit the quantity was referred to as so many gallons, and the rate of flow as gallons per second, but in the electric circuit the quantity of

SIMPLE ELECTRIC CIRCUIT

Fig. 5a. Battery of three cells connected through a switch and ammeter to a variable resistance. Current flow is measured by the ammeter and the voltage of the battery by the voltmeter.

electricity is measured in "coulombs", and the rate of flow in "coulombs per second". Unit rate of flow or unit "current" is "one coulomb per second" and is termed the "ampere", the unit of resistance is the "ohm". Therefore, the words may now be substituted by units:—

$$\text{Current (Amperes)} = \frac{\text{E.M.F. (Volts).}}{\text{Resistance (Ohms)}}$$

Symbols are used for these units as follows: I is used to express current in amperes, E the e.m.f. in volts, and R the resistance in ohms. The previous expression now becomes $I = E/R$, and if two of the values be known, by simple transposition of the formula, the other one may be found. As there are three quantities, the formula may be put into the following forms: $I=E/R$, $E=IR$, $R=E/I$.

This relationship between I,E, and R is of the utmost importance. It is known as "Ohm's law". In Fig. 5B, instruments are shown (connected in a circuit) for measuring amperes and volts. The instrument for measuring amperes is known as an "ammeter", marked A, and that for measuring volts a "voltmeter" and this is marked V.

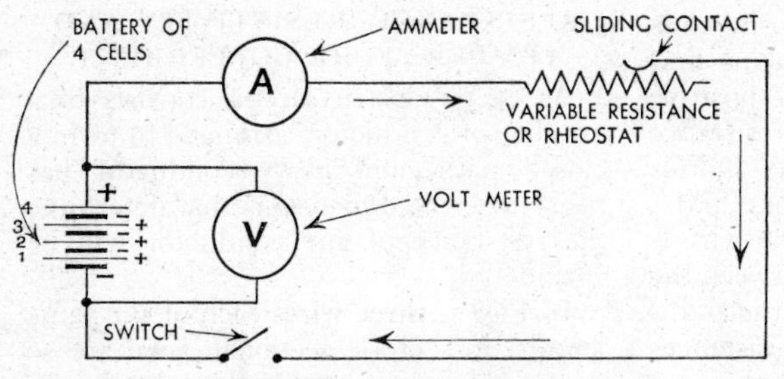

THEORETICAL DIAGRAM

Fig. 5b. Diagrammatic layout of the simple electric circuit shown in Fig. 5a, though in this case a 4-cell battery is illustrated and the switch is depicted in the open position.

Fig. 6 is a circuit which consists of three fixed resistors, R_1, R_2, and R_3, with resistance values of 1, 2, and 3 ohms respectively, connected to a battery of eight cells having a total e.m.f. of 16 volts and internal resistance of 1 ohm, with connecting wires whose total resistance is 1 ohm.

The terms "electromotive force", "potential difference", and "potential" are of importance, and, by the application of "Ohm's law" to the above circuit, definitions for the terms may be found. Applying the expression, current = e.m.f./total resistance, the value of the current will be, $I = \frac{16}{(1+\frac{1}{4}+1+2+3+\frac{3}{4})}$ $= \frac{16}{8} = 2$ amperes.

A current of 2 amperes will flow round the circuit in the direction shown, and

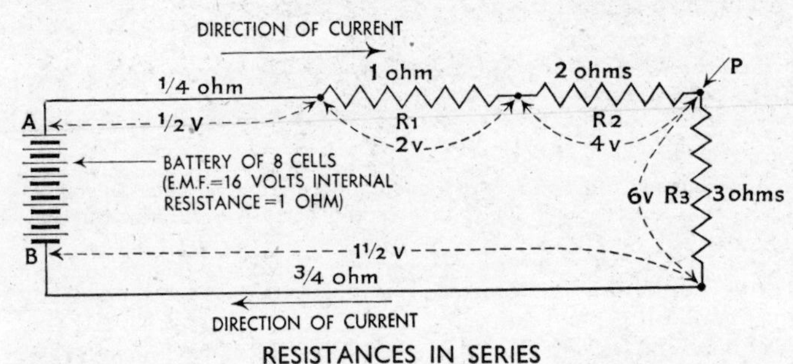

RESISTANCES IN SERIES

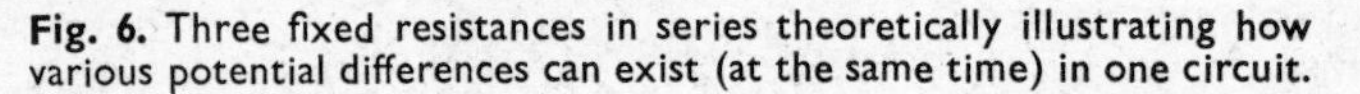

Fig. 6. Three fixed resistances in series theoretically illustrating how various potential differences can exist (at the same time) in one circuit.

starting from the positive terminal of the battery, if Ohm's law is applied to each individual part of the circuit in the form $V = IR$, it will be found that there is a gradual fall in voltage round the circuit. In other words, a "potential difference" is said to exist between the opposite ends of each individual resistance. Taking first the connecting wire between the positive terminal and R_1, the wire has a resistance of $\frac{1}{4}$ ohm. Therefore, applying Ohm's law the potential difference or "p.d." between the opposite ends of the wire is $\frac{1}{4} \times 2 = \frac{1}{2}$ volt, also, the p.d. between the ends of R_1 is $1 \times 2 = 2$ volts, the p.d.'s between the ends of the other resistances are shown in the diagram and if they are added together they will be found to equal the e.m.f.

From the above, potential difference and electromotive force may be defined as follows, the p.d. in volts existing between any two points in a circuit is given by the product of the current flowing and the resistance between the points, and the e.m.f. in volts is the total force acting in the circuit, being the sum of the individual p.d.'s of the various parts of the circuit.

To obtain a definition for potential consider the point P. Between A and P there is a p.d. of $6\frac{1}{2}$ volts, but as the current is flowing from A to P, A is said to have a positive potential of $6\frac{1}{2}$ volts to P, and by similar reasoning B will have a negative potential of $7\frac{1}{2}$ volts to P. Potential is a purely relative value and is meant to express the p.d. between some point in the circuit and a common reference point. This point is usually intended to have zero potential.

In electrical engineering the surface of the earth is considered to be at zero potential. It is usual to connect some point in the circuit to "earth", when the potential of any other point in the circuit can be stated with reference to the "earthed" point. As the volt is the unit of both e.m.f. and p.d., when using symbols the e.m.f. is referred to as E, and the p.d. as V.

RESISTANCE, RESISTIVITY AND TEMPERATURE COEFFICIENT

As every electric circuit consists of a number of conductors arranged to form a closed path, and every conductor has resistance, the dimensions that determine the resistance of any conductor will be considered.

In Fig. 7, three wires each of the same length and cross sectional area are so arranged that one end of each wire is attached to the common point C, the ends A, B, and C being left free. If the lead P is connected to point A the resistance of the copper wire may be determined by taking readings of current and p.d. and applying Ohm's law. If P is moved to A_1, which is in the centre of the wire, and the resistance again determined, it will be found to be one-half of that between C and A, and repeating the experiment with the iron and Eureka wires will give a similar result, proving that the greater the length of the conductor the greater the resistance.

Comparing the resistances of the three wires, it will be found that the iron has about seven times, and the Eureka thirty times the resistance of the copper wire, showing that resistance is dependent upon the material of which the conductor is made. Replacing the wires by three others of the same length but larger cross sectional area will result in smaller values of resistance in each case, but the ratio of the resistances of iron and Eureka wires to the copper wire will still be exactly as in the first case.

From the results it will readily be seen that the resistance of a conductor is directly dependent upon its length and the material of which it is made, and varies inversely with its cross sectional area.

The relationship between resistance and material must be in some form convenient for calculation purposes, and is determined from a conductor in the form of a cube, with each side either one inch or one centimetre (see Fig. 8). A known current is passed and the p.d. between the opposite faces of the cube measured. The value of the resistance between the opposite faces of the cube is then calculated. The resistance of the cube is known as the "specific resistance" or "resistivity" of the particular material, and is used in the calculation of the resistance of any conductor made of that material. The "resistivity" is denoted by the Greek letter "ρ", pronounced "rho".

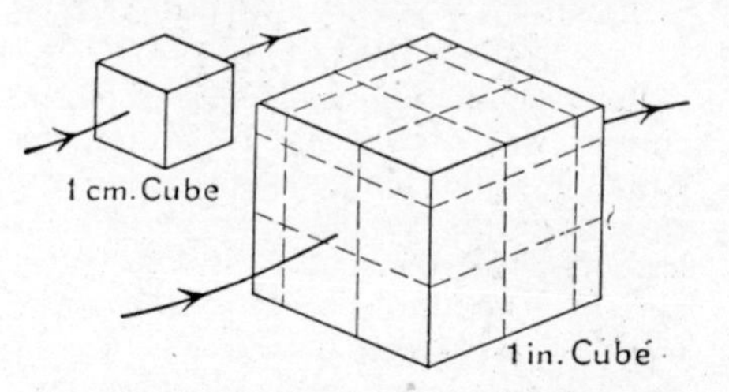

Fig. 8. Metal cubes showing relationship between resistance and material (see text).

The resistance of a conductor may be stated as follows :—

$$\text{Resistance} = \text{resistivity} \times \frac{\text{length of conductor}}{\text{Cross sectional area}}$$

or in symbols, $R = \frac{\rho \times L}{A}$, where ρ is the resistivity, L and A being the length of the conductor and the area of cross section respectively. Since, ρ for an inch cube is only $\frac{1}{2 \cdot 54}$ that of a one centimetre cube, it is important when making calculations that ρ, L and A are all in the same units.

If the resistance of a conductor be determined at some known temperature, and it then carries current for some definite time, it will be found that the temperature has increased, and if the resistance again be measured this also will be found to have increased. Assuming uniform temperature rise and increase in resistance, the increase in resistance per ohm for each degree of temperature rise, which is known as the "temperature coefficient"

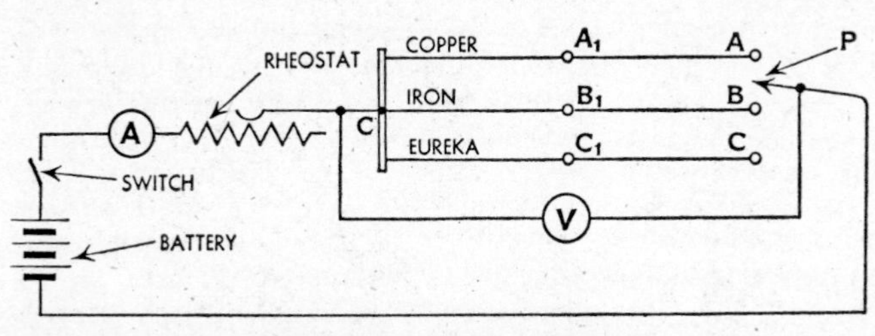

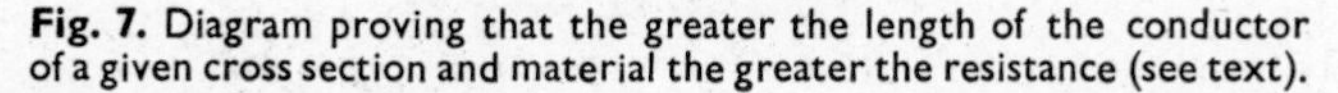

Fig. 7. Diagram proving that the greater the length of the conductor of a given cross section and material the greater the resistance (see text).

of the material, may be found. The resistivity of any material depends upon temperature, and a definite temperature is stated in any table giving resistivities of different materials.

RESISTANCES IN SERIES AND PARALLEL

Referring to Fig. 6, the value of the current was calculated by dividing the e.m.f. by the total resistance in the circuit, and as the individual resistances are joined together end to end the same current flows through each. An arrangement of resistances joined together in this fashion is said to be connected in "series". Therefore, by reference to the circuit and the expression for the current, the following rule must obtain, "the total resistance of a number of resistances connected in series is the sum of the individual resistances," or, if R is the single resistance which when substituted for all the individual resistances would have the same effect in the circuit, then

$$R = R_1 + R_2 + R_3 + \text{etc.}$$

An alternative method of connecting the same resistances is shown in Fig. 9. In this circuit the resistances are so arranged that the individual ends are

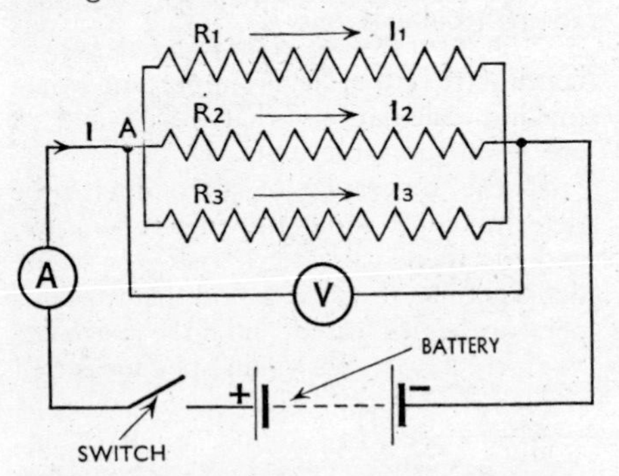

Fig. 9. Alternative method of connecting the resistances shown in Fig. 6. They are now connected in parallel instead of being in series.

joined together to form a common connection at each end. They are then said to be connected in "parallel", and in this case the same p.d. exists between the opposite ends of each resistance. Assuming the total current (I) from the battery flows in the direction shown, at point A, it will divide between the three alternative paths, and the sum of the currents in the separate resistances will be equal to the total current.

If the three resistances are substituted by a single resistance (R) which will have the same effect in the circuit as the joint effect of the three, this single resistance is known as the joint resistance, and its value by Ohm's law given by:—

Joint resistance $(R) = V/I$, or $I = V/R$; therefore, if I_1, I_2 and I_3, be the currents flowing through R_1, R_2 and R_3 respectively, then the total current (I) as stated will be equal to the sum of the individual currents, or, $I = I_1 + I_2 + I_3$,

$$\text{therefore, } \frac{V}{R} = \frac{V}{R_1} + \frac{V}{R_2} + \frac{V}{R_3}$$

$$\frac{1}{R} = \frac{1}{R_1} + \frac{1}{R_2} + \frac{1}{R_3}$$

$$R = \frac{1}{\frac{1}{R_1} + \frac{1}{R_2} + \frac{1}{R_3}}$$

This is known as a reciprocal law, as $1/R$, $1/R_1$, etc., are said to be reciprocals of R, R_1, etc. Also, the value of the joint resistance is less than that of the smallest individual resistance. The above expression for joint resistance may be stated as follows, "the reciprocal of the joint resistance of any number of resistances connected in parallel is equal to the sum of the reciprocals of the individual resistances."

ENERGY AND POWER

Consider the electric radiator circuit in Fig. 10. The radiator has two elements each with a resistance of 40 ohms, and if one of these elements is switched on, by applying Ohm's law, it will be found that a current of 5 amperes will flow. This will result in the wire of which the element is made becoming red hot.

If the radiator is switched on for one hour the current of 5 amperes will flow, and during that time the potential difference of 200 volts will be required to maintain the current. Electrical energy is said to be expended in the circuit, the energy expended being the product of volts, amperes and time in seconds, or, put into symbols, VI × t seconds. The unit of energy is the "joule"; therefore, in this circuit the energy expended is 200 × 5 × 3600 = 3,600,000 joules.

The rate at which the energy is expended is known as the "power", and is energy divided by time, unit power being one joule per second and is termed the "watt". Expressing this statement in symbols, Power (watts) =

$$\frac{\text{Volts} \times \text{Amperes} \times \text{time (secs.)}}{\text{time (secs.)}} =$$

Volts × Amperes, = VI. The power input to the radiator is 200 × 5 = 1,000 watts. By using the forms of Ohm's law, V = IR, and I = V/R, and substituting for V and I respectively in the expression, Watts = VI, the following expressions for power are obtained, Watts = I^2R = V^2/R.

For practical purposes the watt is too small, so that a larger unit is used equal to 1,000 watts or kilowatt (kW). From this larger unit of power a larger unit of energy is derived, by using the kilowatt and the hour instead of the second, which is known as the kilowatt hour (kWh). This is the unit upon which the electricity supply authorities base their tariffs and is referred to as the Board of Trade Unit or (B.O.T.) unit.

HEAT ENERGY

All the energy expended in the radiator element is actually converted into heat energy. It becomes necessary, therefore, to convert from joules to heat units. The unit of heat (upon which calculations are based), is the "gram calorie" usually referred to as the "calorie", and is the amount of heat required to raise one gram of water by one degree Centigrade. It can be proved experimentally that approximately 4·19 joules are equal to 1 calorie. The radiator illustrated in Fig. 10 was taking a power of 1kW.

ONE KILOWATT RADIATOR CIRCUIT

Fig. 10. Measurements of the current flow by means of an ammeter and of the voltage with a voltmeter enable the power input to be calculated. In the above example, the ammeter reads 5 amperes and the voltmeter 200 volts; thus the power is 1,000 watts or 1 kilowatt.

and converts 1 B.O.T. unit into heat energy per hour. This is presuming, of course, that, as before, only the one element is switched on.

MAGNETISM

Certain types of iron ore are known to possess the property of attracting very small pieces of iron. This property is known as "Magnetism", and, as the ore possesses magnetism in its natural state, it is called a natural magnet. A piece of iron or steel may be made into a magnet, or be "magnetised", when it will exhibit the property of attracting unmagnetised pieces of iron or steel in a very pronounced way; in fact, if a magnet is dipped into iron filings, on removal, clusters of filings will be found clinging to the magnet, particularly at the ends where the magnetic force is most intense, and which are termed "magnetic poles".

From the foregoing, magnets may be divided into two classes, natural and artificial. Artificial magnets may be made to any desired dimensions and magnetic strength, and with these the electrical engineer is chiefly concerned. Now it is important to remember that magnets always tend to lose their magnetism. An iron magnet will become demagnetised very quickly; on the other hand a magnet made of hard steel will retain its magnetism for a very long time. Permanent magnets are always made of special hard steels, and may be made into a variety of shapes, very common types being the straight bar and horseshoe magnets, Fig. 11a. The horseshoe type magnet is fitted with a keeper to help retain its magnetism.

Fig. 11b. Diagram showing effect of rupture of bar magnet giving rise to two separate poles.

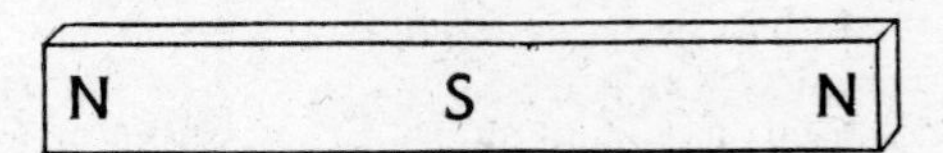

Fig. 11c. Bar magnet with three poles showing the position of the consequent (S) pole.

Fig. 11d. Showing effect of rupture of bar magnet with consequent (S) pole.

Fig. 11a. Bar types of magnets (right) and a horseshoe type fitted with a keeper (left).

MAGNETIC POLARITY

If a straight bar magnet of the type shown in Fig. 11a be suspended so that it is free to rotate in a horizontal plane, and one of its ends be marked to enable it to be easily distinguished, it will be found to take up a very definite position, with one end pointing to the earth's north pole and the other end to the south pole, and no matter how many times the experiment be repeated, the same end will always point to the north pole. This is the principle by which a compass operates. Its needle is a small magnet.

The end or pole which points to the north is called the "north seeking pole", and the pole which points to the south the "south seeking pole". These are usually marked on the magnet as N and S respectively, the terms north and south poles being known as the magnetic polarity of the particular poles of the magnet.

LAWS OF MAGNETIC ATTRACTION AND REPULSION

It has been stated that a permanent magnet will attract pieces of unmagnetised iron and steel. If a piece of unmagnetised iron be held near the north pole of the suspended magnet referred to in the last paragraph, it will be found that the north pole will move towards the iron, the same effect being observed if the iron is held near the south pole. In other words both poles will attract the iron.

Repeating the experiment, but with another bar magnet instead of the unmagnetised iron, will give different results. If the north pole of the second magnet is held near the north pole of the suspended magnet, it will be found that the north pole of the suspended magnet will move away from the second magnet, or a force of "repulsion" is said to exist between the two north poles. The same result will obtain between the two south poles. Holding a south pole near to a north pole will result in "attraction" between the two unlike poles.

These results may be summed up by saying that "like poles repel" and "unlike poles attract" each other, and from these results it will be seen that the only sure test to decide whether a piece of steel is a magnet or otherwise is one of repulsion. This can be tested in the manner shown in Fig. 12.

EFFECTS OF BREAKING A MAGNET

If the bar magnet in Fig. 11a be broken at the centre it will give rise to two separate magnets having polarities as shown in Fig. 11b. A magnet cannot be made with one pole only but may have any number greater than one. Fig. 11c shows a magnet with three poles, a north pole at either end and a south pole at the centre. If the magnet be broken at the middle pole it will result in two magnets with polarities as in Fig. 11d. If a magnet be broken into a number of small pieces each piece will become a magnet having a north and south pole.

In Fig. 13a, a sheet of paper is shown laid on top of a straight bar magnet. Iron filings are sprinkled on the paper by means of a sieve. It will be observed that the iron filings assume a definite arrangement in the form of continuous curves, this clearly indicating that the magnetic forces set up act in definite directions. Any region around the magnet where the force is exhibited is known as the "magnetic field" and, as shown by the density of the filings, the magnetic field is strongest near the magnetic poles.

Fig. 12. Magnetic repulsion and attraction can be demonstrated with two bar magnets, one being suspended and the other held as shown.

The majority of the curved lines assumed by the filings join the north and south poles of the magnet, but those which appear to terminate would be found to join the poles if the apparatus used were sensitive enough; in fact, all the lines are closed paths in space between the two poles. These lines have a particular significance as they are a measure of the strength of the magnetic field, also the direction in which the magnetic forces act.

A small compass needle is a permanent

magnet having north and south poles. Starting from the north pole of the bar magnet place the compass needle in the magnetic field as in Fig. 14. The north pole of the compass needle will be repelled by the north pole of the magnet. If this be repeated in the magnetic field at different points the direction of the needle being noted at each point, and a line described through the points to join the two magnetic poles, it will be similar to the lines of filings. The lines of filings show the direction in which the magnetic force is acting at any particular point, and are known as lines of magnetic force. It may be said that the direction of the magnetic force at any point in the field is the direction in which a north pole would be urged at that point.

UNIT MAGNETIC POLE AND FIELD STRENGTH

By convention, the north pole is regarded as positive and the south pole as negative. The lines of force are said to emerge from the magnet at the north pole, and enter at the south pole (Fig. 13b).

Units are as necessary in studying the effects of magnetic forces as in the case of the electric circuit. It is essential, therefore, to define "unit magnetic pole". If two north poles are placed one centimetre apart and they repel each other with a force of one dyne, the dyne being the unit of force, each north pole would be known as a "unit magnetic pole".

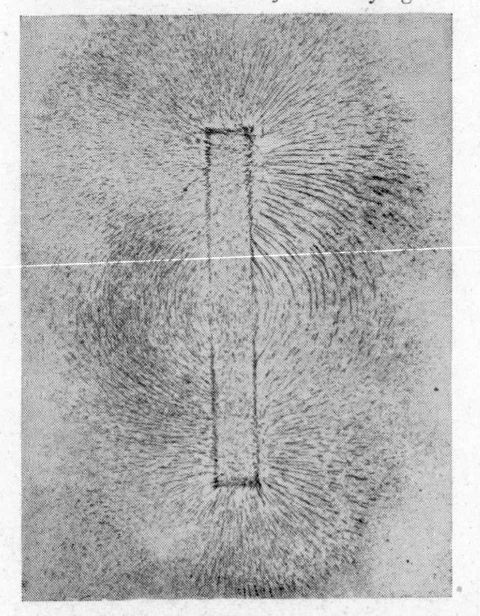

Fig. 13a. Iron filings surrounding a bar magnet give a visual indication of the magnetic field

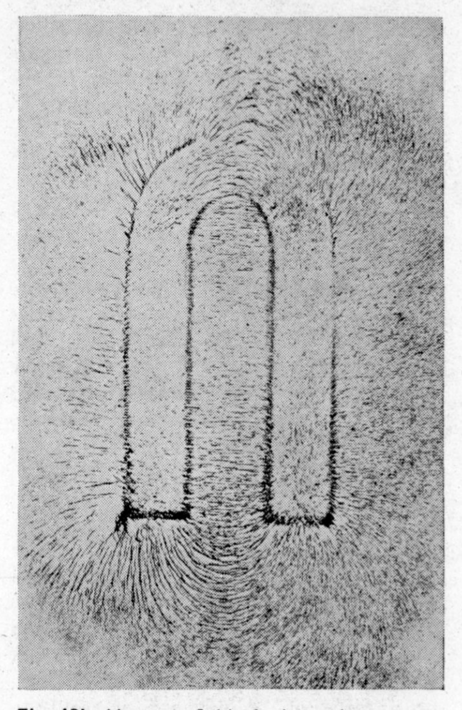

Fig. 13b. Magnetic field of a horseshoe magnet demonstrated by iron filings. Between the iron filings and the magnet is a piece of white paper. Note how the filings centre round the poles.

The force which is exerted between the poles varies inversely as the square of the distance between them, or a unit magnetic pole is one which, when placed one centimetre from a similar pole, exerts a force on it of one dyne.

As the magnetic field consists of a number of lines of force it is necessary to determine the number of lines set up by a unit magnetic pole. The lines leaving a unit north pole are radial to the pole. If, therefore, one line be passed through an area of one square centimetre at right angles to the direction of the line of force, this is known as "unit magnetic field". Also, as the strength of a magnetic field at a point is the force, in dynes, acting on a unit magnetic pole placed at that point, therefore, unit magnetic field, which is one line of force per square centimetre, would exert unit force on unit magnetic pole at a distance of 1 cm.

NUMBERS OF LINES

If a unit magnetic pole be placed at the centre of a sphere of one centimetre radius, then, from the previous paragraph there will be unit magnetic field strength over the whole area of the sphere, or one line of force passing through every square centimetre of area.

As the area of a sphere is $4\pi r^2$ square centimetres, r being the radius in centimetres and "π" being the number of times the diameter will divide into the circumference, the area of a sphere of radius one centimetre is 4π square centimetres. Therefore, the number of lines of force set up by unit magnetic pole is 4π.

All the little particles that make up a piece of magnetic material may be regarded as minute permanent magnets, each having a north and south pole. When the material is unmagnetised the particles are considered to be disarranged such that, at any particular spot there are equal numbers of north and south poles which neutralise each other. It is possible to rearrange these particles and means of doing so will be discussed.

Magnetising the material causes all the

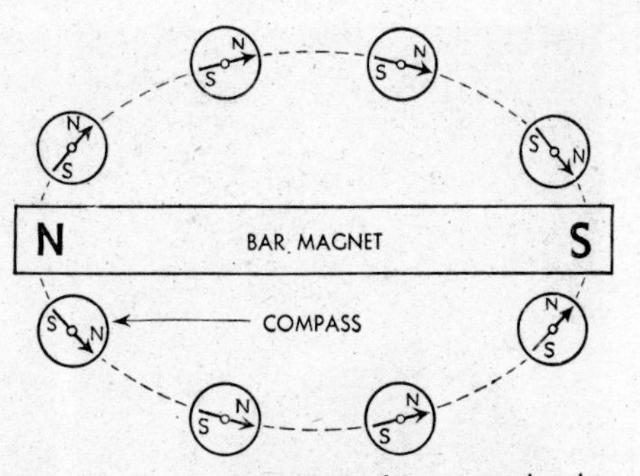

Fig. 14. Lines of magnetic force round a bar magnet plotted with a compass.

particles to arrange themselves in a definite order, with all their north poles pointing one way, and all their south poles in the opposite direction, resulting in a north pole at one end of the magnet and a south pole at the other end.

A piece of iron magnetised by "induction" tends to prove this theory. Fig. 15 illustrates the experiment; the south pole of a magnet is placed near a piece of iron, when a north pole will be set up at the end of the iron nearest to the south pole of the magnet. This, according to the theory, is due to the attractive force between the south pole of the magnet and all the north poles of the particles of iron.

MAGNETISING STEEL

Two methods of magnetising a piece of steel are shown in Fig. 16, the method shown in Fig. 16a is known as "magnetising by stroking", the piece of steel to be magnetised is stroked with one pole of a

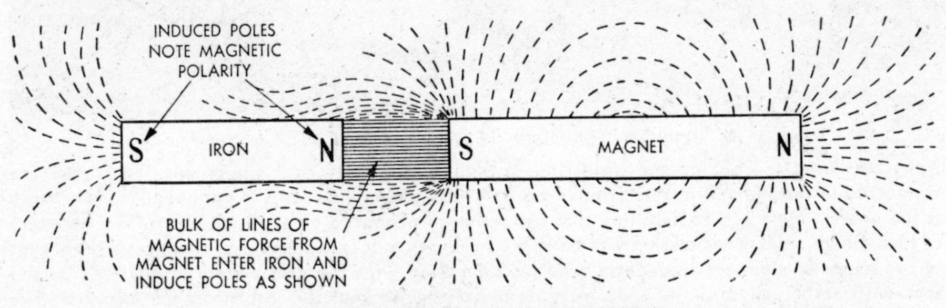

MAGNETISATION BY INDUCTION

Fig. 15. Diagram illustrating how the attractive force of a magnet at south pole causes the rearrangement of the particles in a piece of iron and magnetic poles are induced in it as shown.

HIGH TENSION TESTING APPARATUS

Apparatus used for testing the insulation of high tension electrical equipment. Two units are connected in cascade and in this manner a pressure of one million volts is obtained. The discharge is the nearest approach to lightning that has yet been produced by artificial means. The necessity of such a high voltage for testing will be appreciated when it is remembered that pressures of tens of thousands of volts are frequently used in connection with the grid system of distribution and that with such high tensions wide margins of safety in conductor insulation are essential. The photo. shows an engineer about to test a porcelain insulator. Transformer tests and the testing of switchgear are also carried out with this special type of apparatus. It also has many important laboratory applications especially in regard to the study of the electronic construction of the atom.

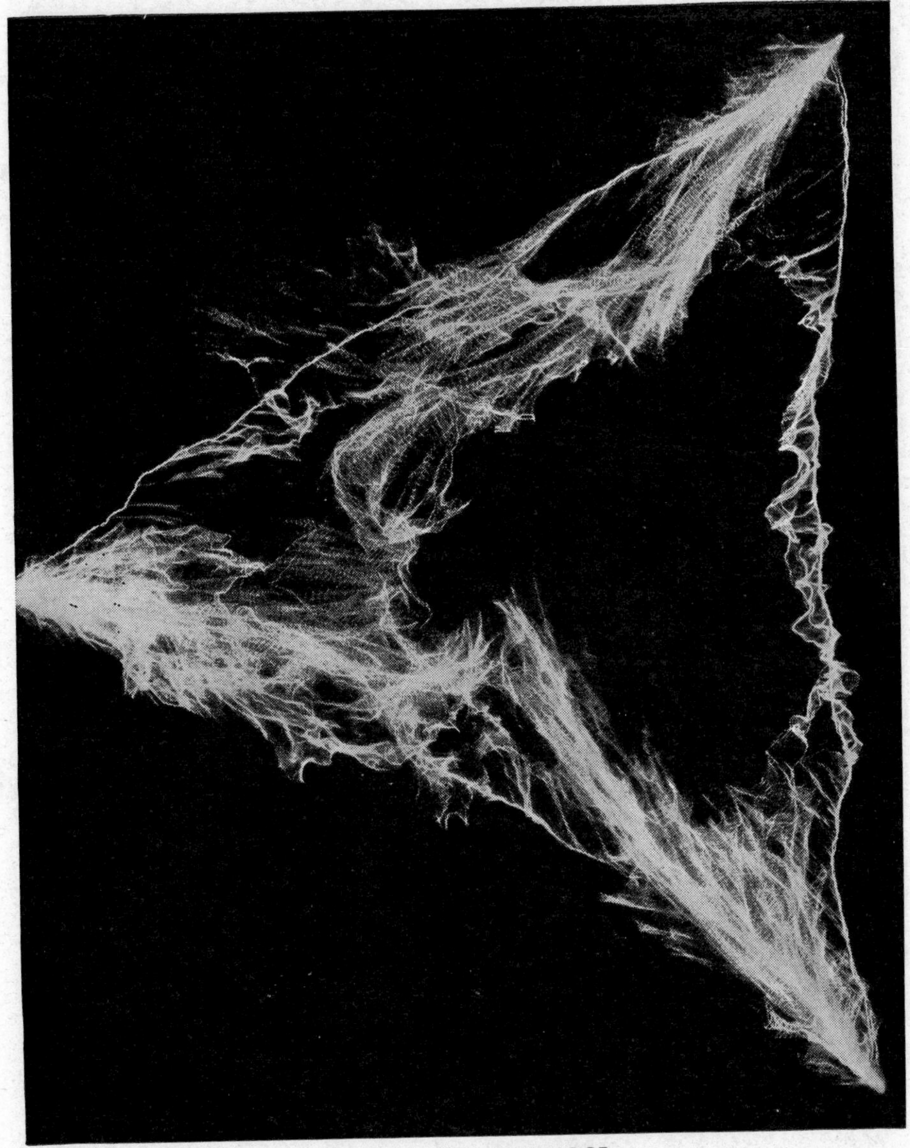

MILLION VOLT DISCHARGE

When the apparatus shown on the opposite page discharges, this is the resulting flash. Special precautions have to be taken during the actual moments of testing and all the engineers retire to some considerable distance from the gear before it is switched on. Odours of ozone, fork flash formation and other features associated with natural lightning effects are all present during the operation of the million-volt apparatus. There is also a violent reverberation similar to thunder. The operation of the apparatus and its effects are, however, strictly under control. Pressures of two million volts have been developed with similar apparatus and are used to test power transmission lines designed to withstand a quarter of a million volts as a normal distribution pressure. The British Grid System, however, does not employ pressures which are in excess of 132,000 volts in normal circumstances.

strong magnet, the polarity of the pole set up in the steel where the stroke finishes being opposite to that of the stroking pole.

The method shown in Fig. 16b is to bridge the poles of an "electromagnet" (see electromagnets), with the specimen to be magnetised, and open and close the circuit several times.

If a glass rod be rubbed with a piece of silk it will be found to attract tiny pieces of paper, hair and sawdust. The rubbing action causes the rod to become "electrified" or "charged" with electricity. Rubbing a piece of ebonite or sealing wax will give similar results. The electricity with which the rods are charged is not in the nature of a current in the sense that it flows, but a charge which is distributed over the surface of the rods and is stationary, or may be regarded as electricity at rest. A glass rod which has been charged, and suspended so that it be free to rotate, will move away from a similarly charged glass rod, but if a charged ebonite rod be brought near the glass rod a force of attraction will result.

These results prove that there are two kinds of charge which are referred to as "positive" and "negative" charges. The glass rod is said to be positively charged and the ebonite rod negatively charged. Unlike charges exhibit a force of attraction analogous to unlike magnetic poles; like charges act similarly to like magnetic poles in exerting a force of repulsion.

Between two oppositely charged bodies a difference of potential exists, the potential difference being measured in volts. The potential difference is dependent upon the quantity of electricity with which the bodies are charged, the unit of quantity being the coulomb, and the capacity of the bodies to hold the charges.

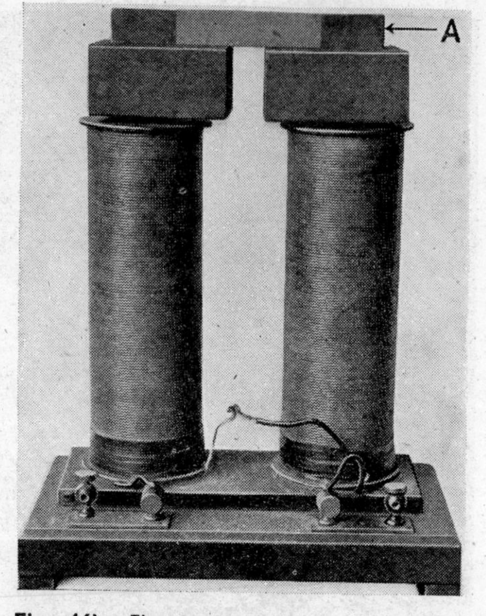

Fig. 16b. Electro-magnet used for making permanent magnets by induction. Specimen to be magnetised is shown at A.

Electricity at rest and current electricity are the same, being measured in the same units. It is not possible to produce a positive charge without an equal negative charge; when rubbing the glass rod the silk became negatively charged. Just as the magnetic field between two magnetic poles is said to be made up of lines of magnetic force, an electrostatic field exists between two oppositely charged bodies of lines of "electric force", and is referred to as the "electric field" as in the case of the condenser in a radio set.

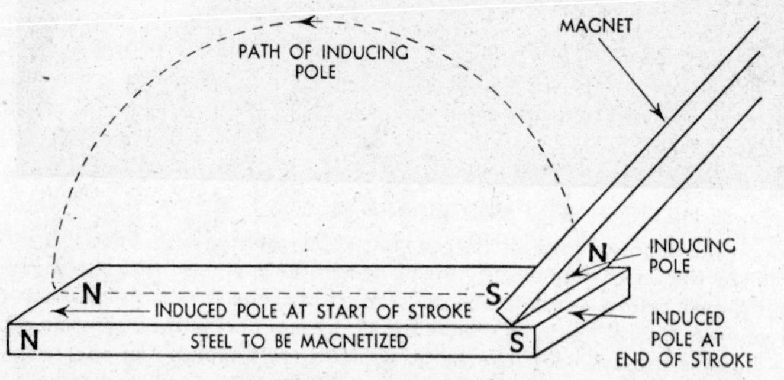

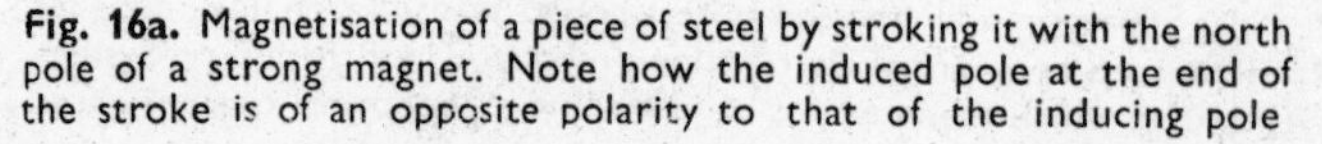

INDUCED MAGNETISM

Fig. 16a. Magnetisation of a piece of steel by stroking it with the north pole of a strong magnet. Note how the induced pole at the end of the stroke is of an opposite polarity to that of the inducing pole

ELECTRON THEORY

THE foundations of the modern theory of electricity were laid in the study of the electric discharge through gases, and in particular the so-called cathode rays. The nature of these rays was first correctly described by Crookes (1879) when he regarded them as negatively electrified particles which were emitted from a metal under the influence of a strong electric field.

Further experiments made on these particles by Perrin (1895) and Sir J. J. Thomson, confirmed that they carried a negative charge and the name "electron" was given to them by Johnstone Stoney, signifying that they were in the nature of atoms of electricity.

It is the movement of these atoms, whether in a conductor or gas, which gives rise to the phenomenon which we call the electric current, and the number of electrons comprising the unit of current has been computed. One micro-ampere is equivalent to the passage of 6 billion electrons per second.

As soon as the existence of the electron was established various experiments were undertaken to measure its mass and the amount of electric charge associated with it. Some of the earliest work was done by Millikan (1917) who found that the charge on the electron was equivalent to $4{\cdot}77 \times 10^{-10}$ absolute electrostatic units. Later work has shown that this figure is nearer 4·8, and the mass of the electron is $9{\cdot}1 \times 10^{-28}$ grams.

ELECTRONS IN ATOMS

The study of chemistry provided evidence that all matter was composed of atoms and that the characteristic properties of substances were due to the structure and nature of the atoms which compose them.

The researches of Sir J. J. Thomson led him to the belief that the atom, regarded hitherto as an indivisible unit of matter, was in turn composed of electrons, the number and grouping of which determined the weight and properties of the atom.

Since the atom in its normal state is electrically neutral and the electron was shown to be negatively charged, it followed that the atom must also contain a core or nucleus which is positively charged and which, as a result, "ties" the negative electron charges to produce a neutral atom.

MINIATURE SOLAR SYSTEM

Lord Rutherford developed a model (see Fig. 17) of such an atom which satisfied the known facts about the behaviour of atoms and electrons and which resembled a miniature solar system with numbers of electrons revolving round a nucleus. Although the nucleus is small compared with the dimensions of the atom, its bulk mainly contributes to the mass of the atom.

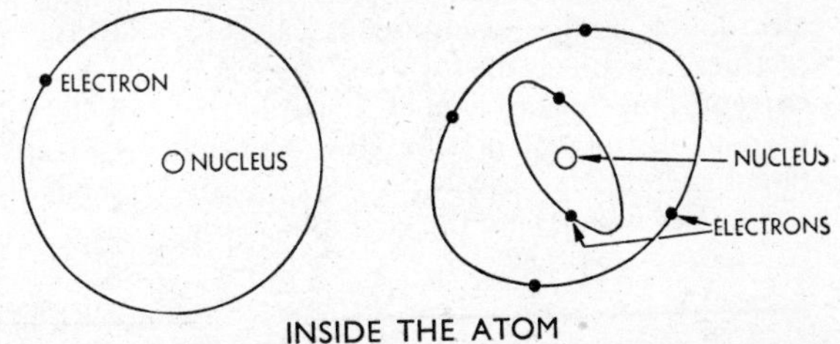

INSIDE THE ATOM

Fig. 17. Diagrammatic representation of electrons in an atom. The hydrogen atom (left) is the simplest, containing one electron and the nucleus. The carbon atom (right) has two electrons near the nucleus and an outer ring of four. The orbits of the electrons are elliptical and are not always necessarily in the same plane.

The electrons nearest to the nucleus are more or less rigidly bound to it, but electrons on the fringe of the atom are less constrained and can probably wander from atom to atom throughout the substance. It is supposed that these electrons are responsible for the conduction of electricity through substances and that in the so-called insulators the electron migration is very slight.

It is not necessary for an individual electron to migrate the length of the conductor in order to form an electric current flow, such a current might be the result of an interchange of electrons among the atoms, the final effect being the surplus of electrons at one end and a deficit at the other.

ELECTRON EMISSION

The reader should remember that an electron, being negatively charged, will move towards that end of the circuit or that part which is termed "positive". The old convention of the electric current flowing from the positive pole or end of a circuit to the negative is thus in direct opposition to the direction of flow of the electrons. The convention is, however, too firmly established to be abandoned, and the current is still assumed to flow from positive to negative. Where there is any doubt, as for example, in valve or rectifier circuits, the words "electron current" or "electron flow" should be used to distinguish it from the conventional current.

The ties which bind the electrons in the atom may be loosened by various agencies such as heat, light, impact of other electrons, and the electrons so freed from their atoms will move from atom to atom through the substance until they find a positively charged atom (or "ion") to which they can attach themselves. The continued application of the exciting agent, such as heat, will cause a continual agitation of electrons and in effect a mass migration throughout the metal.

Before an electron can leave the surface of the metal and escape altogether into the surrounding space (which is usually a vacuum) it must have sufficient energy imparted to it to overcome the forces at the surface, and this kinetic energy is imparted to it by the heat energy applied to the metal. As the temperature is increased, electrons leave the surface in ever-increasing quantities and form a cloud above the surface.

Richardson devised a formula for the number of electrons emitted as a function of the temperature and his formula is a basis of thermionic valve design.

If a positively charged electrode is placed near the heated metal, the electrons will have a further amount of energy imparted to them by the field between the positive electrode and the metal and will travel across the intervening space with a velocity depending on the potential applied (see Fig. 18). Here we have the basis of the familiar diode valve.

Electrons may also be liberated from metals by the action of light (photo-electric effect), or by bombardment by other electrons (secondary emission).

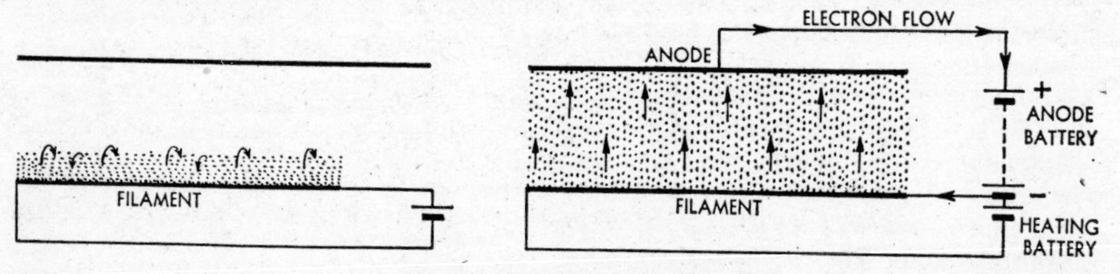

FLOW OF ELECTRONS

Fig. 18. Electrons emitted from a heated wire (left) tend to return after their initial energy has carried them just beyond the surface. If a positively charged plate or anode (right) is mounted above the wire they will be attracted and will migrate across the space and return to the filament by way of the connecting wires and battery.

CONTROL OF ELECTRONS

Free electrons, having left a metal, can be controlled by electric or magnetic fields. These fields may influence the number of electrons per unit area or may guide their movement between the source and the distant electrode to which they are migrating. Both these forms of control are used in thermionic devices such as the valve, cathode ray tube, magnetron and cyclotron.

Within the past few years a great deal of experimental work has been done on the behaviour of electrons in magnetic and electric fields, since the work of Brüche, Ruska, and others. They showed that a stream of electrons under certain conditions can be focused and refracted by electric and magnetic fields in a manner similar to that of light rays, and from their research has developed the theory of electron movement which is known as "Electron Optics".

Since the majority of modern electronic devices employ focusing or deflecting arrangements for their operation, the science of electron optics is of the highest importance at the present time and will probably be productive of many new developments in the next few years particularly in connection with radio direction finding apparatus and systems of television.

DIRECT CURRENTS

When a wire is connected to the terminals of a cell electricity in motion is produced, or, in other words, an electric current flows. One result of this is to be seen in the behaviour of a piece of magnetic material, such as a suspended knitting needle, when placed near to the wire. It is found that the needle will take up some definite position and, because of this, it is known that a force must have been applied to the needle. This force produces effects similar to those of a permanent magnet and is, therefore, known as a magnetic force.

When the current is switched off the force disappears, and if the electric current is reversed, the direction of the magnetic force is reversed also. The space around the wire in which the force can be detected is called the magnetic field. The magnitude of the force at any point, and the direction along which the force acts, can be changed by altering the arrangement of the wire which forms a part of the electric circuit.

The direction of the magnetic force due to a current in a long straight wire is circular with the conductor as centre, as shown in Fig. 19. This can be shown by the use of a compass needle placed at several points round the conductor, the direction in which the needle points is the direction of the force at that point.

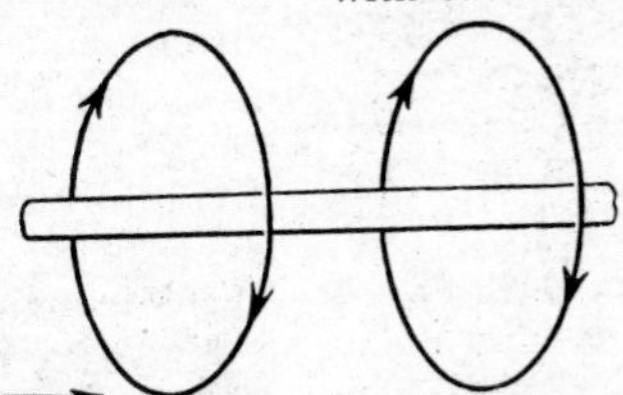

Fig. 19. Lines of magnetic force due to a current in a straight wire. The direction of the current is shown by the arrow.

The direction of the magnetic force can be shown also by the use of iron filings; this is done by placing a straight wire about twelve inches in length through a central hole in a piece of wood about nine inches in diameter. The wood is fixed horizontally and the wire then will be vertical. Pass a current through the wire and then lightly sprinkle some iron filings on to the wood, tapping the wood gently during the process, to assist the filings in taking up their positions. The result will be as shown in Fig. 20, the arrows indicating the direction of the magnetic force.

EFFECT OF COIL

In the two cases so far considered it will be found that the magnetic forces are feeble unless large currents are used. The force can be increased by altering the shape of the current path. This is done by winding the conductor to form a coil, with each turn as close as possible to the next. The lines of force will now take the paths indicated in Fig. 21. The magnetic field is produced in air. It is well known that air is by no means the best medium in which to produce magnetism. Iron and other magnetic substances increase

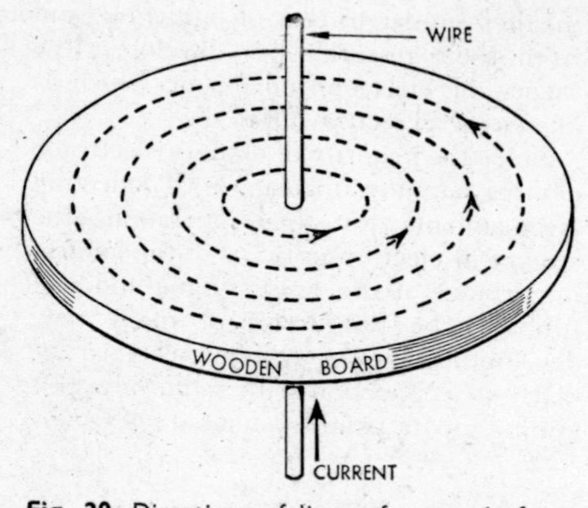

Fig. 20. Directions of lines of magnetic force due to a current in a straight wire, obtained by sprinkling iron filings on to a wooden board

the magnetic strength and for this reason it is usual to find coils wound on iron cores.

Still better results are obtained when the magnetic path is wholly in iron. A complete magnetic path, or circuit, is obtained by winding a coil on a ring of iron, or the circuit may be rectangular as shown in Fig. 22.

USE OF IRON CORE

When a piece of iron is magnetised by the action of the current it is termed an electro-magnet. Many examples of the use of the electro-magnet occur in electrical practice. In bells, electric generators and motors, electrical measuring instruments and sometimes in radio-receivers, electro-magnets are a necessary part of the construction. When a straight piece of iron is magnetised by the action of the current passing round a coil it is in

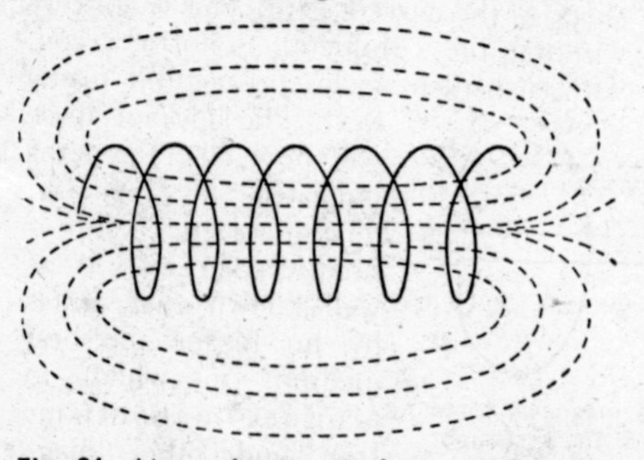

Fig. 21. Lines of magnetic force produced as a result of current flowing through a coil.

all respects similar to a permanent magnet. It possesses poles, North and South, which can be reversed by a reversal of the direction of the current.

Suppose the current is gradually raised from zero, the strength of the magnet will increase rapidly but later the increase rate will be negligible as shown in Fig. 23. The graph indicates the magnetic character of the iron and gives extremely useful information in the design of electro-magnets. It is obvious, therefore, that the strength of an electro-

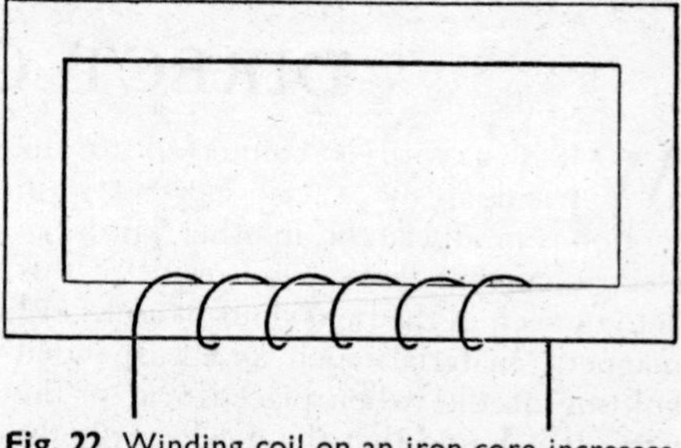

Fig. 22. Winding coil on an iron core increases strength of the magnetic force.

magnet cannot be increased indefinitely by increasing the current. A point is reached where complete magnetic saturation occurs and this cannot be exceeded even though the current is considerably increased.

The strength may be increased, if necessary, by increasing the cross-sectional area of the iron or by using an iron with a better magnetic characteristic.

MAGNETIC CHANGES

Iron is sometimes magnetised by alternating currents. This usually involves very rapid changes in the value of the current and also in its direction. It is necessary, therefore, to investigate the effects of these changes on the magnet strength. Suppose the current in the coil is gradually raised from zero to some convenient maximum value and a graph is drawn as Fig. 23.

The current is now gradually reduced and the changes in magnet strength noted. The resulting graph will be found to lie above the first as shown at G in Fig. 24. It is seen, therefore, that the magnet strength does not fall as the current, for when the current is zero, the magnet has a strength equal to OA. To demagnetise the iron it is necessary to reverse the current and to bring it to a value represented by OB. Fig. 24 shows the complete changes which occur in the magnet strength and the corresponding changes in the value of the current.

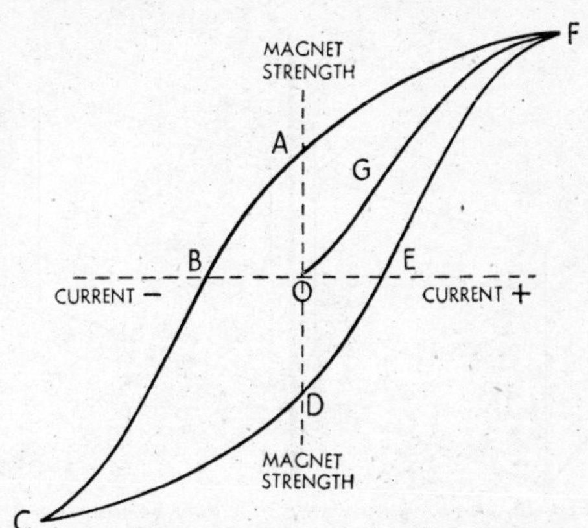

Fig. 24. Hysteresis loop produced in a piece of iron. Horizontal dotted line indicates the current and its direction.

MAGNETIC HYSTERESIS

The magnetic changes do not follow those of the current, but as the graph (Fig. 24) indicates, they lag behind which is due to a phenomenon known as magnetic hysteresis. Hysteresis is due to the inability of the iron molecules to give up their magnetism freely, and the consequence is that the current changes are not followed, in time, by the magnetic changes. The closed curve ABCDEF is known as a hysteresis loop. Energy is required to effect these magnetic reversals and as this represents a loss it is necessary to choose a special grade of iron in which the energy wasted is a minimum. In the section headed electro-magnetic induction, is explained how currents are induced in conductors. Now iron is a conductor of electricity, and since it is used in the construction of machines and apparatus, it is found frequently that induced currents flow in the iron, due to cutting of lines of force. These currents produce heat and raise the temperature of the machine. They are called eddy currents and must be reduced to a minimum, as otherwise they would result in appreciable losses of energy. The reduction of eddy currents can be effected by laminating the iron, that is, by cutting it into a number of thin strips and then insulating each strip from the next. The insulating material may be paper, varnish or even in some cases a thin film of oxide of iron is made to serve the purpose.

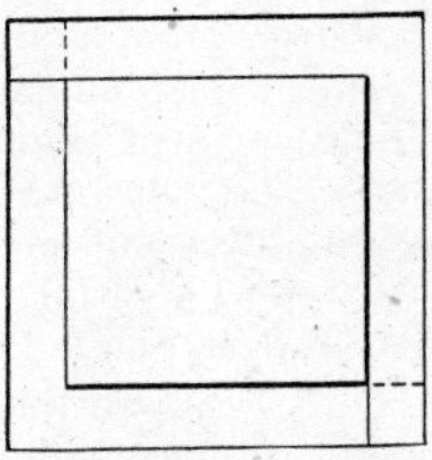

Fig. 25. L-shaped iron stampings arranged so as to form a core around which a coil is wound

In practice the strips are stamped from a sheet of iron, about 20 mils. in thickness, and then placed together to form the required length and cross section.

ELECTRO-MAGNETIC INDUCTION

The stampings may be of various shapes, a common one being that of the letter L and assembled as shown in Fig. 25. It should be noted that each stamping overlaps the next. This is done in order to obtain the best possible magnetic circuit. It should be understood that the magnetising coils are wound on frames or formers and the iron stampings are built up inside the coils thus forming

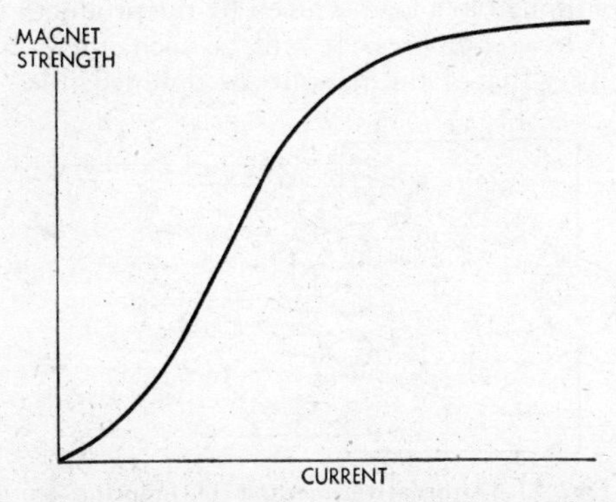

Fig. 23. How magnetic strength in iron varies with changes in values of magnetising current.

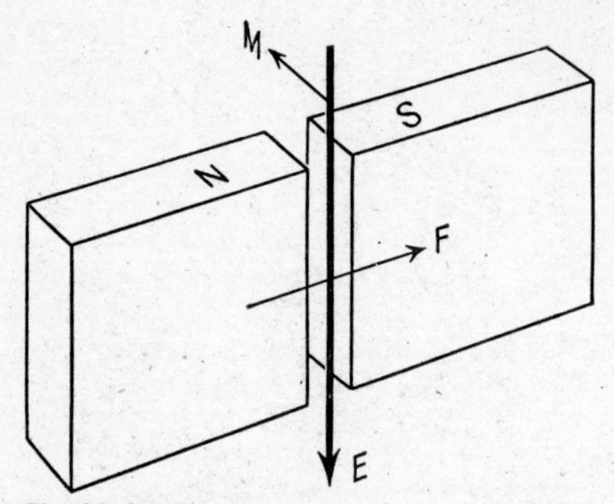

Fig. 26. Showing how an e.m.f. may be induced in a conductor.

the iron cores of the apparatus that may be concerned.

When a conductor moves through a magnetic field, that is, at right angles to the direction of the force, an electric difference of pressure is set up between the ends of the conductor. Should the conductor form part of a closed electric circuit a current will flow, the magnitude of the current depending upon the pressure difference and the opposition offered by the electric circuit.

The direction of the induced e.m.f. is obtained by first noting that the direction of (1) the magnetic force, (2) the motion and (3) the electro-motive force are mutually at right angles.

FLEMING'S RIGHT-HAND RULE

Fleming's Right-Hand Rule enables the direction of the e.m.f. to be obtained in the following manner:—
Place the thumb, first finger and second finger of the right hand in such a way that each is at right angles with the other two. Now point the first finger in the direction of the magnetic force, the thumb in the direction of motion of the conductor, then the second finger will point in the direction of the induced e.m.f. as shown in Fig. 26, where M gives the direction of motion, F gives the direction of the magnetic force and E gives the direction of the induced electro-motive force.

Very large induced voltages may be obtained by using powerful magnetic forces and very long conductors which may be wound in coil form. The coil is rotated in the magnetic field and an electro-motive force is induced. This method is adopted in the electric generator. There is also a Left-Hand Rule which applies to the conditions existing in an electric motor.

ALTERNATIVE METHOD FOR OBTAINING INDUCED E.M.F.

An alternative to the above is obtained if the conductor remains stationary and the magnetic force is varied. In Fig. 27 are shown two coils one placed inside the other.

The coil A is connected to a battery through the switch S, and coil B is connected to a current indicating device G. On closing the switch, G will indicate that a current is induced. G will indicate a momentary current only, for the pointer will return to zero almost immediately. On opening the switch a current will again be induced but this time in the opposite direction. Therefore, two facts emerge from this simple experiment. First, that an e.m.f. is induced when the magnetic force is changing, i.e., being built up from nothing to its maximum value and also falling from maximum to zero. Second, that increasing and decreasing magnetic forces induce currents in opposite directions. This experiment clearly illustrates the action of the transformer.

In direct current distribution the power supplied to a load is given by the product, volts × amperes. It will be seen, therefore, that if the pressure is doubled, the

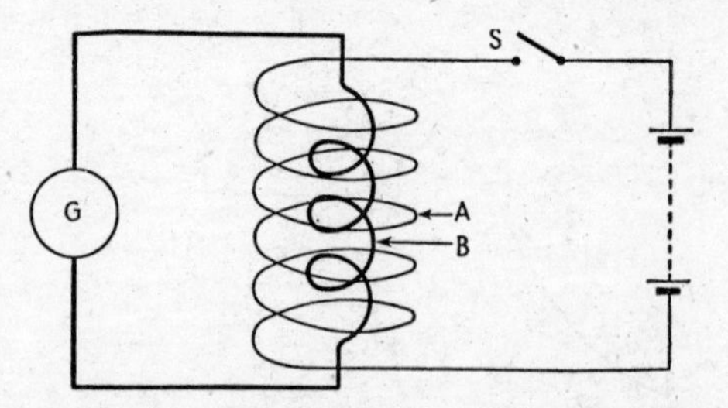

Fig. 27. Alternative method of inducing an e.m.f., the coils being magnetically linked when the switch shown at S is in the closed position.

current will be reduced to one-half, provided the power remains constant. Taking the general case, if the volts are increased x times then the current is reduced to $\frac{1}{x}$ of its previous value.

Some of the power supplied by a generating station is wasted in the cables, therefore let the wasted power be given by I^2R watts, where I is the current in amperes carried by the cable, and R is the total resistance of the cable in ohms.

Since the wasted power is proportional to I^2, it will be an obvious advantage to keep the current as low as possible. The resistance R can be kept down by the use of cables of large cross-sectional area but the larger the cable, the more copper it contains, and, therefore, the cost is greater.

The three-wire system of distribution of power makes possible a considerable reduction in the value of the current, in a given case, with a consequent reduction in the cost of the cable.

Instead of the usual two-wire arrangement, three wires are run from the generator as shown in Fig. 28. The two outer wires are connected to the generator terminals and the potential difference between them is kept at, say, 480 volts. The neutral wire is maintained at a potential midway between that of the two outers and, therefore, the voltage will be 240 between the neutral and either outer. Two voltages are now available, 480 volts for power purposes and 240 volts for lighting.

As far as possible the lighting load is distributed evenly between the two sections as shown. The reason for this is that the current in the neutral wire is the difference between the currents in the positive and negative outers. It is obvious that in an ideal case the neutral would be unnecessary. In practice, however, this is never realised but since the current in the neutral is always less than those in the outers, the cross-sectional area of the neutral is reduced to one-half that of either outer wire.

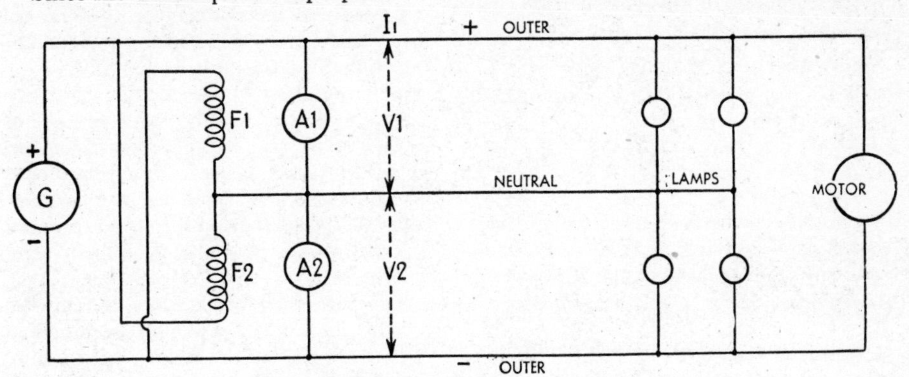

DISTRIBUTING ELECTRICAL ENERGY

Fig. 28. Three-wire system for the distribution of electrical energy. It provides two different voltages, one for lamps and the other for motors. A saving in the cost of the cables is obtained compared with the two-wire system.

SAVING OF COPPER

Let I = current in the 2-wire case.
R = resistance of each main, and
R_1 = resistance of each outer in 3-wire system.

Then power wasted in 2-wire case

$$= 2I^2R \text{ watts.}$$

Then power wasted in 3-wire case

$$= 2\left(\frac{I}{2}\right)^2 R_1 = \frac{I^2R_1}{2} \text{ watts.}$$

For equal efficiencies $2I^2R$ must equal $\frac{I^2R_1}{2}$

Therefore, $R_1 = 4R$

Or each outer is four times the resistance

of each wire in the two-wire system and, therefore, one-quarter of the cross-sectional-area.

Assuming the weight of copper in the two-wire case as 100, we get one-quarter of this as the weight of the outers. To this must be added the weight of the neutral which is one-half that of either outer, that is:—

$$\frac{1}{2} \times 12\frac{1}{2} = 6\frac{1}{4}$$

Total weight of Copper in two-wire case = 100

Total weight of Copper in three-wire case = $25 + 6\frac{1}{4}$, i.e., $31\frac{1}{4}$

For equal current densities:—

The ratio copper in two-wire case to copper in three-wire case =

$$\frac{100}{50 + 12{\cdot}5} = \frac{100}{62{\cdot}5}$$

The three-wire system effects a very considerable saving in the weight of copper used and also in the first cost of the cables.

NEUTRAL AT MID-POTENTIAL

For the successful operation of the three-wire system it is essential that the neutral wire shall be maintained at a potential midway between the two outers. This is made possible by the use of the two shunt wound machines A_1F_1 and A_2F_2 shown in Fig. 28. Used in this way the machines constitute a voltage balancer.

The action of the balancer is:—

When the currents in the two outers are equal the potential differences V_1 and V_2 are also equal and the two machines run as unloaded shunt motors. Suppose that the loads on the two halves are unequal then the two voltages V_1 and V_2 will also be unequal.

EQUALISING LOADS

Consider the case in which I_1 is greater than I_2, then V_1 will be less than V_2. This will result in the voltage across A_1 being lower than across A_2 and since the generator voltage is constant, V_1 will fall by the same amount as V_2 rises.

The armature A_1 tends to slow up, but A_2 tends to rise in speed, because the power to A_2 is now greater than that to A_1 and since the armatures are mechanically coupled, A_1F_1 becomes a generator and A_2F_2 continues to run as a motor.

The result is that the machine A_1F_1 assists the main generator in supplying the heavily loaded side, whilst the machine A_2F_2 adds load to the lightly loaded side, and equality of loads on the two sides is restored and V_1 is again equal to V_2.

The two field windings F_1 and F_2 are cross connected as shown in Fig. 28. This arrangement increases the sensitivity of the balancer to small differences which may be present in the voltages V_1 and V_2.

ALTERNATING CURRENT THEORY

It has already been shown that when a conductor moves so as to cut lines of force (see page 26) an e.m.f. is induced therein, the direction of this e.m.f. being determined by Fleming's right-hand rule. Referring to Fig. 29, in which the conductor P is assumed to be rotating in a "clockwise" direction in the magnetic field provided by the magnet N and S, it will be evident that when the conductor is moving under the north pole, the direction of the induced e.m.f. will be away from the reader and when the conductor is moving under the south pole, the corresponding direction will be towards the reader. Starting at the point A, the conductor P is not, for the moment, cutting the magnetic field but moving parallel with it and thus no e.m.f. is induced. When, however, P moves towards B, as shown, it progressively cuts more and more lines per second until at B it is moving directly across the magnetic field and the number of lines cut per second and, therefore, the induced e.m.f. is a maximum at this instant. As the conductor P leaves position B and approaches C, the induced e.m.f. decreases progressively until, at C, it becomes zero. Thus in one-half of a revolution, the conductor cuts all the magnetic lines emanating from the north pole and, similarly, in the next half revolution, that is from C to A, it cuts all the magnetic lines entering the south pole and the e.m.f. induced during this time will be in the opposite direction as compared with that in the first half revolution.

GRAPHICAL IMPRESSION OF E.M.F. AND CURRENT

Fig. 30 shows, in the form of a curve, the value of induced e.m.f. corresponding to any position of P (Fig. 29), that is, at any instant. For example, assume the conductor P to make one revolution per second, so that the base line corresponds both to one revolution and to one second, as shown, and also, of course, to 360 degrees. The curve is known as a sine curve and it can be shown that this is the most desirable wave form. Consequently, A.C. generators are designed to give an e.m.f. which coincides with a pure sine wave as nearly as possible, and we shall therefore assume that this is realised in practice. Suppose the maximum value of the induced e.m.f. is 100 volts, then the instantaneous values of the sine wave are as given below:—

Deg.	0	15	30	45	60	75	90
e.m.f.	0	25·9	50	70·7	86·7	96·6	100
Deg.		105	120	135	150	165	180
e.m.f.		96·6	86·7	70·7	50	25·9	0

If the conductor P. (Fig. 29) forms part of a closed circuit having a total resistance of r ohms, then the current at any given instant $= \dfrac{\text{voltage at this instant}}{r}$. It is thus evident that the current is directly proportional to the voltage so that the current will also vary in accordance with the sine law. If, therefore, the resistance of the circuit r were 1 ohm, the curve in Fig. 30 would also represent the changes in current to the same scale. Consequently, it has been seen that alternating voltages and currents vary from instant to instant and that they act first in a positive and then in a negative direction, all the changes taking place in one revolution

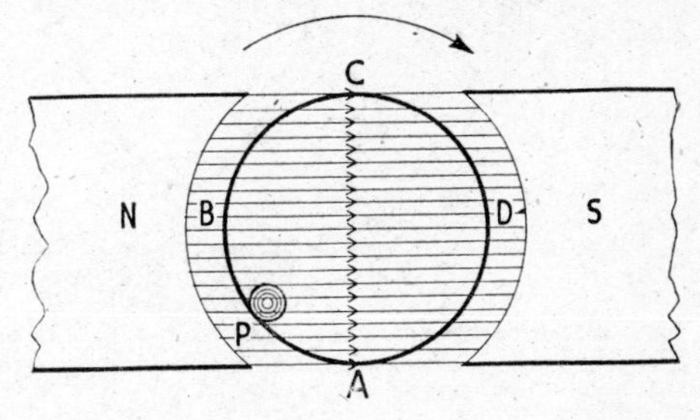

Fig. 29. Rotation of conductor P in magnetic field induces in it an e.m.f. first in one direction and then in opposite direction.

being shown in Fig. 30. The complete curve is called a wave, or more usually a cycle. Thus if conductor P (Fig. 29) were rotated at a speed of 50 revolutions per second, it would evidently complete 50 cycles per second. The number of cycles per second is termed the frequency of the wave. In a two-pole generator, therefore, the frequency is equal to the speed in revolutions per second. In a four-pole field system, the conductor P would evidently complete 2 cycles per revolution and thus the frequency would be twice the speed in revolutions per second and so on. In general, if p is the number of poles, n the speed in revolutions per second and f the frequency in cycles per second, then $f = \dfrac{pn}{2}$.

ELECTRICAL DEGREES

Referring again to Fig. 29, it will be evident that when conductor P rotates from A, through B, to C it will have cut all the flux emanating from the north pole, and it will have moved through 180 degrees. This angle of 180 degrees is called a pole pitch. Obviously, in a four-pole generator, a complete pole pitch occupies only 90 degrees since there must be four pole pitches occupying 360 degrees. It is very convenient to regard a

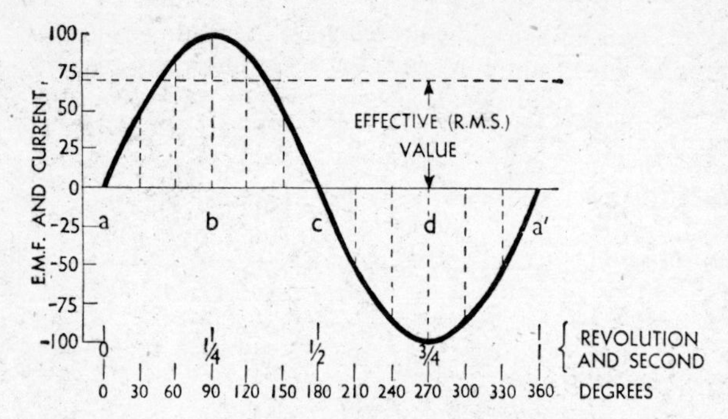

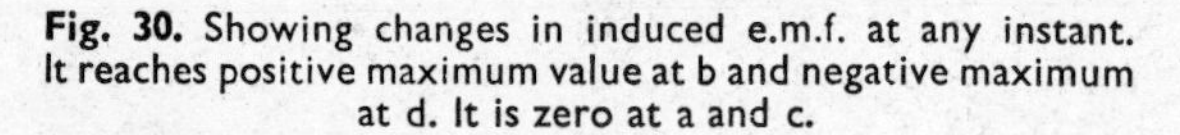
Fig. 30. Showing changes in induced e.m.f. at any instant. It reaches positive maximum value at b and negative maximum at d. It is zero at a and c.

pole pitch always as 180 electrical degrees, whether the generator has two poles or any number of poles. Thus in the case of a four-pole generator, 90 space degrees correspond to 180 electrical degrees and, in general, $A = \frac{1}{2}pB$, where A and B represent electrical and space degrees respectively and p the number of poles.

EFFECTIVE VALUES OF VOLTAGE AND CURRENT

Referring to Fig. 30, suppose the maximum value of the wave is 10 amperes, then evidently the useful value would be less than this, for the maximum current only lasts for a very short time in each cycle. It can be shown that in the case of a sine wave of current, the effective (or useful) value is 0·707 times the maximum value, and the same holds in the case of the voltage. The effective value is that value of the alternating current and voltage whose product would give the same value of power as direct-current values. The effective values are usually referred to as the root-mean square or R.M.S. values, this name being derived from the particular mathematical way of deriving them. Thus, if a sine wave of voltage having a maximum value of 100 volts acts in a circuit of 10 ohms resistance, the maximum current would be 10 amperes and the maximum power would evidently be 1,000 watts. The average power is given by the product of the effective volts and the effective amperes thus $(0{\cdot}707 \times 100) \times (0{\cdot}707 \times 10) = 500$ watts. This will be clear from Fig. 31. Referring first to Fig. 31a, the power curve is obtained by multiplying corresponding instantaneous values of voltage and current and plotting a curve of power in watts, remembering that the product of the two negative quantities is positive. The power curve is reproduced in Fig. 31b and the average power is evidently half the maximum. For the peak A will be found to fit exactly in the "valley" A^1 and the peak BC will fit exactly in the spaces B^1 and C^1. Evidently the area of the rectangle p q r s is equal to the area of the power wave. Or, to put it in other words, the areas of the two peaks will fill exactly the vacant areas below the line represented by the average power.

$$\text{Now P average} = \tfrac{1}{2}\text{ P max.}$$
$$= \tfrac{1}{2}\text{ E max} \times \text{I max}$$
$$= \frac{\text{E max}}{\sqrt{2}} \times \frac{\text{I max}}{\sqrt{2}}$$

since $\left(\frac{1}{\sqrt{2}} \times \frac{1}{\sqrt{2}} = \frac{1}{2}\right)$; therefore,
P average $= 0{\cdot}707$ E max $\times\ 0{\cdot}707$ I max.
$= E \times I$

E and I are thus the R.M.S. values, so that in the case of 100 volts and 10 amperes (maximum values) their corresponding R.M.S. values are 70·7 and 7·07. These values are thus equivalent to 70·7 D.C. volts and 7·07 D.C. amperes, since in both A.C. and D.C. cases they produce an average power of 500 watts. R.M.S. values will be assumed in future, unless otherwise specified.

AVERAGE VALUES OF CURRENT AND VOLTAGE

The average (or mean) value of a sine wave is easily obtained by measuring the ordinates of the positive half of the wave, adding them together and then dividing by the number of ordinates taken. If this is done accurately, the mean value will be found to be 0·637 times the maximum value. This number 0·637 is usually expressed as $\frac{2}{\pi}$, ($\pi = 3{\cdot}1416$). These and other expressions are of great practical value in alternating current work.

INDUCTANCE

The theoretical circuit (Fig. 32a) shows a solenoid supplied from an A.C. generator. At a given instant, a current of i amperes flows in the coil and this gives rise to a certain value of magnetic field or flux. These lines of force link with the turns of the coil and the term "linkages" is given to the product of flux and turns. The number of linkages per ampere is termed the "inductance" of the coil. The practical unit of inductance is the "henry" and a coil has an inductance of 1 henry if it sets up 100,000,000 linkages per ampere. Thus inductance in henries (represented by L),

$$= \frac{\text{Flux} \times \text{turns}}{\text{current} \times 100{,}000{,}000}$$

It will be remembered that when a coil is cut by lines of force, an e.m.f. is induced therein and thus when the flux rises and collapses with the current, an e.m.f. is induced in the coil. This e.m.f. is evidently proportional to the rate at which the flux changes; it is a maximum when the current and flux are zero and it lags behind the current and flux by 90 degrees, i.e., the e.m.f. reaches its maximum (or zero) value 90 degrees after the current. This is shown in Fig. 32b. Assuming the coil to have no resistance, the voltage required from the generator must be equal and opposite to the induced voltage. Another way of showing this is given in Fig. 32c, in which a current is represented by a line OI, its length being proportional to its magnitude. Another line, lagging by 90 degrees behind the current represents the induced e.m.f. Ei, and a third line leading the current by 90 degrees gives the applied voltage Ea. This diagram is known as a vector diagram and such diagrams are extensively employed in alternating currents. The arrow on the diagram indicates that Ea leads the current I and, similarly, I leads the induced e.m.f. Ei. It can be shown that the value of the induced and the applied voltages is $Ea = Ei = 2\pi fLI$, where f is the frequency, L the inductance in henries and $\pi = 3{\cdot}1416$. Thus $I = \frac{Ea.}{2\pi fL}$

The quantity $2\pi fL$ is called the inductive reactance of the coil and is denoted by the symbol X. The unit of reactance is the ohm.

RESISTANCE

In this case the applied voltage only has to overcome the voltage drop due to resistance, so that $E = I \times R$. Thus when I is zero, E must be zero, and when the current is a maximum, the applied voltage must be a maximum. Thus the voltage and current evidently go through their changes at the same instants, or in other words they are in phase with each other. This condition is shown in Fig. 33

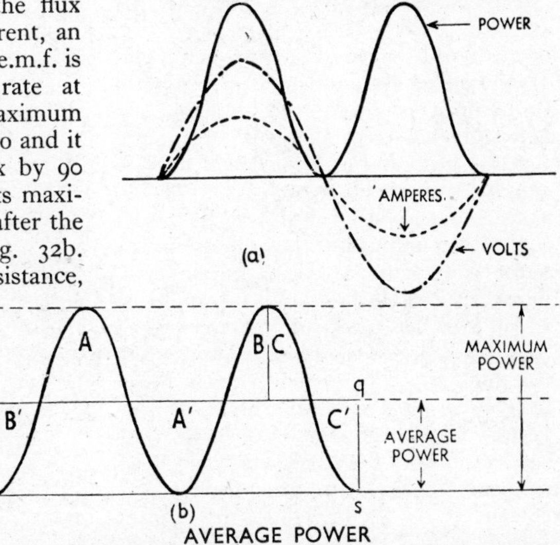

Fig. 31. Power curve in (a) is obtained by multiplying corresponding instantaneous values of volts and amperes. This power curve redrawn at (b) shows that average power is half maximum power as a peak exactly fits a valley.

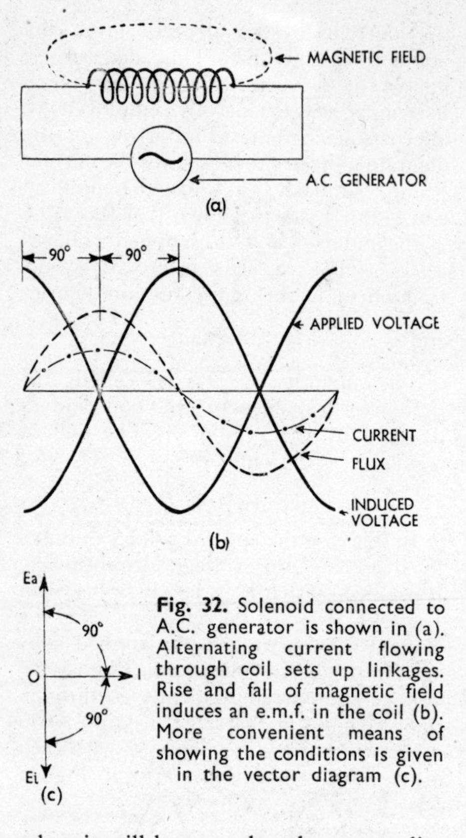

Fig. 32. Solenoid connected to A.C. generator is shown in (a). Alternating current flowing through coil sets up linkages. Rise and fall of magnetic field induces an e.m.f. in the coil (b). More convenient means of showing the conditions is given in the vector diagram (c).

when it will be seen that the vector diagram assumes its simplest form. A circuit containing resistance and inductance is given in Fig. 34a and it will be evident that the generator voltage E will have to supply two components. $V_R = IR$ to overcome the resistance and $V_L = 2\pi fLI$ the voltage induced in the coil due to the latter being cut by the magnetic field. These two voltages V_R and V_L cannot be added together, for it will be remembered that V_L leads the current by 90 degrees (see Fig. 32c). The applied voltage E can be got by vector addition. Referring to vector diagram Fig. 34b, the two voltages V_R and V_L have been drawn respectively in phase with and leading the current by 90 degrees and the applied voltage E is obtained by completing the rectangle o a b c, when E = the diagonal ob. It is seen that E leads I by the angle ϕ (phi) which lies between 0 degrees and 90 degrees. This is reasonable, since with resistance only (Fig. 33) the angle is 0 degrees and with inductance only the angle is 90 degrees. With both resistance and inductance in the circuit, the angle between the applied voltage and the current is between these limits, the greater the resistance the smaller the angle and vice versa. It can be shown that

$$E = I\sqrt{R^2 + (2\pi fL)^2} = IZ$$

$$Z = \sqrt{R^2 + (2\pi fL)^2}$$ and

is termed the impedance of the circuit,

$$\text{thus } I = \frac{E}{Z}.$$

CAPACITANCE

When two metal plates are separated by a layer of insulating material, the arrangement is known as a condenser. Fig. 35a shows the two plates A and B with the insulation between them connected to a D.C. generator. Suppose first the double-pole switch S is open and the generator voltage E is 500 volts. There is, of course, no potential difference between the plates of the condenser. If, now, the switch S is closed, there is evidently a potential difference of 500 volts across the condenser plates A and B, and it is interesting to consider how the plates became charged up to this voltage. At the instant of closing the switch, the potential of plate A is lower than that of the

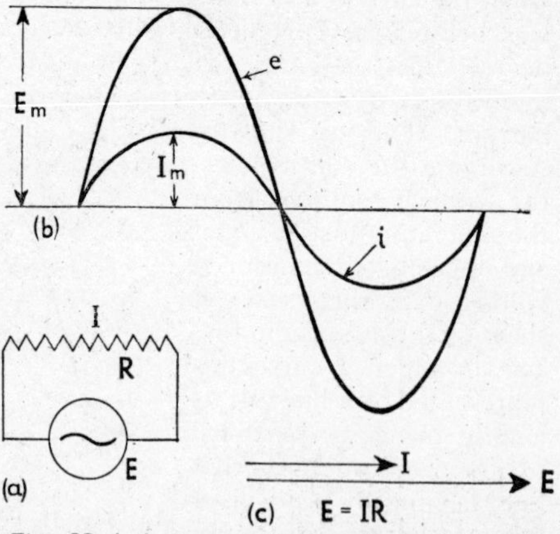

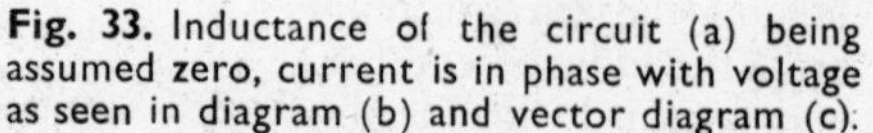

Fig. 33. Inductance of the circuit (a) being assumed zero, current is in phase with voltage as seen in diagram (b) and vector diagram (c).

positive terminal of the generator, and the potential of plate B is higher than that of the negative terminal. Consequently a current must flow from B towards A until the potentials of A and B are equal to the potentials of the corresponding generator terminals, when the current will cease. During this time a quantity of electricity, Q coulombs, is displaced since $Q = i \times t$, where t is the time in seconds and i is the average current during this time. It is thus seen that a condenser can only be charged by a movement of electricity. If V is the voltage across the condenser corresponding to the charge Q, then V is evidently proportional to Q, or V is $\frac{1}{C} \times Q$, so $Q = CV$. C is called the capacitance of the condenser, the unit of capacitance being the farad (symbol F). In practice a much smaller unit, the microfarad (μF) equal to one-millionth of a farad is usually employed (μ = the Greek letter m).

If this condenser is now connected to the terminals of an A.C. generator giving a sine wave of e.m.f. (see Fig. 35b) it will be evident that since the applied voltage is continuously varying, the charge in the condenser must correspondingly vary. This means, of course, that the current must be varying continuously. When the condenser was connected to the D.C. generator by closing the switch, it was obvious that the current started flowing *before* the voltage was built up across the plates A and B. In other words, the current *leads* the voltage applied to the condenser. When the current is alternating, then the current leads the applied voltage by 9c

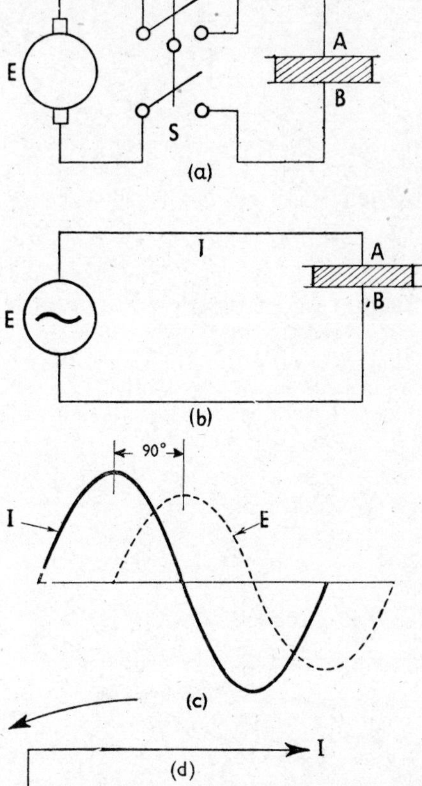

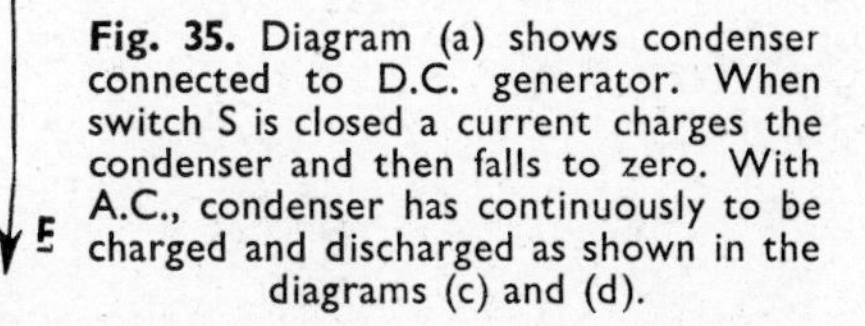

Fig. 35. Diagram (a) shows condenser connected to D.C. generator. When switch S is closed a current charges the condenser and then falls to zero. With A.C., condenser has continuously to be charged and discharged as shown in the diagrams (c) and (d).

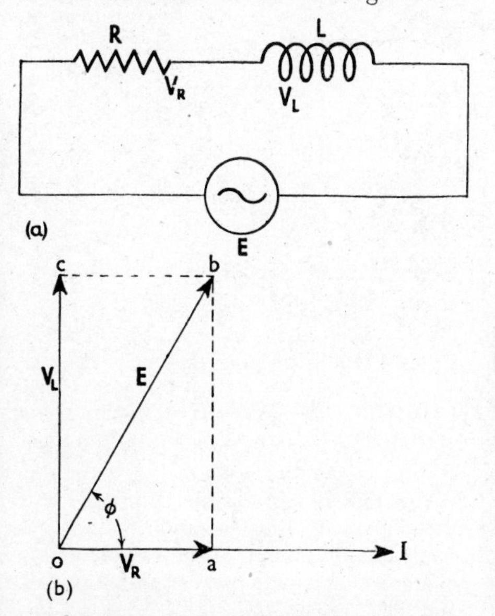

Fig. 34. Diagram (a) shows circuit with resistance and inductance. Vector diagram (b) should be studied carefully in conjunction with the vector diagrams in Figs. 32(c) and 33(c).

degrees. This is shown in Figs. 35c and d. The voltage $E = \frac{I}{2\pi fC}$ where C is in farads. The quantity $\frac{1}{2\pi fC}$ is called the reactance of the condenser, and the unit is also the ohm. Condenser reactance is, like inductive reactance, denoted by the symbol X, thus $E = I \times \frac{1}{2\pi fC} = IX$.

CIRCUIT CONTAINING RESISTANCE AND CAPACITANCE

Fig. 36 is similar to Fig. 34 and the two should be compared carefully. The only difference is that V_C lags behind the

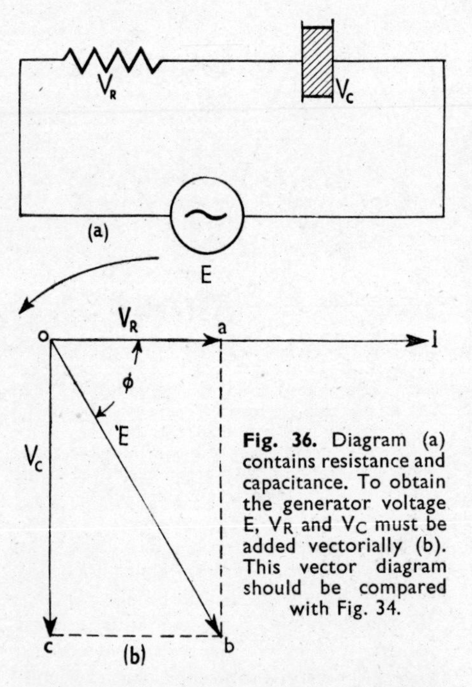

Fig. 36. Diagram (a) contains resistance and capacitance. To obtain the generator voltage E, V_R and V_C must be added vectorially (b). This vector diagram should be compared with Fig. 34.

current by 90 degrees whereas, in Fig. 34, V_L leads the current by 90 degrees. Fig. 36a shows the circuit and it will be seen that the applied voltage E has to supply two components, V_R to overcome the resistance and V_C to charge the condenser, so that the two must, as in the case of Fig. 34, be added vectorially to give the generator voltage E. This is done in Fig. 36b. It can be shown that

$$E = I\sqrt{R^2 + \frac{1}{(2\pi fC)^2}}$$
$$= I\sqrt{R^2 + X^2} = IZ$$

where Z is again the impedance of this circuit. The current leads the applied voltage by the angle ϕ.

CONDENSERS IN SERIES AND PARALLEL

Fig. 37a shows three condensers connected in parallel. Let the charges in the condensers be Q_1, Q_2 and Q_3 respectively and the total charge in all the condensers be Q, then evidently $Q = Q_1 + Q_2 + Q_3$.

If C be the total capacitance of C_1, C_2 and C_3 then by substitution,

$$CE = Q = C_1E + C_2E + C_3E$$
$$CE = E(C_1 + C_2 + C_3)$$

Dividing both sides of this equation by E, we obtain $C = C_1 + C_2 + C_3$

If the condensers are connected in series, as shown in Fig. 37b, then evidently, $E = E_1 + E_2 + E_3$

Since all the condensers are charged in series, they will all have the same charge. Let this be Q. If C represents their combined capacitance, then since $E = E_1 + E_2 + E_3$, substituting $\frac{Q}{C}$ for E, $\frac{Q}{C_1}$ for E_1, $\frac{Q}{C_2}$ for E_2 and $\frac{Q}{C_3}$ for E_3, we get

$$\frac{Q}{C} = \frac{Q}{C_1} + \frac{Q}{C_2} + \frac{Q}{C_3} = Q\left(\frac{1}{C_1} + \frac{1}{C_2} + \frac{1}{C_3}\right)$$

Dividing both sides of this equation by Q, we get $\frac{1}{C} = \frac{1}{C_1} + \frac{1}{C_2} + \frac{1}{C_3}$. If $C_1 = C_2 = C_3$ it will be obvious that $E_1 = E_2 = E_3$.

CIRCUIT CONTAINING RESISTANCE INDUCTANCE AND CAPACITANCE

This circuit is shown in Fig. 38, and its vector diagram should be compared with those given in Figs. 34 and 36 since it is really a combination of the two. It will be evident that since the components OV_L and OV_C are in opposition they tend to neutralise one another and thus the applied voltage OE may be less than either. OE is obtained by adding vectorially

OV_L, OV_C and OV_R, and this is done by first subtracting OV_C from OV_L and then combining this resultant $(V_L - V_C)$ with OV_R. The applied voltage

$$E = I\sqrt{R^2 + \left(2\pi f L - \frac{1}{2\pi f C}\right)^2} = IZ$$

OE leads the current by the angle ϕ and a little consideration will show that if OV_C should be greater than OV_L, OE would lag behind the current. It will also be evident that OV_L may be equal to OV_C when the resultant $(OV_L - OV_C)$ would be zero. In this case, OE would be equal to OV_R, and thus the current and the applied voltage would be in phase, and the circuit is said to be tuned or in resonance.

In the resonant condition $I = \frac{V_R}{R} = \frac{E}{R}$ so that the circuit obeys Ohm's law, although clearly both OV_L and OV_C may be very large, indeed many times greater than the applied voltage OE. For resonance V_L must be equal to V_C and therefore $2\pi f L I = \frac{I}{2\pi f C}$. Dividing both sides by I we get:—

$$2\pi f L = \frac{1}{2\pi f C}$$

$$(2\pi f)^2 = \frac{1}{LC}$$

$$2\pi f = \frac{1}{\sqrt{LC}}$$

$$f = \frac{1}{2\pi\sqrt{LC}}$$

Thus with given values of L in henries and C in farads, resonance will occur at one frequency, f. Resonance is of very great importance in radio engineering.

POWER IN A CIRCUIT CONTAINING REACTANCE

It had been shown (see Fig. 31) that when the voltage and current are in phase, the average power is given by multiplying together the R.M.S. values of voltage and current. This is not the case when there is a phase difference between the voltage and current. Referring to Fig. 39a, where the voltage leads the current by 90

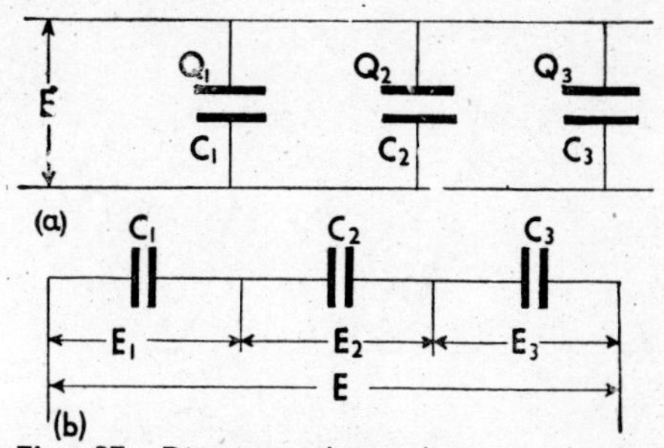

Fig. 37. Diagrams show three condensers connected (a) in parallel and (b) in series.

degrees, it will be evident that the average power is zero, i.e., the powers in positive and negative directions are equal. This will be clear when it is remembered that the product of a positive and a negative quantity is negative; the product of two negative quantities is positive. Thus between p and q both e and i are positive; between q and r the current is positive and the voltage is negative giving negative power; between r and s both e and i are negative, giving positive power; between s and t the voltage is positive and the current is negative giving negative power. Referring to Fig. 39b which repre-

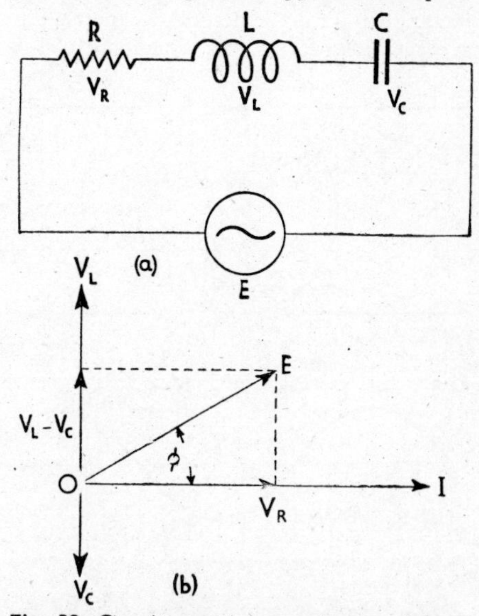

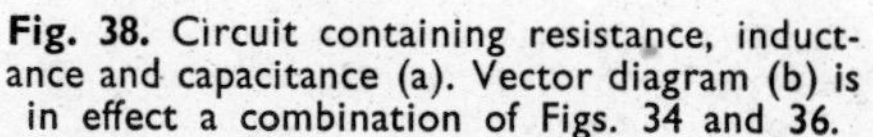

Fig. 38. Circuit containing resistance, inductance and capacitance (a). Vector diagram (b) is in effect a combination of Figs. 34 and 36.

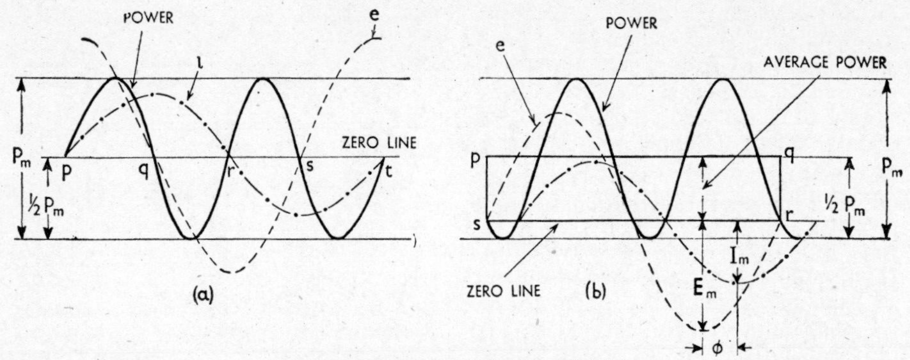

INSTANTANEOUS POWER VALUES

Fig. 39. Diagram (a) shows instantaneous values of power when current lags behind voltage by 90 degrees. In diagram (b) current lags behind voltage by angle between zero and 90 degrees.

sents the case of the current lagging behind the voltage by an angle ϕ, less than 90 degrees, it will be clear that there is more positive than negative power, but the average power will still be half the maximum power taking into account the negative power. This can be obtained in the same way as was done in Fig. 31, which should be compared with Fig. 39a in which half the maximum power brings us up to the zero line and in Fig. 39b, half the maximum power gives the rectangle p q r s, the height of which is the average power and this is evidently less than that in the case of the one shown in Fig. 31.

In all cases where the voltage and current are not in phase, the power can be obtained by connecting a wattmeter in the circuit. In all circumstances the wattmeter will indicate the average power. If a voltmeter and ammeter are also connected in the circuit, and their readings are multiplied together, the result is termed the apparent power, that is, $E \times I$ (R.M.S. values). The ratio of the average power to the apparent power is called the power factor of the circuit, thus:—

$$\text{Power Factor} = \frac{\text{Watts}}{E \times I} \text{ so that Watts} = E \times I \times \text{Power Factor.}$$

When the phase difference between E and I is 90 degrees, the current either lagging or leading, the average power is zero (Fig. 39a) and thus the power factor is zero. The power factor (assuming sine waves of current and voltage) is also given by the cosine of the angle of phase difference between the voltage and current, so that Watts $= EI \cos \phi$. ("Cosine" is invariably referred to as "cos"). Referring to Figs. 34, 36 and 38,

$$\cos \phi = \frac{V_R}{E} = \frac{IR}{IZ} = \frac{R}{Z}$$

Polyphase systems are formed from a combination of single-phase systems having the same frequency but differing in phase. For example, suppose in Fig. 29 another conductor similar to P was

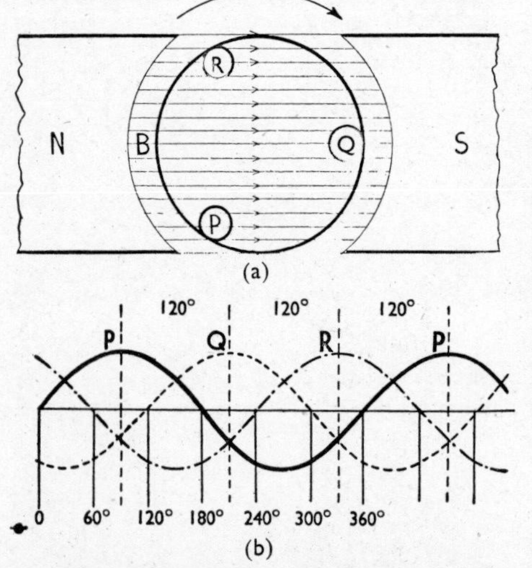

Fig. 40. Diagram (a) shows an elementary A.C. generator with three moving conductors. The waves of e.m.f. induced are seen at (b).

placed between B and C, the angle between the two conductors being 90 degrees. Then an e.m.f. would be induced in this new conductor which would be in all respects similar to that induced in P, but leading it by 90 degrees, that is, it would reach its positive maximum value at a (Fig. 30), zero at b, negative maximum value at c, zero at d and again its positive maximum at a^1. This combination would form a two-phase system, but such a system is now of minor importance and will not be further considered. The only important polyphase system is the three-phase system, which is the standard employed for power work. For this reason, we shall devote considerable attention to it.

THREE-PHASE SYSTEM

Fig. 40a shows three conductors P, Q, and R, suitably mounted and rotated in a clockwise direction. The three conductors are all the same distance from one another, i.e., the angle between any two is 120 degrees. As they are rotated, P will be the first to arrive at position B under the north pole when, of course, maximum e.m.f. will be induced in it. When P has rotated through 120 degrees from position B, Q will have maximum e.m.f. induced in it, and after the system has rotated through a further 120 degrees, R will be in position B. Thus all three conductors will have the same wave of e.m.f. induced, but the instants at which each reaches maximum e.m.f. are displaced by 120 degrees. This is shown in Fig. 40b.

STAR CONNECTION

For the transmission of three-phase power, it would appear at first sight that six conductors are necessary, two for each phase. Imagine the three single conductors P, Q and R in Fig. 40a to be replaced by three windings of a three-phase A.C. generator, the windings, of course, being displaced in space from one another by 120 degrees. Referring now to Fig. 41a, the windings will have three-phase e.m.f.'s induced in them as depicted in Fig. 40b. Each winding is

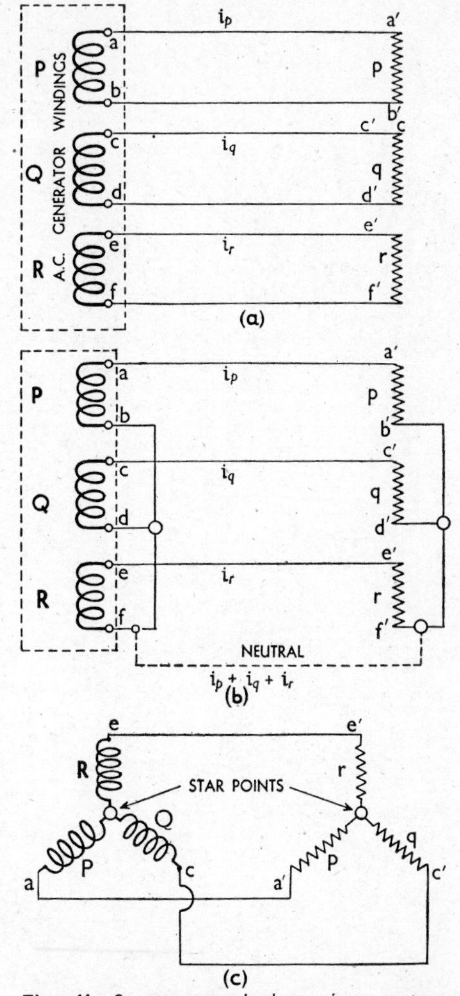

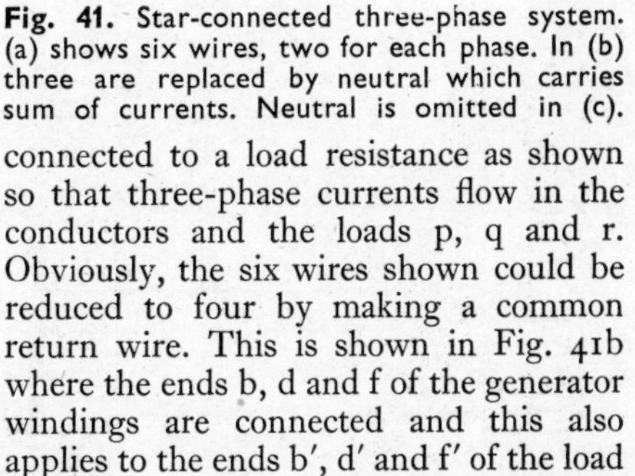

Fig. 41. Star-connected three-phase system. (a) shows six wires, two for each phase. In (b) three are replaced by neutral which carries sum of currents. Neutral is omitted in (c).

connected to a load resistance as shown so that three-phase currents flow in the conductors and the loads p, q and r. Obviously, the six wires shown could be reduced to four by making a common return wire. This is shown in Fig. 41b where the ends b, d and f of the generator windings are connected and this also applies to the ends b′, d′ and f′ of the load resistors. Between these two common points the common return wire (or neutral wire) is connected, and this wire

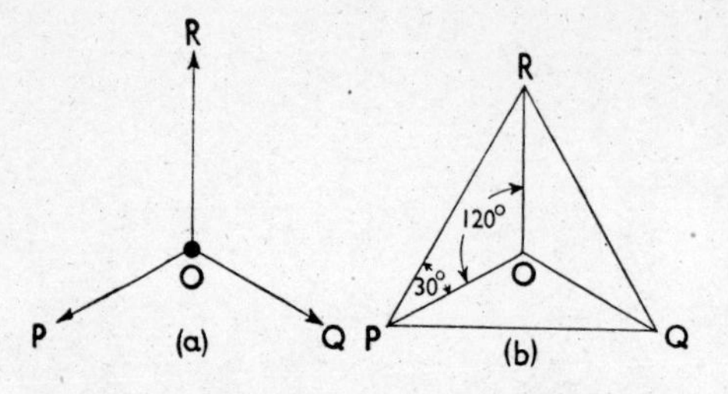

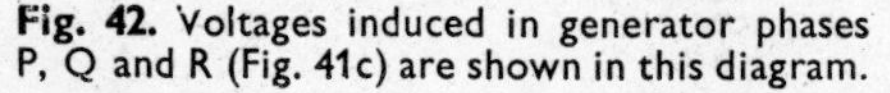
Fig. 42. Voltages induced in generator phases P, Q and R (Fig. 41c) are shown in this diagram.

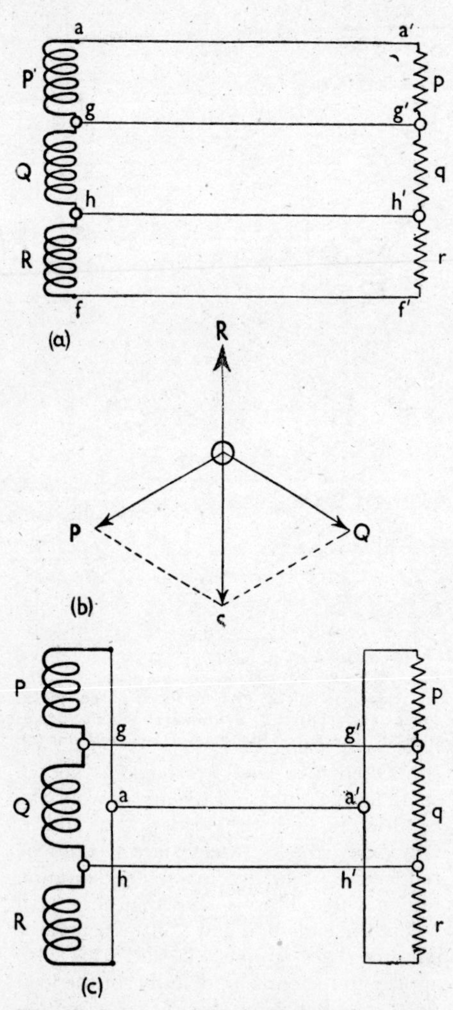

Fig. 43. Delta method developed (a), vector treatment is at (b), and elimination of wire at (c). See also Fig. 44.

will evidently carry the sum of the currents i_p, i_q and i_r at any instant. These currents are, of course, displaced in phase by 120 degrees just as are the induced e.m.f.'s, and thus the three waves in Fig. 40b labelled P, Q and R can represent the currents i_p, i_q and i_r. Now let us examine these current waves more closely; if we consider the instant when i_p has attained its maximum value in the positive direction, then the currents i_q and i_r will each be equal to half their maximum values but in the negative direction. Again, consider the instant when i_p is zero (at 180 degrees) then i_q is equal to i_r but i_q is positive and i_r is negative. The reader should similarly check the conditions at other instants when it will be found that at every instant the algebraic sum of the currents is zero. Thus when i_p is at its maximum value $i_p = -(i_q + i_p)$, or $i_p + i_q + i_r =$ zero; when $i_p = 0$, then $i_q = - i_r$ so that $i_q + i_r = 0$ and obviously again $i_p + i_q = i_r = 0$. We thus can see that the current in the neutral wire in Fig. 41b, is zero, and it consequently follows that there is no necessity for this conductor, and it has been omitted in Fig. 41c. Thus only three conductors are necessary for three-phase transmission with this method of interconnecting the wires which is known as the star connection. The common points of the generator windings and the loads are called the star points or neutral points. Fig. 41c is identical to Fig. 41b with the exception of the neutral wire which in 41b is shown as a dotted line.

LINE AND PHASE VOLTAGES IN STAR-CONNECTED SYSTEM

Since the ends of the generator windings b, d and f in Fig. 41 are connected together, these points are connected to a common potential. The induced e.m.f.'s can therefore be represented as shown in the vector diagram of Fig. 42 since these voltages are displaced in phase by 120 degrees. Obviously the potential of the point a (Fig. 41c) is P and that of e is R; thus the *potential difference* between lines a and e is PR. Similarly the potential differences between lines e and c and between lines c and a are RQ and QP respectively. It will be noticed that there is an inherent phase angle of 30 degrees between the generated, or phase, voltages and the line voltages. If the load power factor is unity, therefore, the currents will be in phase with the generated voltages. They will then be displaced by an angle of 30 degrees from the line voltages. If the voltages are measured, it will be found that the line voltages are 1·73 times the phase voltages. Calling the line and phase voltages V_L and V_P respectively, the relationship is $V_L = \sqrt{3}V_P$, since 1·73 is the square root of 3.

the wires dd′ and ee′ (Fig. 41) are replaced by the single wires gg′ and hh′ respectively. Thus the points b and c of the two generator windings are reduced to the same potential, and the same applies to the two points d and e, so that the number of conductors has at once been reduced from six to four.

Fig. 43b shows the generated voltages OP, OQ and OR and obviously the voltage between the points a and h is OS as shown in the diagram. It will be seen that OS is equal in magnitude to OP, OQ and OR, and in phase opposition to OR. Similarly, the voltage between the points f and a will be obtained by adding

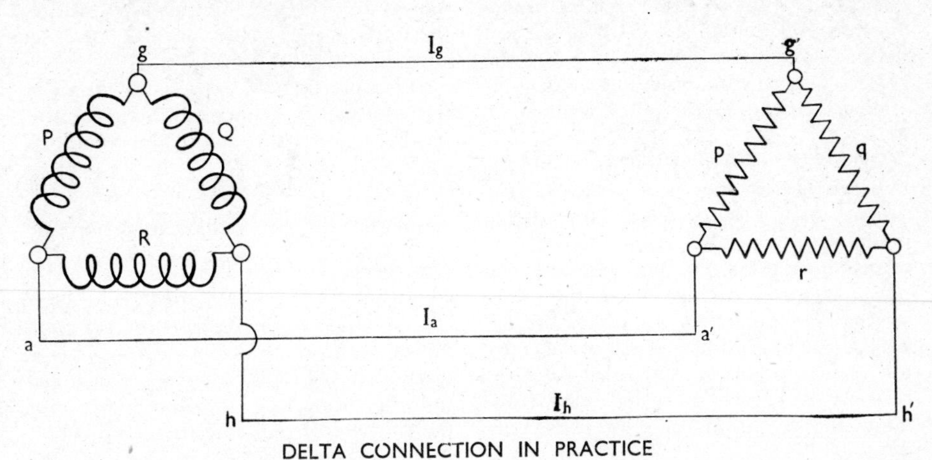

DELTA CONNECTION IN PRACTICE

Fig. 44. Alternative way of depicting a delta-connected three-phase system which is largely employed in practice. Compare this diagram with Fig. 43c which is theoretically identical.

Since the points a, c and e are each connected to their respective conductors, the line currents are evidently the same as the currents in the winding and loads, so that line current equals phase current.

DELTA-CONNECTED THREE-PHASE SYSTEM

An alternative method of reducing the number of conductors required for three-phase transmission is to connect the windings in delta or mesh. Referring first to Fig. 41a, the three A.C. generator windings P, Q and R can obviously be connected as in Fig. 43a, from which it will be seen that the wires bb′ and cc′ and

vectorially the voltages between the points a and h and between h and f, i.e., by adding vectorially OS and OR. Clearly this resultant is zero and since, therefore, there is no potential difference between the points f and a, these points can be connected together and the conductor ff[1] dispensed with. This has been done in Fig. 43c and thus, as in the case of the star connection, the number of conductors has been reduced to three. Fig. 44 is identical to Fig. 43c and shows the alternative method of representing the three-phase delta-connected system.

It will be clear from a study of Fig. 44 that each line must carry the resultant

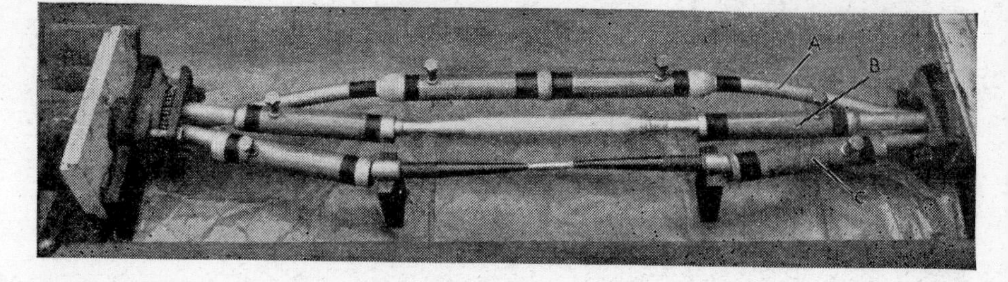

HIGH TENSION CABLES

Fig. 45. Showing cables which can carry an electrical pressure of 33,000 volts. The three-phase system described in the accompanying text is a standard method of high tension distribution.

of the currents in two phases. For example, I_g is the resultant of the currents in windings P and Q. It can be shown that the line current is equal to $\sqrt{3}$ times the phase current while the line voltage is obviously equal to the phase voltage.

POWER IN THREE-PHASE SYSTEM

Referring to Fig. 41a, suppose the loads p, q and r each consist of three equal impedances, i.e., the magnitudes of the three impedances are the same and the power factor of each circuit is the same, so that all the currents are equal and lag behind their respective phase voltages by the same angle ϕ. This, for obvious reasons, is known as a balanced load. Thus the power in each phase is $V_p I_p \cos\phi$, and the total power in the three phases is evidently obtained by adding the watts in each phase, or total power $= 3V_p I_p \cos\phi$.

It is convenient to express the power in terms of the line voltage and current and in the case of the star connection this becomes $3\frac{V_L}{\sqrt{3}} I_L \cos\phi = \sqrt{3}\, V_L I_L \cos\phi$

Similarly with the delta connection the total power $= 3\, V_L \frac{I_L}{\sqrt{3}} \cos\phi = \sqrt{3}\, V_L I_L \cos\phi$. Thus the expression for the total power is the same in both cases. This is obvious as the total power is not changed by interconnecting the conductors for the purpose of reducing their number.

SPECIAL INSULATION NEEDED

Fig. 46. Laying beside a railway line a special oil-filled cable for distributing power at high tension. Subsequently, the voltage is reduced by transformers for local distribution to consumers.

CHAPTER 2

SIMPLE APPARATUS AND MEASUREMENTS

Galvanometers. Ammeters and Voltmeters. Moving Iron Instruments. Dynamometers. Thermal Instruments. Electrostatic Voltmeters. Potentiometers. Measurements of Capacitance and Self-Inductance. Frequency Meters. General Considerations of Instruments. D.C. Meter Construction. Ampere-Hour Meters. Meters and Metering. Conductors. Insulating Materials. Magnetic Materials. Testing. Primary Cells. Accumulators and Accumulator Charging. Maintenance of Batteries.

THIS chapter, as the name implies, gives details of the various methods of measuring electricity and deals with the working and use of appliances for this purpose. It also describes various electrical materials as well as the best methods of storing small quantities of electricity. The Electrical Engineer should fully understand these subjects before studying the more complicated aspects of the generation of power which are dealt with in Chapter 3.

INSTRUMENTS AND MEASUREMENTS

CURRENT can be measured with a tangent galvanometer although it is not a very sensitive device. The value of the current in amperes is

$I = \frac{10\,H\,r}{2\pi n} \tan\phi$. For the detection of very small currents it is necessary to modify the construction so that the instrument is more sensitive. It can be seen from the above equation that to measure small currents the quantity $\frac{H\,r}{n}$ must be small. H represents the controlling magnetic force, n the number of turns on the coil and r the coil radius.

In sensitive galvanometers, the number of turns is greater than in the tangent galvanometer and the effect of the earth's field is reduced by the use of a control magnet or by using an astatic system. A control magnet is a bar magnet placed in such a position that the suspended galvanometer needle lies at an almost neutral magnetic point.

The astatic system reduces the control due to the magnetic field by the use of two magnets, one vertically above the other, and having equal magnetic moments. The couples are opposite due to the earth's field and are nearly equal, since the magnets are placed with opposite poles adjacent as shown in Fig. 1. A given current will now produce a much larger deflection than would be obtained by the use of a single magnet. The movement of the magnets may be magnified many times by the use of a mirror attached to the moving system.

A beam of light is projected on to the mirror and the reflected light is thrown on to a scale.

MOVING COIL GALVANOMETER

When a plane mirror is turned through an angle θ, the reflected beam is turned through an angle 2θ. The spot of light, on the scale, turns through twice the angle made by the magnets. In addition the beam is equivalent to a long pointer, which greatly increases the deflection for a given current.

When a current-carrying coil is suitably placed in a magnetic field, it tends to set

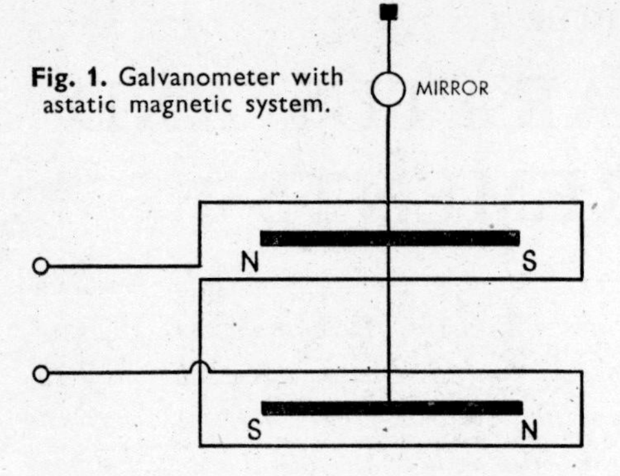

Fig. 1. Galvanometer with astatic magnetic system.

itself so that the plane of the coil is perpendicular to the lines of force. This fact is made use of in the moving coil galvanometer shown diagrammatically in Fig. 2. A light coil C is suspended between the poles of a permanent magnet, by a phosphor bronze strip D. This strip and the ligament B are used to carry the current to and from the coil. The angle through which the coil deflects is proportional to the current.

Galvanometers are usually employed to indicate a condition of balance, i.e., when zero potential difference exists between two points as, for example, in a bridge network. In this case it sometimes happens that the current through the galvanometer coil is excessive and so to prevent damage a conductor is placed in parallel until the current is reduced to a safe value. A conductor used for this purpose is called a shunt.

UNIVERSAL SHUNT

If I_G is the current in the galvanometer, I_S the current in the shunt and I the total current, then $I = I_G + I_S$. The ratio $\frac{I}{I_G}$ is the multiplying power M of the shunt.

Therefore $M = \frac{I_S + I_G}{I_G} = \frac{I_S}{I_G} + 1$

$= \frac{R_G}{R_S} + 1$ where R_G = resistance of galvanometer and R = shunt resistance.

A universal shunt can be used with any galvanometer and gives in each case the same multiplying power. The shunt consists of a resistance connected across the galvanometer terminals as shown in Fig. 3a. When the main current leads are connected to terminals T_1 and T_3 the galvanometer current $I_G = I \times \frac{R_S}{R_S + R_G}$

If now T_1 and T_2 are used I_G becomes

$$I \times \frac{R_S/n}{\left(R_G + R_S - \frac{R_S}{n}\right) + \frac{R_S}{n}}$$

$$= I \times \frac{R_S}{n(R_G + R_S)}$$

The current I_G is now one *nth* of its previous value. Therefore by tapping the resistance R_S at a number of points such as T_2 various multiplying powers can be obtained.

AMMETERS AND VOLTMETERS

For the measurement of current or voltage it is a great convenience to employ an instrument in which a pointer, moving across a scale, indicates directly the magnitude of the quantity.

Such instruments are called ammeters or voltmeters. There is no real difference in principle between them, as all the operating mechanisms are common to both. There is however one exception, this will be referred to later. The methods by which the movable system is made to deflect are used to denote the various

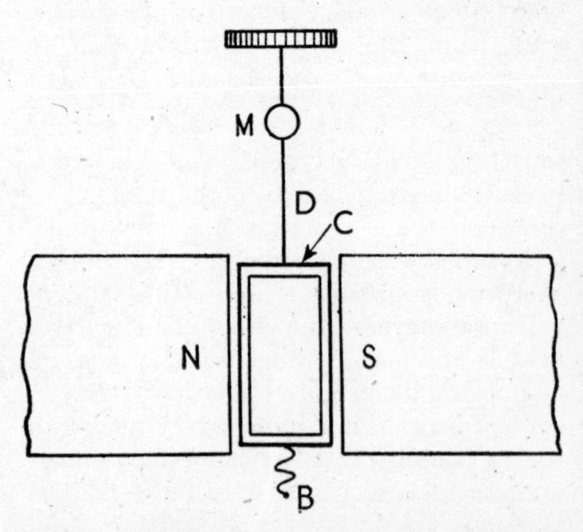

Fig. 2. Moving coil galvanometer. Readings are by reflected light beam from a small mirror, M.

types of instruments. The following types are in common use:—

(1) Moving coil permanent magnet, (2) Moving iron, (3) Thermal, (4) Electrostatic, (5) Induction and (6) Dynamometer. Numbers 2, 3, 4 and 6, can be used on either direct or alternating current circuits. No. 1 is suitable for measurements of direct current and No. 5 for alternating current only.

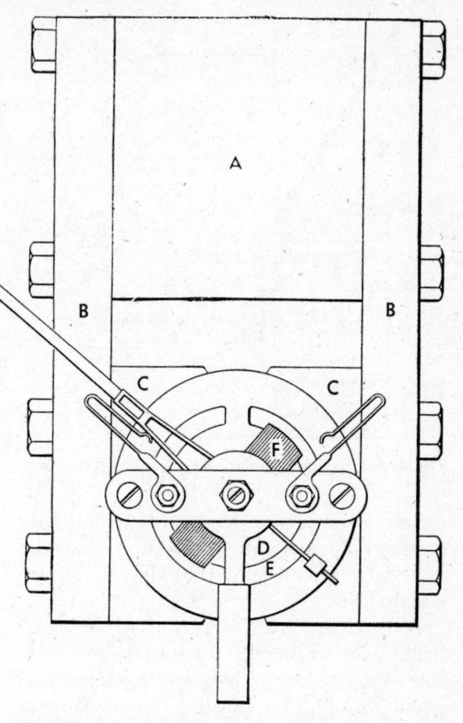

Fig. 3b. Everett-Edgcumbe moving-coil permanent-magnet instrument. Operating principle is similar to that illustrated in Fig. 2.

PERMANENT MAGNET

The moving coil type of permanent magnet instrument is very similar in design to that of the galvanometer in Fig. 2.

The general arrangement is shown in Fig. 3b. A is the permanent magnet of block form made from alnico steel. The extension pieces B.B. terminate in the poles C.C. In the space bounded by the poles is placed the core iron D, leaving a gap E in which the coil F is free to move.

The deflecting torque which is produced when current is passed through the coil is opposed by two flat spiral springs (not shown). The springs also serve as the flexible connection between the moving coil and the external circuit. Since the radial length of E is uniform, the flux density will be uniform also. The deflecting torque is proportional to the flux density B, and to the current I. It is equal to K B I where K is a constant depending on the length and breadth of the coil and the number of turns. Since, for a given instrument, B is constant, it follows that the deflection is equal to K I.

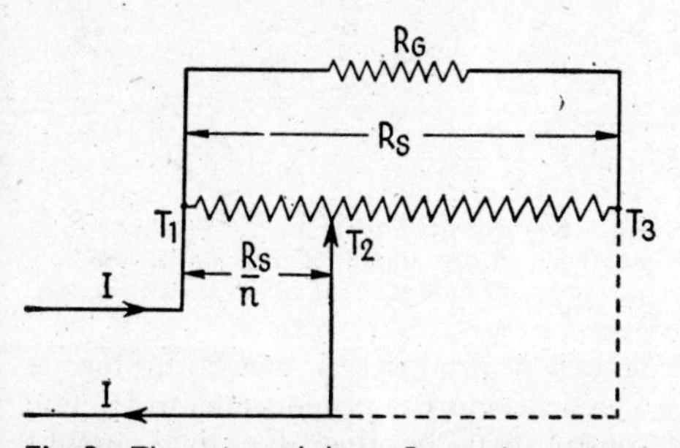

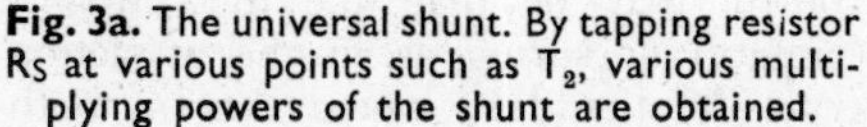

Fig. 3a. The universal shunt. By tapping resistor Rs at various points such as T_2, various multiplying powers of the shunt are obtained.

Therefore, the scale of amperes or volts is uniformly divided.

MOVING IRON INSTRUMENTS

There are two types in general use, these are:—(1) attraction; and (2) repulsion. In the former, a piece of iron is drawn towards the centre of a current-carrying coil, while the latter depends upon the repelling force produced by two similarly magnetised iron rods.

Attraction Type. Reference to Fig. 4 will show that this instrument consists of the coil A which carries the current to be measured, and the moving system comprising the soft iron disc B, the pointer C and the two weights $D.D_1$. The damping system E, which is of the air type, is to prevent the unnecessary oscillation of the moving system. When current passes round the coil a magnetic force is set up which magnetises the iron B. A deflecting

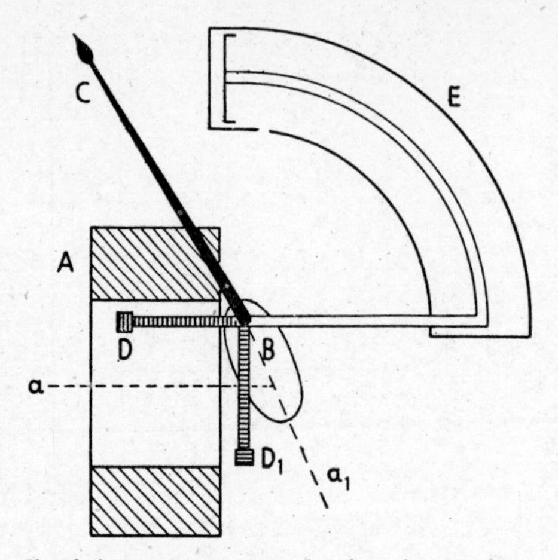

Fig. 4. Attraction type moving iron instrument.

torque is now produced and the moving system takes up a position such that the deflecting torque and that due to D_1 are equal.

It is clear from Fig. 5 that the controlling or restoring torque is given by the weight $D_1 \times$ distance r_1 which is equal to $D_1 \times r \sin \theta$. The restoring torque is, therefore, proportional to the sine of the angle through which the system has moved from its zero position. The weight D is used to balance the moving system, that is, to bring its centre of gravity through the axis of the spindle F. A flat spiral spring is employed sometimes to provide the necessary control, and therefore, it has the same function as the weight D_1. The magnetisation of the moving iron and the magnetic field within the coil are each proportional to the current, and consequently the deflecting force is proportional to I^2. The deflecting torque however depends upon the shape of the iron and its position relative to the axis of the coil. When the axes of the iron and coil are perpendicular the theoretical torque is zero, increasing to a maximum at 45° and falling again to zero when the axes are co-incident, or deflecting torque is given by $I^2 \sin 2\theta$ where θ is the angle between the axes a and a_1. Fig. 4 illustrates this point.

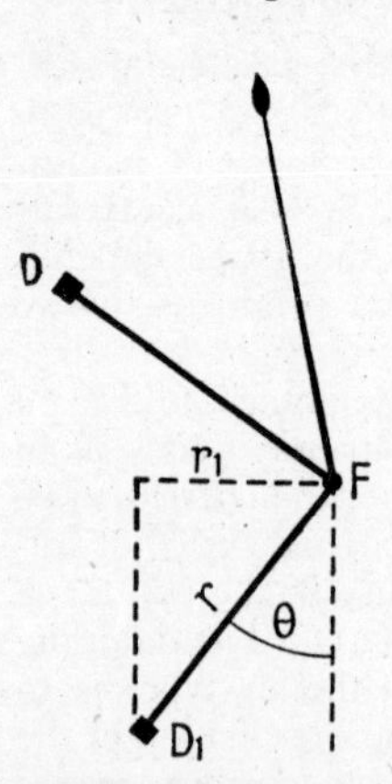

Fig. 5. Gravity control system of instrument shown in Fig. 4.

DEFLECTING TORQUE

In the repulsion type two irons are used and are fixed as shown in Fig. 6. The moving iron is usually rectangular whilst the fixed iron is tapered as shown. The two irons are magnetised when current flows in the coil and the force of repulsion produces a deflecting torque which as before is proportional to I^2. The control may be that due to a weight (gravity) or spring as in the attraction type. It should be noted that in both

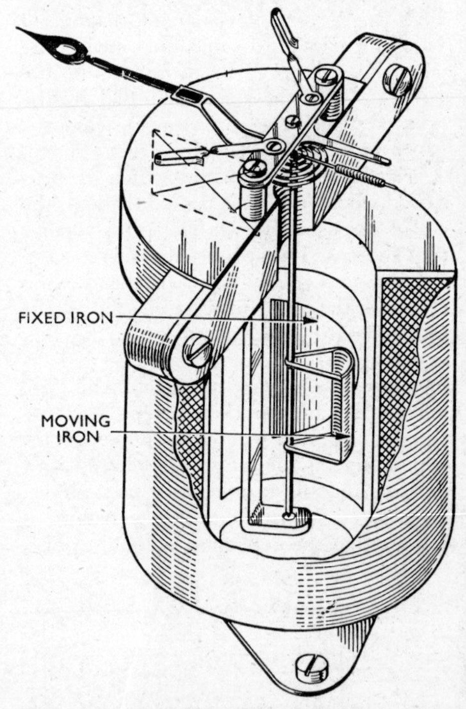

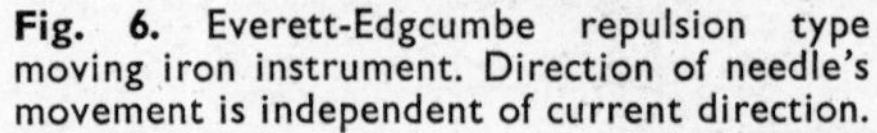
Fig. 6. Everett-Edgcumbe repulsion type moving iron instrument. Direction of needle's movement is independent of current direction.

types the deflection is independent of the direction of the current.

Dynamometer instruments do not as a rule make use of iron in their operation. The usual principle of such instruments is that of the interaction of magnetic fields produced by a fixed coil or coils and a movable coil. The arrangement is illustrated in Fig. 7. When current is passed through the two coils the resulting magnetic forces cause a clockwise movement of the movable coil, if the directions of the forces are as shown.

When the axes of the coils are parallel the deflecting torque is zero and when perpendicular, the torque is maximum. The controlling torque is provided by two flat spiral springs which serve, also, as the supply leads to the moving coil. The deflecting torque is proportional to the product of the two magnetic forces and, therefore, in an ammeter the torque is proportional to the square of the current. For this reason, dynamometer instruments are suitable for use on alternating as well as on D.C. circuits.

D.C. CALIBRATION

When they are used as ammeters the fixed and moving coils are connected in parallel as shown in Fig. 8. When calibrated on direct current, the resistances R_1 and R_2 of the parallel paths 1 and 2 will decide the ratio $\frac{If}{Im}$, but on alternating current it is the impedances Z_1 and Z_2 which settle this ratio.

In order that the instrument may read correctly on both circuits the ratios $\frac{R_1}{R_2}$ and $\frac{Z_1}{Z_2}$ must be the same.

To obtain this the two non-inductive resistances Rm and Rf are included as shown in Fig. 8.

When calibrating, the instrument is first tested on a direct current circuit and the deflection with a known current is observed. This is repeated with the same value of alternating current and, if necessary, adjustments are made on Rm or Rf. For use as voltmeters the two coils are connected in series, this combination being in series with a high non-inductive resistor.

The dynamometer construction is used with great success in one form of wattmeter.

For this purpose, the fixed coils are

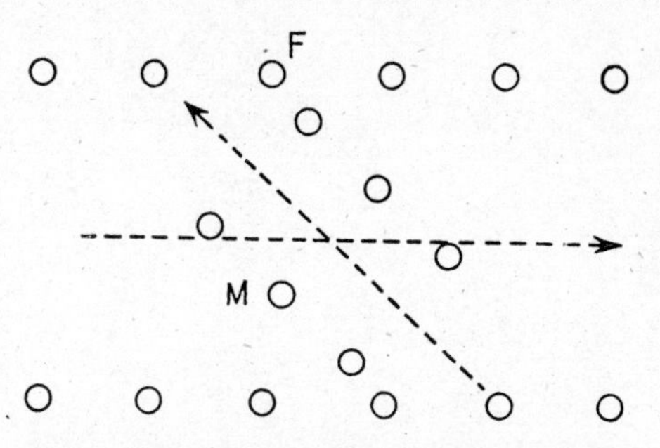

Fig. 7. Principle of the dynamometer instrument with fixed coil F and movable coil M.

put in series with the load, and the movable coil is connected across the load.

The movable coil has a high resistance in series and the current through it is proportional to the voltage across the load. The deflection of the pointer is proportional to the product of volts and amperes multiplied by the cosine of the angle of

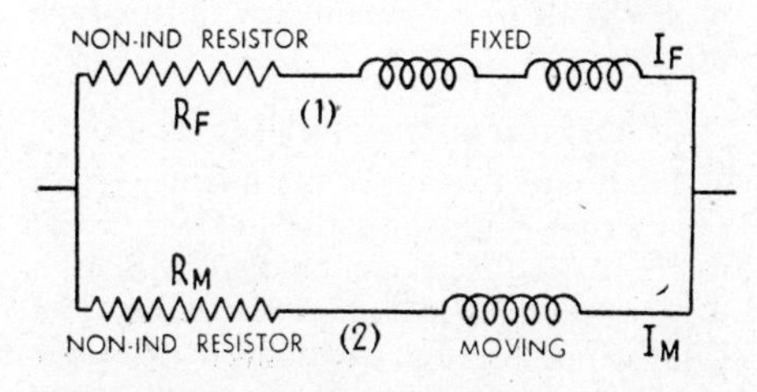

Fig. 8. Connection of the fixed and moving coils in the dynamometer ammeter.

phase difference between the voltage and the current, or watts = VI cos ϕ.

A typical wattmeter construction is shown in Fig. 9. The current coil C surrounds the moving coil MC. Air damping is employed as shown at N, and S is the control spring. The current enters and leaves the moving coil by means of the two silver ligaments B.B. which have a

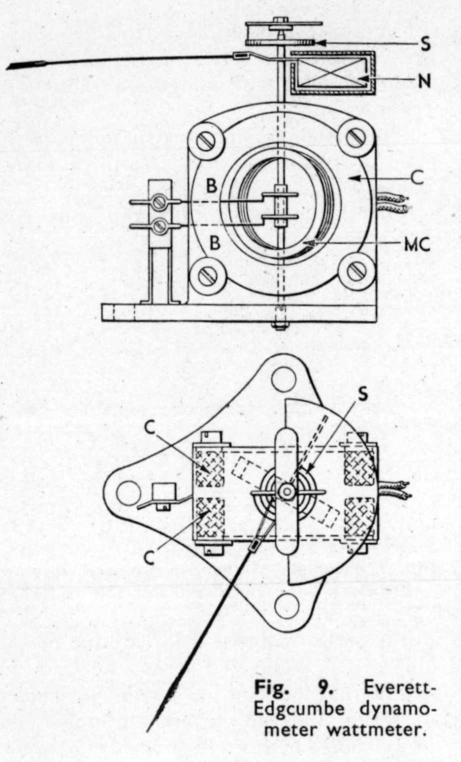

Fig. 9. Everett-Edgcumbe dynamometer wattmeter.

negligible effect on the moving parts of the meter. As will be seen the needle has a knife edge enabling very close readings on the scale to be obtained with this type of meter.

THERMAL INSTRUMENTS

There are two types (1) hot wire, and (2) thermo-couple. In the hot wire type, the heat produced by a current through a wire causes expansion of the wire. The lengthening is used to deflect a pointer across a scale of amperes or volts. Since the extension of the wire in a modern instrument is small, it becomes necessary to use a device to ensure a reasonable pointer deflection. Reference to Fig. 10 will show the general arrangement. The current to be measured is passed through the wire A by connection to the terminals TT. Attached at the point B is a second wire the other end of which is fixed at C. Joined at the point D is a silk thread which is passed round a pulley on the pointer spindle. When the wire is heated the sag is taken up by the spring S the silk thread being wound round the pulley, and the pointer is moved.

Thermo-couple instruments depend for their operation on the fact that if a closed circuit is made of two dissimilar metals and the temperature of one junction is raised or lowered relative to the other, an electromotive force is set up and a current will flow.

UNIVERSAL APPLICATION

The temperature of one junction is raised by a heater coil which carries the current to be measured. A permanent magnet moving coil instrument is inserted in the circuit formed by the dissimilar metals. The scale markings relate to the currents in the heater coil. A large number of materials is suitable for this purpose. An antimony-bismuth couple gives the largest E.M.F. Copper-constantan and manganin-constantan couples are in general use. The instrument deflection is proportional to the square of the heater current and, for this reason, the thermo-couple instrument can be used on both A.C. and D.C. circuits.

When a difference of potential is applied between two bodies a mechanical force is set up tending to bring the bodies together. The electrostatic voltmeter

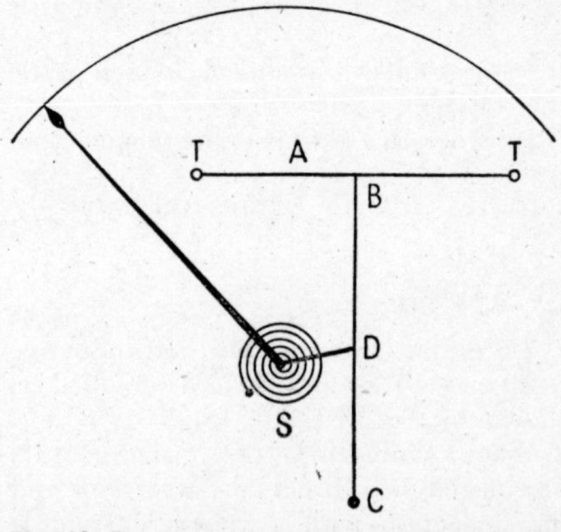

Fig. 10. Diagram showing the general arrangement of the hot wire principle. Currents up to 5 amperes are passed through the wire A, shunts being used for larger ones.

depends for its action on the production of such a force. The general construction of the instrument is therefore settled. It consists mainly, Fig 11, of two parts (1) fixed metal vane or vanes A, (2) movable metal vane or vanes B. When a difference of potential is applied between A and B the force set up causes the vane B to move in the direction of A. The opposing force is provided by a weight or spring. The two vanes form a condenser and, as is well known, when a potential difference is applied between the plates a quantity of electricity is displaced in the circuit. This displacement causes a lowering of the potential of one plate and a rise in the potential of the other, until the difference is equal to the applied voltage.

MULTI-CELLULAR VOLTMETER

This displaced quantity of electricity is in reality a migration of electrons from one plate to the other. Therefore, one plate becomes richer in electrons by the same number as the other plate becomes poorer. The force set up between the plates depends upon this fact and since both the increase and the decrease in the

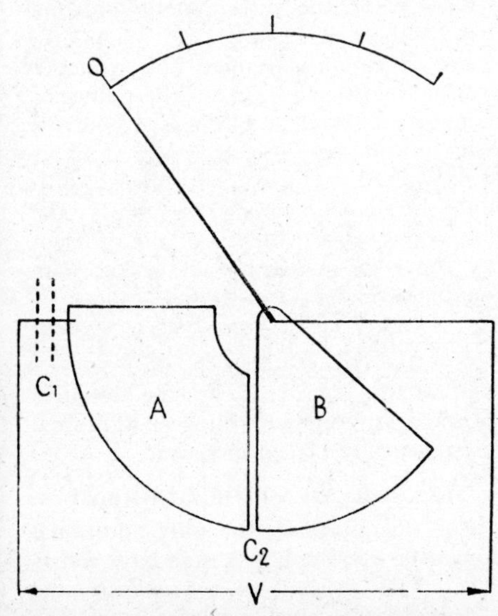

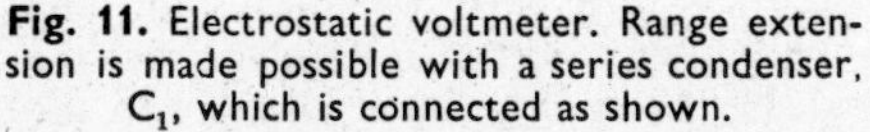

Fig. 11. Electrostatic voltmeter. Range extension is made possible with a series condenser, C_1, which is connected as shown.

number of the electrons is proportional to the voltage, the deflecting torque is proportional to the square of the voltage. In practice this provides the advantage

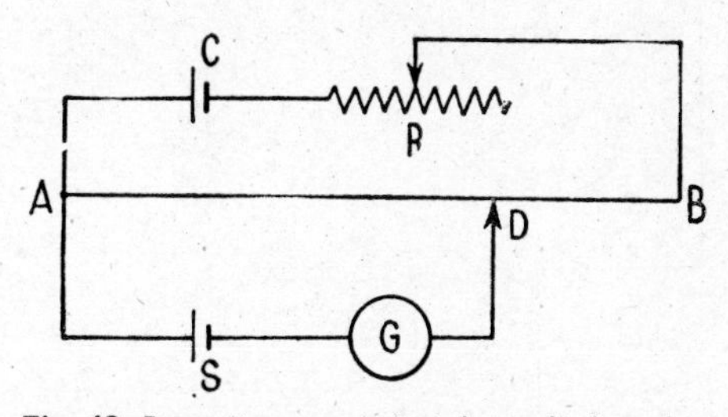

Fig. 12. Potentiometer principle applied to the measurement of voltages with the aid of a standard cell and a galvanometer.

that the instrument can be applied to either direct or alternating current circuits. For the measurement of low voltages of the order of two to three hundred, the working forces are extremely small if one pair of plates only is employed. In such a case, the number of fixed and movable plates is increased and is termed the multi-cellular voltmeter. The electrostatic voltmeter is sometimes used with a step-up transformer thus enabling low voltages to be measured by an instrument designed for much high pressures and, therefore, with larger working forces. The range of a given instrument may be extended by the use of a series condenser as shown dotted in Fig. 11. The voltage V_2 across the instrument is given by $V \times \frac{C_1}{C_1 + C_2}$ since the potential difference across each part is inversely proportional to its capacitance.

POTENTIOMETERS

A potentiometer is an instrument for the measurement of voltages. The principle is that of opposing a known against an unknown voltage. The known is that of a standard cell. The basis of the arrangement for direct current work is shown in Fig. 12.

The slide wire AB is connected to a battery C through a variable resistor R.

The slide wire is of uniform cross

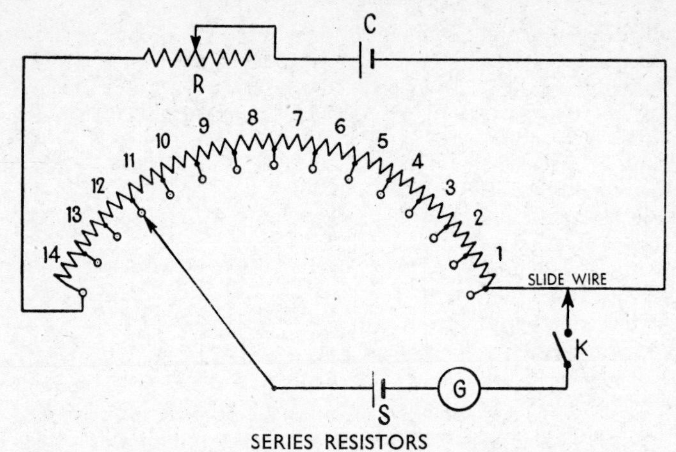

Fig. 13. Effective length of slide wire is increased by use of series resistors each having the same resistance.

section and, therefore, when it is carrying current, the potential difference across any part of the wire will be proportional to the length of that part. The standard cell is shown at S in series with a galvanometer G. The battery C represents the unknown voltage to be measured by this potentiometer method.

USE OF RESISTORS

The sliding contact D enables a point to be found on the slide wire at which the E.M.F. of the standard cell balances the potential difference across a part of the wire. Assume, for example, that the length of AB is 200 cms., and the length AD, at which the two voltages balance, is 101·83 cms. and the standard cell has an E.M.F. of 1·0183 volts. It follows, therefore, that the potential difference per cm. of wire is $\frac{1 \cdot 0183}{101 \cdot 83} = 0 \cdot 01$ volts, or 2 volts across the ends of the slide wire. If now an unknown voltage replaces that of the standard cell, a new point D can be found on the wire at which the two voltages are equal. Equality is indicated by the galvanometer G which is usually of the centre zero type. A high degree of precision in the measurement can be obtained by a simple method of increasing the effective length of the wire AB. This is done as shown in Fig. 13. The slide wire is connected in series with a number of resistors 1, 2, 3, etc., each having the same resistance as the slide wire. It follows that if there are say 14 resistors and the potential difference is adjusted to 0·1 volt per resistor the total voltage is therefore 1·5. Suppose the slide wire to be 100 cms. in length the addition of the resistors gives an effective length of 1,500 cms.

In setting up the instrument, the first thing to do is to set the movable contacts to the points corresponding to the E.M.F. of the standard cell. The resistor R is then adjusted to such a value that on closing the switch K no deflection of the galvanometer is observed. The standard cell is then replaced by the source whose e.m.f. is to be measured. The settings of the movable contacts which produce no deflection on the galvanometer indicate directly the new E.M.F.

For the measurement of voltages greater than that for which the potentiometer is adjusted, in the above case 1·5 volts, a volt ratio-box is required. This is illustrated in Fig. 14. It consists of a high resistance connected across the unknown source which is of the order of say 100 volts. A tapping at the 100 ohm point is brought out as shown.

The ratios $\frac{v}{V}$ and $\frac{100}{10000}$ are equal and therefore $V = v \times 100$. For the measurement of still higher voltages additional resistances are placed in series.

MEASUREMENT OF CURRENT

For this purpose, the only additional apparatus required is a standard resistance. The method is to measure the potential difference by means of the potentiometer across a standard resistor and, by the application of Ohm's law, the current can be calculated. The value in ohms of the standard resistance must be such that the current produces a volt drop across the resistance of the order of 0·5 to 1·0 volt. This method is used in the calibration of standard ammeters.

To measure an unknown resistance, it is connected in series with a standard resistance. A suitable current is then passed through the two, and the potential differences are measured. The ratio of the volt-drops is equal to the ratio of the two resistances.

MEASUREMENT OF CAPACITANCE

Many different methods are available for this measurement. The best usually involve some form of alternating current bridge. The magnitude of the capacitance also affects the choice. One of the simplest however is by ammeter and voltmeter, when a sine wave-form of voltage is available. A suitable ammeter is placed in series with the condenser and the two are connected across a supply of known frequency. A voltmeter, preferably of the electrostatic type, is joined across the terminals of the condenser. If the voltmeter indicates V volts and the ammeter I amperes and the frequency is f cycles per sec. then $I = 2\pi fCV$ and $C = \frac{I}{2\pi fV}$ where C is the capacitance in farads.

When the capacitance being measured is small, the parallel capacitance of the voltmeter cannot be neglected. Its value must be known and subtracted from that obtained for C above. A further difficulty arises due to the fact that the capacitance of the voltmeter varies with its deflection.

When a potential difference of V volts exists across the plates of a condenser of C farads, the displaced quantity of electricity Q coulombs is given by $C \times V$. The same displacement may be made to take place with two condensers of different capacitances, since $Q = C_1V_1 = C_2V_2$ and $\frac{C_1}{C_2} = \frac{V_2}{V_1}$. Therefore, if the two condensers are charged so that the potential difference across each is inversely proportional to its capacitance they will then hold equal charges. The test is carried out in the following manner. In the diagram, Fig. 15, R is a high resistance connected across the battery B. The movable contact A enables different voltages to be applied to the two condensers C_1 and C_s. The two voltages V_1 across C_1, and V_s across C_s, are proportional to R_1 and R_2 respectively.

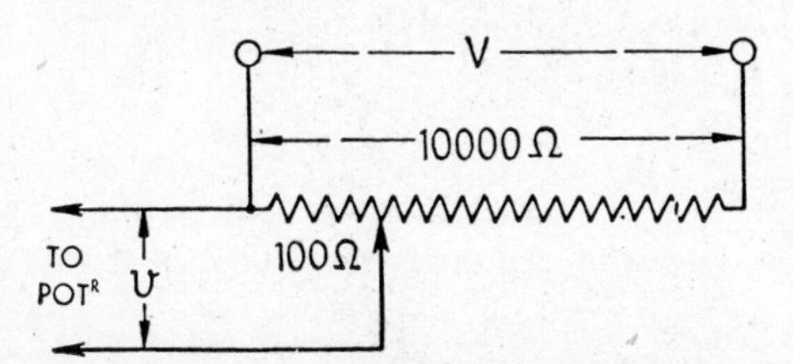

Fig. 14. Volt ratio resistor for widening scale of voltage measurements.

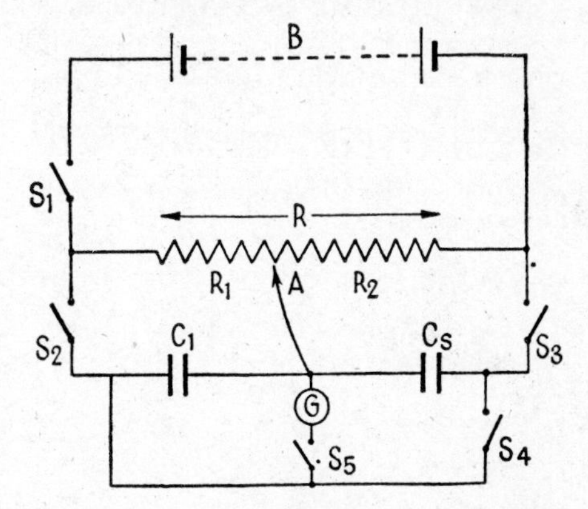

Fig. 15. Circuit for measurement of capacitance by mixture method.

MIXING OF CHARGES

When S_1 is closed a current passes along R producing the two volt drops V_1 and V_s. By closing the two switches S_2 and S_3 for a short period the condensers are charged. Now, switch S_4 is made and the two charges allowed to mix. When mixing is complete the switch S_5 is closed and if the original charges were equal the galvanometer will remain at zero. If a deflection is produced the ratio $\frac{R_1}{R_2}$ is changed and the test repeated. This procedure is continued until some ratio is found that, on closing S_5, the galvanometer deflection is zero. Then $C_1 = \frac{C_s R_2}{R_1}$. It is, of course necessary that the resistance should be smoothly and continuously variable and not one that is tapped at widely separated intervals.

MEASUREMENT OF INDUCTANCE

One method is based on the fact that the current I in an inductive circuit is given by $I = \frac{V}{Z}$ where V is the difference of potential across the circuit and Z is its impedance.

Now $Z = \frac{V}{I} = \sqrt{R^2 + (2\pi fL)^2}$ where R is the resistance, f the frequency, and L the inductance in henrys.

Therefore $L = \frac{\sqrt{\left(\frac{V}{I}\right)^2 - R^2}}{2\pi f}$

Potentiometer Method. This is a more precise method than that described above, and in addition to the inductance, the phase angle can be obtained. A non-inductive resistance R, of known value, must be connected in series with the coil and the potential differences V_1 and V_2, as shown in Fig. 16, must be measured.

The current is given by $\frac{V_1}{R}$ and Z (of coil) $= \frac{V_2}{V_1} R$. If the coil resistance is R_1

then $L = \frac{\sqrt{\left(\frac{V_2}{V_1} R\right)^2 - R_1^2}}{2\pi f}$

Let the phase angle of V_2 with respect to V_1 be ϕ, then $R_1 = \frac{V_2}{V_1} R \cos \phi$ and the reactance $X = 2\pi fL = \frac{V_2}{V_1} R \sin \phi$

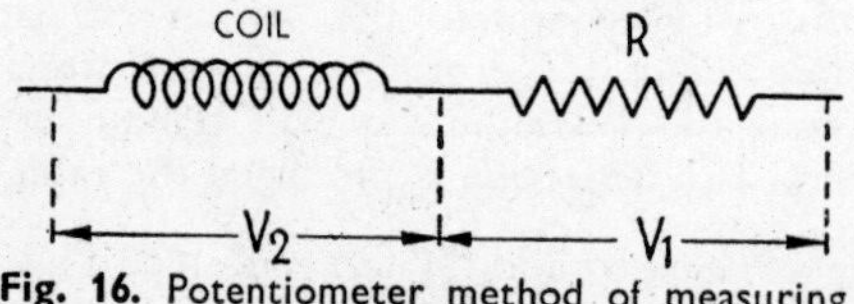

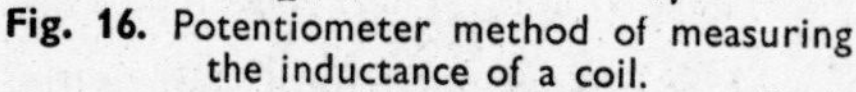

Fig. 16. Potentiometer method of measuring the inductance of a coil.

The power taken by the coil is given by $\frac{V_2 V_1}{R} \cos \phi$.

Bridge Methods. These are based on the original Wheatstone bridge so largely used in the measurement of resistance. In the measurement of inductance (or capacitance) alternating currents are employed. It follows, therefore, that to

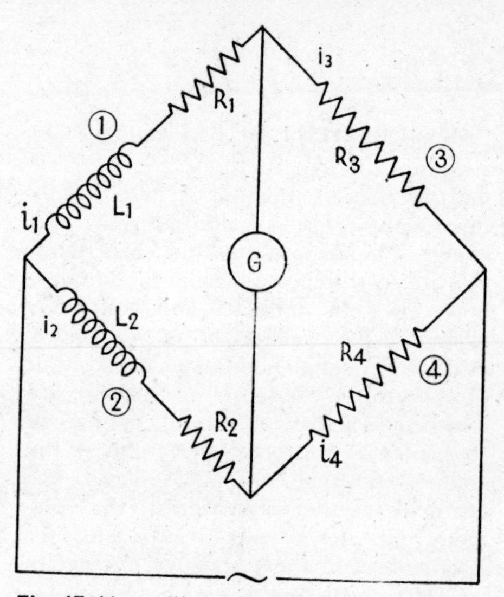

Fig. 17. Maxwell's bridge for the measurement of self-inductance based on the Wheatstone bridge which is widely used for the measurement of resistance.

obtain a balance, not only must the potential differences be identical in magnitude, but they must have the same phase also.

Maxwell's Method. It will be seen in the diagram, Fig. 17, that when balance is obtained the volt drop across circuit (1) is equal to that across circuit (2) and that across (3) is equal to that across (4). It follows that $(R_1 + j\omega L_1)i_1 = (R_2 + j\omega L_2)i_2$

and $R_3 i_3 = R_4 i_4$

also $(R_1 + j\omega L_1)i_1 \times R_4 i_4 = (R_2 + j\omega L_2)i_2 \times R_3 i_3$

At balance $i_1 = i_3$ and $i_2 = i_4$

Therefore $(R_1 + j\omega L_1)R_4 = (R_2 + j\omega L2)R_3$

$= R_1 R_4 + j\omega L_1 R_4 = R_2 R_3 + j\omega L_2 R_3$

In order to satisfy the requirements of

phase and magnitude, mentioned above. we have

$$R_1R_4 = R_2R_3 \text{ and } L_1R_4 = L_2R_3$$

$$\text{and } \frac{R_1}{R_2} = \frac{R_3}{R_4} = \frac{L_1}{L_2}$$

Resonance Method. In this, three arms of the bridge are non-inductive resistors, the fourth comprising an inductance L, and condenser C in series denoted by R_1 Fig. 18. At some particular frequency

$2\pi fL = \frac{1}{2\pi fC}$ and the circuit is in resonance and, therefore, non-reactive. The bridge is balanced in this condition

when $R_1R_4 = R_2R_3$ and $L = \frac{1}{\omega^2 C}$

FREQUENCY METERS

These meters indicate directly the frequency of the supply, to which they are connected. In the vibrating reed type, Fig. 19, a number of tuned steel reeds are made to link with the magnetic flux produced by a current carrying coil. The reeds are fixed securely at one end and they are adjusted to have a particular natural period of oscillation. When this natural period of oscillation corresponds to twice that of the current in the coil, the reed will vibrate. The amplitude of vibration will rapidly fall as the frequency of the current is varied. Therefore, a number of reeds will cover a definite range of frequencies. The frequency to which a particular reed vibrates can be read on a suitably placed scale.

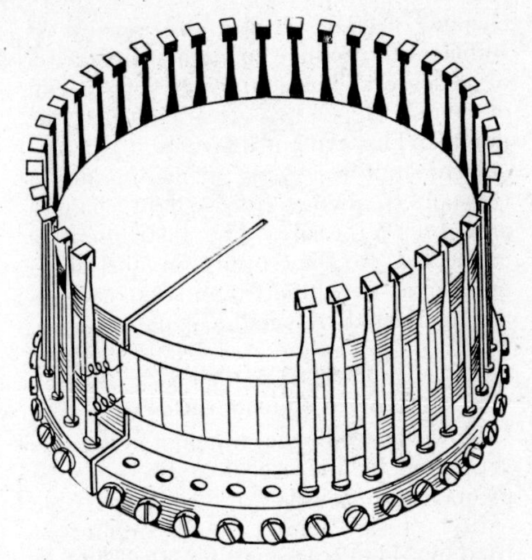

Fig. 19. Everett-Edgcumbe vibrating reed frequency meter which embodies tuned steel reeds linking with the magnetic flux.

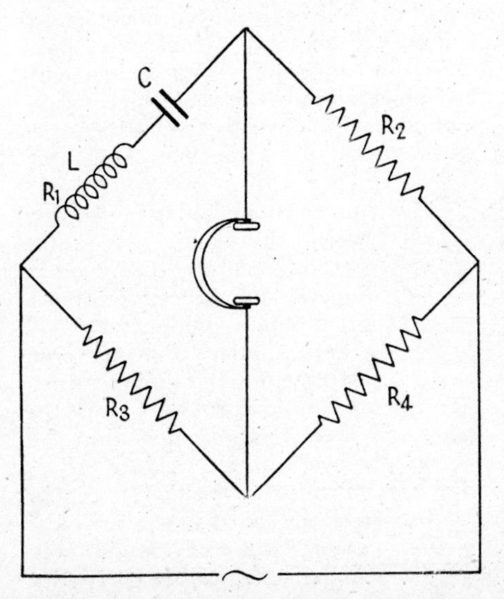

Fig. 18. Resonance method of inductance measurement using three non-inductive resistors.

DEFLECTIONAL FREQUENCY METERS

Among several meters of this type one of the best known is that due to Colman (Everett-Edgcumbe). It consists, as shown in Fig. 20 of two coils, A and A_1 each of which is connected in series with a condenser and inductor. Included also is a pair of moving irons BB so placed as to swing freely inside the coils. The irons will be pulled one way or the other depending upon the currents in the two coils. A pointer is fixed to the same shaft as the irons, and this moves across a scale marked in cycles per second. The circuit A_1 is tuned to a frequency a little above and circuit A a little below the upper and lower marked frequencies. With this arrangement a considerable deflection is possible with quite a small change in frequency. For example, a change of four cycles per second is sufficient to produce an angular deflection of 90 degrees. The actual scale length will, of course, depend on the length of the pointer. This type of instrument is particularly suitable for use in maintaining a constant frequency, since slight changes are observed easily. The instrument is connected to the supply in the same manner as a voltmeter, and its readings are unaffected by small voltage changes.

INSTRUMENTS
(General Considerations)

However well the moving system is supported by the use of highly polished pivots and jewels, it is impossible entirely to prevent a small amount of friction. The frictional force set up is dependent on the weight of the moving system and it must be masked by providing a large deflecting force. To this end, use is made of the torque/weight ratio. The value of this ratio for a given instrument is such that the effects of friction are kept within acceptable limits. In some cases it is possible to get the desired result easily, in others difficult or impossible.

F. E. J. Ockenden gives the following values as typical. For a 6 in. moving coil, permanent magnet instrument, the torque, at full scale deflection of 100 deg. is 500 mg. cms., the weight of the moving system being 3 grs. The torque/weight ratio is, therefore, 0·0017 gr. cms. per degree, per gr. weight.

For a 6 in. moving iron instrument the corresponding figures are:—torque, 140 mg. cms., weight 2 grms. and torque/weight ratio 0·0007 grm. cms. per degree per gr. weight. These figures are for ammeters and voltmeters. For dynamometer wattmeters the torque/weight ratio is 0·0012.

The flux densities required for satisfactory operation, depend to a great extent on the type of instrument, and the precision required. In the case of a moving coil, permanent magnet ammeter or voltmeter the flux density in the gap is roughly 1500 lines per sq. cm. which is raised to approximately 2000 for recorder types.

FLUX DENSITIES

In moving iron instruments, the flux density varies according to the permissible errors. For example, in instruments of the sub-standard class, the flux densities rarely exceed 500 lines per sq. cm. since immunity from wave-form errors is important. With switchboard instruments however, where high torque is of primary importance the flux densities are increased to as much as 2000 lines per sq. cm.

For a 6-in. switchboard type moving coil instrument the figure is 0·6, the maximum current being 0·025 ampere, and the coil resistance is 1·0 ohm.

For similar moving iron instruments, the ampere turns are approximately 350, the power required for the coil being 1·5 to 2·0 watts.

Pivots are made of carbon steel not less than 1·2 per cent. carbon, since only in this way can be obtained the necessary strength and hardness to resist wear due to continuous use.

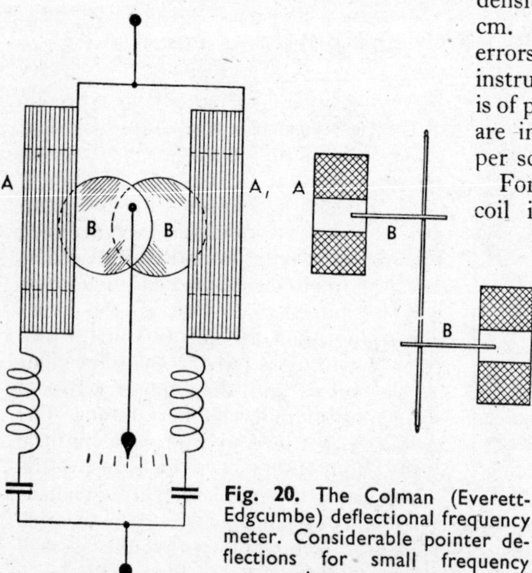

Fig. 20. The Colman (Everett-Edgcumbe) deflectional frequency meter. Considerable pointer deflections for small frequency changes are given.

METERS AND METERING

Electricity is a form of energy, that is, it is capable of doing work. In order to assess the value of any such work done, it is necessary to make measurements. One important electrical quantity to be measured is the Board of Trade Unit which is equal to 1,000 watt-hours. This unit involves a measurement of power and time. Instruments for this purpose are called electricity supply meters. They consist of two main parts: (1) that dealing with the power, and (2) that taking account of time.

D.C. METER CONSTRUCTION

Most meters for the purpose of measuring Board of Trade Units are really small electric motors. The construction consists, therefore, in the main of a current carrying conductor lying in a magnetic field so arranged that the direction of the current is perpendicular to the direction of the magnetic force. It is well known that under such conditions the conductor will experience a mechanical force and, if it is free, movement will take place. The force which is set up is proportional to the current in the conductor and to the magnitude of the magnetic flux. This force is equal to a constant multiplied by the magnetic flux and the current. The power, in watts, at any instant in an electric circuit is equal to the product of volts and amperes. If, therefore, the magnetic flux is proportional to the electric pressure, and the current in the conductor is proportional to the current to be measured then, from what has been said above, the force exerted on the conductor will be proportional to the power in the circuit.

The supply pressure at consumers' terminals is required by law to be maintained within $\pm$ six per cent. of the declared pressure. For small consumers, this fact makes it possible to construct a meter of simpler form than that required for large installations.

When the electric pressure varies but little, or even up to the maximum permissible, it is assumed in one well-known range of meters that the pressure does not vary at all. It is then possible to construct the meter with a permanent magnet to provide the necessary magnetic field and, then, with the addition of the current carrying conductor we have the required components for the measurement of the power. Such a meter is called an ampere-hour meter.

The best and most popular form of ampere-hour meter, for direct current circuits, consists of a permanent magnet and a disc of copper which is immersed in mercury and placed between the poles of the magnet, as shown in Fig. 21.

The current to be measured enters the mercury bath at the terminal J, passes

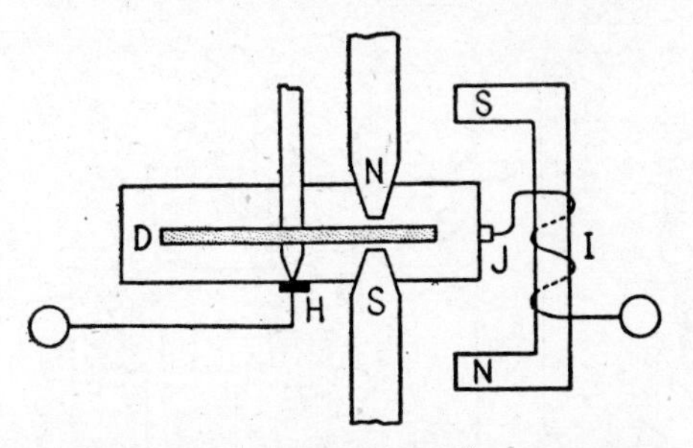

Fig. 21. Mercury motor meter. Current passes radially across the disc D between the poles of the permanent magnet.

across the mercury to the copper disc and then leaves the disc via the spindle and the terminal H. It will be seen from this construction that rotation of the disc is obtained, and the speed, when the meter is correctly adjusted, is proportional to the current passing through the disc. The speed of the disc will depend upon the force acting on the disc and the speed will remain constant when the applied force remains constant. The applied force multiplied by the distance from the spindle at which the force acts is called the turning moment, or the torque, and this torque is opposed by an equal and opposite braking torque. The braking torque is produced automatically because as the disc rotates magnetic lines of force are cut and eddy currents are induced in the disc. These react on the magnetic force producing them and tend to retard the movement of the disc.

The maximum speed of the disc which, of course, occurs at maximum disc current is approximately forty revolutions per minute. It is found, however, that there is a tendency at the higher currents for the speed to fall away. This is due to the friction which occurs between the disc and the mercury, the friction increases rapidly as the higher speeds are reached. To overcome this, the strength of the magnet is reduced by the action of the solenoid shown at I in Fig. 21.

The action of this solenoid is as follows:—The iron core of the solenoid has poles as shown and the magnetic strength of the core will depend on the strength of the current. The stronger the iron core the larger will be the diversion of magnetic flux from the permanent magnet.

Now since the driving torque is proportional to the flux passing across the disc and the braking torque proportional to the square of this flux, the net result will be a relative increase in the driving torque. Therefore, at the higher currents the linear relationship between current and speed will be maintained. Since the speed of the disc is proportional to the power, assuming constant voltage, the number of revolutions of the disc in a given time will be, therefore, proportional to power multiplied by time. Therefore the number of revolutions of the disc can be converted directly into watt-hours and from these into kilowatt hours or Board of Trade Units.

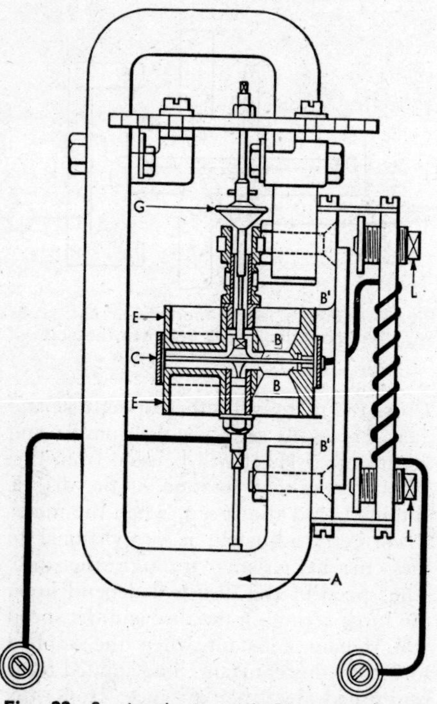

Fig. 22. Sectional view of Chamberlain and Hookham mercury motor ampere-hour meter. Its principle of operation is essentially similar to that illustrated in Fig. 21.

WATT-HOUR METERS

In Fig. 22 is shown, in section, the complete meter manufactured by Chamberlain and Hookham, Ltd. The permanent magnet A is fitted with wrought iron poles pieces B^1 B^1 which terminate in the circular poles B B.

The space, between the two brass castings E E is filled with mercury and in this bath is placed the copper disc or armature. The pole pieces B B are screwed into the castings and project into the mercury. The metal ring C, which is lined with leather, surrounds the two brass castings and forms the side of the mercury chamber. The brass weight G is to prevent the armature floating on the mercury.

The two screws L L enable slight adjustments to be made in the amount of flux diversion, and so obtain fine speed variation.

For currents greater than 10 amperes, the meter is shunted.

In the case of large consumers or where there is a large fluctuation in the voltage, a true watt-hour meter is required. For this purpose, a modification of the ampere-hour meter design is adopted. To do this it is necessary to

FIXED CHARGE COLLECTOR

Metering of electricity supplies for domestic premises involves the use of some very interesting apparatus to meet the requirements of modern tariffs and hire-purchase schemes. Here, for example, is a Sangamo fixed charge collector which operates on the principle of subtracting over a given period a predetermined sum from the amount credited by a prepayment meter.

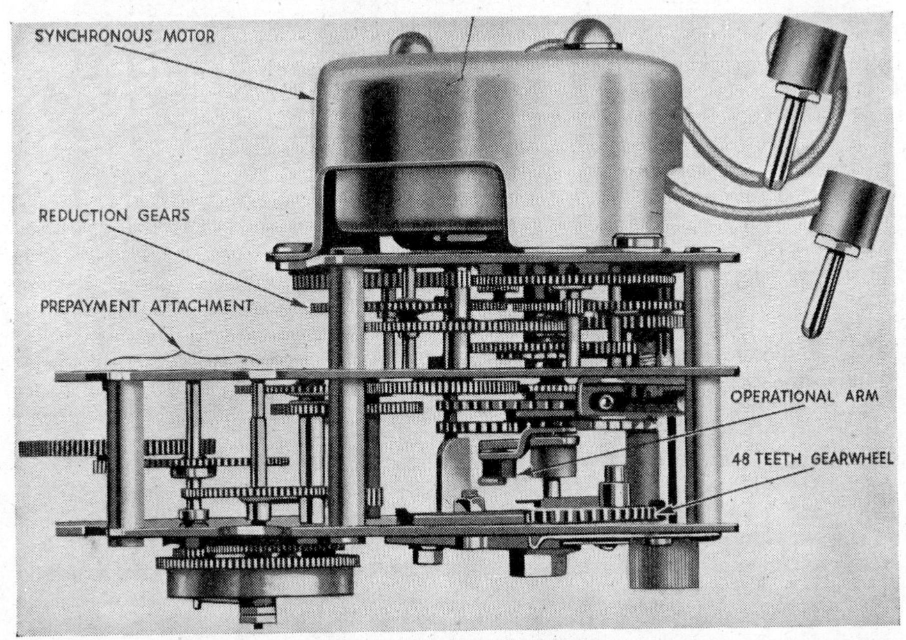

MECHANISM OF COLLECTOR

Showing the driving motor and reduction gearing of the British Sangamo fixed charge collector. This unit is housed together with a prepayment attachment and meter element in the one compact bakelite casing. By means of a simple adjustment the collector can be made to collect any sum from ½d. to 7/6d. per week in ½d., 1d. or 2d. increments

replace the permanent magnet by an electro-magnet, the permanent magnet being retained for braking purposes.

The construction of the meter can be seen by reference to Fig. 23. The armature A is a copper disc and is immersed in mercury. The magnetic field is set up by the two coils G G placed on the laminated electro-magnet K. They are connected across the load, the energy to which is being measured. The magnetic field which is set up passes through the disc A and the magnetic circuit is completed by the iron ring Q. A band of insulating material W is fixed between the two portions of the mercury chamber, and by means of the terminals X X the current is conveyed to and from the armature A. The braking disc O and the armature A are fixed to the vertical spindle B, the lower end of which rests on the jewelled bearing set in the screw F. The clock or counting mechanism is driven by the pinion N. The speed at which the armature rotates is proportional to the current passing through it and to the strength of the magnetic field produced by the coils G G. The speed is proportional, therefore, to the power supplied to the load.

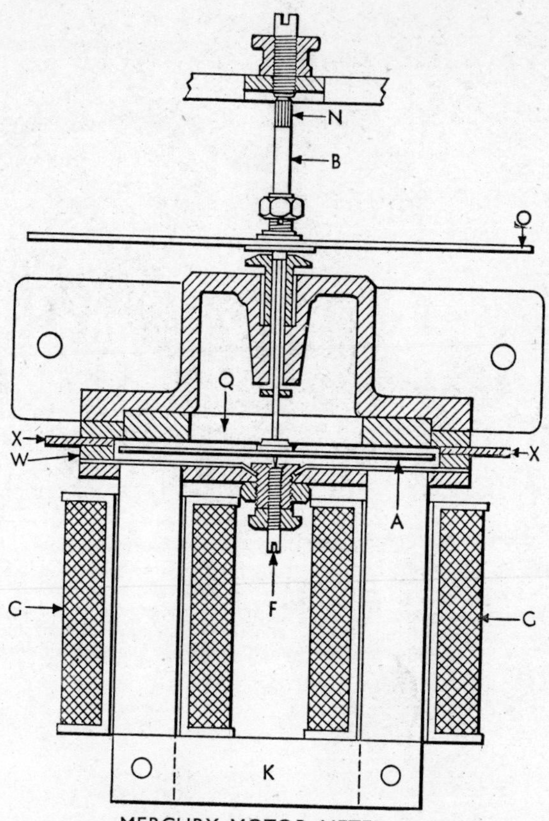

Fig. 23. Chamberlain and Hookham mercury motor watt-hour meter for direct current. Electro-magnet replaces the permanent magnet which is retained only for braking purposes.

A.C. METERS

Induction Type Single-Phase Watt-Hour Meter. This meter consists of three main parts:—

(1) The voltage element. That which produces a magnetic force proportional to the voltage of the mains.

(2) The current element. That which produces a magnetic force proportional to the current in the mains.

(3) An aluminium disc which is rotated by the interaction of currents and magnetic forces. The voltage element consists, as shown in Fig. 24, of a coil C of many turns wound on a laminated iron core A. The inductance is made large and the resistance is kept low, in order that the phase angle of the coil shall be as big as possible. The current element consists of a coil B, of a few turns, wound also on a laminated iron core. The aluminium disc D is mounted between the two elements.

In order to understand the working principle consider first the two elements separately.

The voltage element has an iron circuit which is complete, except for the two air gaps E E, Fig. 24. The magnetic potential across the gaps is large and this causes

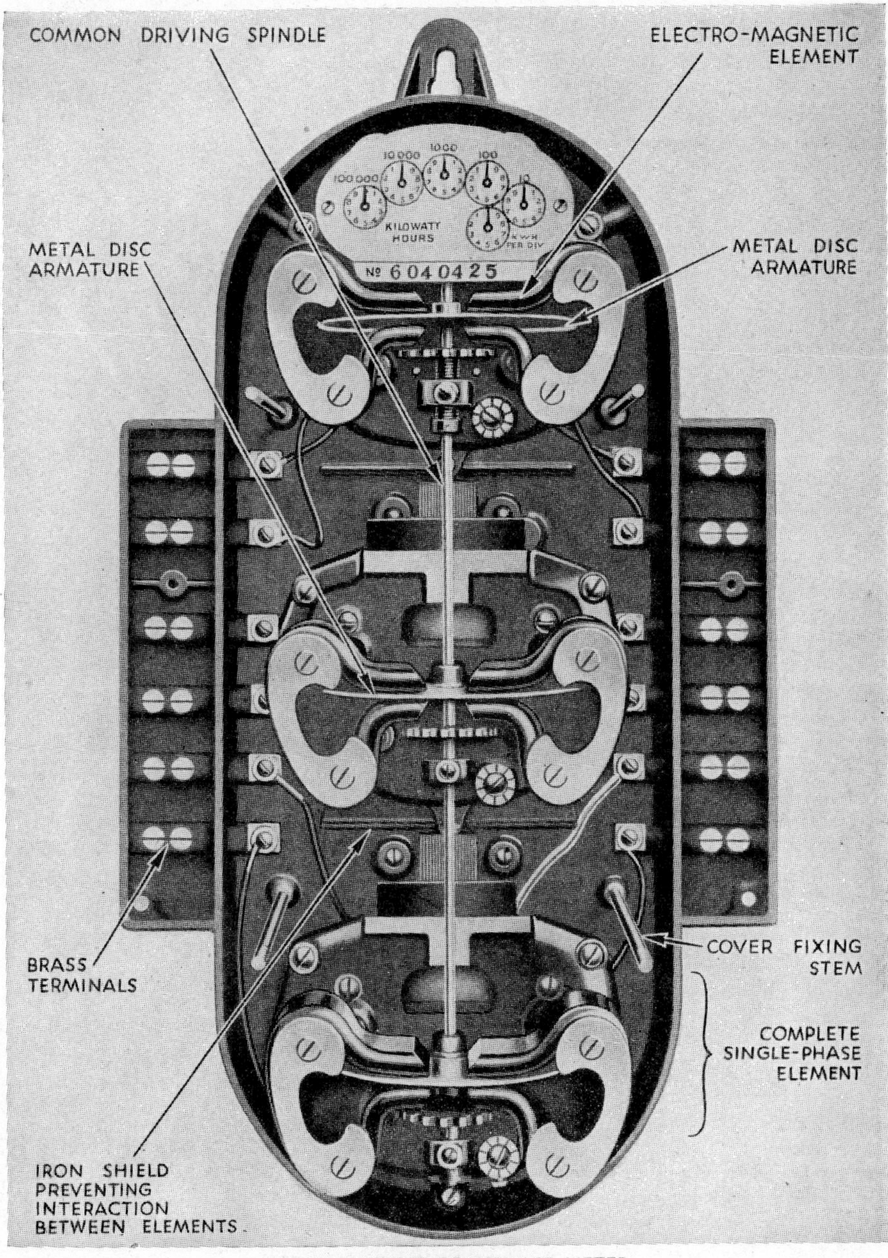

THREE-ELEMENT POLYPHASE METER

As is explained on page 59, the problem of metering three-phase supplies can be solved by regarding it as simply that of making three simultaneous single-phase measurements. It is not necessary, however, to use separate meters. The three meter elements can be built together and made to operate a common spindle and thus provide a total energy reading. This is the principle embodied in this British Sangamo three-element, four-wire polyphase watt-hour meter.

some of the lines of force to cut the disc, as shown by the dotted line. Since the magnetic force is alternating, eddy currents are induced in the disc at F. This fact is important as it is an essential condition for the production of torque on the disc.

The magnitude of the eddy currents is proportional to the rate of change of the magnetic force and consequently a 90 deg. phase angle exists between these two quantities.

The purpose of the voltage element is the production of eddy currents in the disc which shall be proportional to the applied voltage and in phase with it.

This is obtained in the following way:—

When the potential difference for which the coil is designed is applied to its terminals, a current will flow. This current is proportional to, and nearly 90 deg. lagging on the voltage. The current and resulting magnetic force are in phase. Therefore, the applied voltage is in quadrature with the magnetic force. The eddy currents being at 90 deg. with respect to the magnetic force, it follows that the applied voltage is in phase with the eddy currents induced in the disc.

It will be seen from Fig. 24 that eddy currents are induced in the disc by the current element also. It will be noted, however, that the coil current and the eddy currents are 90 deg. out of phase. Reference should now be made to the vector diagram Fig. 25. The applied voltage V gives rise to the current I_S, which produces the magnetic force Φ_S. The eddy currents I_E, being at 90° with respect to Φ_S, are consequently in phase with V. Assuming the power factor of the load to be unity the main current I_C will be in phase with V, as also is the magnetic force Φ_C set up by the current element. The eddy currents due to rate of change of Φ_C are shown by I_{EE}. The phase relationships of the following quantities should be noted specially. The eddy currents I_E are in phase with Φ_C and the eddy currents I_{EE} are in phase with Φ_S.

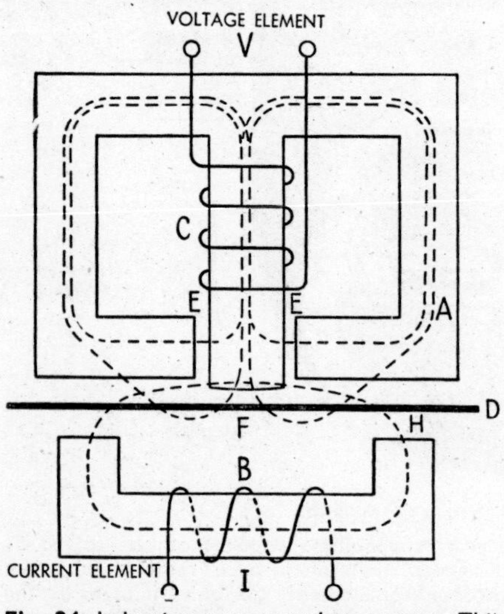

Fig. 24. Induction type watt-hour meter. This can be used on alternating current circuits.

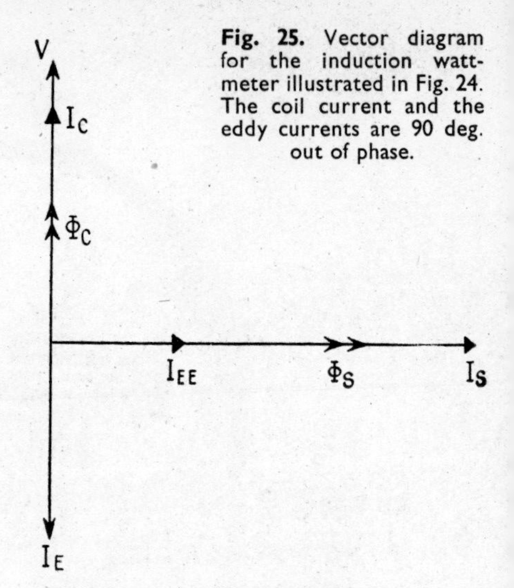

Fig. 25. Vector diagram for the induction wattmeter illustrated in Fig. 24. The coil current and the eddy currents are 90 deg. out of phase.

METERING OF SUPPLIES

The interaction of these quantities of similar phase produces a torque on the disc. In each case, one quantity is made proportional to the applied voltage and the other proportional to the current, therefore, the torque is proportional to the product, volts × amperes.

When the load is not wholly resistive, it can be seen, by an appropriative change in the vector diagram, that the torque on the disc is proportional to VI cos ϕ which is the power in the load, ϕ being the phase angle between V and I_c.

Measurement of the energy supplied to a load is one of the most important operations connected with the supply of electricity. Metering of supplies involves not only the use of an accurate meter, but also its correct connection in the circuit.

When the current in the line and the potential difference across the lines are greater than those for which the meter is designed, care and skill are needed to ensure that a true miniature or known percentage of the larger quantity is being passed through the meter.

D.C. TWO-WIRE SUPPLIES

For small loads, such as those of private consumers, an ampere-hour meter is frequently used and is connected in the circuit as if it were an ammeter. Since the meter possesses two terminals only, there is little likelihood of error in connecting up, but care must be taken to see that the leads to the meter are screwed into the proper terminals, otherwise the armature will rotate in the wrong direction.

For bigger loads a true watt-hour meter is employed, the connections being as shown in Fig. 26. When the current in the line is greater than 10 amperes a shunt is employed. This is usually internal up to currents of 50 amperes and external for currents above this figure.

Shunts are made in standard sizes up to about 10,000 amperes. Larger shunts are made as required.

The pressure circuit can be made for direct connection to supplies at a voltage up to 550 volts, and may be used on any

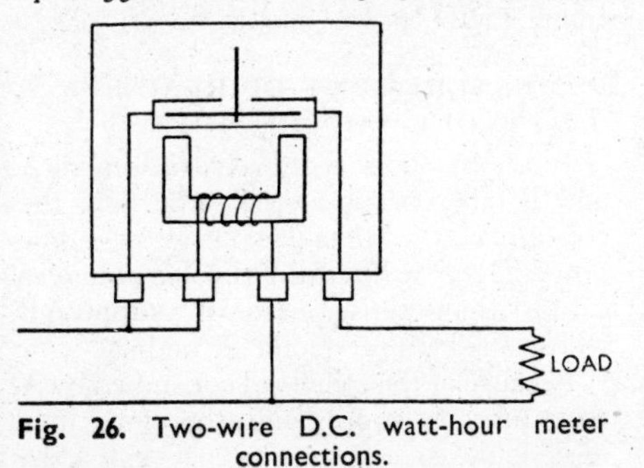

Fig. 26. Two-wire D.C. watt-hour meter connections.

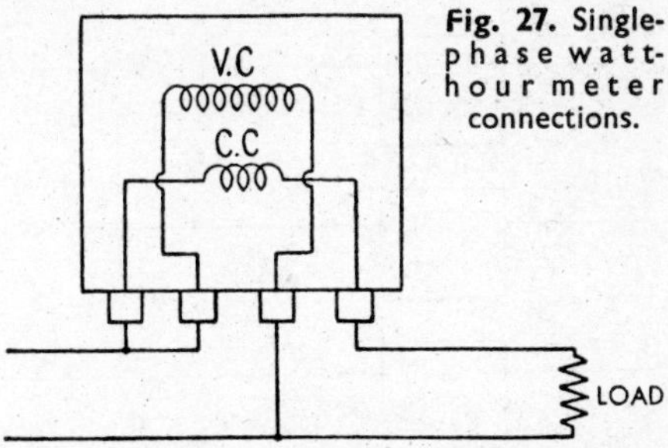

Fig. 27. Single-phase watt-hour meter connections.

voltage within 20 per cent. above or below that for which the meter is adjusted.

For the measurement of energy in three-wire direct current supplies, it is usual to use two two-wire meters. Each meter is wound for the voltage between outer and neutral conductors and therefore the total energy is given by the sum of the readings of the two meters.

SINGLE-PHASE METERS

The connections are arranged as shown in Fig. 27 there being one current and one pressure winding. The meter reads the energy in the circuit independently of the power factor.

THREE-PHASE METERS

Unbalanced Load. The problem of metering three-phase supplies, can be solved by regarding it as simply that of making three simultaneous single-phase measurements. Therefore, this can be done by the connections shown in Fig. 28 in which three single-phase meters are employed.

The current coils are connected, one in each line and the pressure coils between one line and the neutral point NP. The total energy is given by the sum of the three meter readings.

An unbalanced three-phase load can be obtained by connecting two resistances across the points AB and BC, Fig. 28, with the load shown first removed. Under these new conditions the line 2 serves as a common lead to the two resistances. Therefore, it is apparent that if two single-phase watt-meters are placed, with their current coils in lines 1 and 3 and their voltage coils between lines 1 and 2, and 2 and 3 respectively, the total

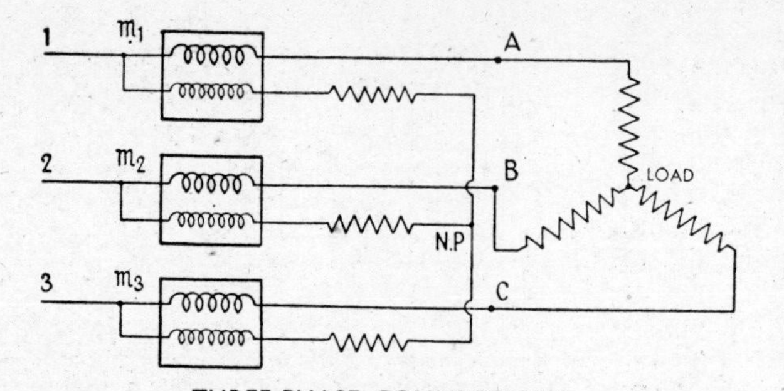

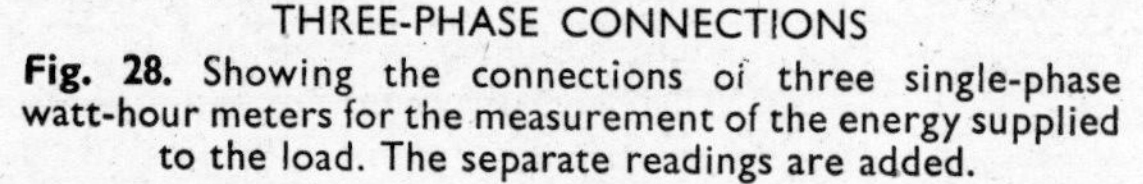
THREE-PHASE CONNECTIONS

Fig. 28. Showing the connections of three single-phase watt-hour meters for the measurement of the energy supplied to the load. The separate readings are added.

energy will be given by the sum of the two readings.

It is usual to fit the two meters in one case and arrange for the two discs to operate on a common spindle and thereby obtain the total energy direct.

For three-phase four-wire supplies the arrangement of Fig. 28, i.e., three watt-hour meters, is necessary.

THREE-PHASE BALANCED LOAD

When a three-phase load is balanced, that is when the three currents are equal and similarly the three voltages, the total energy taken by the load can be obtained by measuring the energy consumed by one phase only. This is done by a single-phase meter, the actual energy passed through the meter being one third of that taken by the load. The current coil is connected in one line and the voltage coil between the same line and the neutral point.

A second method is to divide the current coil into two sections. Then connect one section in line (1) and the other section in line (2) this latter coil being reversed relative to the other as shown in Fig. 29. The vector diagram Fig. 30 for this arrangement shows that the combined effect of the currents 1 and 2 in the two sections is identical with that produced by the one 1—2. This is $\sqrt{3}$ times the value of the separate currents and is in phase with the voltage V which is applied to the pressure coil. The meter reads directly the three-phase energy consumed.

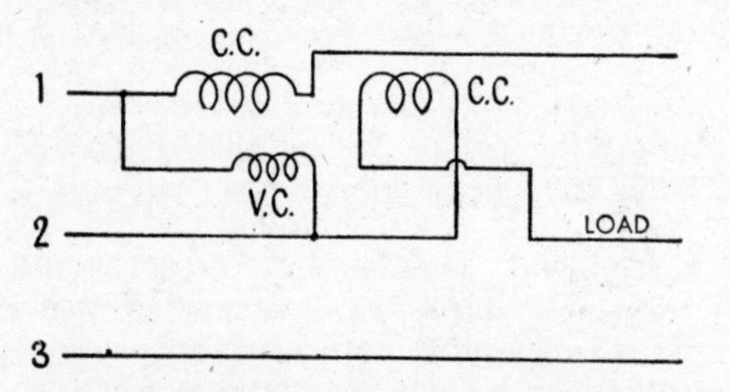

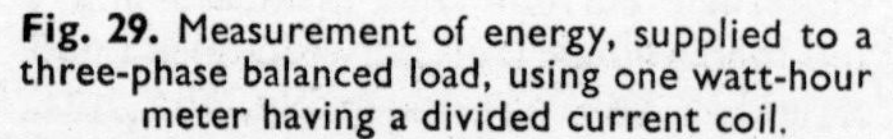
Fig. 29. Measurement of energy, supplied to a three-phase balanced load, using one watt-hour meter having a divided current coil.

The cost of supplying electrical energy depends to some extent on the power factor of the load. The current required for a given power is inversely proportional to the power factor.

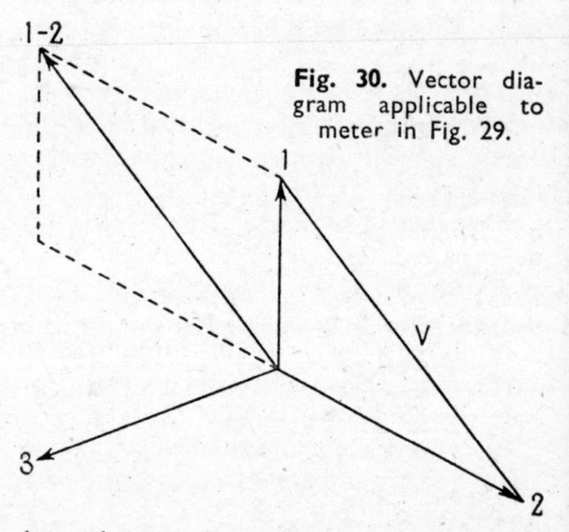

Fig. 30. Vector diagram applicable to meter in Fig. 29.

MEASUREMENT OF REACTIVE VOLT-AMPERE HOURS

It is obvious that if, say, consumers A and B take energy at the same rate, the consumer A who takes energy at a low power factor will require the use of bigger cables than those used to supply B whose load power factor is higher.

Because of this, the load consumed by A costs more to supply and, therefore, it is reasonable to ask him to pay extra. In addition to the need for bigger cables the supply authority has to face additional losses in generators, transformers, etc.

The vector diagram, Fig. 31, shows the current in, and voltage across an inductive load, the phase angle being ϕ. The current I can be resolved into two components I_1 in phase with V and I_2 at right angles with V.

The power supplied to the load is VI_1, which is equal to $VI \cos \phi$.

The current I_2 is called the reactive component of I and this multiplied by V gives the reactive volt-amperes (VAR). The total volt amperes $V \times I = V\sqrt{I_1^2 + I_2^2}$ and the ratio $\frac{VI_2}{VI_1}$ gives the tangent of the angle ϕ.

The product VAR × hours (VARh) and the Watt Hours can be measured by similar meters and the readings enable the total VA and the power factor of the load to be obtained.

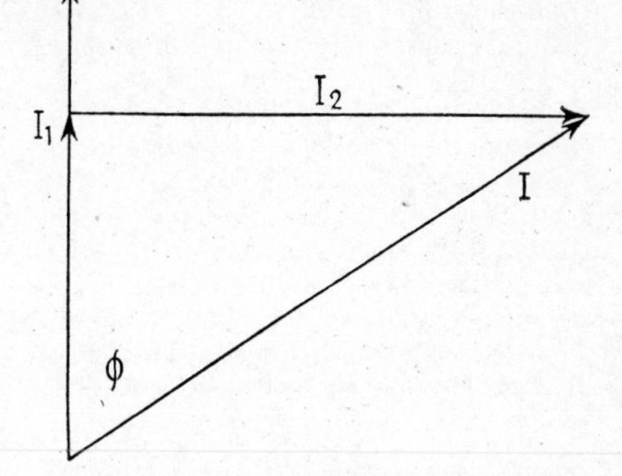

Fig. 31. Vector diagram showing how a lagging current can be resolved into power and reactive components as at I_1 and I_2.

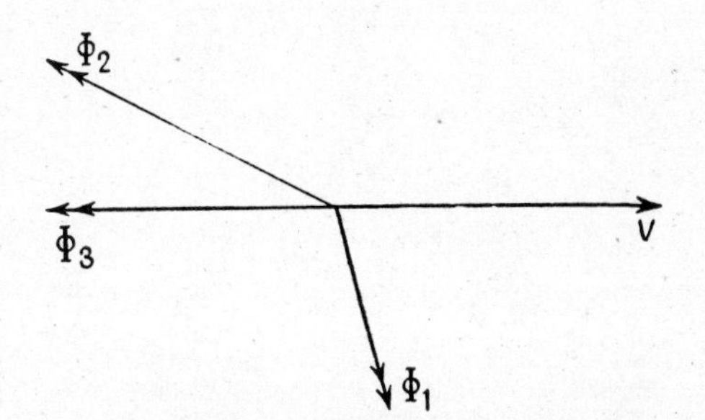

Fig. 32. Modification in magnetic flux phase due to the voltage coil enables the meter to measure reactive volt-ampere hours, single-phase.

INDUCTION ENERGY METER

In an induction energy meter the magnetic flux produced by the pressure element is made to lag by 90 deg. on the voltage applied. Now if this flux is made to lag a further 90 deg, this modification will result in the registration of reactive volt-ampere hours.

The necessary modification of the flux in a single-phase meter can be obtained by the use of a double coil, the two sections being wound in opposite directions. The resulting magnetic force Φ_3 and the two component forces Φ_1 and Φ_2 are shown in Fig. 32.

The phase angle of the coil which produces Φ_2 can be varied by the use of a series resistance, and the resultant Φ_3 is made to be in phase opposition to V. This makes phase of Φ_3 differ by 90 deg. from that required for the measurement of energy and, therefore, suited to the measurement of reactive volt-ampere hours, that is $VI \sin \phi \times$ hours.

We have seen that to measure VARh it is necessary to change the phase of the voltage element flux by 90 deg. from that required for energy measurement.

This is done in three-phase metering

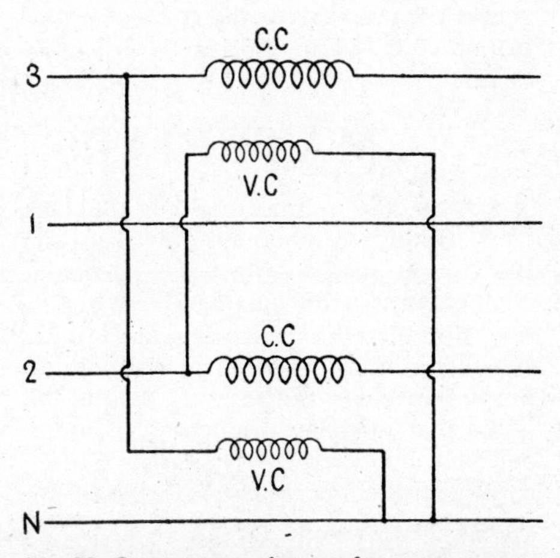

Fig. 33. Connections of meter for measurement of three-phase reactive volt-ampere hours.

by choosing voltages of the proper phase from the supply itself.

Suppose, therefore, that in a three-phase energy meter the current coils are connected in lines (3) and (2) respectively the corresponding voltage coils would be connected across lines 3—1 and 2—1. In a three-phase reactive meter if the current coils are connected in lines (3) and (2) the corresponding pressure coils are connected across line 2 and N and line 3 and N as shown in Fig. 33. The vector diagram Fig. 34 shows that the voltages

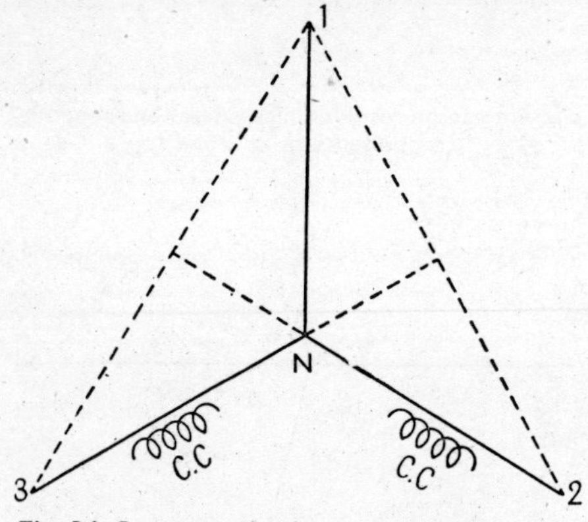

Fig. 34. Current and voltage phase relationships in the meter illustrated in Fig. 33.

applied to the two pressure coils are 90 deg. displaced from the phase required for energy registration. For the latter the vector 1—2 represents the voltage applied to one coil, but in the reactive case the

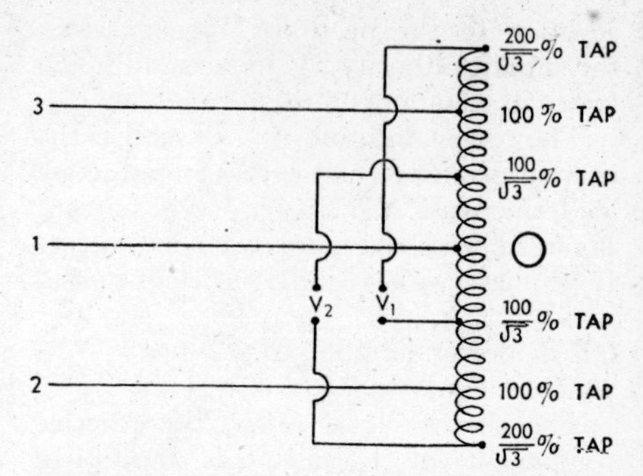

Fig. 35. Two auto-transformers connected in open delta used to adjust phase angle of magnetic flux produced by voltage coil.

voltage applied to the same coil is represented by the vector 3—N. These two voltages 1—2, and 3—N are in quadrature. Similar changes are made in the connection to the other voltage coil, after which the meter will register VARh.

The above method is suitable only if the neutral is available.

AUTO-TRANSFORMER METHOD

A second method of obtaining the required voltages is by the use of two auto-transformers connected in open delta as shown in Fig. 35. The voltages V_1 and V_2 are those applied to the meter pressure coils, and it should be noted that they are in quadrature with voltages 1—2 and 1—3 respectively, and also that they are of the same magnitude.

MATERIALS AND TESTING

WITH any engineering job the best results are obtained only by using the correct material for each particular component. In this chapter the materials used for electrical purposes are simply considered in the light of their suitability for a particular purpose. It should be noted that in many instances the purely mechanical properties of materials assume considerable importance in addition to their electrical characteristics.

Conductors are used to provide definite paths for electric currents in all types of apparatus, also to enable electrical energy to be supplied to consumers from generating plants. Conductors used for the windings of electrical machines and the transmission of electric power should have the following characteristics.

They should have very low specific resistance, see chapter on Electricity Explained, in order that the electrical losses due to resistance are kept as low as possible. They must be strong enough mechanically for the particular job and the materials of which they are made must be able to be drawn out into considerable lengths of uniform cross section.

They must be capable of being easily jointed together, either by fittings or soldering, and able to stand up to temperature changes. In the case of outdoor conductors they must be able to withstand weather conditions, all types should be easily and economically produced.

The following table gives a list of materials in the order of their conducting properties, and the relative resistance of each material to copper for a given length and cross section.

Material.	Comparative resistance. Copper = 1
Silver	0·97
Copper	1·0
Aluminium ..	1·7
Tungsten	3·16
Zinc	3·8
Iron . ..	6·5
Mercury	55·0
Carbon	2400·0

Silver. From the above table it will be observed that silver is the best conductor, its comparative resistance being 97 per cent. that of copper; in other words, it will only require for a given length, a silver conductor having a cross-sectional area 97 per cent. that of a copper conductor to pass a given current. Silver is not employed as a conductor in the general sense as it is too costly, but is sometimes used in the manufacture of instruments.

Copper is by far the most frequently used conductor being used for cables, windings of machines and apparatus, and conducting parts of switchgear. It is also easily soldered.

Aluminium on the other hand has a comparative resistance 1·7 times that of copper or, for a given length, an aluminium conductor will require a cross sectional area 1·7 times greater than a copper conductor to pass a given current. It is used for overhead lines, is very light and a cheaper conductor but, due to its higher comparative resistance and consequently greater bulk, if it has to be insulated the cost of additional insulation outweighs its cheaper production, also it is more difficult to solder than copper.

Tungsten is a conductor used for filaments in electric lamps and various types of valves.

Zinc is employed in the manufacture of primary cells, and iron and steel find special uses as outdoor lines.

Mercury is particularly suitable for liquid contacts, such as the make-and-break contacts in time switches and automatic cut-outs used for stationary battery charging.

Carbon is suitable for contacts where rubbing takes place such as brushes for machines, as it tends to be self-lubricating, also it will stand big changes in temperature as caused by excessive sparking at contacts.

Alloys of metals are used considerably in electrical work, and the following table of the principal alloys shows the comparative resistance of each alloy to copper.

Alloy.	Comparative Resistance. (Copper = 1)
Brass	6 to 9
Constantan (Eureka)	30
Platinoid	24
German Silver ..	15 to 20
Manganin	30

Brass, an alloy of copper and zinc which when used individually are good conductors, has a higher comparative resistance than copper. It is used very considerably in various electrical apparatus, particularly for contacts and connections in switchgear and fuses. If for instance, various types of fuses be examined in which brass contacts are used, it will be found that the dimensions of the brass contacts are very large compared with the conductors used for the fuses. This is owing to the greater resistance of the brass and to prevent overheating of the contacts. Another example is brass cable sockets used for making off the ends of stranded copper cables.

Constantan or Eureka is another high-resistance alloy containing copper and nickel, the nickel giving mechanical strength. Wire made of this alloy is used for resistances and elements of radiators.

Manganin, containing copper, manganese and nickel, is another high-resistance alloy and is used for the resistances of motor starters. Both constantan and manganin are suitable for components which have to dissipate heat, as changes in their resistance values for changes in temperature are very small.

Platinoid and German Silver are high-resistance alloys which find practical application in various types of electrical apparatus.

LIQUID CONDUCTORS

There are certain liquid conductors used in electrolytic processes, such as primary and secondary cells, silver, copper and chromium plating. These liquid conductors are called electrolytes, see sections on Primary Cells and Accumulators. Examples of electrolytes are sulphuric acid, sal-ammoniac and copper sulphate. Water to which soda has been added is used in liquid motor starters for certain types of alternating current motors.

INSULATING MATERIALS

Insulating materials may be said to be used for the purpose of restricting electric currents to definite paths, such as enclosing the conductors with insulating materials or by mounting uninsulated conductors on special insulators.

The properties which insulating materials should possess may be stated generally as follows:—They should have high specific resistance and a high dielectric strength or they will break down when subject to high potentials. Dielectric strength is usually expressed in thousands of volts per millimetre thickness. They should be able to withstand reasonable temperature changes with a minimum loss of insulating properties, they should be non-ageing or age very slowly and they should be suitable for the particular job for which they are to be used.

The following table gives the dielectric strengths of insulating materials frequently employed in electrical engineering:—

Material.	Dielectric strength in thousands of volts per millimetre thickness.
Asbestos	2 to 5
Ebonite	10 to 30
Glass (2mm. thick) ..	16
Cotton	3 to 5
India Rubber, pure ..	20 to 40
„ „ vulcanised	15 to 20
Mica	15 to 50
Oil	3 to 8
Paper, oiled	5 to 20
Paraffin Wax	9 to 11
Porcelain	9 to 30
Presspahn	5 to 20
Shellac	10 to 20

Asbestos. Pure asbestos is used extensively in the Electrical Industry as an insulator in fuse boxes, etc. It is a fibrous material and is fire-proof. Other types of this material sometimes interwoven with cotton are used for armature windings, mining motors, insulated fire-resisting cables, etc.

Ebonite. Many uses are made of ebonite particularly in radio and instrument work.

Glass finds uses as an insulator, its biggest disadvantage being that moisture condenses very easily on glass surfaces giving rise to electrical leaks.

Cotton is used for covering wires, particularly those used in the windings of machines. As it absorbs moisture very quickly, which results in loss of insulating properties, it must be protected by varnishing or other means. Owing to the fact that it tends to char it should not be subjected to large changes in temperature.

Pure India-Rubber, used largely for insulating joints on vulcanised india-rubber cables, becomes very brittle when exposed to air for any length of time and must be covered with some form of protective covering.

Vulcanised India-Rubber is principally used in electrical work for insulating the cables used for wiring indoor installations known as V.I.R. cables. The sulphur it contains attacks the copper, therefore, it is usual to place a layer of pure india-rubber between the vulcanised india-rubber and the copper. Tinning the copper conductors gives further protection.

Mica has many uses as an insulator in machines and radio, as in the construction of formers for coils, insulation for commutators and the dielectric of condensers. It will withstand high temperatures and is practically unaffected by moisture.

Oil specially treated to exclude all moisture is used further to insulate the windings of transformers, the contacts in certain types of switchgear, starters for slip-ring motors, and in certain types of condensers. This type of insulating oil is very thin and highly inflammable, it vaporises easily with temperature changes, the fumes given off being explosive in air. Oil-filled gear is totally enclosed in a tank, the tank being fitted with a special type of breather.

Oiled or Impregnated Paper has high-insulating qualities and is principally used for insulating the conductors of cables used for power transmission. As this type of insulating material absorbs moisture very easily it is necessary to enclose it in a protective covering which, in the case of cables, takes the form of a lead sheath; if subjected to big changes in temperature it becomes dry and brittle.

Paraffin Wax which does not absorb moisture is often used to impregnate cotton-covered windings which are not subject to temperature changes, it also finds a big field in the manufacture of fixed condensers for radio work.

Porcelain is used chiefly for insulators for supporting bare conductors, examples being supports for conducting parts of ironclad switchgear, busbar sections of switchboards, insulators for outlets of cable-end boxes, fuse handles, and insulators for outdoor lines. Its disadvantage is its liability to crack.

Presspahn is used in the construction of formers for various types of coils, slot insulation for armature windings, and insulating metallic supports in apparatus not intended to conduct. It is liable to warp through changes in temperature and tends to absorb moisture.

Shellac is a base in the manufacture of insulating varnishes used for protecting cotton-covered wires from damp.

Slate which should be free from metallic veins is used as panels for switchboards, motor starters, and terminal blocks on machines. It should not be used in outdoor positions where it may be subjected to changes in weather conditions as in damp weather it gives rise to surface leaks.

Miscellaneous.—There are many other types of insulating materials including moulded materials, insulating tapes and compounds which have their particular uses.

MAGNETIC MATERIALS

All electrical devices whose functions are based upon the principle of electromagnetic induction, such as transformers, generators, motors and electromagnets have magnetic circuits as well as an electric circuit. It is just as important to use the correct magnetic material for each part of a magnetic circuit as it is to use the correct conductor with proper insulation in an electric circuit.

Soft iron magnetises very easily and intensely but will not retain its magnetism, whereas hard steel retains its magnetism under proper conditions indefinitely. A self-excited direct current generator relies for its initial electro-motive force upon residual magnetism, its field coils are, therefore, mounted on pole pieces made of pole core steel.

As soft iron magnetises very easily, definite paths for magnetic forces may be made with it. It is usual to construct with soft iron armature cores of direct current machines, transformer cores, and stator cores for alternating current machines in order to reduce what are termed "Iron Losses". Instead of making the cores in one solid piece of soft iron, they are made up of a number of thin sheets of soft annealed iron or steel called "laminations"; special alloys are often used one being known as "Stalloy".

Cast iron is a magnetic material that was frequently used in the construction of yokes for machines. It has now been superseded by cast steel which magnetises much more intensively; the use of cast steel effects economies in construction and gives greater mechanical strength. Permanent magnets such as those used for magnetos are made of special hard steels in order that they provide a definite magnetic field while in use.

TESTING

Particular materials are used for particular purposes, the suitability of a material for some purpose being determined by specially designed tests and experiments. These tests include investigation of conducting and insulating properties, effects of temperature changes and magnetic tests.

Tests for conducting properties of various materials may be said to be the determination of specific resistances of materials. Some conductors have to be roughly handled during installation.

Effects of temperature on conductors are very important, as temperature changes result in changes in resistance values for given conductors. There are many instances where resistance values must remain constant over wide temperature ranges, an example being the shunts used in certain types of instruments; only materials whose resistance values are practically unaffected by temperature changes could be used in these particular cases.

With insulating materials tests are again necessary to determine specific resistances, for good insulators these must be high; dielectric strengths of various materials must be ascertained by subjecting specimens to high potentials.

Temperature effects are equally important with insulating materials, as temperature increases during operation tend to reduce insulating properties, also effects of bending and stretching must be carefully considered.

The surroundings in which completed apparatus is used often has some effect on the various components which make up the apparatus, and is a subject for investigation.

With magnetic materials the intensity to which specimens of iron and steel may be magnetised is important, also the behaviour of specimens when subjected to rapidly changing magnetic forces.

From the foregoing it may be said that a research department to study effects and carry out the various tests is a necessary part of any manufacturing organisation.

PRIMARY CELLS

If two plates, one of copper and the other of zinc, be immersed in a jar containing dilute sulphuric acid, H_2SO_4, and a voltmeter be connected to the external parts of the plates as shown in Fig. 36a, it will be found that there is a potential difference between the plates.

The current flowing in the circuit is only that required to deflect the voltmeter and is very small. The reading in volts shown on the instrument is termed the "electromotive force" or "e.m.f." of the cell. This type of cell is known as a simple cell as there is a minimum of parts used in its construction.

Copper and zinc are both called "elements". The element which most easily combines with, or has the greatest affinity for the oxygen in the sulphuric acid, which is known as the exciting fluid or the "excitant", is said to have the highest heat value in chemical combination and will produce the greatest e.m.f. Zinc combines more easily with oxygen than copper and will give a higher e.m.f.

E.M.F. INSIDE CELL

The e.m.f. inside the cell acts from zinc to copper, so that the zinc is known as the positive element and the copper as the negative element. Any two elements having different affinities will produce an e.m.f. between them when placed in an excitant, but it is advantageous that the negative element should have as low an affinity as possible, or be inert. This results in a higher e.m.f. being available at the terminals of the cell.

If a resistance be connected between the plates as shown in Fig. 36b, a current will flow in the circuit starting from the zinc (positive element) through the excitant to the copper (negative element), up the copper plate to the external terminal or pole, through the resistance and terminal of the zinc plate to the zinc,

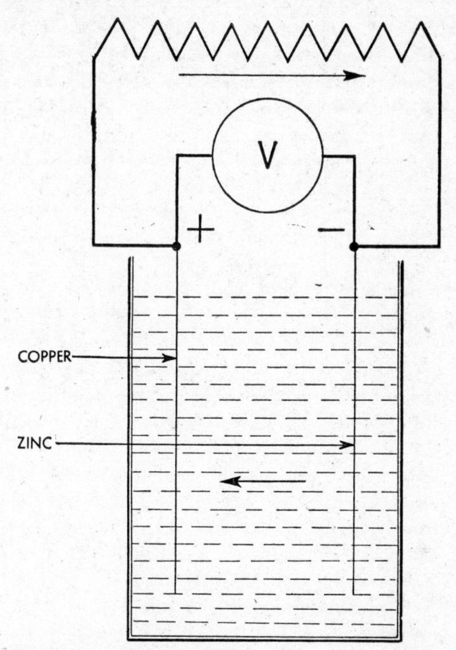

Fig. 36b. Diagrammatic arrangement of simple cell with resistance connected between the plates. Arrows show direction of current flow.

as the current always flows from a higher to a lower potential. While the copper plate inside the cell is the negative element its external terminal is the positive pole, the terminal of the zinc plate being the negative pole.

The flow of current causes the zinc to dissolve in the excitant, therefore, when the whole of the zinc has dissolved the cell can not supply any further energy or, in other words, chemical energy is converted into electrical energy.

As the functioning of the cell depends upon the chemical reactions between the elements and the excitant, this type is known as a primary cell, the name being applied to all cells of a similar type.

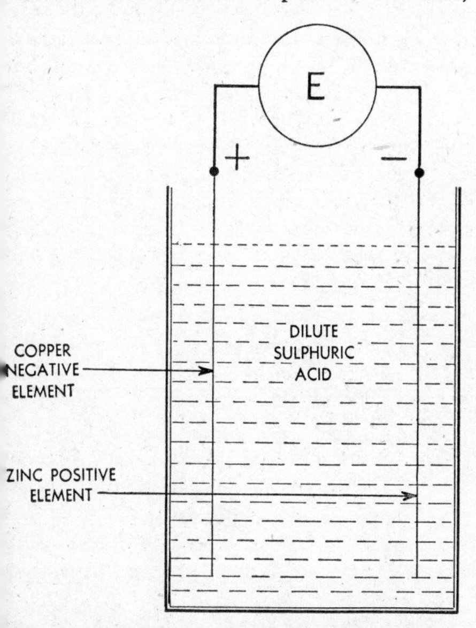

Fig. 36a. Diagrammatic arrangement of simple cell with voltmeter indicating in terms of e.m.f. potential difference set up between plates.

LOCAL ACTION

Zinc usually contains impurities in the form of particles of iron and other metals, these impurities having different heat values to the zinc. Little primary cells are actually set up between each impurity in the excitant and the zinc, with the result the zinc is dissolved much more quickly than if the impurities were not present. The little cells contribute nothing to the main current taken from the cell their action being a local action, this disadvantage is known as "local action". Local action is eliminated by giving the zinc a coating of zinc amalgam. It will then act chemically as pure zinc, and as the zinc is dissolved under normal working conditions the impurities will come to the surface of the zinc and then fall off.

Fig. 37. Leclanché porous pot type cell. Positive and negative elements are respectively zinc and carbon and sal-ammonia solution is used as an exciting fluid or excitant.

POLARIZATION

As current flows through the cell hydrogen is liberated at the copper plate. The heat value of hydrogen is much higher than that of the copper, therefore an e.m.f. is set up between the hydrogen and the excitant which will oppose the main e.m.f. of the cell, resulting in the main e.m.f. being reduced with a consequent reduction in current.

Hydrogen is a gas having a very high resistance, it will tend to insulate the copper plate from the current and increase the internal resistance of the cell. This reduction in e.m.f. due to the action of the hydrogen is known as "polarization". If a cell is to work well polarization must be eliminated as much as possible, or the cell must be "depolarized", this is usually accomplished by introducing an agent into the cell which will free oxygen to combine with the hydrogen to form water. Of the many types of primary cell the principal difference between the various types is the method used to effect depolarization, though the principle is exactly the same in each case. The agent used to supply the necessary oxygen is called the depolarizer.

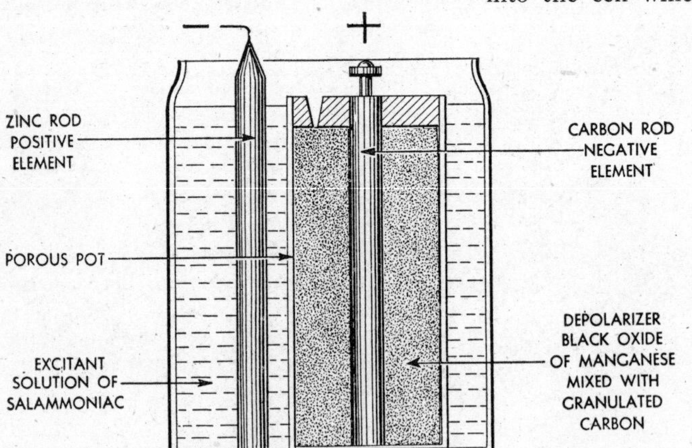

Fig. 38. Leclanché type of primary cell in section. The purpose of the depolarizer is to absorb the hydrogen which would otherwise reduce the current output of the cell. However, hydrogen is released faster than it will combine with the oxygen of the depolarizer so the cell will not maintain a constant current for long.

In the first paragraphs it was stated that the voltmeter reading, in Fig. 36a, was the e.m.f. of the cell. In Fig. 36b a

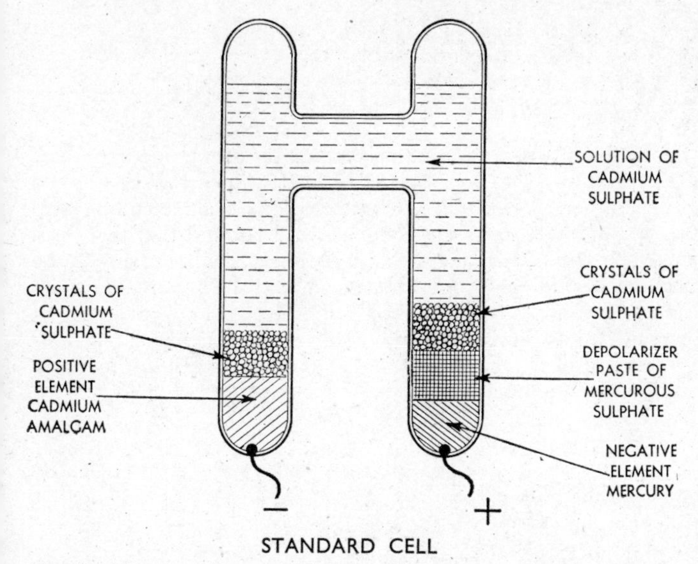

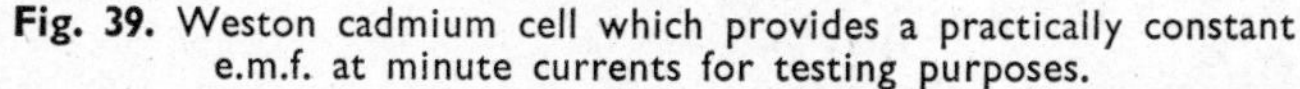

Fig. 39. Weston cadmium cell which provides a practically constant e.m.f. at minute currents for testing purposes.

resistance is connected between the terminals of the cell, and as current is flowing it will be found that the voltmeter reading will be less than for the conditions of Fig. 36a. The difference between the two readings is a measure of the voltage lost inside the cell due to its "internal resistance".

The internal resistance is made up of the resistances of the plates and the resistance of the excitant. To reduce the voltage lost inside the cell when current is flowing the internal resistance must be reduced to a minimum.

LECLANCHÉ CELL

One of the most common primary cells in use is the Leclanché porous pot type shown in Fig. 37, and in section in Fig. 38. The positive and negative elements are zinc and carbon respectively, the excitant is a solution of sal-ammoniac, and the depolarizer a black oxide of manganese mixed with granulated carbon, and packed round the carbon rod inside the porous pot. When current flows the hydrogen, which is liberated, travels through the pores in the porous pot and combines with some of the oxygen of the depolarizer. Hydrogen is liberated faster than it can combine with the oxygen, therefore, the cell will not maintain a constant current for any length of time. For this reason, and the high internal resistance of the cell, it is only suitable for intermittent duty, such as the operation of electric bells.

Dry cells are similar in operation, having their excitants and depolarizers in the form of pastes, which renders this type of cell portable. Thus, strictly speaking, they are not "dry". Due to its compactness the dry cell has a lower internal resistance than the wet type, various types of dry cells are used for torches and portable radio sets.

STANDARD CELLS

Primary cells used as sources of e.m.f. for testing purposes, particularly in laboratories, are known as standard cells, giving a practically constant or standard e.m.f. as only very minute currents are taken from them. One of the most common types is the Weston Cadmium cell shown in Fig. 39, which has an e.m.f. of 1·01823 volts at 20° C. The positive element is cadmium amalgam and the negative element mercury, being immersed in a solution of cadmium sulphate, and using a paste of mercurous sulphate as the depolarizer.

Connections to the elements are normally made by wires fused into the bottom of each tube portion of the glass container. The cell is usually housed in a container, the wires being joined to a pair of external connections. It will be appreciated that standard cells have no practical applications beyond those of a laboratory nature.

ACCUMULATORS AND ACCUMULATOR CHARGING

When discussing the simple primary cell, it was shown that if two dissimilar metal plates be immersed in sulphuric acid, H_2SO_4, a difference of potential would exist between the plates due to their different chemical affinities, and, if an external resistance be connected between the plates a current would flow round the circuit until either the plate with the greatest affinity, or the excitant is used up. No further energy is then available until either a new plate or excitant is supplied.

If two lead plates be immersed in dilute sulphuric acid and a current passed through the cell as shown in Fig. 40a, it will be found that the sulphuric acid will be partly decomposed, the hydrogen travelling with the current and the oxygen going in the reverse direction. The plate where the current enters the cell is called the "anode" meaning "way in", the other plate being the "cathode" meaning "way out", the hydrogen will be given off in little bubbles at the cathode, while the oxygen will travel to the anode and attack its surface, covering it with a layer of lead peroxide, PbO_2, which is chocolate brown in colour. The lead peroxide is known as the active material.

This action of decomposing the sulphuric acid is known as "electrolysis", the acid is called the "electrolyte", the process of electrolysis resulting in changing the surface of the anode into lead peroxide. If the flow of current be stopped and a voltmeter be connected between the plates it will be found that there is a potential difference, this being due to the fact that lead and lead peroxide have different affinities. The process of charging has set up chemical reactions resulting in similar conditions to those existing in the simple primary cell but, whereas the potential difference between the plates in the primary cell was due to the chemical reactions inside the cell, in the case of the lead-acid cell the chemical reactions were due to the passage of current supplied from an external source or, in other words, they are secondary reactions. This type of cell is known as a secondary cell or accumulator.

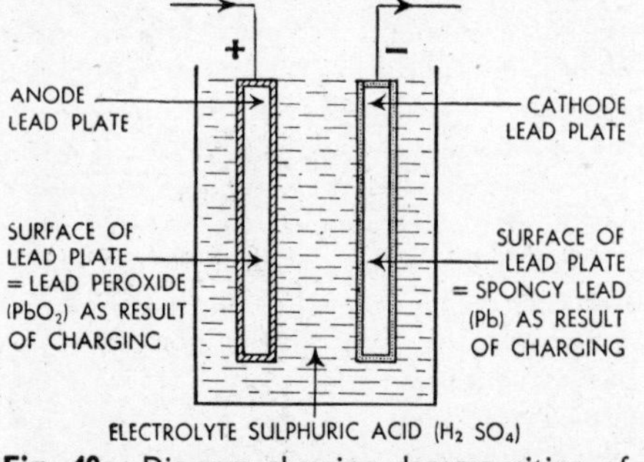

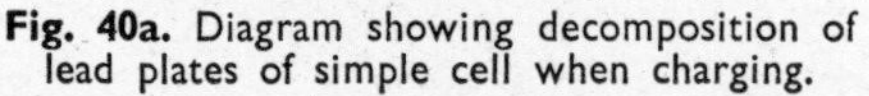
Fig. 40a. Diagram showing decomposition of lead plates of simple cell when charging.

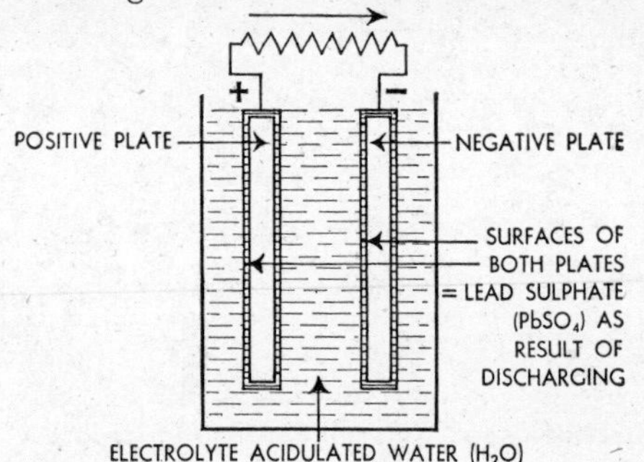

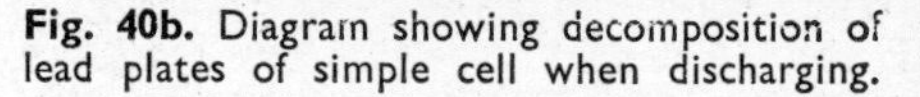
Fig. 40b. Diagram showing decomposition of lead plates of simple cell when discharging.

CHEMICAL REACTIONS

Connecting a resistance between the external terminals of the plates will result in a current flowing from the terminal of the anode, through the resistance to the terminal of the cathode and through the cell as shown in Fig. 40b. The cell will discharge. The discharge current will decompose the electrolyte, the hydrogen travelling to the anode where it will combine with the lead peroxide and acid, forming lead sulphate and water, while the sulphur and oxygen combine with the

BATTERY CHARGING UNIT

Fig. 41a. Crypton three "Bus Bar" constant voltage battery charging unit.

lead cathode and also form lead sulphate. With both plates coated with lead sulphate no difference of potential will exist between them, therefore, no further current will flow, or the cell is discharged.

Repeating the charging and discharging process will give increased depth of lead peroxide on the anode, with the result that the duration of flow of discharge current will lengthen with each successive discharge.

The complete cycle of events may be stated thus, during charging electrical energy is converted into chemical energy, and during discharge chemical energy is converted into electrical energy.

The actual changes which take place in a lead acid cell during charge and discharge are complex, but the main reactions are given below:—

From the foregoing there are two indications of the state of the cell, the first is the potential difference between the plates, and the second the "density" or "specific gravity" of the electrolyte. When charging the cell the charging should be continued until the potential difference between the plates is about 2·6 volts measured while the current is flowing. The specific gravity of sulphuric acid is higher than that of water, so during charging the specific gravity rises.

A hydrometer for indicating the specific gravity is necessary, see Fig. 41b, when the cell is charged the specific gravity should read 1·22, on some types of hydrometer the reading will be 1,220. The specific gravity of the electrolyte immediately surrounding the plates will be higher than that which is more remote,

Cell Charged.		
Anode, positive plate. Lead peroxide (PbO_2)	Electrolyte. Sulphuric acid ($2H_2SO_4$)	Cathode, negative plate. Spongy lead. (Pb)
Cell Discharged.		
Lead sulphate ($PbSO_4$)	Acidulated water ($2H_2O$)	Lead sulphate ($PbSO_4$)

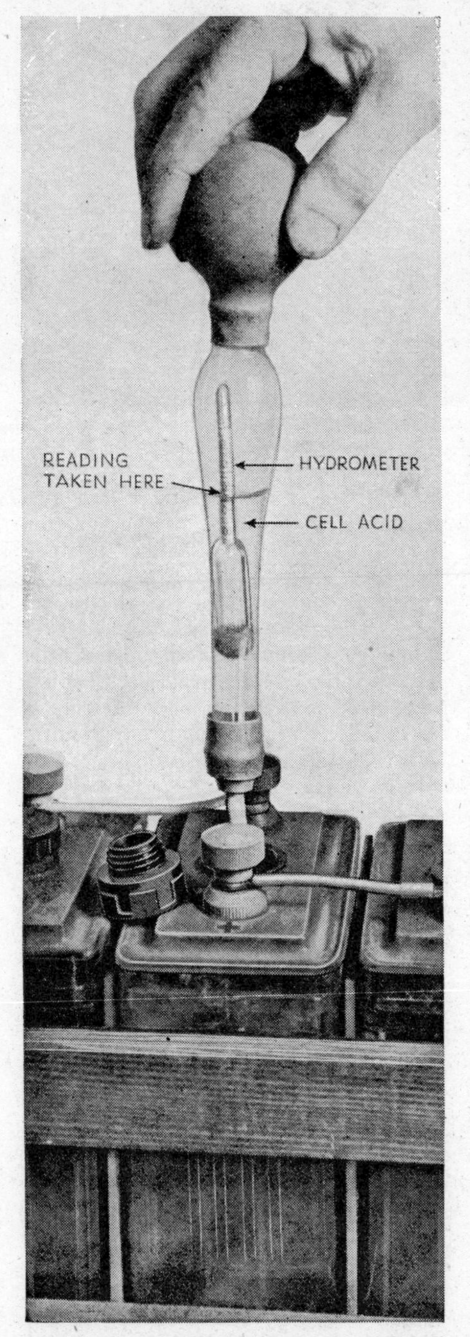

Fig. 41b. Reading specific gravity of secondary cell, to obtain an indication of its state of charge, by means of hydrometer.

therefore, when the charging is completed the stronger acid will tend to mix with the weaker, which will result in a fall in the specific gravity and a fall in e.m.f. to about 2·1 volts. The cell in this condition is ready for discharge

The state of discharge is determined by the amount of lead sulphate formed on both plates and, as lead sulphate is a hard non-conducting material which is only removed by prolonged electrolytic action, a limit must be fixed to the amount of lead sulphate to be formed in order that it may be oxidised into lead peroxide during normal charging. A cell should not be further discharged when the potential difference between the plates has fallen to 1·8 volts measured while the current is flowing, the specific gravity should then have fallen to about 1,190. Lead sulphate is easily discernible due to its greyish white colour

TYPES OF PLATES

The type of plate described, in which the depth of lead peroxide is obtained by repeated electrolytic action is known as a "formed" or "Planté" plate, the principal advantage of this type of plate is that the lead peroxide is an integral part of the plate, its depth being fixed by considerations of mechanical strength. This forming process is lengthy and costly. There is another type of plate known as a "pasted" or "Faure" plate which requires only one forming or first charge after which the cell is ready for use.

With the pasted type of plate a lead grid is cast, a little white metal being added to increase mechanical strength, and the paste is then applied to the grid. The paste used for the positive plate is red lead or minium mixed with sulphuric acid; that used for the negative plate being yellow oxide of lead or litharge mixed with sulphuric acid. When red lead is mixed with sulphuric acid a mixture of lead sulphate and lead peroxide is formed; mixing yellow oxide of lead with sulphuric acid gives lead sulphate.

Two freshly pasted plates, one positive and the other negative, immersed in

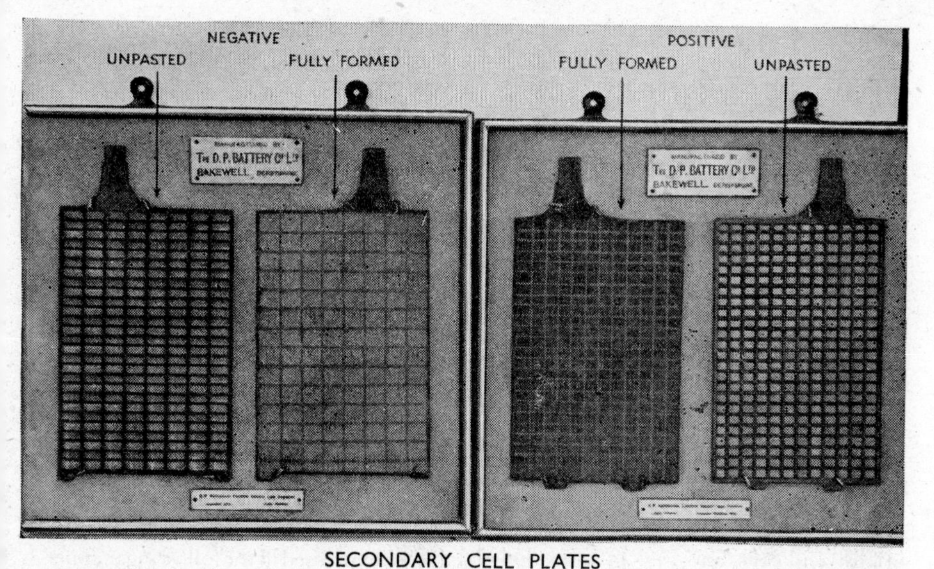

SECONDARY CELL PLATES

Fig. 42. Both unpasted and fully formed negative and positive plates are to be seen in this photograph. They are mounted on display backings for purely illustrative purposes.

sulphuric acid represent a cell in a discharged condition; if the cell be now charged the red lead of the positive plate will be changed to lead peroxide, and the litharge of the negative plate reduced to spongy lead.

The principal advantage of the cell with the pasted plates is the larger energy output for a given weight compared with formed plates, owing to the different rates of expansion of the pastes and lead grids. Repeated charging and discharging, particularly with large currents, will cause the paste to break away from the grids, this is especially the case of the paste on the positive plate. Cells which are used for heavy duty usually have formed plates for positives and pasted plates for negatives. Fig. 42, shows types of formed and pasted plates.

INTERNAL RESISTANCE AND CAPACITY

Secondary cells possess resistance and, to reduce the amount of potential lost inside the cell when current is flowing, the internal resistance must be reduced to a minimum.

The length of time that current may be taken from the cell is determined by the amount of lead peroxide available for conversion into lead sulphate on discharge. The product of the current in amperes and the time in hours, during which the cell may supply current until the e.m.f. falls to 1·8 volts is called the "capacity" of the cell and is stated in ampere-hours, denoted by the symbol Ah.

If a number of positive plates be connected to a common bar, and a number of negative plates treated in the same way, and then the plates are interlaced, this arrangement will result in increased capacity and decreased internal resistance. There is always one more negative plate than positive, or a negative at both ends, this gives mechanical strength and ensures that both sides of each positive are active. With this arrangement the plates are very close together, a positive must be prevented from touching a negative otherwise an internal short circuit will result, this is done by placing separators between adjacent plates.

Separators for small cells including cells for car batteries, may be of wood, ebonite, or hard rubber, while large stationary cells usually have glass rods,

the type of cell described is called a "multiplate" cell.

The containers for small cells such as those used for radio purposes are usually of glass, those for car batteries of moulded material, and for stationary cells either glass or lead lined teak boxes. To allow for expansion there should be ample clearance in the container, especially at the bottom to prevent pieces of active material which have broken away from the plates causing internal short-circuits.

A battery of given e.m.f. is made by joining a number of cells in series, in the case of car batteries the connections between cells are in the form of lead bars burnt on to the cell connections to ensure good joints, while in the case of stationary cells specially prepared connecting bolts are used. Figs. 43 and 44 show two types of lead acid cells, and Fig. 45 an exploded view of a typical Lucas Car Battery in which the main constructional details can be seen.

As the capacity of a cell is determined by the ampere-hours on discharge, a measure of the efficiency of a cell may be calculated by comparing the ampere-hour input during charge to the ampere-hour output, this is known as the capacity or ampere-hour efficiency.

The ampere-hour efficiency expressed as a percentage may be stated thus,

Ah, efficiency per cent.

$$= \frac{\text{Ah on discharge}}{\text{Ah on charge}} \times 100$$

This is not a true efficiency, as true efficiency should be in terms of energy output to energy input. Energy is the product of watts and time and the true efficiency or the watt-hour, Wh, efficiency can be expressed in the following manner:—

SELF-INDICATING BATTERY

Fig. 43. Exide multiplate cell which itself indicates its condition of charge by hydrometer action.

Wh, efficiency per cent.

$$= \frac{\text{Ah discharge} \times \text{average volts during discharge}}{\text{Ah charge} \times \text{average volts during charge}} \times 100$$

In both numerator and denominator the term average volts appears as, during discharge, the e.m.f. falls from about 2·1 volts to 1·8 volts and during charge rises from 1·8 volts to about 2·6.

The following rules may be of use to those responsible for the maintenance of secondary cells of the lead-acid type:—

(1) Cells must not be discharged below 1·8 volts per cell measured while the discharge current is flowing,

(2) Discharge carried beyond this point will result in the formation of lead sulphate, or sulphating, which can only be removed by repeated slow charging,

(3) Rates of charge and discharge should be observed as stated by makers.

(4) Cells should gas freely during charge, the specific gravity rising to its correct value as shown on a hydrometer, the charging being completed when the e.m.f. per cell has risen to 2·6 volts to 2·7 volts measured while the charging current is flowing,

(5) The level of the electrolyte, which will fall due to evaporation, should only be made good with distilled water, acid should not be added, and

(6) Cells should not be left in a discharged condition for any length of time

Fig. 44. Exide "Mass" type cell showing glass container and with plate group partly removed.

ALKALINE CELLS

Alkaline batteries are used for a large variety of purposes. They have almost every advantage over the lead-acid type, except that of first cost which is much higher. As, however, an alkaline battery will outlast an indeterminate number of lead-acid batteries, it is actually the cheaper in the end.

The two types of alkaline cell in general use are the nickel-iron and the *nickel-cadmium*. Both cells have the same type of positive plate, of which the active material is nickel-hydroxide, and both use the same electrolyte, which is a potassium hydroxide solution with a specific gravity of 1·190. The specific gravity does not vary during charge or discharge. In the Edison (nickel-iron) cell, the negative plate is iron and in the cell known commercially as the NIFE, the negative plate is cadmium. The NIFE plates are constructed in the form of flat steel tubes, perforated by a large number of small holes for entry of the electrolyte. The construction of the cell and the arrangement of the plates is shown in Fig. 46. The active material is pressed into the tubes. It will be clear that this construction results in a very strong plate, so that buckling is practically unknown in alkaline cells. Sediment formation is also negligible. The cell case is usually steel, on which the electrolyte has no action, but the outer surface of the cell is sometimes plated to prevent atmospheric corrosion.

The absence of any form of acid in this type of cell obviously makes it very safe to handle. Also there is an absence of such dangerous fumes as with the lead-acid types. Nevertheless, considerable gassing takes place during charging so that it is essential that the vents be removed during that process.

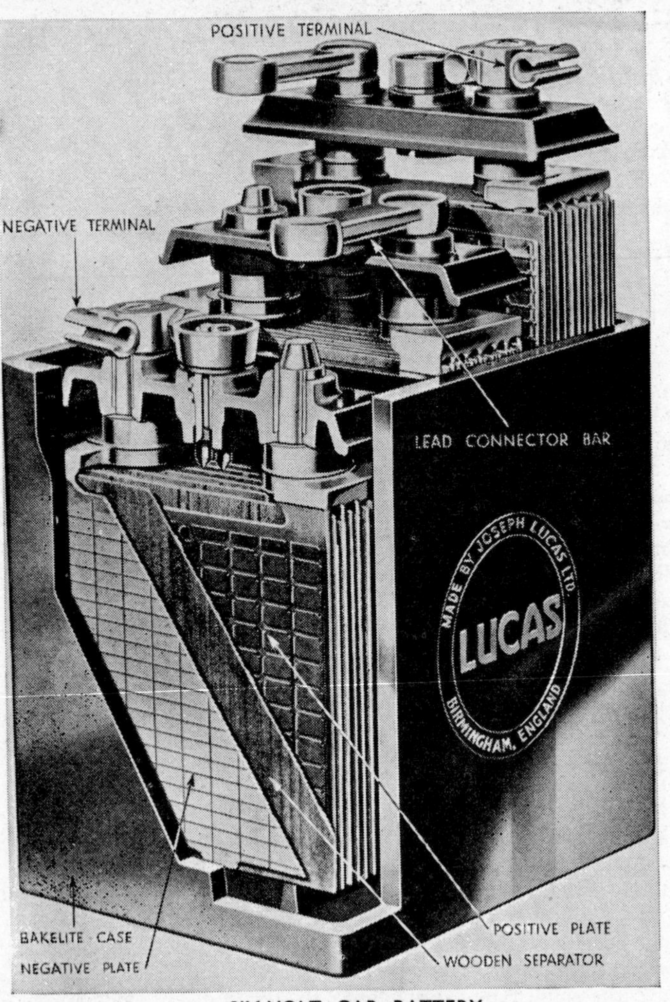

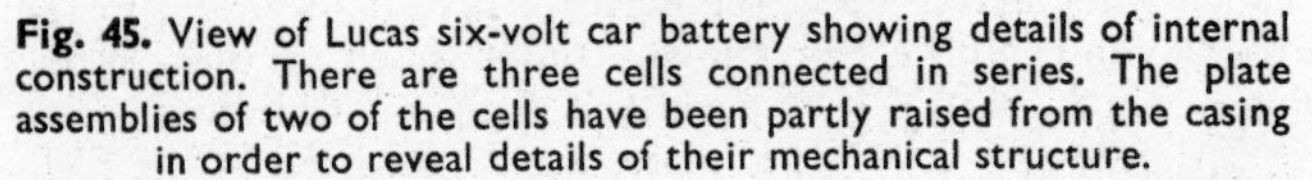
SIX-VOLT CAR BATTERY

Fig. 45. View of Lucas six-volt car battery showing details of internal construction. There are three cells connected in series. The plate assemblies of two of the cells have been partly raised from the casing in order to reveal details of their mechanical structure.

The voltage characteristics of the Edison and NIFE cells are shown in Fig. 47. It is usually taken that 1 volt is the lower limit of discharge, but this is more with reference to the usefulness of the e.m.f. than to the interests of the cell, which is not harmed by some further discharge. It will be seen from Fig. 47 that the nickel-cadmium type is the more suitable for floating duties in conjunction with a charging dynamo, the difference between charging and discharging e.m.f.'s being too great in the case of the nickel-iron.

To make up a battery of nominal 12 volts, either nine or ten NIFE cells in series are employed according to the particular case. As with any other type of secondary cell the capacity of an alkaline cell depend

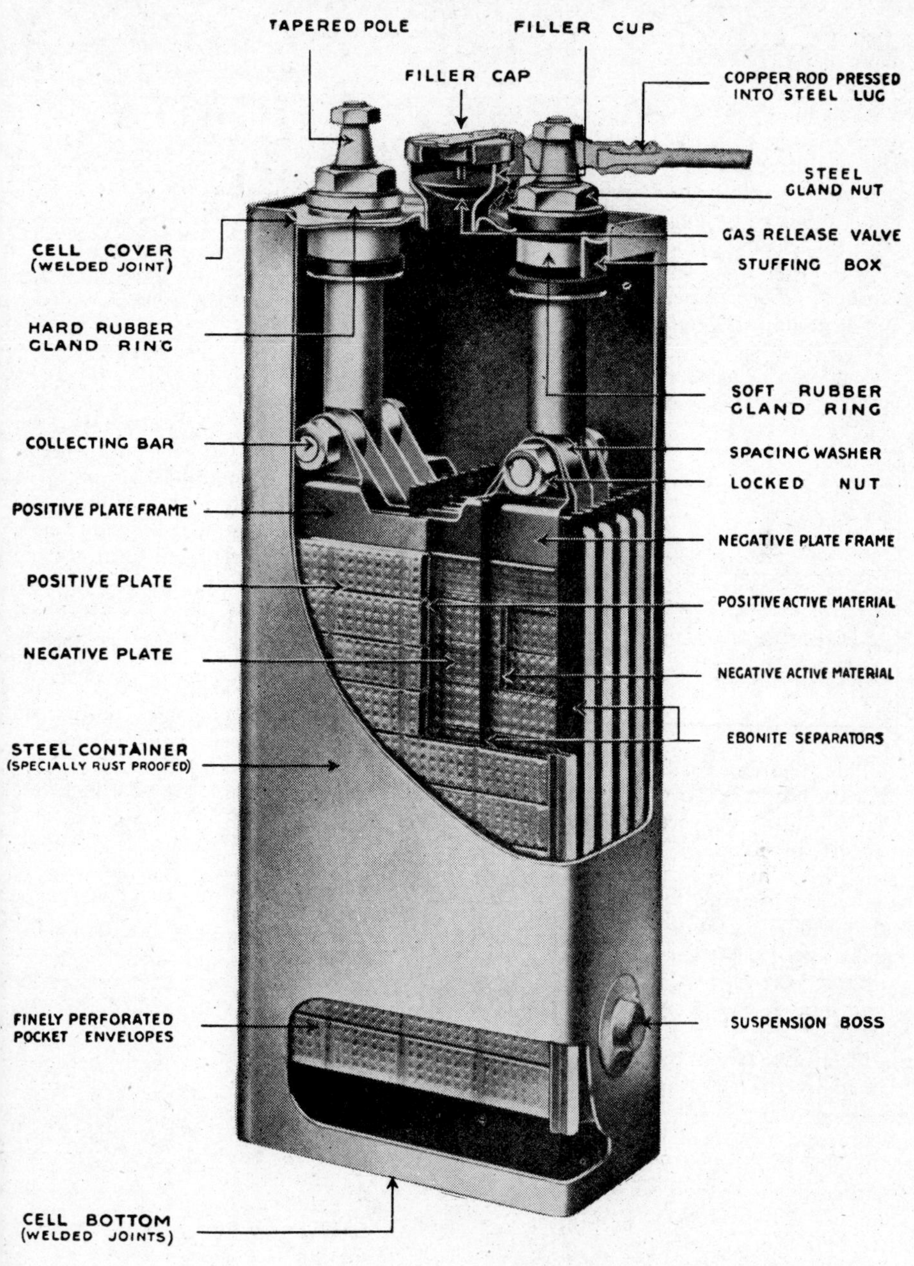

NICKEL CADMIUM CELL

Fig. 46. Secondary cell which uses neither acid nor lead. This type of accumulator, the NIFE, has several advantages over the more familiar lead-acid types. It is lighter and is not damaged by periods of idleness. The specific gravity of its electrolyte does not vary during charge and discharge.

upon the amount of active material in it, and also varies with the rate of discharge. The alkaline cell is however much better than the lead-acid in this respect.

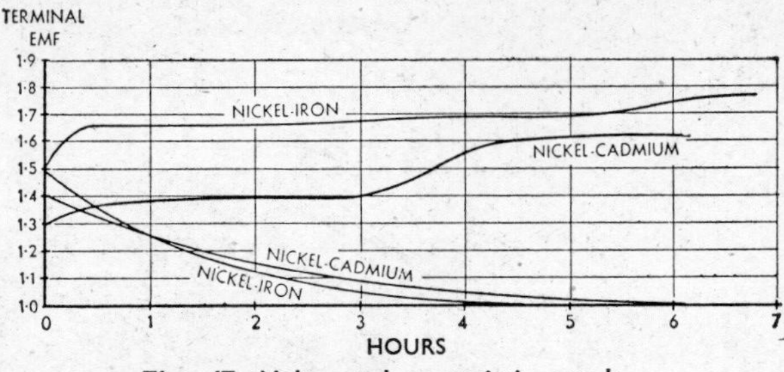

Fig. 47. Voltage characteristic graph.

From Fig. 48 it will be seen that at really heavy discharge rates the alkaline cell retains a high percentage of its capacity. The ampere-hour and watt-hour efficiencies of alkaline cells are not as good as those of lead-acid cells, as the following comparative percentage figures will show:

Cell.	*Ampere-hour efficiency.*	*Watt-hour efficiency.*
Lead-acid ..	90%	75%
Nickel-cadmium	80%	65%
Nickel-iron ..	72%	58%

This apparent disadvantage is however almost completely outweighed by the fact that alkaline cells are not sensitive to periods of idleness. They require so much less "nursing" than lead-acid batteries that, taking all factors into account, their efficiency is at least as great, and from many aspects much greater.

Electrolyte level is maintained by the addition of distilled water. Not less than once per year it is advisable to dismantle the battery, flush out each cell, and refill with fresh electrolyte. The outer surface of the cells should be coated with petroleum jelly unless the cells are plated.

Terminal e.m.f. on load is the only guide to the state of charge, because the specific gravity of the electrolyte does not vary. Provided the cell temperature does not rise too far (95° Fahrenheit is safe), very high charging rates can be used. Gassing on charge is fairly heavy, and continues for 10 to 12 hours after charging. In cases when alkaline cells are fitted with air-tight vents, these must not be replaced until gassing has ceased.

Alkaline batteries must be kept well apart from lead-acid types at all times. The fumes from a lead-acid cell are very detrimental to an alkaline battery, whilst the acid itself will of course destroy an alkaline cell. A separate hydrometer, syringe, glass beaker, etc., must be kept in the charging room for use with alkaline cells, and rags used for wiping lead-acid cells must on no account be applied to alkaline batteries. The process of

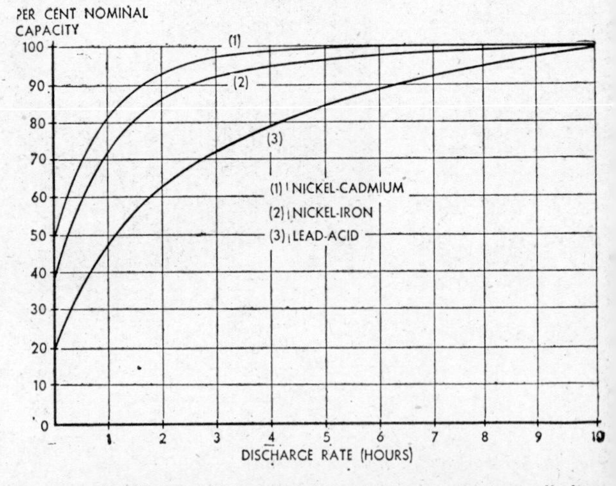

Fig. 48. Showing how at heavy discharge rates an alkaline cell retains a high percentage of its capacity.

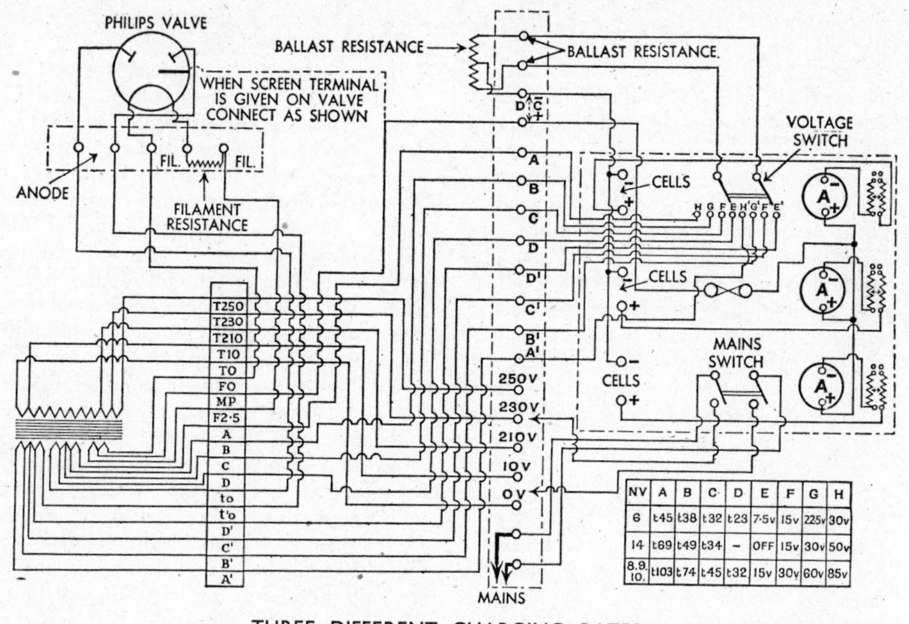

NV	A	B	C	D	E	F	G	H
6	t45	t38	t32	t23	7·5v	15v	22.5v	30v
14	t69	t49	t34	–	OFF	15v	30v	50v
8.9. 10.	t103	t74	t45	t32	15v	30v	60v	85v

THREE DIFFERENT CHARGING RATES

Fig. 49. Wiring diagram of Crypton 3-circuit rectifier. Three different charging rates can be obtained by means of transformer tappings. There are no losses due to regulating resistances.

charging cells is the same for all types, the passage of an electric current through the cell, the current entering at the positive terminal and leaving at the negative; the charging current must flow in the reverse direction to the current supplied by the cell when discharging. It is necessary that a voltage higher than that of the cell be applied before charging current will flow. In other words, the value of the charging current is determined by the difference between the applied voltage and the voltage of the cell divided by the internal resistance of the cell.

During the charging the voltage of the cell will rise as stated earlier in this chapter, therefore, if a cell is to be charged with a constant current arrangements must be made to compensate for this change in voltage which ranges from about 1·8 to 2·6 volts. When charging car and radio batteries the charging current is usually obtained from public supply mains; there are two types of public supply, namely, direct and alternating current.

Cells may be charged from direct current mains by connecting them in series, the value of the charging current being regulated by means of a variable resistance placed in series with the cells and mains. The regulating resistance often takes the form of a number of lamps connected in parallel, varying the number of lamps varies the charging current. As very often happens many of the cells will require different

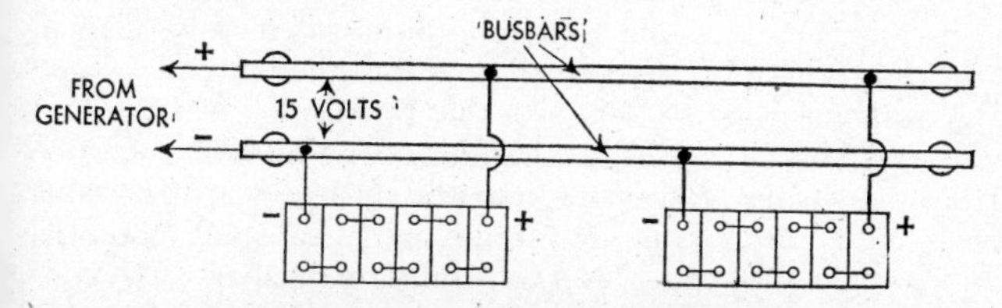

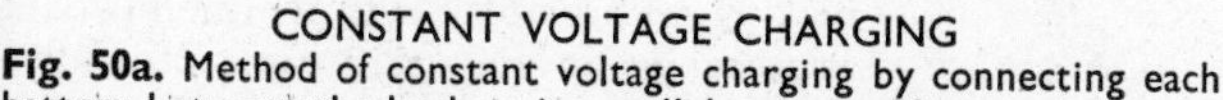

CONSTANT VOLTAGE CHARGING

Fig. 50a. Method of constant voltage charging by connecting each battery between the busbars in parallel across a fifteen volt supply.

charging currents, therefore if they are all connected in series some will be under-charged and some over-charged. To overcome this it is necessary to arrange cells in a series-parallel combination those taking the same current being in series, and then the series groups connected in parallel, the number of cells in each series group being the same. Unless there is a large number of cells to be charged this method is not efficient as it is possible that a substantial portion of the energy supplied from the mains will be expended in the regulating resistance. When the supply is alternating current this must first be converted to direct current, and this is usually done by either a valve or metal rectifier.

SPECIAL CHARGING UNITS

One type of charging unit with a valve rectifier, has three different charging rates, by which car and radio batteries may be charged at the same time, one circuit charging twelve cells at six amperes, the second circuit twelve cells at three amperes, and the third circuit twelve cells at one ampere.

This type of unit is very efficient, there are no losses in regulating resistances, independent circuits have various charging rates, as may be seen from the wiring diagram, Fig. 49, charging rates are adjusted by transformer tappings, also the number of cells in each circuit may be varied. The principal disadvantage of series charging is that every cell in a series group must take the same current irrespective of its state of charge.

By far the most efficient method of charging is the "constant voltage" method as the charging current at any instant is determined by the conditions of the cell. To charge a cell correctly it should take a big current at the start of the charge when there is maximum active material for chemical conversion, the current falling to a small value at the end of the charge when the available active material has been converted, this method of charging ensures this automatically.

Car batteries are made in either 6-volt or 12-volt units respectively having three and six cells connected in series, allowing 2·5 volts per cell when charged; for a 12-volt battery this would give 15 volts when the battery is fully charged. If a constant potential difference of 15 volts be applied to a 12-volt battery, at the start of the charge the current will be a maximum as the difference between the applied and battery volts is a maximum, until at the end of the charge the difference between the applied and battery volts is a minimum when only a small current will flow into the battery.

This is the principle of constant voltage charging, any number of such batteries may be charged at the same time by supplying a constant potential to a pair of common busbars and connecting each battery between the busbars as is shown in Fig. 50a. Fig. 50b shows a similar method using three busbars

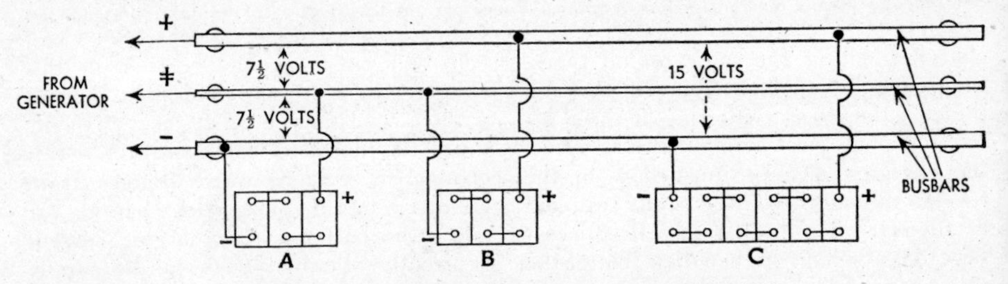

Fig. 50b. Diagram showing three-busbar method of constant voltage charging. The 6-volt batteries are connected between one outer and one middle busbar and the 12-volt batteries between the two outer busbars. In this manner the load can be balanced with batteries of different voltages.

CHAPTER 3

GENERATION OF POWER

Generating Plant. Speed of Prime Mover. Rotating Field Systems. Low-Speed Generator Construction Turbo-Generator Construction. Stator Windings. Sizes and Voltages of A.C. Generators. Exciters. Supplies to Power Station Auxiliaries. Voltage Regulation of A.C. Generators. Automatic Voltage Regulators. Parallel Operation and Synchronising of A.C. Generators. Synchroscope Connections in a Power Station. Converting Plant. Circuit Breakers. Arc Control Devices. Outdoor Switchgear. High-Voltage Circuit Breaker Bushings. Busbars Reactors Between Busbar Sections. Metal-Clad Switchgear. Control Rooms. Hydro-Electric Schemes Pelton Wheel Turbine Element. Impulse Turbine. Francis Turbine. Governors.

INCREASING density of population necessitates the provision of power for manufacturing purposes; rapid and reliable transport for passengers and also for food and other commodities; and lighting, heating and cooking. Since these fundamental necessities can best be supplied through the medium of electrical energy, large electric power stations have been constructed and these are interconnected by means of transmission lines which now cover the major part of Great Britain. Consequently, an enormous amount of capital has been expended in the development of this service which is of paramount importance to the community. In this chapter we shall consider the equipment of power stations, such as generators, switchgear, etc., together with their main auxiliary and control plant.

GENERATING PLANT

IT is, of course, necessary for an electric generator to be driven by a prime mover, and various types employed may be classified as follows:—

(1) Steam, i.e., Turbines and Reciprocating Engines,

(2) Internal Combustion, i.e., Oil and Gas Engines, and

(3) Hydraulic, i.e., Water Turbines.

Large A.C. generators are invariably driven by means of turbines which have the advantages of relatively low cost per kilowatt, low maintenance, small floor area per kilowatt, and high efficiency. Also turbines can be built for the largest sizes and for the highest speeds required for A.C. generators. For the above reasons, the turbine has almost entirely displaced the reciprocating engine, although the latter is occasionally employed for low-speed generators. The Diesel engine, which utilises crude oil vaporised at high pressures, is also employed to drive low-speed generators, and gas and petrol engines are employed for generators of small output, usually direct-current. The water turbine, which is used where the natural energy of a waterfall is available, or where water power is artificially made available, will be referred to at the end of this chapter.

SPEED OF PRIME MOVER

It will be evident from Fig. 29 (see Chapter 2) that in a 2-pole machine, each conductor passes through one complete cycle in one revolution, while in the case of a 4-pole machine, the conductor will pass through two cycles per revolution. If, therefore, the armature rotates at, say, 300 r.p.m. or 5 revolutions per second, the frequency in the case of the 2-pole machine will be 5 cps., in the case of the 4-pole machine, 10 cps. The fre-

Number of poles	2	4	6	8	10	12	16	20	30	40
Speed R.P.M.	3,000	1,500	1,000	750	600	500	375	300	200	150

quency f clearly depends upon the number of poles p and the speed n, thus $f = \frac{pn}{120}$ where n is in revolutions per minute. The standard frequency for supply to consumers for power and lighting in accordance with the grid system is 50 cps. and it will be evident that the A.C. generator with a given number of poles can only be run at one particular speed if the frequency is to be maintained constant. The speed corresponding to the frequency for which the generator is designed is known as the "synchronous speed" and since the generator operates exclusively at this speed, it is referred to as a "synchronous" generator. For a frequency of fifty cycles per second (50 cps.) the relationship between speed and numbers of poles is as given in the above table.

18,000 kW LOW-SPEED STATOR

Fig. 1. B.T.H. stator of 300 r.p.m. generator wound for three-phase working. Note the large diameter and relatively short horizontal length.

Usually turbine-driven generators have two or four poles, or in very large sizes 6-pole machines are occasionally used. 2-pole generators are built up to 60,000 kilowatts. Diesel-engine-driven generators have as many as forty poles, the number of poles increasing as the size increases, while generators driven by steam engines of the reciprocating type may have as many as twenty poles in large sizes.

In the case of a D.C. generator a commutator is necessary, and thus the armature must be the rotating member, the pole magnet system being, of course, stationary. With an A.C. generator no such restriction applies since there is no commutator, and either the field magnet system or the armature can be rotated. In both cases the armature conductors are cut by the magnet flux, and since the rotating field system possesses important advantages, it is almost invariably employed. Thus the armature is the stationary member and is always referred to simply as the stator. The rotating field system is similarly called the rotor. The terms "stator" and "rotor" are employed irrespective of whether the armature or field system rotates, so that in a rotating armature machine, the field system would be the stator and the armature the rotor. The advantages of the rotating field construction will now be considered in some detail.

THIRTY-POLE ROTOR

Fig. 2. In this 30-pole rotor, manufactured by Messrs. Metropolitan Vickers, Ltd., the poles are secured to the rotor wheel by bolts. Note leads from field winding which pass through hole in shaft and thence to slip rings. As the poles project they are known as salient poles.

Since the armature winding is placed outside the field system, there is clearly space for an increased number of slots and thus the space available for the armature conductors is increased. This will be apparent from Fig. 1 if it is imagined that a rotor, similar to that shown in Fig. 2, is inserted. It will be obvious that it is easier to make a sound mechanical construction of the field poles and windings, since the end connections of the armature windings, if rotated, would tend to be displaced owing to the large centrifugal forces. Also it will be appreciated that since generators are commonly wound for voltages of the order of over 6,000 volts per phase, and in some cases as high as 20,000 volts per phase, it is preferable to have the high voltage windings stationary. Finally, a rotating field requires only two low-voltage slip rings and brushes, to lead the current into and out of the field winding. These slip rings are shown in Fig. 2 on the shaft adjacent to the field poles. With a rotating armature wound for three-phase supply, three high-voltage slip rings would, of course, be required.

GENERATOR CONSTRUCTION

Low-speed generators are generally driven by reciprocating steam engines or Diesel engines. Referring again to Fig. 1, the function of the stator frame is to hold the armature stampings, or laminations, in position. The latter are formed of annular rings with the slots on the inside as shown. In the case of large machines, these annular rings will be built up in sections. The stampings are tightly clamped together between a number of mild steel clamping plates. Bolts pass through the clamping plates thereby rigidly holding the stampings together. The end connections of the windings are supported by being securely lashed to insulated steel rings, these being sup-

STATOR UNDER CONSTRUCTION

Fig. 3. General Electric stator of 50,000 kilowatt, 11,000 volt, three-phase 1,500 r.p.m. generator. The complete generator is shown in Fig. 5.

insulated by a mica sleeve. This type of construction in which the poles project outwards, is known as a "salient pole" rotor. Since turbines are designed to operate at high speeds, the generators are generally equipped with 2- or 4-pole rotors and thus the rotor diameter is much smaller as compared with that of a low-speed generator. As a consequence, the stator diameter is also smaller and thus the armature winding space is more limited.

ported by brackets from the stator frame.

The rotor construction will be understood from a study of Fig. 2. The rotor body consists of a steel wheel, with holes in the web to reduce the weight, the wheel being keyed to the shaft. Thus it will be evident that the major portion of the weight is concentrated in the outer rim so that there is a considerable flywheel effect. Since engines of the reciprocating type do not operate at a consistently steady speed, the torque being transmitted to the shaft by a series of piston impulses, this flywheel effect is utilised to smooth out irregularities in the speed. The poles are built up of steel laminations and are bolted to the wheel by means of steel bolts inserted from the under-side as shown, so that any one pole can be removed without disturbing the others. The field coils are wound with copper strip on edge, adjacent turns being insulated from each other with insulating material specially shaped to fit the copper strip. The slip rings are made either of bronze or steel and are shrunk on to a cast-iron bush from which they are

Due to a reduced number of stator slots, there will evidently be fewer armature conductors and in order that sufficient voltage may be generated each armature conductor must be of increased length. While, therefore, a low-speed generator has a large diameter and a short length, a turbo-generator has a small diameter and is long horizontally. To give some idea of leading dimensions, the following particulars of a 60,000 kW. 1,500 r.p.m. turbo-generator may be interesting:

Dimensions (overall).	Generator.	Turbine.
Length ..	37 feet	44 feet
Height ..	10 feet	13 feet

The overall length of the turbo-generator is thus 81 feet (or 27 yds.), and the weights of the stator and the 4-pole rotor are respectively 91 and 58 tons.

Fig. 3 illustrates the stator of a

50,000 kW generator and Fig. 5 shows the complete turbo-generator set giving a good idea of the great overall length. The machines in the foreground are auxiliary generators direct-driven from the main shaft and will be referred to later. The main generator is behind the main bearing placed between it and the auxiliary generators and the turbine is in the background. The stator construction follows substantially that of a low-speed generator, but the rotor construction is very different and will now be referred to in detail. Fig. 4 illustrates the construction of a two-pole rotor. The core consists of a number of steel rings which are shrunk on to the shaft and slotted after assembly. The rotor windings are placed in the slots and the unslotted portions of the rotor iron at the top and bottom form the north and south poles. The method of winding the rotor will be evident from Fig. 6 from which it will be seen that the slots are closed by means of bronze wedges which are driven into dovetails cut in the mouths of the slots. The end connections of the rotor windings are protected against the centrifugal forces by

AIR-COOLED ROTOR

Fig. 4. Unwound two-pole non-salient type rotor, manufactured by the British Thomson-Houston Co., Ltd. Portion of the shaft which receives core-plates is fluted and core-plates are separated from each other as shown. Thus cooling air can be drawn in along shaft and circulated between core-plates.

G.E.C. COMPLETE 50,000 kW TURBO-GENERATOR SET

Fig. 5. Steam turbine is in background next to A.C. generator. The 1,500 kilowatt, 400 volt house service generator is in front of the main generator. There are five separate machines in all.

enclosing them in non-magnetic steel end-rings (see Fig. 7). This type of construction is very sound from the mechanical viewpoint and is thus suitable for high speeds and for two, four, or six poles. The rotor is known as a "non-salient pole" (or "cylindrical" type).

PARTLY ASSEMBLED ROTOR

Fig. 6. Non-salient two-pole rotor showing pole windings formed from copper strip. Manufactured by British Thomson-Houston Co.

STATOR WINDINGS

The windings used for A.C. generators are of the open-circuit type, whilst closed-circuit windings are used in D.C. generators, but otherwise A.C. and D.C. windings are very similar. For example, wave and lap windings are often employed in A.C. machines. Fig. 8a illustrates the wave winding for a 4-pole A.C. generator. In all windings it is, of course, necessary to connect a conductor lying under a north pole to one lying under a south pole thereby obtaining addition of the induced e.m.f.'s. Thus, starting from T_1, the e.m.f.'s in the four conductors connected between the points T_1 and A are added. The conductor A is then connected to A^1 and the conductor B to B^1 so that all conductors are in series between terminals T_1 and T_2. Fig. 8b shows a lap development and again it will be seen that all conductors between the terminals T_1 and T_2 are in series. The coils are diamond-shaped and a special end connection or jumper connects successive coils together. The relation between these coils and the four poles are to be seen in the diagram where the polarities are clearly to be seen.

The windings shown are, of course, single-phase only. Practically all generators are now wound for three-phase

COMPLETED NON-SALIENT ROTOR

Fig. 7. Completed British Thomson-Houston 4-pole 1,500 r.p.m., non-salient rotor for 40,000 kilovolt-ampere A.C. generator. Note the nickel-manganese-steel (which is non-magnetic) retaining rings for supporting rotor end turns from the effect of centrifugal forces.

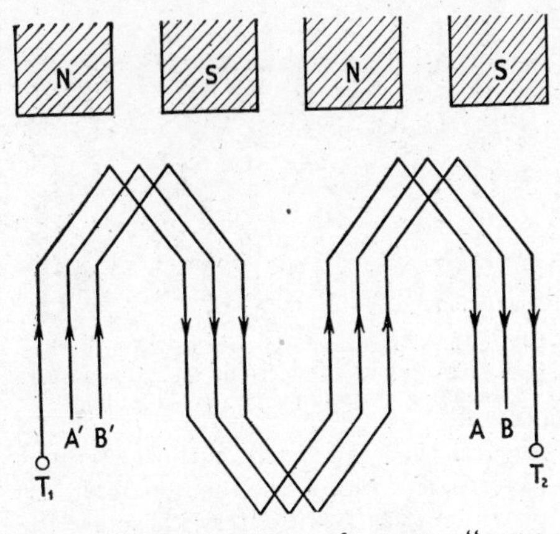

Fig. 8a. Development of stator "wave-winding" for A.C. generator.

working and so three separate and distinct windings are necessary. Suppose we consider the case of a 4-pole generator having 24 stator slots. The number of slots per pole pitch is therefore 6 (Fig. 9). The three-phase windings are named red, blue and yellow. Taking the red phase, the back end of conductor 1 would be connected to the back end of conductor 1′, the latter lying under the south pole. The front ends of 1′ and 2 would be connected together and the rear ends of 2 and 2′ would also be connected. The front end of 2′ would then be connected by means of the jumper to the next coil. This development is, of course, the lap connection in Fig. 8b or alternatively the wave connection could be employed. The developments of the blue and yellow phases are exactly similar to that of the red winding.

SPAN OF POLE PITCH

Referring again to Fig. 9 and remembering that one pole pitch spans 180 electrical degrees (see page 29), it will be evident that the red, yellow and blue phase windings each occupy $\frac{180}{3}$ or 60 electrical degrees. Imagine the pole magnet system to be moving from left to right as shown. It will be clear that the pole flux will first move past conductors 1 and 2 of the red phase, then past conductors 3 and 4 of the blue phase and lastly past conductors 5 and 6 of the yellow phase. Consequently the e.m.f. induced in the red phase will be 60 deg. ahead of that in the blue phase, while the e.m.f. induced in the yellow phase will lag behind by a further 60 deg. These e.m.f.'s are shown in the vector diagram of Fig. 9 as E_R, E_B and E_Y respectively.

PHASE DISPLACEMENT

In a three-phase system we require a phase displacement between the voltages of 120 degrees and this condition is very easily satisfied by the external connections of the windings. Since three-phase A.C. generator windings are almost invariably connected in star, the necessary external connection will be evident from a study of Fig. 8b. The terminals T_2 of the red phase and T_2 of the yellow phase are connected to T_1 of the blue phase to form a star point, the corresponding terminals being, of course, T_1 (red), T_1 (yellow) and T_2 (blue). Thus it will be evident that the blue phase winding has its connections reversed as compared with those of the red and yellow phases and the

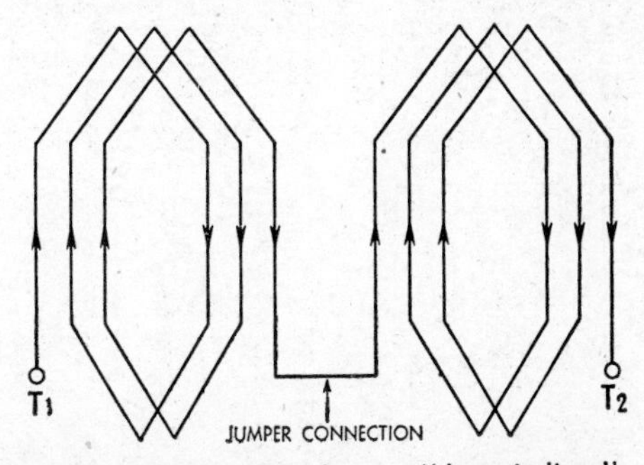

Fig. 8b. Development of stator "lap-winding" for A.C. generator. Lap and wave-windings are similar to those used for D.C. machines, but while D.C. windings form completely closed circuits, A.C. windings are open-circuited.

result is clearly a reversal of the blue phase voltage. The latter will, therefore, be represented by—E_B as shown in Fig. 9a and the system voltages will then be represented by E_R, E_Y and—E_B mutually spaced 120 deg. apart just as we said was desired. In order to avoid the fouling of the end connections of the three phases, which must evidently cross one another, the end connections are bent upwards (Fig. 9b), two shapes being employed.

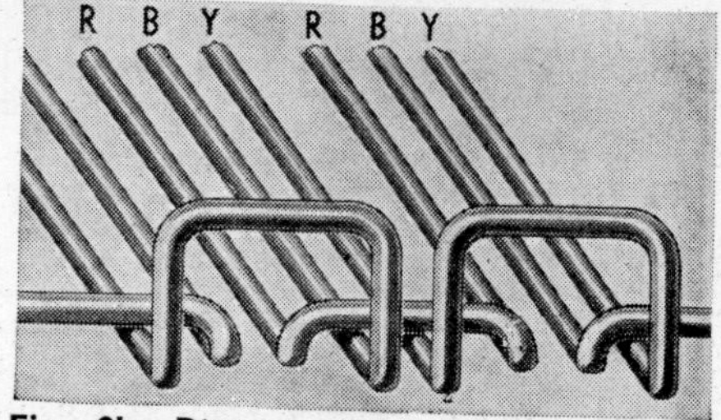

Fig. 9b. Diagrammatic arrangement illustrating how end connections in a three-phase winding are arranged to avoid fouling.

SIZES AND VOLTAGES OF A.C. GENERATORS

For large and important power stations generators of about 50,000 to 75,000 kW appear to represent standard practice while for smaller stations 30,000 kW sets are usually employed. The largest set in this country is 100,000 kW. The most usual voltage is of the order of 11,000 volts between terminals, but a number of generators operating at 33,000 volts have been in successful service for some years. (Fig. 10 shows the layout of the turbo-generators in a large power station.)

EXCITERS

The field windings of an A.C. generator must, of course, be supplied with direct-current and, for this purpose, a D.C. generator known as an exciter forms an integral part of each turbo-generator. Referring to Fig. 5, the main generator is provided with two exciters, these are the first and third machines from the right, the latter being the main and the former the auxiliary exciter. The A.C. generator field winding is supplied from the armature of the main exciter. Since the main exciter is a large machine, having a full-load rating of 176 kW, the field current of this machine is supplied from the armature of a self-excited auxiliary exciter. Since the operation of the main generator depends upon the exciters, the design of the latter machines must in all circumstances receive very careful consideration.

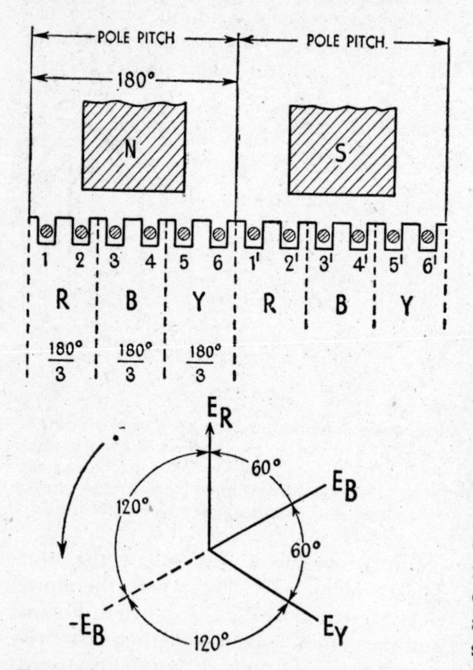

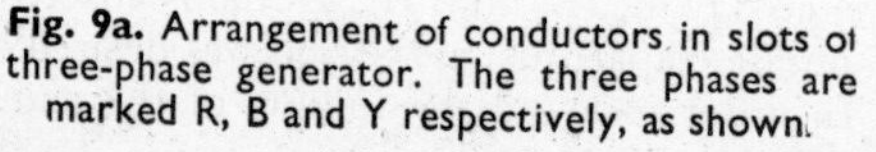

Fig. 9a. Arrangement of conductors in slots of three-phase generator. The three phases are marked R, B and Y respectively, as shown.

SUPPLIES TO POWER STATION AUXILIARIES

In a large power station, there are many electric motors, some of considerable size, which provide various necessary services. For instance, motors are required to drive the boiler feed pumps which keep the boiler drums supplied with water. In order to stimulate the boiler fire, fans are employed to increase the air draught. The grate conveying fresh coal to the fire is electrically driven and coal is brought to the hopper of the boiler by means of a coal conveyor also electrically driven. In addition, further motors are employed in connection with each turbine and electrically driven fans are necessary for ventilating the power station itself. Also the power station will require power for lighting and other purposes. It is clearly of supreme importance that the supply of power for these purposes shall be absolutely reliable and great care must therefore be exercised in the layout of an auxiliary supply scheme. A unit which is widely employed for the generation of power for auxiliary supplies is the house-service generator driven either by the main turbine or by a small independent turbine. The former scheme is shown in Fig. 5, the house service generator being placed between the main generator and the exciter previously referred to. The output of this generator is 1,500 kW, so that if four such turbo-generator sets were installed in a power station having a capacity of 200,000 kW the corresponding house service generator capacity would be 6,000 kW.

MODERN POWER STATION

Fig. 10. Interior view of Clarence Dock Power Station which supplies energy for power and lighting to a large area in Liverpool. The two generating sets in the foreground are of 51,250 kW each, while the two just visible in the background are of 51,000 kW each.

VOLTAGE REGULATION

In the case of a separately excited D.C. generator, the terminal voltage decreases as the load increases due to two reasons, namely the IR drop due to armature resistance and the decrease of airgap flux due to armature reaction. In an A.C. generator, the reactance must be considered so that the terminal voltage falls due to the impedance drop, IZ, in the winding. Armature reaction, due to the magnetic field set up by the stator ampere-turns, occurs as in D.C. machines, but its effect is dependent upon the power factor of the load. With a lagging power factor, the effect of the armature field is to decrease the airgap flux and, therefore, the generated voltage, the lower the power factor the greater is the demagnetising effect. Conversely, the effect of a leading power factor is to increase the airgap flux and the generated voltage. Usually an A.C. generator operates at a lagging power factor, however, and thus the terminated voltage decreases considerably as the load current is increased. The voltage regulation is defined as the voltage rise which takes place when full-load current is thrown off, the power factor being specified. The regulation is thus $= \frac{E - V}{V}$ where V is the normal terminal voltage at full-load and E is the corresponding voltage at no-load. Thus

E — V is the voltage drop. Since the variation of terminal voltage is generally considerable, it is modern practice to equip A.C. generators with voltage regulators which function automatically to keep the terminal voltage constant.

AUTOMATIC VOLTAGE REGULATORS

Various types of automatic voltage regulators are employed and forms used in conjunction with large A.C. generators are described in more advanced text books. A simple type of voltage regulator suitable for fairly small A.C. generators will serve to give the reader an idea of the operating principle of a more elaborate type. Referring to Fig. 11 two stacks of rectangular carbon plates connected in series, form the resistance element of the regulator, and these are in series with the exciter field circuit, as shown. Near the front end of each carbon plate, and passing right through it is a silver contact b and near the rear end is an insulating spacer c. Under each plate is a metal spacer d which acts as a fulcrum upon which the carbon plates can be rocked backwards or forwards by means of a rod e and lever f pivoted at g. It will be seen that the control coil carries a current which is proportional to the terminal voltage of the A.C. generator. Suppose, now, the generator is loaded and the terminal voltage is at its normal value. Under this condition approximately the upper half of each stack of carbon plates is tilted forward and a corresponding number of the silver contacts are closed. If the generator load is decreased, the terminal voltage, and thus the current in the control coil, will rise. The resulting increase in the control coil ampere - turns will cause the iron core to be attracted and thus the lever f will rotate counter-clockwise raising the rod e and opening the closed silver contacts in succession thereby inserting more resistance in series with the exciter field circuit. Consequently, the exciter armature voltage and, therefore, the A.C. generator voltage decreases

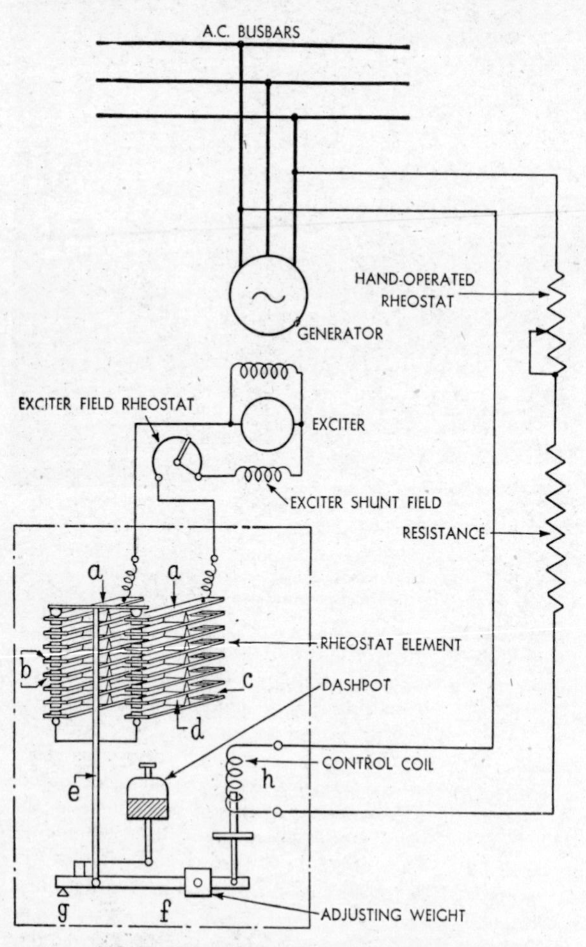

VOLTAGE REGULATOR OPERATION

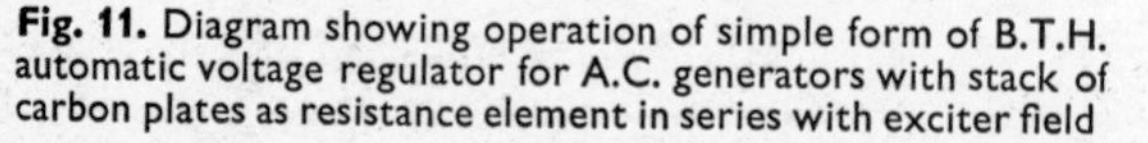
Fig. 11. Diagram showing operation of simple form of B.T.H. automatic voltage regulator for A.C. generators with stack of carbon plates as resistance element in series with exciter field

AUTOMATIC VOLTAGE REGULATOR

Fig. 12. Case and internal mechanism of B.T.H. automatic voltage regulator. This should be compared with Fig. 11. Note that cover is of expanded metal so that heat generated may be more readily dissipated

so that the latter is restored to its normal value. Conversely, if the A.C. generator voltage falls, the iron core sinks and an increased number of the silver button contacts are closed causing the exciter and generator voltages to rise until the normal voltage is re-established.

In the high-resistance position, the exciter field current passes through all the carbon plates and the metal spacers d, all the silver contacts being separated. In the low resistance position, with the front end of the carbon stacks depressed, the silver contacts form a continuous silver path thereby reducing the resistance to a negligible value. Thus a wide range of resistance is obtainable from this carbon plate arrangement which permits of a large adjustment of the exciter field current. An adjusting weight is provided which can be moved along the lever f and the position of this weight will evidently determine the terminal voltage of the generator. For example, suppose it is desired to maintain the generator voltage at a higher value, then the adjusting weight would be moved further to the right. A further means of adjustment for the same purpose is the hand operated rheostat shown in series with the control coil. The action of the regulator is damped by connecting the lever f to the piston of the dashpot through a flexible coupling. The object of this damping is, of course, to eliminate vibration in the mechanism of the device. Usually a dashpot consists of a piston fitting loosely in a cylinder of oil. Fig. 12 illustrates the appearance of an automatic voltage regulator.

As in the case of D.C. generators, A.C. generators are required to operate in parallel since in a power station there are generally a number of turbo-generator sets installed. Fig. 13a illustrates the arrangement of two generators 1 and 2, the former being connected to the busbars to which the feeders conveying the current to the load are also connected. From time to time the demands which are made on the installation will vary considerably. Suppose now, that the load is increasing, and consequently it becomes necessary to run up generator 2 and connect this generator in parallel with 1 in order to deal with the increased load. Before 2 can be connected to the busbars, the following condition must be satisfied:—

(1) the e.m.f. of generator 2 must be the same as the busbar voltage.

(2) the e.m.f. of generator 2 must be in phase with the busbar voltage.

(3) the frequency of generator 2 must be the same as the busbar frequency.

In the case of D.C. generators only condition 1 has to be fulfilled, but with A.C. generators their voltages are varying from instant to instant and, consequently, the remaining two conditions must also be satisfied thus ensuring that the

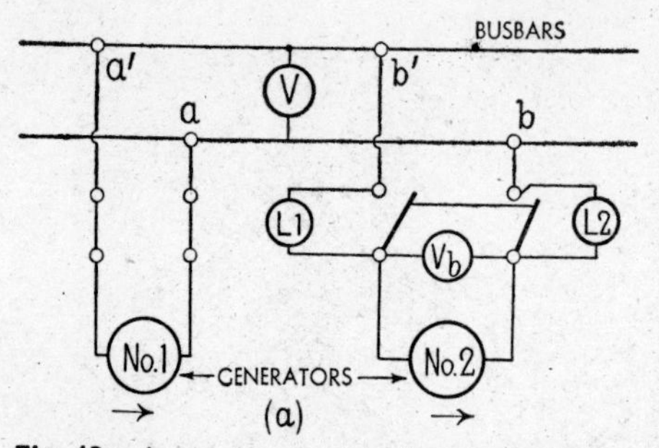

Fig. 13a. Apparatus required for synchronising A.C. generators by means of lamps, showing connections for the "lamps dark" method.

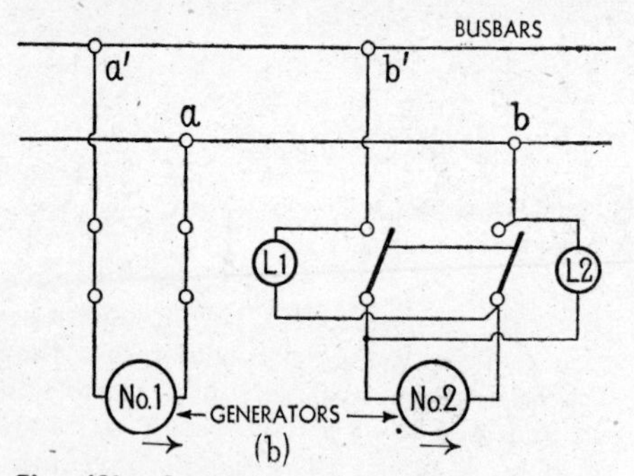

Fig. 13b. Connections for "lamps bright" method. Switch of machine 2 is closed at instant when lamps give maximum brilliancy.

voltages are the same at every instant. Condition 1 will evidently be satisfied when the busbar voltmeter V indicates the same voltage as the generator voltmeter V_b but in order to indicate when conditions 2 and 3 are satisfied some form of synchronising gear is necessary, or in other words, generator 2 has to be synchronised.

SYNCHRONISING CIRCUITS

The simplest form of synchronising gear consists of two lamps, each of the same voltage as the busbar voltage. Each lamp L is connected across the terminals of one pole of the generator switch (Fig. 13a). Obviously, if, when generator 2 is running and generating an e.m.f. the lamps remain consistently dark, this means that there is no voltage difference between the machine and busbar voltages and evidently the switch can safely be closed because all three of the above conditions are complied with. Imagine, for instance, the instant when the voltages of both 1 and 2 are passing through their maximum values, and the direction of these maximum voltages are towards the right-hand terminals of the generators. This instantaneous condition is represented by the arrows directed from left to right. These two voltages will, of course, tend to send a current through the closed circuit provided by the two machines, lamps and busbars. Tracing through this circuit and starting at a′, we first pick up the voltage of generator 1 in the sense of left to right, through the busbar a to b, through lamp L_2, through generator 2 in the sense of right to left, through L_1 and busbar b′ to a′. We thus see that in this closed circuit the two voltages are equal and in opposition and the resultant voltage which would give rise to a current in the circuit is zero. Since this condition holds when the voltages are maximum, the same applies at every other instant assuming the voltage waves of the two generators are in phase and have the same frequency.

Suppose, now, the speed of generator 2 is increased so that it is, say 10 per cent. higher than that of generator 1. If both are 4-pole machines and the speed of the latter is 1,500 r.p.m., then its frequency

$$= \frac{4 \times 1{,}500}{120} = 50 \text{ cycles per second.}$$

Since the speed of generator 2 is 1,650 r.p.m. its frequency will be 55 cycles per second. Thus in $\frac{1}{10}$ second, the voltages of the two generators will trace out 5 and $5\frac{1}{2}$ cycles respectively (see Fig. 14a) in which e_a and e_b are the voltage difference between the generators but at the instant b, the voltage difference is practically twice that of each machine. Consequently the synchronising lamps (see Fig. 13a) will be dark at instant a and fully bright at instant b; thus the light will vary between zero and maximum brilliancy every $\frac{1}{10}$ second. If the speed of generator 2 is reduced slightly, the synchronising lamps will flicker more slowly, showing the frequencies are becoming more nearly equal. Fig. 14b shows the condition when the two frequencies are equal, but have a constant angle of phase difference between them. Since the average voltage difference per cycle is the same, the lamps will glow with constant brilliancy, the latter increasing as the phase difference increases. If the phase difference was 180 deg., as shown in Fig. 14c, the lamps would evidently give their maximum brilliancy continuously. Thus the lamps not only show whether the generators are in synchronism or not, but they give some indication of the conditions before synchronism is reached. In practice, the voltage of the incoming generator is adjusted until it is equal to the busbar voltage, then its speed, and, therefore, its frequency, is adjusted until the lamps flicker slowly and uniformly, the machine switch being closed at the instant when the lamps are dark. It is assumed at this instant that the voltage difference is zero, but this instant cannot accurately be judged because the lamps are not very sensitive to changes of voltage when the voltage is near zero. When the voltage applied to the lamps is near maximum, however, a change in voltage will produce a much greater change in the amount of light, and thus the instant of synchronism can be judged much more

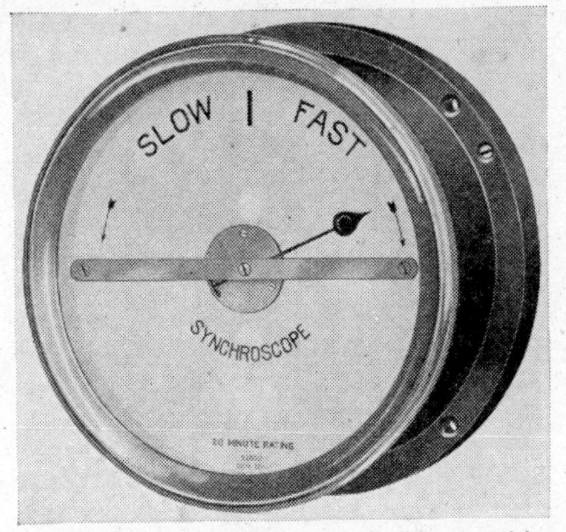

Fig. 15. Typical synchroscope, manufactured by B.T.H. One revolution of pointer corresponds to difference of one cycle per second.

accurately by cross-connecting the lamps, Fig. 13b. Tracing out the closed circuit provided by the generators, lamps, and busbars as before, it will be evident that the two generator voltages now act in series with respect to the lamps instead of in opposition. Consequently synchronism will be reached at the instant when both lamps attain their maximum brilliancy, and this instant can now be judged more accurately. For large turbo-generators, the operation of synchronising must be carried out very accurately and a special instrument called a "rotary synchroscope" is invariably employed. This consists essentially of a small motor, housed inside an instrument case, with its shaft connected to a pointer. The stator winding of the A.C. motor is connected to the busbars and the rotor to the terminals of the incoming generator. A difference of frequency causes the pointer to rotate in a clockwise direction if the speed of the incoming machine is too high and in a counter-clockwise direction if the incoming machine speed is

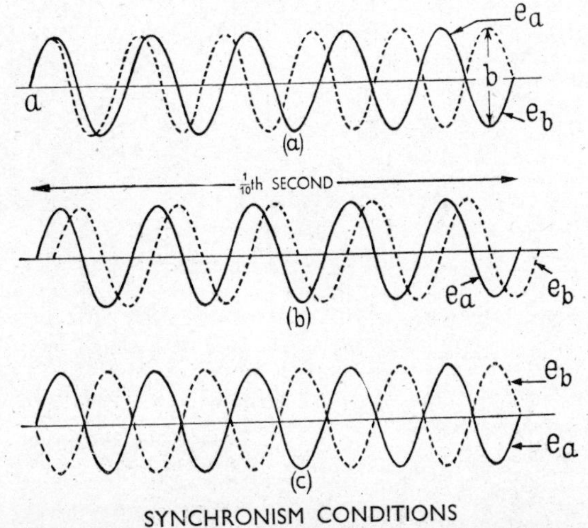

Fig. 14. Diagram showing three different conditions before synchronism between the generators has been reached.

too low. When the two frequencies are identical, the pointer remains stationary at a position proportional to the phase difference between the two voltages. When synchronism is reached, the pointer stands vertically upright. Fig. 15 illustrates a typical synchroscope, the black mark between "slow" and "fast" being the position of synchronism. The connections to the coils of the A.C. motor are made through step-down voltage transformers (see page 125) when the busbar voltage is high.

SYNCHROSCOPE CONNECTIONS IN A POWER STATION

It is usual to provide only one synchroscope in a power station and to arrange for this instrument to be connected to any of the A.C. generators at will. Fig. 16 illustrates the connections for this purpose. Only two generators are shown but it will be obvious that the scheme could be extended to include any larger number. The synchroscope is connected to the busbars and to the incoming machine through potential transformers PT, either 4-pin plugs or small double-pole switches being used for this purpose. If plugs are employed they must be so designed that it is impossible to insert them incorrectly.

Imagine generator No. 1 to be connected to the busbars, its main switch being closed as shown and No. 2 generator is to be paralleled with the busbars.

The synchroscope is connected to the busbars and incoming generators, the latter having first been run up to its normal speed and its terminal voltage adjusted. The speed of the incoming machine is now adjusted until the synchroscope pointer rotates very slowly indicating a very small frequency difference. When the pointer is just approaching the vertical position the main switch is closed and the operation is complete. The synchroscope is now disconnected from the busbars and from the machine. It will be evident that the voltages between two lines only are synchronised and this is all that is necessary since if these are in phase, the remaining line voltages will also necessarily be in phase.

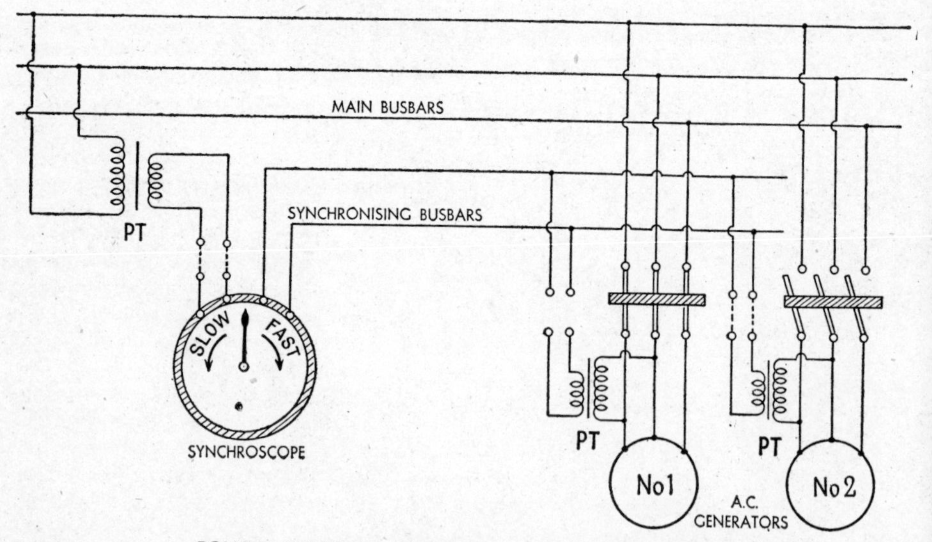

POWER STATION SYNCHROSCOPE CONNECTIONS

Fig. 16. Synchroscope is connected to busbars and also to machine to be synchronised through voltage transformers. Synchronising busbars facilitate connection of synchroscope to every generator in station at will. If 4-point plugs are used for connecting, the pins should be set at the corners of an oblong to prevent incorrect insertion, thereby short-circuiting the generator.

MERCURY-ARC RECTIFIER SUB-STATION

Fig. 17. Large mercury-arc rectifier sub-station supplying energy for electric traction purposes. Each rectifier gives output of 2,000 kilowatts at 630 volts. The rectifiers are of steel tank type and water cooled. Mercury chamber proper is housed in outside shell which acts as water jacket. Cooling of the anodes is effected by means of water-filled radiator tubes mounted on top of rectifier tanks. Each rectifier is supplied from a bank of three single-phase air-blast-cooled transformers.

The high-voltage windings of the voltage transformers PT must be protected by fuses (these are not illustrated).

CONVERTING PLANT

It is frequently necessary to convert from alternating to direct currents. Direct currents are necessary for some industrial applications, particularly where motors are required to give their outputs at varying speeds, the speed being under the control of the operator.

Another very important case is that of electric traction in which D.C. series-wound motors are almost invariably employed. Since electrical energy is generated as three-phase A.C., converters are installed, generally in sub-stations near the load, to convert the energy to D.C. The input to the sub-station is given at high voltage so that transformers must be employed to reduce the voltage to a value suitable for the converting plant.

One form of converter, the mercury-arc rectifier is, of course, a static apparatus but another form of rectifier which is widely employed is the rotary converter. This machine is essentially a D.C. generator, but on the end of the shaft remote from the commutator, slip rings are mounted, and these are connected to appropriate points of the armature winding. When these slip rings are supplied with three-phase currents, the machine runs as a synchronous motor, i.e., it functions as the reverse of a synchronous generator just as a D.C. generator will function equally well as a D.C. motor. It will be understood that the machine must be synchronised with the system from

ROTARY CONVERTER SUB-STATION

Fig. 18. Each machine gives an output of 2,000 kilowatts at 500 volts. The starting motor is in foreground and behind it are one main bearing, the slip rings and A.C. brushgear. Commutator and D.C. brushgear are located on the other side of armature. Appearance of the D.C. side is similar to that of a D.C. generator. The complete installation was manufactured by the General Electric Co., Ltd.

which it is to be supplied. D.C. supplies may then be taken from the commutator as in the case of a D.C. generator. Since the machine can only operate at its synchronous speed, special arrangements must be made for starting it, and one such means is to employ a separate A.C. motor, erected on a shaft extension outside the main bearing. This motor is also used, of course, to adjust the speed to its correct value and to enable the converter to be brought into synchronism. The starting motor is on the right of the rotary converters, as shown in Fig. 18. Note that this illustration also shows the D.C. side of the machines.

CIRCUIT BREAKERS

It is well known that when a circuit carrying a large current is broken, an arc occurs at the point where the contacts are separated. The arcing is, as would be expected, especially severe when high voltages are involved, and if a short-circuit occurs on, say, a high-voltage cable which is supplied from a large power station, the arc would be sufficiently powerful to bridge the contacts of the switch and destroy it by burning. For this reason, an alternating current circuit is broken under oil, the switch contacts being enclosed in a steel tank containing oil, and the device is known as an oil circuit breaker. An oil circuit breaker possesses the valuable property of always breaking an alternating current at or near its zero value, because when it parts and an arc is formed, the oil exerts a hydrostatic pressure on the arc. Naturally the arc is weakest when the current is small and so the pressure of the oil quenches the arc when the current passes through its zero value. Since a short-circuit current is, of course, many times greater than the normal load current, oil circuit breakers must evidently be designed so that they are able safely to break the most severe short circuit current that can occur. Indeed, the size of a circuit breaker is based upon the short-circuit current and not upon the full-load current, and many ingenious devices have been evolved for the purpose of controlling the arc under the severe conditions which have been mentioned.

Fig. 19 illustrates a three-phase oil circuit breaker with the tank removed. The breaker consists essentially of fixed contacts A which pass through insulating tubes D to the terminals F. When the breaker is closed, each pair of fixed contacts is bridged by a moving contact B, the three moving contacts being simultaneously operated from a common horizontal cross-bar, housed in the top frame E, which carries the three insulated tension rods C. It will be seen that the fixed contacts A consist of three short and one long finger, the latter making contact with the arcing contact G. Since arcing inevitably occurs when the breaker interrupts a current, the arc is made to occur between these arcing contacts, both of which are arranged to facilitate easy renewal. Thus the function of the main contacts is restricted to the carrying of the current. The operation of the arcing contacts is clearly shown in Fig. 20. The circuit breaker of Fig. 19 is suitable only for low power and is operated manually by means of the handle shown, the catch on the handle holding the breaker in the closed position. When the breaker is closed, coiled springs, which act on the tension rods, are compressed. When the catch is released,

HAND-OPERATED CIRCUIT BREAKER

Fig. 19. Johnson & Phillips' 300 ampere, 6,600 volt oil circuit breaker. High speed of break is obtained by means of accelerating springs. The apparatus is suitable for only low power and is operated by means of the handle which can be seen on the right.

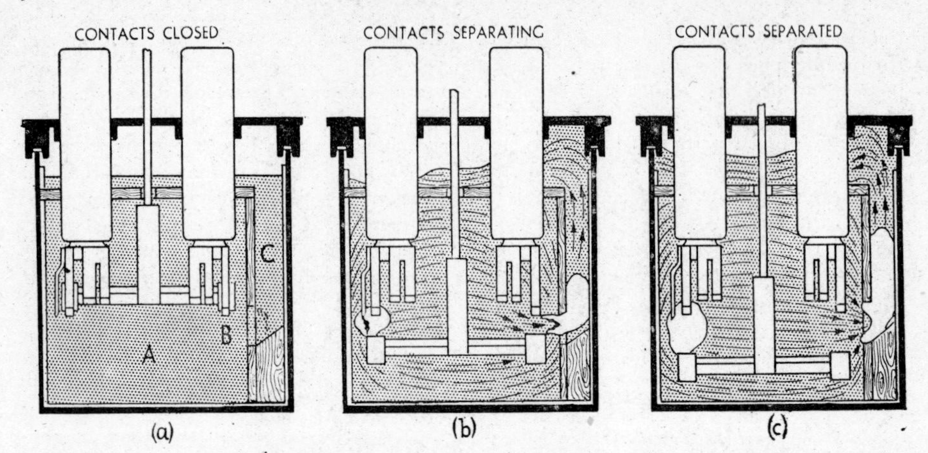

OPERATION OF B.T.H. CROSS-JET BOX

Fig. 20. Arc is drawn out in enclosure A and resulting generation of gas puts surrounding oil under pressure. Consequently cool oil is forced across path of right-hand arc and thence into chimney B.

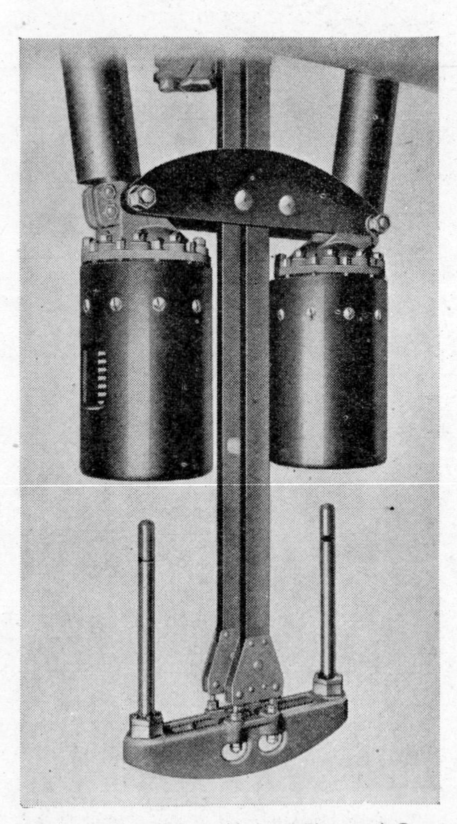

Fig. 21. Metropolitan Vickers Electrical Company's moving contacts and cross-jet pot for one phase of a 66,000 volt circuit breaker.

the springs open the breaker quickly. The contacts are, as previously mentioned, immersed in a tank fixed to the top frame, and it will be seen that above the oil is a certain volume of air, known as the air cushion, between the surface of the oil and the top frame (Fig. 20). Large circuit breakers are not manually but electrically operated, the breaker being opened and closed either by means of an operating motor or by a solenoid, this making remote control possible. A modern development is to use compressed air for the purpose.

ARC CONTROL DEVICES

When an arc occurs, the oil in its path is vaporised, and the gas thereby generated exerts a pressure on the surrounding oil. This pressure is utilised in arc control devices to cause a movement of fresh cool oil cross the path of the arc thereby efficiently assisting its interruption. One of the simplest arc control devices is the cross-jet box (Fig. 20) from which it will be seen that the contacts are enclosed in a special enclosure A which is housed inside the main oil tank. This enclosure is completely filled with oil, but has a single outlet or orifice B which communicates with the chimney C. When the breaker opens arcs are drawn out between the arcing contacts (Fig.

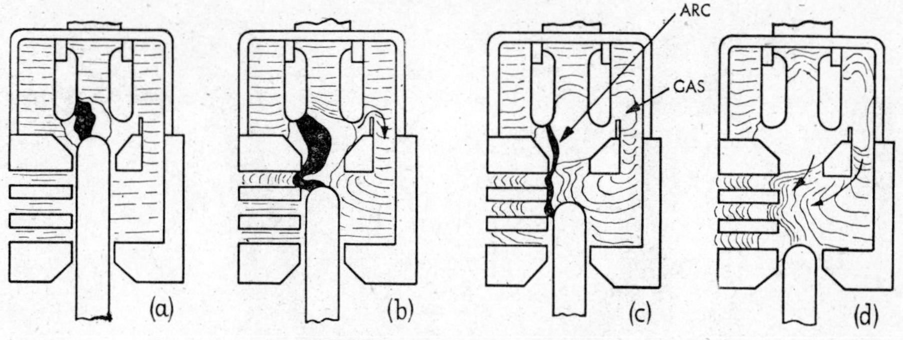

ACTION OF CROSS-JET POT

Fig. 22. An arc is drawn between the contacts as they separate, thereby putting the oil in this Metropolitan Vickers' cross-jet pot under pressure. When the horizontal vents open the gas pressure forces the arc against the vents, thus it is attenuated and finally extinguished.

20b). The arc generates gas which sets up a pressure in the arcing chamber and since the only outlet for the oil is through the three orifices B (one for each phase) the oil is forced directly across the arc path through the orifice and into the chimney, taking the gas products with it (Fig. 20c). In this manner the arc is first of all weakened and then finally extinguished.

For larger and higher voltage circuit breakers, cross-jet pots are employed instead of the cross-jet boxes, one cross-jet pot being employed on each break (Fig. 21). It will be seen that the contacts are of the plug and socket type (see also Fig. 22) and are enclosed in a chamber constructed from a fibrous material. Referring to Fig. 22, the four diagrams illustrate progressively the action of the device. Since the clearance between the moving plug contact and the throat of the chamber through which it passes is very small, the oil is forced out

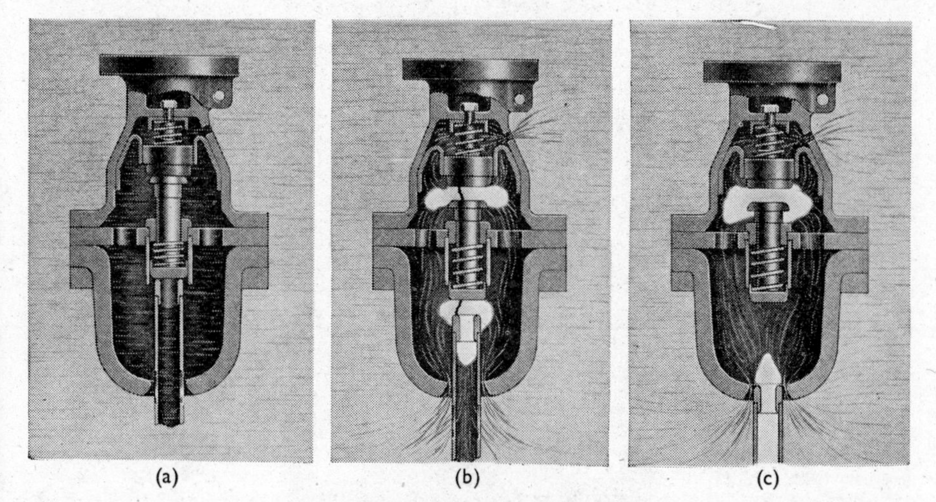

B.T.H. OIL-BLAST EXPLOSION POT

Fig. 23. Ingenious arc control device of the pot type. Two breaks per phase are obtained with a "butt" contact comprising upper, intermediate and lower members. Upper and intermediate contacts part first (B) and draw arc and create gas pressure. Second arc forms when intermediate and bottom contacts part (C) and across this is forced pressure generated in upper chamber.

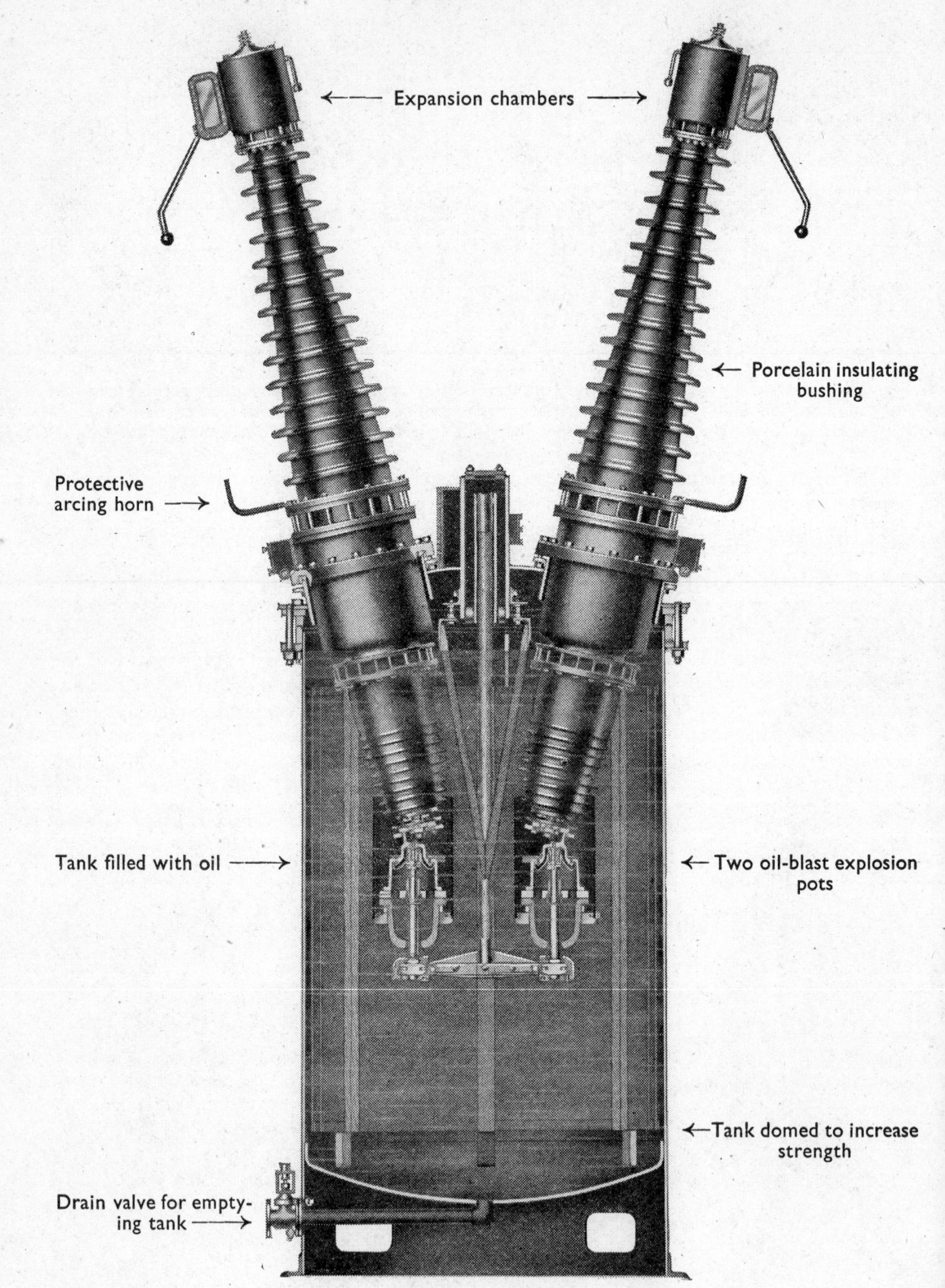

HIGH POWER CIRCUIT BREAKER

Fig. 24. This high-power circuit breaker was designed by Messrs. British Thomson-Houston Co., for 132,000 volt service and equipped with oil-blast explosion-pot contacts.

MET. VIC. THREE-PHASE OIL CIRCUIT BREAKERS

Fig. 25. Installation of 132,000 volt, three-phase oil circuit breakers of large capacity outside a large power station. The steelwork is for the purpose of supporting overhead equipment and connections.

of the chamber through the horizontal vents. As shown in the diagrams, the arc is driven on to the insulating barriers. At (b) the moving plug contact has just opened the first horizontal vent and the oil and gas are being expelled through it from the arcing chamber. At (c) the second vent has been opened while (d) shows the final arc extinction. High voltages are catered for by increasing the number of vents and intervening arc splitters, the function of the latter being to provide cutting edges across which the arc is attenuated, weakened and finally interrupted. It will be clear that the action of the cross-jet pot is similar to that of the cross-jet box, but in the former greater accuracy of "shooting" of the oil and gas across the path of the arc is achieved.

An ingenious arc control device is the oil-blast explosion pot (Fig. 23). The contacts, which are of the "butt" type, consist of upper, intermediate and lower members so that two breaks per phase are obtained. When the breaker begins to open, the upper and intermediate contacts part thereby drawing out an arc and generating a gas pressure. The intermediate and bottom contacts then part and a second arc is therefore created (see Fig. 23b). The pressure generated by the arc in the upper chamber forces oil across the lower arc and through the lower moving contact rod, which is hollow, thereby extinguishing the arc (as shown in Fig. 23c).

OUTDOOR SWITCHGEAR

Fig. 24 illustrates a large circuit breaker for an outdoor installation. It is employed on 132,000 volt service and three such breakers are employed to form a three-phase unit. The contacts are of the oil-blast explosion pot type described above, and the large porcelain bushings projecting above the oil tank provide the necessary degree of insulation for this

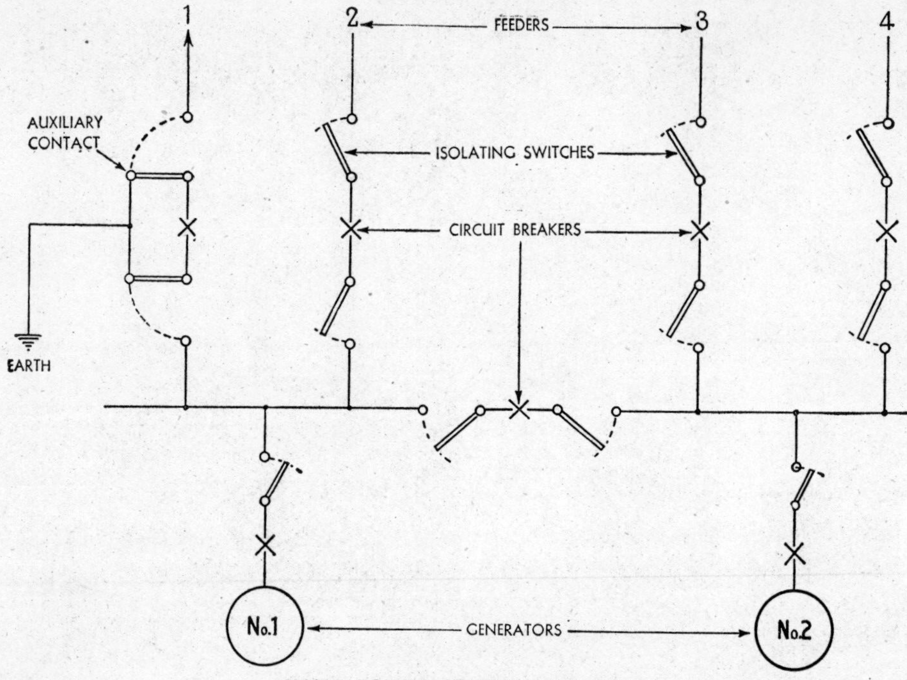

SMALL POWER STATION BUSBARS

Fig. 26. Scheme for the busbars of a medium-sized or a small power station. One busbar only is illustrated, but the other two busbars, for the remaining two phases making a three-phase system, are precisely similar. The section circuit breaker divides the busbar into two halves.

voltage. It will be seen that both top and bottom of the tank are domed to increase the strength, and a drain valve, attached at the lowest point of the domed bottom, allows the tank to be completely emptied. The bushings are provided with arcing horns, the airgap between them being dimensioned so that a flash-over occurs between the horns and is thereby kept away from the surface of the porcelain. The overall height to the top of the bushings of this type of breaker is of the order of 16 feet. Fig. 25 illustrates an installation of this class of switchgear outdoors together with the structure supporting overhead equipment.

BREAKER BUSHINGS

High-voltage bushings are confined to two main types; the oil-filled and condenser types. The oil-filled type is illustrated in Fig. 24 and as the name implies, the bushing is filled with oil, thereby enhancing its insulating properties. The oil space inside the bushing is split up by means of concentric insulating tubes with oil spaces between them so as not to interfere with the free circulation of oil. An expansion chamber and an oil gauge, the latter giving a visual indication of oil level, are provided at the top of each bushing. The expansion chamber is, of course, to allow for the variation in the volume of the oil which occurs with changes of temperature. Condenser type bushings are constructed with alternate layers of insulating material and tinfoil, the length of the tinfoil cylinders decreasing as their diameters increase so as to keep the total area of each tinfoil cylinder the same. The metal cylinders, together with the insulation between them thus form a number of condensers in series each having precisely the same capacitance. The voltage across each condenser will thus be the same (see A.C.

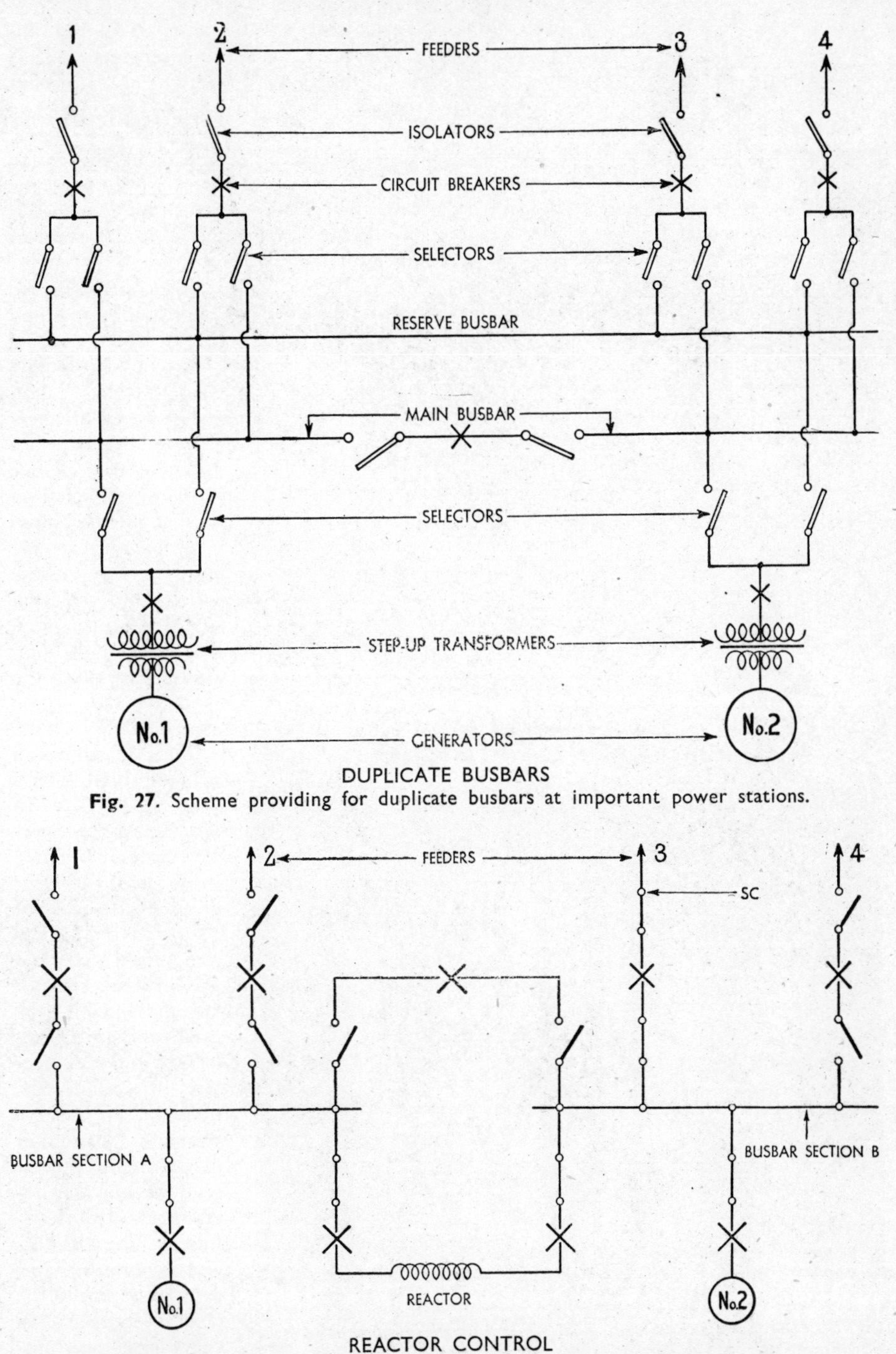

DUPLICATE BUSBARS

Fig. 27. Scheme providing for duplicate busbars at important power stations.

REACTOR CONTROL

Fig. 28. Limiting by reactor control current supplied to short circuit.

section, page 34) and so no part of the insulation will be overstressed. The outward appearances of a condenser type and an oil-filled bushing are very similar.

Referring to Fig. 24, it will be evident that current transformers of the unwound primary type (see Fig. 23b, Chapter 4) can be accommodated on the lower part of the bushing near the top of the inside of the tank, for the working of instruments, thereby saving the separate insulation which these transformers would otherwise require.

In a power station it is evident that all the generators and outgoing feeders must be capable of being connected together or disconnected at will. Consequently, such connections are made through busbars. The arrangement of the busbars depends upon a number of considerations which can only receive a brief reference here. Fig. 26 shows a diagrammatic busbar arrangement suitable for a medium-sized or small power station. For simplicity the connections of only one phase are given and all instrument connections are omitted. It will be understood that the connections of the remaining two phases of a three-phase system are precisely similar. The busbar is divided into two sections, the sections usually being coupled together by means of the section circuit breaker. At times of light load, the section circuit breaker can be opened and one section busbar made dead for cleaning and inspection or for circuit alterations, the live section continuing to supply the load through the remaining feeders.

Air break isolating switches are usually installed on either side of the section circuit breaker and feeder circuit breakers so that when any of those breakers are opened they can be isolated from all live parts when the breaker can be worked on with safety. Since all instrument transformers and other auxiliary gear are placed between isolating switches, these can also be isolated. The isolating switches are so arranged that, in the open position, the blades are earthed through an auxiliary contact thereby earthing the disconnected zone (see feeder No. 1).

REACTOR CAST IN CONCRETE

Fig. 29. Winding of this B.T.H. reactor is cast inside sector-shaped slabs of concrete and the structure stands on porcelain insulating feet. This method of construction contributes great mechanical strength.

Fig. 27 shows a scheme suitable for a power station in which it is not permissible to immobilise half the generators. It will be seen that the busbars are duplicated and the airbreak selector switches fulfil the dual function of isolation and connection to either the main or the reserve busbars. Thus either of the main busbar sections may be de-energised by transferring the feeders and generators connected thereto to the reserve busbar. In very large and important stations, not

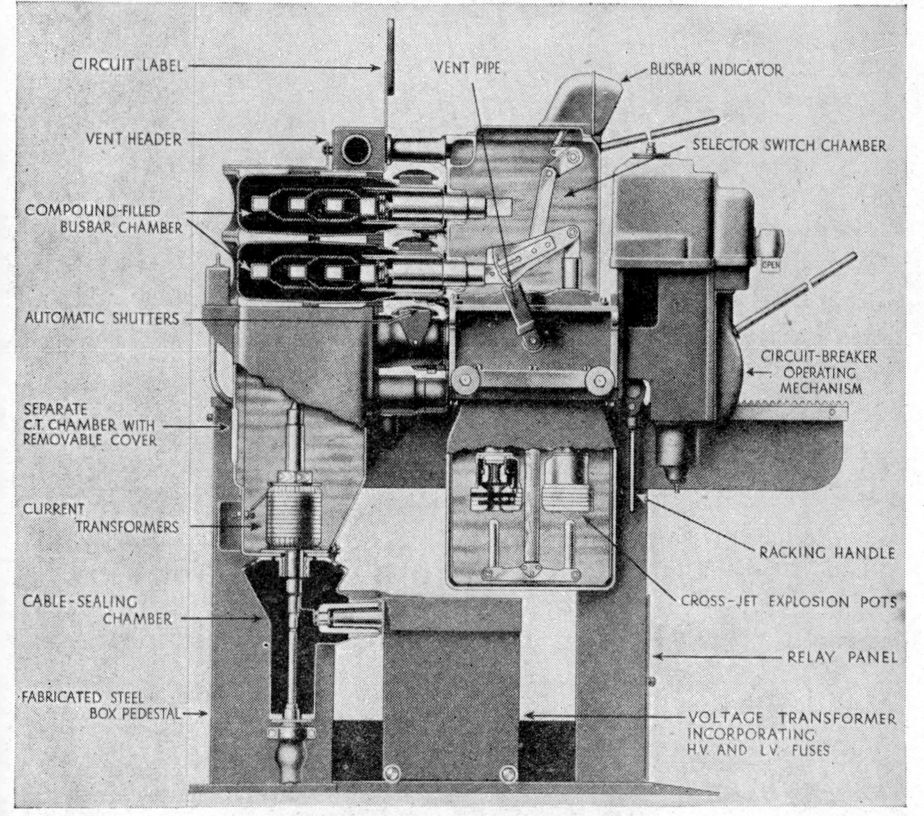

TYPICAL METAL CLAD SWITCHGEAR

Fig. 30. Note the compactness of this Met. Vic. unit which includes circuit-breaker, selector switches, current and voltage transformers, main and reserve busbars and cable chamber. Isolation of the gear is effected by "racking out" the circuit-breaker and components. The voltage transformer can also be isolated. As will be seen cross-jet explosion pots are used (see Fig. 22).

only the airbreak switches but also the oil circuit breakers are duplicated so that if a breaker fails, the service of an important feeder or generator is not lost while the breaker is being repaired. In Fig. 27, each generator is equipped with a power transformer to step up the voltage from the generating to the switching voltage which, in some instances, may be as high as 66,000 volts.

REACTORS BETWEEN BUSBARS

In the case of large stations, the busbars are divided up into sections, but instead of the sections being directly connected through section circuit breakers as shown in Figs. 26 and 27, they are connected through coils having high values of reactance and low resistance, such coils are termed "reactors" and their function is to limit the current flowing into a short-circuit occurring on a feeder or generator from generators connected on neighbouring sections. Referring to Fig. 28, imagine, for example, a short-circuit to occur on feeder No. 3, generator No. 2 will supply current to the short-circuit direct, but the current from generator No. 1 must pass via the reactor. As has been seen from the section on alternating current theory, the addition of reactance to a circuit reduces the current. The value of reactance in ohms is chosen low enough to permit currents up to the full load value of generator No. 1 to pass to the feeders connected to the other section, but high enough to prevent generator No. 1 from supplying anything like its short-circuit current to this section.

One form of reactor (Fig. 29) is known as the air-cored, cast-in-concrete type. It will be seen that the winding is cast in sector-shaped slabs of concrete and mounted on porcelain insulators. The advantage of this type of construction is its great mechanical strength. Another form of reactor follows standard transformer practice, the flux set up by the coil traversing a magnetic circuit which is partly in iron and partly in air, the airgap being included to prevent the iron from becoming saturated by the heavy short-circuit currents.

METAL-CLAD SWITCHGEAR

In this country the practice is to house not only the circuit breaker but also the busbars and auxiliary gear inside a metal enclosure. The advantage of this gear is that it occupies less space than other types. In one unit (Fig. 30) it will be seen that isolation of the circuit breaker is effected by "racking out" the breaker and selector switches bodily from the busbars and cable chambers, the circuit being broken at plug and socket connections. In the isolated position, automatic shutters, shown in the photograph, protect the busbars and cable sockets. The voltage transformer can be similarly isolated by moving it to the right on the rails provided. Fig. 31 illustrates a number of these units installed in a large power station. The breakers shown in the photograph form one group out of a total of four. It is customary to sub-divide the switchgear into sections corresponding to busbar sections. For example, referring to Fig. 26 the switchgear belonging to the generator and all the feeders of the left-hand busbar section would be in one room, and that of the right-hand busbar section in a separate room. A further section of the switchgear can be seen in

SECTIONISED SWITCHGEAR

Fig. 31. Typical Met. Vic. installation of metal-clad switchgear in a large power station. The individual units are as shown in Fig. 30. In order to prevent the whole of the switchgear from being involved should a fire occur it is divided into four sections, two of which can be seen above.

POWER STATION CONTROL ROOM

Fig. 32. Note the instrument panels with the mimic circuit diagrams above them. These diagrams show the actual system connections. Operating desk in the foreground contains the controls of the turbo-generators (Metropolitan Vickers Electrical Co., Ltd.).

the background of Fig. 31. The advantage of switchgear sectionalisation is the reduction of fire risk. Arcing of faulty connections may start an oil fire which might involve the whole of the switchgear in a general conflagration, and bearing in mind the fact that the switchgear is the veritable "nerve centre" of an electric power system, it is evident that such a risk could not be tolerated.

CONTROL ROOMS

In the largest power stations, separate switch houses, one for the switchgear of each busbar section, are employed.

Control boards should be placed in a separate room, remote both from the switchgear and the turbo-generator house so that the operator is not distracted at the moment of emergency. Fig. 32 illustrates part of the control room of a large power station. At the top of the panels, is a mimic diagram showing what circuit breakers are closed, and underneath are located the various instruments so that the operator has before him complete information concerning the system. Any change in the system conditions, such as the operation of a breaker, is brought to the operator's notice by the change oı the colour of a lamp which represents the breaker on the mimic diagram. The desk-type board is used for the control of the generators and from this desk, the operator can alter the load on any generator and watch the effect on the others.

HYDRO-ELECTRIC SCHEMES

In some countries where coal is scarce, such as Switzerland, Norway and Sweden, large hydro-electric plants have been developed. The modern tendency, even in countries such as Great Britain and America, possessing abundant resources of coal, is to develop their water power resources for economic reasons, and in Great Britain a relatively large amount of hydro-electric development has taken place in recent years. Of the total water power available in Great Britain, approximately 80 per cent. is located in Scotland, this country being mountainous and having a comparatively high average rainfall. It also possesses a considerable number of lochs at high elevation which can be used as reservoirs.

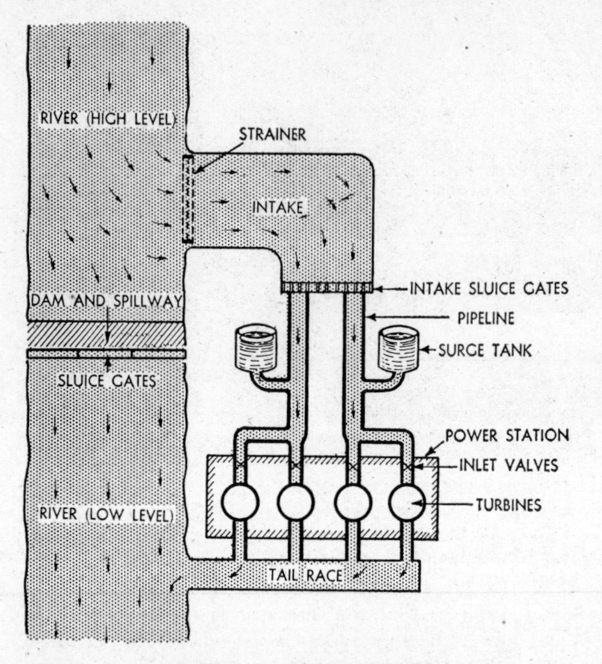

HYDRO-ELECTRIC PLANTS

Fig. 33. Water level is raised by means of dam and passes through the strainer into the intake canal and thence to the turbine pipeline. The water finally leaves by the tail race.

Fig. 33 gives a general idea of the component parts of a hydro-electric scheme. A dam is constructed across a river to raise its height, and the surplus water spills over the head of the dam or "spillway" thereby taking the floodwater to the lower level. Sluice gates are also provided at the dam to assist this purpose and also to provide a means of uncovering the bottom of the intake sluice gates for inspection and overhaul.

The intake is a small pool or canal and is for the purposes of linking the river with the pipelines. At the river end of the canal is a metal screen or strainer which prevents solid matter and rubbish from entering the pipelines, and at the other end are the sluice gates which are for the purpose of isolating the pipelines from the water supply. The closing of the sluice gates enables either of the pipelines to be drained, thereby giving access to the pipes, surge tanks and inlet valves for inspection and repair. The pipelines are generally of reinforced concrete for low heads when the head does not greatly exceed 100 feet, but riveted steel pipes are used for high head schemes or for very high heads steel pipes with welded seams must be employed on account of the very high internal pressures. With steel pipes, expansion joints must be used to allow for the changes in length of the pipes which occur, of course, with changes of temperature. Automatic valves are also installed on all pipes and these operate to shut off the water if a pipe bursts. When the normal pipe pressures are high, surge tanks which consist of open water tanks of large capacity are utilised as shown in the diagram, so that if the inlet valves to the turbines are closed, the excess pressure can be taken by the surge tanks. The walls of the pipelines are thickened as the height decreases so as to withstand the increasing pressure.

Near the power station, the pipelines are resolved into distributors, one for each turbine. The water, after passing through the turbine runner, makes its way back to the low level part of the river.

The scheme is substantially the same in outline either for high or low heads. The source of power for a high head scheme is generally a waterfall, which provides a natural dam and spillway.

CLASSIFICATION OF SCHEMES

It is usual to classify water power schemes roughly under three headings:—

1. High head schemes utilising heads varying between 500 and 5,000 feet,
2. Low head schemes where the head varies from 100 feet down to a few feet.
3. Medium from 100 to 500 feet.

The power available at the intake valve of the turbine can easily be calculated. Let C be the number of cubic feet of water per second passing through the pipeline. Since 1 cubic foot of water weighs 62·4 lbs. the weight of water passing through the pipeline is 62·4 C lbs. per second and if H is the head, or height, through which the water falls, the power is 62·4 C.H. foot-lbs, per second. Since there are 550 foot-lbs. per second in one horse-power, the horse-power is

$$\frac{62{\cdot}4\ C.H.}{550}$$

Thus, for the same power in both cases, a high head scheme would evidently be characterised by a small volume of water per second and a low head scheme by a large volume of water per second, and the same type of turbine would not be suitable for both schemes. For high heads, the Pelton wheel, or impulse turbine, and for low heads, the Francis, or reaction turbine are employed. These two types will now be considered.

Fig. 34 illustrates a Pelton wheel together with the rotating field system of the A.C. generator. The wheel consists essentially of a number of specially shaped buckets of the "Dobie" type, from which a portion has been cut away, as shown, in order to allow the water, which is delivered to the wheel in the form of jets, to impinge on that part of the bucket where it can most effectively drive it. Consequently, the power is supplied to the wheel by a continuous series of impulses, as one bucket after another receives the jet of water. Thus the Pelton wheel operates on the "impulse" principle and is therefore termed an impulse turbine. The width of the buckets is 3 to 4 times the diameter of the water jet and since the maximum practicable jet diameter is about 12 inches, it will be evident that the volume of water that can be handled, and therefore the turbine output, is limited with low heads. In some cases two jets are employed and thus the power is approximately doubled. The two sets of buckets may, however, be mounted on separate wheels as, if they are placed on the same wheel, the splash from one jet

PELTON WHEEL TURBINE ELEMENT

Fig. 34. British Thomson-Houston Company's Pelton wheel together with the rotor of an A.C. generator. The wheel has a number of specially shaped buckets fixed around its periphery. Water jets are made to impinge on the buckets thereby driving the wheel.

interferes with the other, thereby reducing the turbine efficiency.

Pelton wheels are almost invariably constructed with horizontal shafts, since the horizontal type affords simplicity of construction and facility for inspection.

FRANCIS TURBINE

The Francis turbine is shown in Fig. 35. The wheel has a spiral steel cover and the water passes from the inlet valve into this casing, and it will be seen that the diameter of the spiral casing continuously decreases to suit the diminishing volume of water as the latter passes the turbine blades. The water then passes through the centre of the wheel to the discharge pipe or drought tube (foreground of Fig. 35) and thence to the tailrace. The development of power is by the continuous pressure of the water against the blades of the runner and, therefore, the Francis turbine is of the "reaction" class.

The quantity of water passing into the runner is controlled by a number of gates or guide vanes which are placed inside the spiral casing adjacent to the runner. The gates are opened and closed by the governor mechanism.

The Francis turbine is constructed either with a horizontal or vertical shaft, but in the latter case a specially strong thrust bearing, capable of carrying the weight of the whole set, must evidently be provided.

REACTION TURBINES

Fig. 35. Hydyo-electric power station utilising three English Electric Company's 4,750 h.p. turbines. These turbines are suited to dea'ing with large quantities of water and are thus utilised for low head schemes.

GOVERNORS

It will be understood that the flow in the pipeline is independent of the load and thus when the generator load decreases, the generator speed tends to increase largely. Hence sensitive governors are required for water turbines. Unfortunately, due to the weight of the moving parts, a large amount of power is required to operate an hydraulic valve, and so the governor, operated by the changing speed of the shaft, is made to open or close the valve of a cylinder containing oil under pressure, and the corresponding movement of the oil works the water regulating gear. In the case of the Francis turbine, as previously mentioned, the gear consists of a number of gates adjacent to the runner. When the load on the Pelton wheel decreases, the oil pressure is made first to deflect the jet partly away from the buckets while the inlet valve closes; this immediately decreases the input so preventing an excessive rise of speed and water pressure. After the adjustment of the inlet valve to the reduced load conditions has taken place, the jet is re-directed on to the buckets. When the load increases, the inlet valve is opened by the governor.

CHAPTER 4

TRANSMISSION OF POWER

Transmission Voltages. Transformers. Action of a Transformer. Voltage Ratio. Current Ratio. Reversibility. Magnetic Circuit Construction. Construction of the Coils. Three-Phase Transformers. Operation of Three-Phase Transformers in Parallel. Auto-Transformers. Transformer Losses. Cooling. Conservators and Breathers. Buchholz Protective Device. Instrument Transformers. Mercury Arc Rectifiers. General Operation of Equipment. Operation of Rectifier. Transformer Connections. Three-Wire Operations. Voltage Adjustment and Grid Control. Backfiring and Surges. Protective Switchgear. Interference with Communication Circuits. Types and Performance of Rectifiers. Transmission Lines. Construction and Jointing of Underground Cables. Testing and Operation of Cables.

ONE of the chief advantages of alternating currents is the ease and efficiency with which power at low voltage may be transformed into an almost similar amount of power at high voltage and *vice versa*. Since power = volts × amperes × power factor, it will be evident that a large amount of power can be transmitted by overhead lines or underground cables at high voltage with a small current. Since a small current means a small size of conductor, a saving in cost of the copper required for this purpose will, in practice, evidently be achieved.

TRANSFORMERS

IN a large power station, power may therefore be generated at a voltage of, say, 10,000, this voltage being raised by means of a transformer to 100,000 and then transmitted to a point many miles distant at which the power is required for use in factories and houses. At this point, a further transformer is employed to reduce the voltage to a value suitable for use in consuming devices such as 230 volts for lighting or heating, or 400 volts for motors. We see, therefore, that the transformer is an indispensable link.

ACTION OF A TRANSFORMER

Suppose we have a winding surrounding a closed magnetic circuit. Fig. 1 shows such a magnetic circuit as a complete iron ring and the winding at present being considered is represented by P, the other winding S being ignored for the moment. Suppose P is connected to the terminals of an A.C. generator which is giving a voltage. A current will therefore flow through P and the resulting ampere-turns of this winding will set up a flux in the ring. Now it will be evident that since the current is alternating, the lines of force will rise and collapse with the current, also reversing when the current reverses and, in so doing, the flux will cut the winding four times during each cycle. Due to the varying flux, an e.m.f. is induced in the winding and this e.m.f., by Lenz's law, must oppose the change in the flux. Neglecting the voltage drop due to resistance, the applied voltage from the generator must be equal and opposite to this induced voltage.

Now consider a second winding S which, for the moment, is open circuited. Since the flux also cuts this winding, a similar voltage will be induced in every turn and thus the total voltage induced will

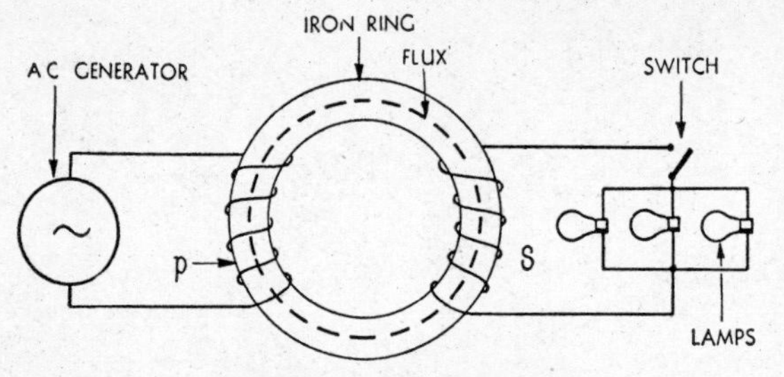

Fig. 1. Primary and secondary windings, P and S respectively, are linked by the magnetic flux in the iron ring.

be the induced volts per turn multiplied by the number of turns. The two windings are termed the primary and secondary respectively, and it will be obvious that since each turn of both windings is cut by the same flux, exactly the same voltage will be induced in every turn wound on the ring, irrespective of whether it is located in the primary or in the secondary.

Now suppose the switch in the secondary circuit is closed so that the lamps are connected to the winding; the latter will now supply a current which will flow through the lamps and the resulting secondary ampere-turns will tend to set up a flux which will oppose that due to the primary ampere-turns and it will be obvious that the resultant flux in the core will be weakened. Consequently, the primary induced e.m.f. will be reduced, and since the generator voltage is constant, the excess of applied voltage to the primary will cause an increased current to flow therein. This increase of primary ampere-turns will be sufficient to magnetise the core to its former value and stability will result. If the load current is increased, the same action will again occur. On the other hand, if the load current is decreased, the core flux, and therefore the primary induced e.m.f. will tend to rise thereby decreasing the primary current. It is thus seen that whenever the load current changes, corresponding momentary changes in the core flux occur

CORE FOR MEDIUM-POWER TRANSFORMER

Fig. 2. B.T.H. three-phase, three-leg core for medium-sized power transformer with top yoke removed ready for assembling the windings.

which have the result of always readjusting the value of the primary current in accordance with the new value of the secondary current.

This action of the flux might be compared with that of an inlet valve on a steam engine; when an increase of load is demanded from the engine, the speed drops because the input is insufficient to supply the increased load. This change in speed is made to open the inlet valve wider, thereby increasing the steam supply. A decrease of load will cause the speed to rise and the inlet valve to close. In this manner the input is varied in direct proportion to fluctuations of the load.

Suppose the primary has a voltage of 100 volts applied and it consists of 100 turns, thus each turn will have a pressure of one volt across it. Since this voltage balances the induced voltage, it follows that each turn of both the primary and secondary windings has an e.m.f. of one volt induced in it. If the secondary winding consists of 50 turns, then the total e.m.f. induced in this winding will be 50 volts. Hence the secondary induced voltage will be one-half of the primary applied voltage because the number of turns in the secondary winding of the transformer is one-half of the primary turns.

Since the secondary voltage is lower than the primary voltage, the transformer would be known as a step-down transformer. Similarly, had the number of secondary turns been 200, the secondary voltage would have been twice the primary voltage and in this case, the transformer would be termed a step-up transformer because it is used to increase the voltage; in general, if T_1 and T_2 and V_1 and V_2 represent the primary and secondary turns and voltages respectively, it will be clear that the following relationship holds:—

$$\frac{V_1}{V_2} = \frac{T_1}{T_2}$$

$\frac{T_1}{T_2}$ is termed the turns ratio and $\frac{V_1}{V_2}$ the voltage ratio, and if the turns ratio and one of the voltages is known, the other voltage can evidently be calculated.

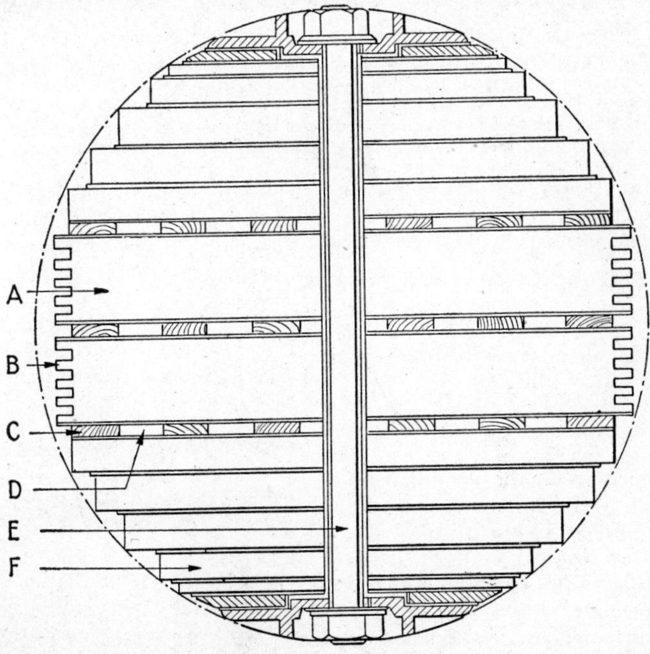

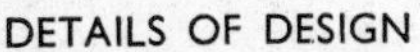
DETAILS OF DESIGN

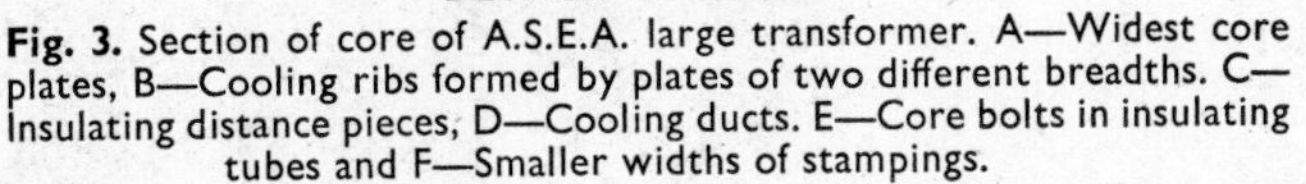
Fig. 3. Section of core of A.S.E.A. large transformer. A—Widest core plates, B—Cooling ribs formed by plates of two different breadths. C—Insulating distance pieces, D—Cooling ducts. E—Core bolts in insulating tubes and F—Smaller widths of stampings.

From the above ratio it will be clear that $\frac{V_1}{T_1} = \frac{V_2}{T_2}$ or the voltage per turn of the primary is equal to the voltage per turn of the secondary, as has already been stated.

Neglecting any power loss in the transformer, the power input must be equal to

LARGE CORE UNDER CONSTRUCTION

Fig. 4. Large A.S.E.A. transformer core under construction. This should be compared with Fig. 3. Note the cooling ducts which are integral with the design. The complete structure is shown in Fig. 5, where it will be seen that the yokes are square in section. A core of this type is employed in three-phase transformers each limb accommodating single-phase windings.

the power output or, at unity power factor, $V_1I_1 = V_2I_2$ where I_1 and I_2 are the primary and secondary currents respectively. Therefore, $\frac{V_1}{V_2} = \frac{I_2}{I_1}$ but it has already been shown that $\frac{V_1}{V_2} = \frac{T_1}{T_2}$ and thus $\frac{I_2}{I_1} = \frac{T_1}{T_2}$ so that the currents in the windings are inversely proportional to the numbers of turns. It is also seen that $I_1T_1 = I_2T_2$ or the load ampere-turns of the primary equals the ampere-turns of the secondary. Of course, this neglects the current which magnetises the core when the secondary load current is zero; this magnetising current is independent of any load current.

It will be obvious that the transformer, like the direct current machine, is reversible. Either of the two windings may be fed from the supply voltage, and thereby act as the primary, the output being taken from the remaining winding which will, of course, act as the secondary. Suppose the voltage ratio, primary to secondary, is 100 to 200, then if the primary is supplied at 100 volts it will give a load output at 200 volts, but if the secondary is connected to a 200-volt source, then the secondary winding will become the primary winding and the 100-volt winding will give the output at this voltage.

The iron ring shown in Fig. 1 is not used as the magnetic circuit of a practical transformer since such a form of construction would be very wasteful of material. Consequently, the iron core is built up in rectangular form. Fig. 2 shows the construction of an iron core for a three-phase transformer in which the

READY FOR WINDINGS

Fig. 5. Completed core of an A.S.E.A. Electric Ltd's. 45,000 kVA transformer. The laminations of the three limbs are arranged to approximate to circular forms.

HIGH VOLTAGE COIL CONSTRUCTION

Fig. 6. Primary and secondary coils are wound on the same limb of this Bruce Peebles 3-phase transformer. At A is seen the low voltage insulating cylinder which, B, holds the low voltage winding. Over this in turn is the high voltage cylinder and winding as shown at C.

three vertical limbs are enclosed by windings while horizontal limbs, both at top and bottom, are for the purpose of completing the magnetic circuit. Of course, in the case of a single-phase transformer, two vertical limbs only would be provided and half the primary and half the secondary turns would be placed on each limb. In either case, however, the illustration will serve to show the method of assembly.

Since the changing flux will cut the iron itself and induce e.m.f.'s therein in a direction at right-angles to that of the flux, large currents would flow in the iron. These are known as eddy currents and would result in the heating of the iron and, of course, of the coils which surround it, thereby causing deterioration of the winding insulation. In addition, a loss of power equal to I^2r, where r is the resistance of the eddy current path and I is the current therein, would occur, thus reducing the efficiency of the transformer.

CORE LAMINATIONS

For the above reasons, the iron structure is built up of thin iron sheets or laminations, each sheet being about $\frac{1}{64}$ in. thick. Adjacent iron sheets are insulated from each other and are rigidly bolted together by means of bolts passing through insulating tubes.

The horizontal limbs, termed yokes,

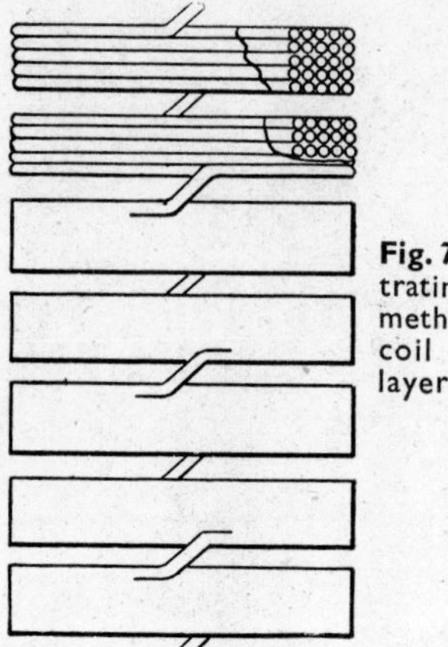

Fig. 7. Diagram illustrating the Met. Vic. method of winding a coil of the multi-layer section type.

are clamped between steel members as shown in the illustration (Fig. 2) from which it will also be seen that there are four different widths of stampings so arranged as to allow the whole of the limb to approximate to a circular cross-section. It is obvious that a circular coil will enclose a maximum cross-section of iron if the latter is also circular. Putting this in another way, we may say that for a given cross-section of iron, the average length of turn of both windings will be a minimum if the iron section is circular. Fig. 3 illustrates the section of the core of a very large transformer in which six different breadths of stampings are employed. By studying the diagram carefully it will be noticed that the central stampings are of two different breadths so that the wider stampings form ribs which assist in the cooling of the core. It will also be noticed that three ducts are formed in the core by the placing of wooden distance pieces at intervals. These ducts, of course, are also for the purpose of cooling. Since the yokes are not surrounded by windings, these can be and always are of rectangular cross-section and larger than the cross-section of the vertical limbs. Fig. 4 illustrates the core under construction and Fig. 5 the complete structure with the laminations arranged to give approximately a circular form.

CONSTRUCTION OF THE COILS

The two most important types of coils are the spiral coil which is suitable for large currents and is, therefore, almost invariably used for low-voltage windings, and the section coil which is usually employed for high-voltage windings. Referring to Fig. 6 the centre limb shows a spiral coil and this consists of a con-

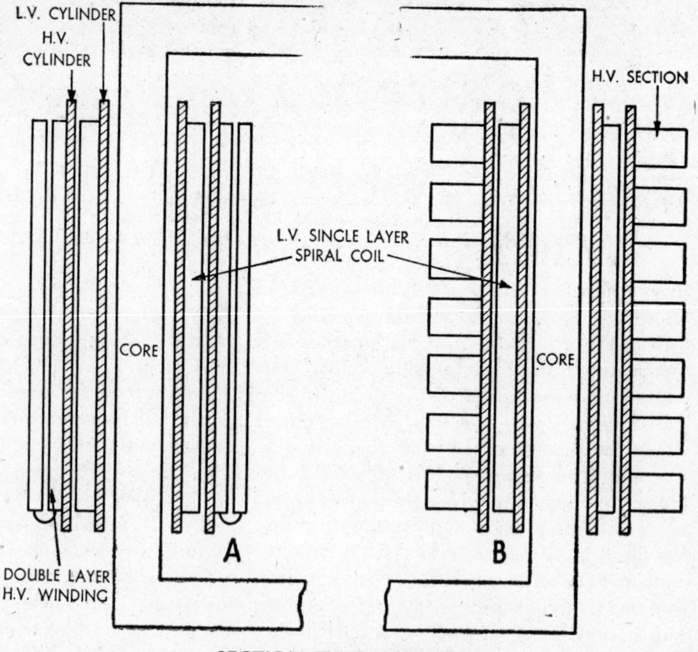

SECTION TYPE WINDINGS

Fig. 8. Diagram illustrating advantage of seven-section type windings for high voltage coils as compared with a double layer spiral winding.

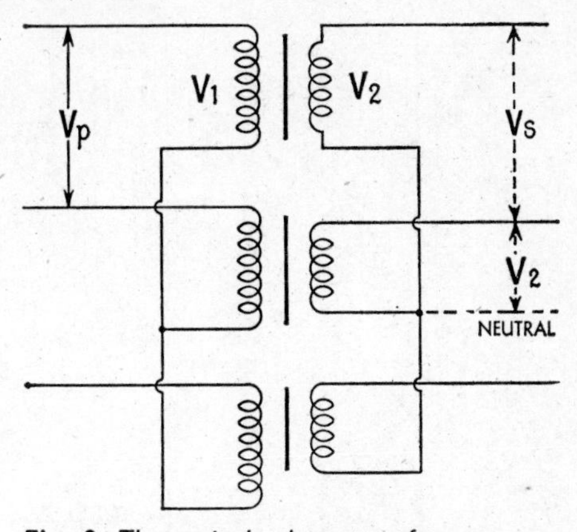

Fig. 9. Three single-phase transformers connected star-primary and star-secondary for three-phase transformation.

ductor formed of one or more strands of insulated copper wire, generally of rectangular cross-section, wound in a closely spaced spiral. If the number of turns is too great for a single layer, a double layer coil is used. The coil is wound on to an insulating cylinder (see right-hand limb, Fig. 6) so that the coil is effectively insulated from the core. As previously mentioned, both the primary and secondary windings are wound on the same limb, and the low-voltage coil is always placed next to the core. Referring again to Fig. 6, the high-voltage coil is shown on the left-hand limb and this is wound on another insulating cylinder of larger diameter which is then slipped over the low-voltage coil. Thus the high-voltage coil is effectively insulated from the low-voltage coil and has double insulation, consisting of the two insulating cylinders, with respect to the core. The high-voltage coil is of the section type and its construction will be clear from an inspection of Fig. 7. As the name implies, the coil is wound in sections. Starting with the top section, we wind five turns downwards, these turns having the largest diameter; then five turns upwards, these turns having the next largest diameter and so on until we come to the inner, or smallest diameter turns which are wound downwards, thereby finishing the top section. The second section is then commenced in like manner but in this case the inner turns are started first winding five turns downward thus finishing off this section with the maximum diameter turns which are also wound downwards.

ADVANTAGE OF SECTION COIL

The advantage of the section coil for high-voltage windings will be apparent from Fig. 8. Referring first to A, suppose the high-voltage winding was of the spiral type with a double layer consisting of a total of 140 turns and 10 volts per turn. The total voltage of this winding is therefore 1,400 volts or 700 volts per layer. The voltage between the two layers at the bottom is only 10 volts since the two layers are connected in series at this point, but at the top end of the winding the voltage between layers is 1,400. If the winding insulation were to break down, it would probably do so where the potential difference was greatest and thus the turns near the top of the winding form the danger point. Referring now to B, when the high-voltage winding is broken up into seven sections and the voltage and turns per section are respectively 200 and 20. These turns are arranged as in Fig. 6, but there are five turns per layer and four layers. It will be evident in this case that the maximum potential difference between adjacent layers is only 100 volts and thus the danger of breakdown is minimised. Naturally, the danger of insulation breakdown is greater in the case of high-voltage windings and since a transformer must be as reliable as possible, it is obviously an advantage to sectionalise such windings. This is, in fact, a general practice in modern transformer design.

It has already been shown (see page 37) that there are two separate ways of connecting three single-phase systems to form a three-phase system and it will be obvious that three single-phase transformers can be so connected. Fig. 9 illustrates the primary and secondary windings of three single-phase transformers, the magnetic circuits being represented simply by means of a line between the two windings, so as to

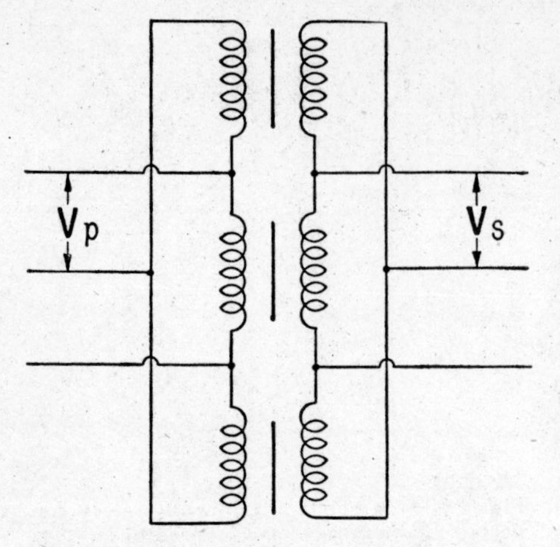

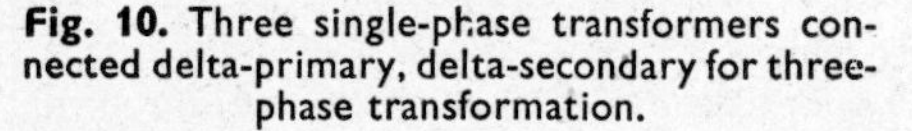

Fig. 10. Three single-phase transformers connected delta-primary, delta-secondary for three-phase transformation.

simplify the diagram. Both the primaries and secondaries are connected in star. Suppose the voltage ratio v_1/v_2 is 2,300 to 230, or 10 : 1, then evidently the line voltages $v_p = \sqrt{3} \times 2{,}300 = 4{,}000$ and $v_s = \sqrt{3} \times 230 = 400$, so that $\frac{v_p}{v_3} = \frac{4{,}000}{400} = 10 : 1.$ Thus the line voltage ratio is the same as the transformer voltage ratio. Fig. 10 shows the same three single-phase transformers, but now the primaries and secondaries are connected in delta. A study of the diagram will reveal that since each primary and secondary winding is connected respectively between two lines, the line and transformer voltage ratios are identical, i.e., 2,300/230. But the current in each delta-connected winding is $\frac{1}{\sqrt{3}}$ times the current in the lines (see page 40) and it will be obvious that the delta connection is suited to low voltages and large currents; while the star connection is suited to high voltage systems since the voltage across each winding is only $\frac{1}{\sqrt{3}}$ times the voltage between lines. Consequently, for a given voltage transformation between lines, it will be clear that the number of turns required for the star connection is only $\frac{1}{\sqrt{3}}$ times the number of turns required for the delta connection. On the other hand, each winding when connected in star must carry the full line current, and a greater cross-section of conductor in the winding is necessary as compared with the delta connection.

An obvious advantage of the star connection is that the choice of two voltages is made available by running a fourth conductor from the neutral point.

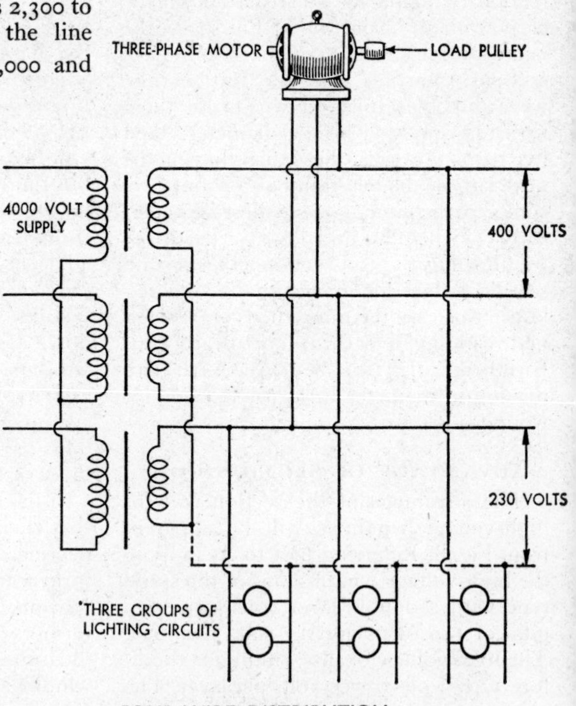

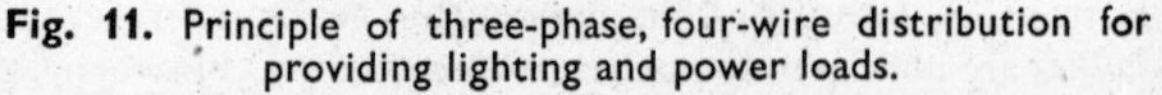

FOUR-WIRE DISTRIBUTION

Fig. 11. Principle of three-phase, four-wire distribution for providing lighting and power loads.

Referring again to Fig. 9, suppose the transformers were used to supply both electric motors and lamps. The motors could be of the three-phase type which are cheaper and more efficient than single-phase motors, and could be fed from the three 400-volt lines, whilst lighting could be supplied from any one line and the neutral. The scheme is clearly shown in Fig. 11, and this system is now the standard employed for distributing electrical energy to consumers.

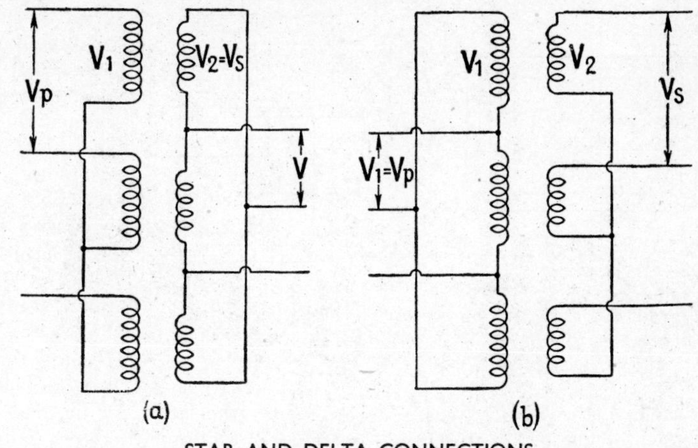

STAR AND DELTA CONNECTIONS

Fig. 12. Diagram (a). Three single-phase transformers with their primaries connected in star and secondaries in delta. Line voltage ratio is 17.32; 1. In (b) the primaries are connected in delta and the secondaries in star with the result that line voltage ratio now becomes 5.77 to 1.

Frequently, primary windings are connected in star and secondaries in delta and *vice versa* and in such cases the line and transformer voltage ratios are evidently different. Fig. 12a shows the same transformers connected in star-delta and in Fig. 12b the connections are changed to delta-star. Taking the first case, assume that $v_1 = 2{,}300$ volts and $v_2 = 230$ volts. Thus $v_p = \sqrt{3}v_1 = 4{,}000$ volts and $v_s = v_2$, so that the line voltage ratio is $4{,}000/230 = 17{\cdot}32 : 1$ instead of $10 : 1$ as was the case with similar primary and secondary connections. In the case of the delta-star connection (Fig. 12b) $v_p = v_1 = 2{,}300$ volts and $v_s = \sqrt{3}v_2 = 400$ volts and the line voltage ratio is $2{,}300/400$ or $5{\cdot}77 : 1$.

Three single-phase transformers forming a three-phase group are seldom employed, as a single three-phase transformer is cheaper, lighter in weight and has a higher efficiency. The core of a three-phase transformer is shown in Fig. 5 and this is represented by one set of windings in Fig. 13. Suppose the three windings of this transformer are fed from a three-phase alternator. Since the three currents i_1, i_2 and i_3 are balanced, we may assume that the three fluxes ϕ_1, ϕ_2 and ϕ_3 are balanced. It will therefore be evident that at any instant $\phi_1 + \phi_2 + \phi_3$ will be zero or $\phi_1 = -(\phi_2 + \phi_3)$. Thus, when ϕ_1 is passing through its maximum value, ϕ_2 and ϕ_3 each have values equal to half their maxima in the opposite direction. Clearly, then, the maximum value of the flux which each limb has to carry does not exceed that of each independent magnetic circuit of the three single-phase transformers. The amount of iron thus required for three single-phase trans-

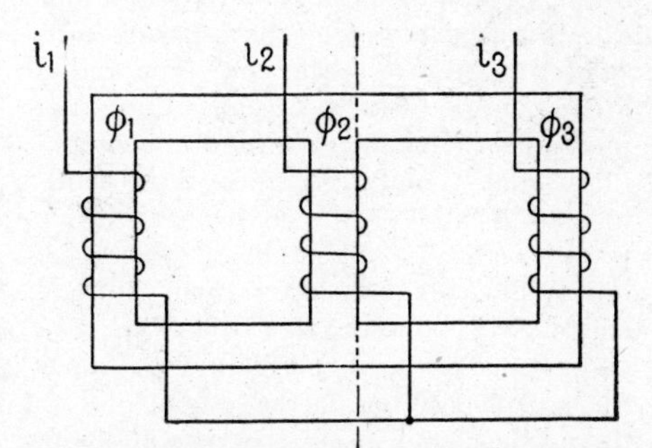

Fig. 13. Illustrating magnetic circuit of three-phase core-type transformer. Primary windings only are shown. The iron to the right of dotted line represents that extra to convert one single-phase into three-phase transformer core.

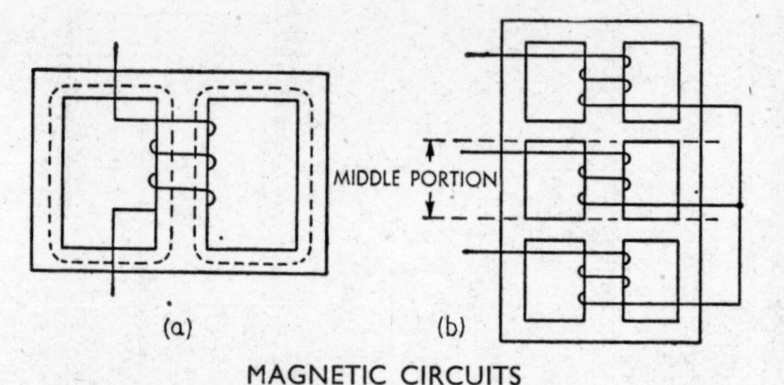

Fig. 14. Diagrammatic representation of single-phase (a) and three-phase (b) shell-type transformer magnetic circuits. In (a) the dotted lines represent the flux paths.

formers is evidently three times that shown on the left of the dotted line (Fig. 13) and thus the three-phase transformer requires only a little more than 50 per cent. of the iron necessary for three single-phase transformers for the same power. Since the iron losses increase with the volume of iron, these are clearly much less and, consequently, the efficiency is higher while the weight, size and cost are naturally less. It should be appreciated that these are not merely theoretical economies. Such losses could be very considerable and in early designs it is possible that kilowatts of power were wasted per transformer in this manner.

SHELL TYPE MAGNETIC CIRCUIT

Another form of magnetic circuit is occasionally employed. This is known as the shell type in which, as the name implies, the magnetic circuit surrounds the windings. The type already considered is known as the core type and is much more widely used. Fig. 14a illustrates the magnetic circuit of a single-phase shell-type transformer. Both windings are located on the centre limb which is twice the cross-section of the outer limbs. The flux paths are shown "dotted" and it will be seen that there are two magnetic circuits in parallel. Fig. 14b is the corresponding arrangement for a three-phase shell-type structure and Fig. 15 illustrates a single-phase shell transformer for an output of 50 kVA.

In the case of very large transformers of the core type, the overall height is so great that transportation may be difficult, owing to the clearances of railway or road tunnels being insufficient. To reduce the overall height of such large units, two more magnetic paths are added, making a total of five limbs as shown in Fig. 16. The three inner limbs contain the three-phase windings and the two outer limbs provide parallel flux paths so that the fluxes passing through the top and bottom yokes are reduced and the latter can be made of smaller cross-section thereby reducing the height. This expedient is only employed when transformers of normal construction cannot be brought within permissible loading gauges.

TRANSFORMERS IN PARALLEL

It is frequently necessary to operate transformers in parallel. Consider, for instance, a factory requiring a maximum load of 500 kW, the load consisting of lamps, radiators, motors, etc. This load would possibly be supplied by means of

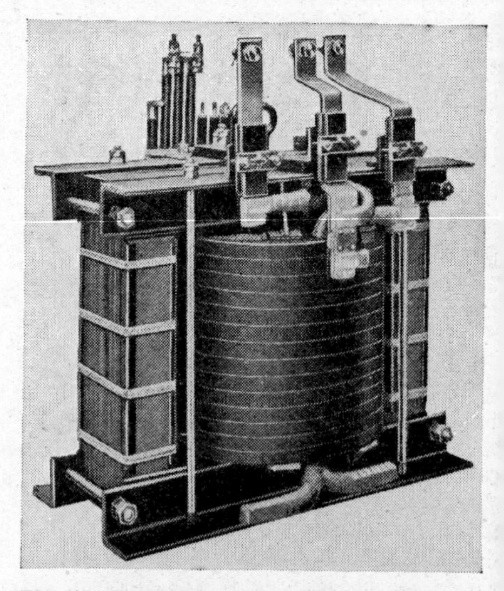

Fig. 15. Illustrating the magnetic circuit and windings of a G.E.C. single-phase shell type transformer with an output of 50 kVA.

FIVE-LIMBED CORE CONSTRUCTION

ig. 16. Showing the five-limbed core construction of a very large Hackbridge three-phase trans-rmer in which mechanical strength and rigidity are essential factors of design. The three inside nbs are wound and the two outside limbs provide shunt paths for magnetic fluxes. Consequently, e top and bottom yoke sections can be reduced, thereby reducing height of the transformer.

vo transformers operating in parallel so at during periods of light load, one of e transformers could be switched out ereby saving its losses.

It has already been seen that primary nd secondary windings may have the me connections, for example, both may e connected in delta, or both in star. On e other hand, the primary and second-ry windings may be connected in delta nd star respectively. Only certain con-ections can be operated in parallel, and mongst these are obviously the trans-ormers with identical connections. For xample, a star-star connected trans-rmer can evidently be operated in arallel with another star-star connected ransformer and the same holds if both transformers have their windings connected delta-delta. Also if the first transformer has its primaries connected in star and its secondaries connected in delta, then a second transformer can be connected in parallel if its windings are connected either in star-delta or in delta-star.

The rule giving permissive connections for parallel operations may be stated as follows. If the connections of the primary and secondary windings of the first transformer are the same, then the primary and secondary connections of the second transformer must be the same, but if the connections of the first transformer are different, for example star-delta, then the primary and secondary connections of the second transformer must be different, either star-delta or delta-star. Thus a star-star connected transformer cannot be connected in parallel with a transformer connected delta-star.

AUTO-TRANSFORMERS

It has been stated that the induced voltage in each turn of a transformer is the same irrespective of whether the turn is located in the primary or in the secondary winding. Now consider the arrangement shown in Fig. 17a in which we have one

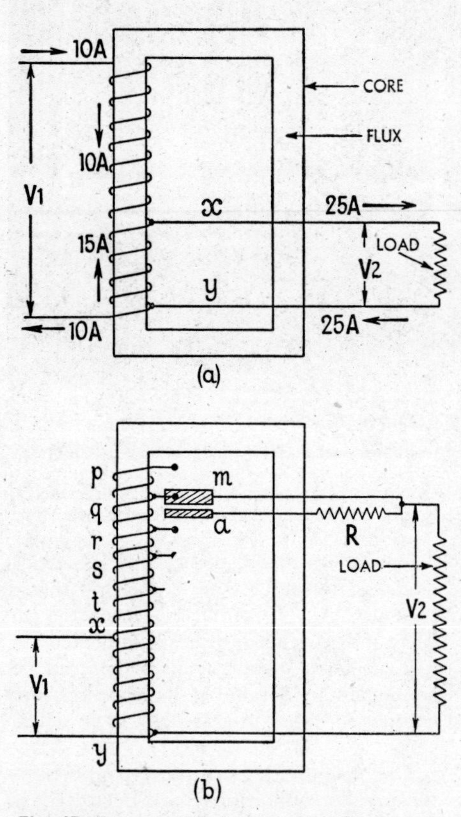

Fig. 17. Diagram (a) shows a step-down auto-transformer. The common portion of the winding carries both primary and secondary currents. The primary current is 10 amperes and flows downwards and the secondary current is 25 amperes and flows upwards. Their sum is thus their arithmetic difference. (b) Shows step-up auto-transformer. Primary voltage V_1 is now applied to the points x and y and the secondary voltage V_2 will obviously be higher.

winding only on a magnetic circui Suppose the winding consists of 100 turr and the applied voltage $V_1 = 100$ volt so that the volts per turn is unity. If th winding is tapped at x so that betwee xy we have 40 turns, then the voltage V between these two points will be 40 volt If, now, a load of 25 amperes is connecte between xy, a current corresponding t this must be taken from the suppl Remembering that the ampere-turr of the primary must equal the amper turns of the secondary, then the primar

$$\text{current} = \frac{\text{secondary ampere-turns}}{\text{primary turns}}$$

$= 1000/100 = 10$ amperes. The curren distribution will be as shown in the dia gram, and it will be evident that th portion of the winding common to bot the primary and secondary currents, tha is, the portion xy, carries only the difference. Thus a saving of copper achieved by this arrangement as compare with a transformer with separate primar and secondary windings. In the latter cas we should require 100 turns, each carry ing 10 amperes and 40 turns carrying 2 amperes. In the auto-transformer 6 turns carrying 10 amperes and 40 turn carrying 15 amperes only would b required. A little consideration will sho that the nearer V_2 is to V_1 the greater wi be the saving in copper. Thus if $V_2 =$ V the saving in copper would be 100 pe cent. because no transformer would b required in this case. This is fortunat because when V_2 differs considerab from V_1 a double-wound transform would be required since it would b necessary to insulate the low volta circuit from the high-voltage circuit.

STEP-UP AUTO-TRANSFORMERS

Fig 17b shows a step-up auto-tran former. In this case V_1 is the low voltage and is applied across the poin xy. Since the flux links with the whole the turns, the secondary voltage V_2 wi evidently be higher than the primar voltage. In the diagram, part of th winding is equipped with tappings p.q.r etc., so that V_2 can be varied by a propriate movement of the tapping switch. The latter has two contacts, a main contact m and an auxiliary contact a, connected to m through a resistance R. Suppose the main contact is to be moved from the position shown in the diagram, q, to the position r. In the intermediate position, m would make contact with q and a with r and there would be a current provided by the voltage due to the turns between qr round the circuit which includes the resistance R. Thus while the tapping switch is being moved, the load circuit is never interrupted. If the auxiliary contact, a, were omitted, and m was made wide enough to bridge two adjacent contacts such as q and r the turns between them would be short-circuited during a movement of the tapping switch resulting in a heavy local current which, when broken, would cause arcing and burning of the tapping switch contact and terminal studs. Such a transformer arranged for variable secondary voltage is known as a booster transformer, and is widely used for raising the voltage on a feeder, thereby compensating for the voltage drop which, of course, increases with the load current.

TUBES FOR COOLING

Fig. 18. Large transformers have plain tanks with external tubes to assist heat dissipation. In the Ferranti type (shown above) the tubes are welded to the top and bottom of the tank.

Directly a transformer is connected to the voltage of supply, a current flows in its primary winding and the flux is established in the magnetic circuit. Since this flux is changing continuously, iron losses occur and those losses are due to eddy currents and to hysteresis. When the transformer is loaded, there are I^2r or copper losses in both windings. These losses will, of course, have to be supplied from the generator so that the transformer output will be less than the input. Nevertheless, the efficiency of a medium-sized transformer is very high, being of the order of 97 to 99 per cent. Taking the case of a 5,000 kVA transformer having an efficiency of 98 per cent., it will be evident that the losses are 2 per cent. of 5,000 or 100 kW. Now these losses cause the temperature of the iron and copper to rise, and the temperature rise must obviously not be so great as to cause damage to the insulating materials employed in the construction. While the iron losses are practically constant whatever the value of the load, the copper losses, being proportional to the square of the load current, clearly increase rapidly as the load increases. Consequently, the output that a transformer can safely give is limited by the allowable temperature rise.

If the transformer is loaded, the active materials above referred to will, however, tend to conduct the heat to the surrounding air (or oil, if the transformer is oil-immersed), and it will be evident that the final temperature of the coils and iro will depend not only upon the powe losses, i.e., upon the rate of putting i heat into these materials, but also upo the rate at which the heat can be cor ducted away from them. The final tem perature will obviously be reached whe the rate of generating heat equals the rat at which the heat can be dissipated by th copper and iron.

It will therefore be obvious that if th windings and core can be cooled by som means, the output could be increased, an the various methods of cooling adopte in practice will now be considered. A these methods are based on the sam general principle.

The great majorit of transformers, wit the exception of th smaller sizes, ar housed in steel tank which are filled wit a mineral oil. Th oil, in addition t augmenting the in sulation, is a coolin agent which con ducts the heat fron the copper and iron The heated oil rise to the top of th tank and is thu replaced by coole oil. Consequently, natural circulation o oil is maintained Also the heated oi comes into contac with the surface c the tank whence th heat is dissipated t the outside air. Thi action can be in creased by increas ing the area of th tank surface, and fo this purpose the tan sides are either cor rugated or, alterna tively, are equippe with metal strips o cooling fins welde

JOHNSON AND PHILLIPS' TRANSFORMER

Fig. 19. Auxiliary oil tanks are fitted to high-voltage transformers in order to prevent contamination of the oil through direct contact with the atmosphere. As the oil level falls in the conservator the air is drawn through calcium chloride which absorbs all the moisture in it. Thus, only dry air is admitted and the insulating quality of the oil remains unaffected.

ertically to the ınk surface. For ıe larger sizes plain .nks are used with ›ws of external ıbes, either round : elliptical section, elded into the tank : the bottom and at ıe top. Such a tank shown in Fig. 18. 'he heated oil rises ı the tank, then asses into the tubes 'hich are, of course, ı contact with the utside air. The oil : thus cooled and gain enters the tank t the bottom.

For sizes of trans- ɔrmers exceeding bout 5,000 kVA the adiator method of ooling is adopted ince it is difficult to nd the necessary pace for a suffi- ient number of cool- ıg tubes. In this ıethod the tubular ank shown in Fig. 9 is replaced by a lain tank fitted with .etachable radiators. 'he radiators are illed with oil and ransported separately thereby reducing he bulk of the transformer. Fig. 20 hows a 15,000 kVA transformer with he radiator units assembled. The ction is the same as in the tubular ank, the heated oil entering the tubes ›y means of the upper busbar pipe, hen sinking in the vertical tubes and e-entering the tank by means of the ower busbar pipe.

MIXED COOLING SYSTEM

Fig. 20. This Hackbridge Electric Company's transformer with radiator tubes assembled is rated at 15,000 kilovolt-amperes and is "mixed cooled". The blower is seen in front. Above approximately half-full load cooling air is delivered to the risers which have nozzles for distributing air on the surfaces of the radiator tubes.

In the case of very large transformers, .here is insufficient space available on the ›ides of the tank for the direct mounting ›f the necessary radiator banks, and in ›uch cases the radiators are assembled in ›eparate banks in a position near the transformer, the necessary pipework and valves communicating between the trans- former and the radiators. This system is shown in Fig. 21.

In some large transformers, the mixed cooling system has been adopted. This scheme is illustrated in Fig. 20. Up to about half-full load, the transformer operates as an oil-cooled unit, but when the load increases above this value, the load current is made to close an automatic switch which starts up the motor driving a blower. Thus cooling air is blown round the channel at the base of the transformer in both directions, and thence up the risers shown between the radiator banks.

The motor speed is made to vary with the load current and thus the volume of cooling air per minute varies with the output. This system is obviously an advantage when the transformer is required to operate at low loads for considerable periods, and is largely employed on the National Grid System.

CONSERVATORS AND BREATHERS

In small low-voltage transformers it is general practice to leave a small air-space in the tank above the oil level, but the oil surface may become contaminated by contact with the air. The oil volume increases, of course, with the oil temper ture due to expansion with the result th the transformer "breathes" new ai together with moisture, into the tar when the oil temperature is reduced. Th action tends to reduce the insulatin property of the oil and thus cannot b tolerated in high-voltage transformer A means to prevent this is to provide a auxiliary tank located above the mai transformer tank and connected theret by means of a pipe as shown in Fig. 1 The oil level is brought up to about ha or two-thirds in this auxiliary tank, th main tank being, of course, complete

G.E.C. TRANSFORMER WITH SEPARATE RADIATORS

Fig. 21. Vertical pipe shown is closed by means of thin metal diaphragm. If a breakdown of trans former insulation occurs, gas may be generated from the oil through arcing, but excess gas pressur is relieved by diaphragm bursting. Note the separate bank of radiators with this transformer

ll. When the oil level in the conservator lls, air is drawn in from the outside rough an oil seal into the breather (see g. 19) containing a charge of calcium loride, which is for the purpose of sorbing the moisture. Thus only dry r enters the conservator.

BUCHHOLZ PROTECTIVE DEVICE

The principle of this device is based on e fact that transformer breakdowns, ch as short-circuits between turns or rth faults, are accompanied by the sification of the oil. The device, shown Fig. 22, is connected in the pipe tween the main tank and the conserva-r and is thus normally full of oil. In ese circumstances, the hollow float is in e position shown so that the mercury vitch inside it is open. The flap valve, nged at the top and located in the axis the pipe is also in the position shown ith the mercury switch open. If, now, a inor fault occurs, bubbles of gas are nerated which rise from the main tank, ass through the pipe to the top of the uchholz device. Consequently, the oil vel falls and the hollow float follows the l level, ultimately closing the mercury vitch contacts thereby ringing an alarm ell. If the fault becomes dangerous, using the gas generation to become rrespondingly violent, the flap valve is eflected, thereby closing the contacts of e lower mercury switch which in its rn closes the tripping circuit. The latter perates to open the main transformer vitches on both the primary and condary sides.

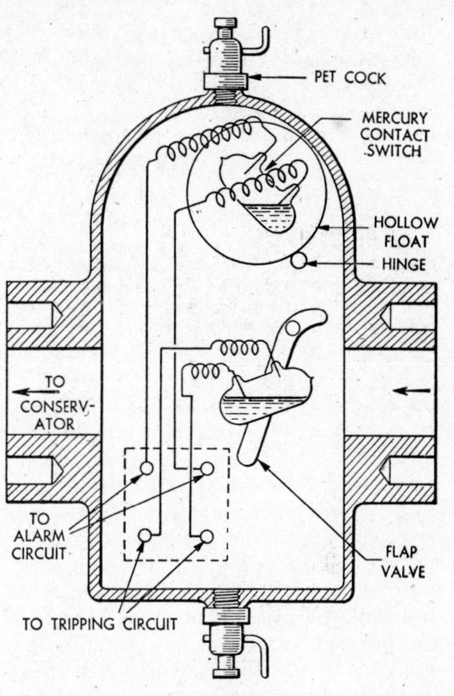

Fig. 22. Metropolitan Vickers Electrical Company's Buchholz protective device. When gas bubbles move slowly (minor fault) they rise to top of housing and close upper mercury switch. If speed is sufficiently high (dangerous fault) the flap valve is deflected and the lower mercury switch closes the tripping circuit.

INSTRUMENT TRANSFORMERS

Instrument transformers are invariably mployed in connection with high-oltage circuits to enable voltage and urrent measurements to be made. The oltage transformer has its primary inding connected to the high-voltage ircuit and the turns ratio is arranged so hat when the line voltage is at its normal alue, the secondary voltage is 110 volts. uppose the primary voltage is 11,000, hen the turns ratio would be 100 : 1. The cale of the voltmeter would be marked in terms of the primary voltage, so that when 110 volts was actually applied to the voltmeter terminals, the pointer would indicate at 11,000, which value would be marked on the scale.

Current transformers are used in conjunction with ammeters, and in this case the primary winding is connected in series with the high-voltage circuit whose current is to be measured, and the secondary winding is connected to an ammeter as shown in Fig. 23a. It was shown at the beginning of this chapter that, neglecting the magnetising current which is very small indeed in this case, the ampere-turns of the primary winding must always be equal to the ampere turns of the secondary winding. Suppose the full-load current in the line and, therefore, in the primary, is 400 amperes and the number of primary turns is 3. Thus the

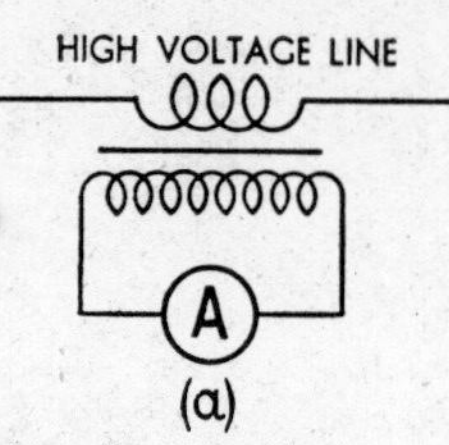

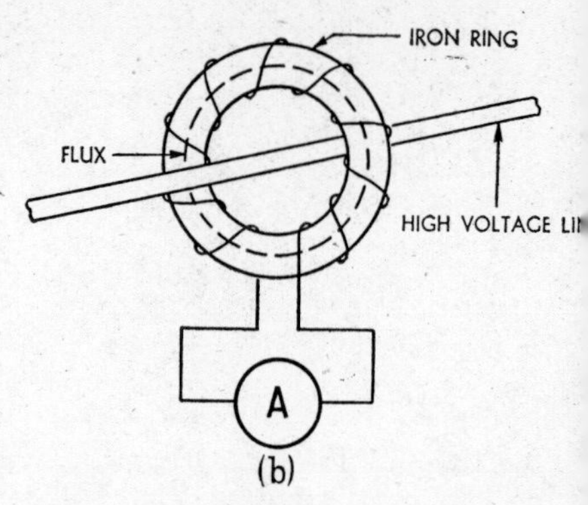

Fig. 23. Diagram shows the connections of a current transformer with, (a), wound primary and, (b), without a primary winding. This latter type is used only when the line current is greater than about 300 amperes.

full-load primary ampere-turns is 1,200. If the secondary winding contains 240 turns, the secondary ampere-turns will be 1,200 when the secondary current is 5 amperes and, therefore, the ammeter will give an indication proportional to 5 amperes. This point on the instrument scale is, however, marked 400 amperes and thus the instrument is made to read the primary current. Since the primary winding carries the line current, it must be thick and comprise only a few turns.

When the primary current is large, th primary winding may be dispensed wi and the line conductor itself is passe through a laminated iron ring whic contains a secondary winding, Fig. 23 The flux set up by the line current in th iron ring cuts the secondary winding an induces a voltage therein. Obviously, th arrangement is equivalent to a prima winding with a single turn. The arrang ment is, however, known as a busbar (unwound primary) current transformer

MERCURY ARC RECTIFIERS

The use of rectifiers is widespread for the supply from alternating current mains of direct current power where this is necessary for industrial purposes, traction, electrolysis, and radio and telephonic communication. The rectifying characteristic of passing current in only one direction is also employed in numberless control and communication circuits.

Three main types of rectifier are in general industrial use: first, the mercury arc rectifier with mercury pool cathode; second, the hot cathode mercury vapour rectifier; and third, the so-called metal rectifier employing copper oxide or selenium elements. Neither the second nor third type is used for any considerable power and, therefore, only the mercury arc rectifier will be considered in detail in this section.

The mercury arc rectifier has taken over many applications formerly assigned to the rotary converter. The spac occupied by the complete equipment comparable with that for the rotar converter, but the building and founda tions may be of lighter constructio Moreover, maintenance and supervisio are slight, and automatic or unattende operation is more easily arranged.

GENERAL OPERATION

The rectifier equipment consists of th transformer, the rectifier itself, and th necessary alternating and direct curren switchgear. The secondary of the trans former supplies alternating current to th rectifier, which feeds current into th D.C. system and so back to the neutra point of the transformer, which forms th negative of the D.C. system. A typica installation operating with glass bul rectifiers is shown in Fig. 24.

The transformer both isolates the direc current circuits from the alternatin

:urrent system, and also supplies alternat-ng current to the rectifier at the required voltage. The transformer can be con-nected to the alternating current system by means of an oil switch, or by a switch-fuse in the case of very small equip-ments.

Since the valve action of the rectifier allows current to pass in only one direc-ion, one-half only of the alternating current wave can pass through the rectifying path into the direct current system. By the provision of an additional rectifying path, both halves of the alternating current wave can be passed unidirectionally into the direct current system; and similarly by the provision of further paths all the phases of a three-, six- or twelve-phase transformer winding can be utilised. The application of two rectifying paths giving full-wave recti-fication from a single-phase supply is shown diagrammatically in Fig. 25. During one-half of the wave current passes through path A, and during the other half of the wave through path B. Thus a fully rectified wave passes into the direct current system and back through the transformer neutral.

OPERATION OF RECTIFIER

The rectifier, shown diagrammatically in Fig. 26, consists of a vacuum chamber in which the rectifying path is from the positive pole, or anode, to the negative pole, or cathode, which is a pool of mercury. For efficient rectification the pressure of the residual gas in the vacuum chamber must be only about 1 micron—that is, ·001 millimetre of mercury—and

COMPLETE RECTIFYING INSTALLATION

ig. 24. Two B.T.H. 100 kW 500 volt D.C. glass bulb rectifier units supplying power to a factory. ote the transformer in the foreground and the A.C. and D.C. switchgear between the two units.

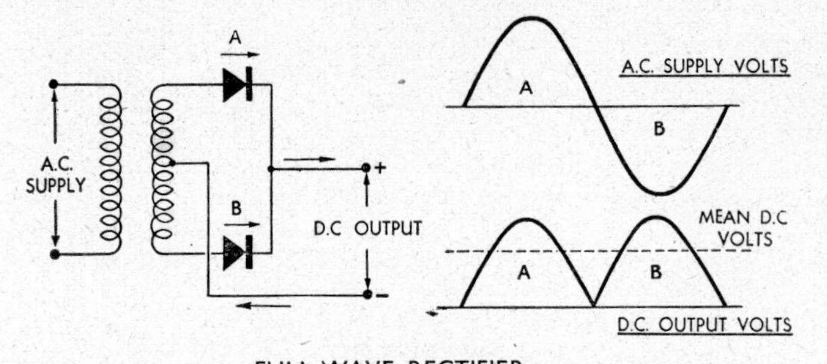

FULL-WAVE RECTIFIER

Fig. 25. Diagram showing how single-phase full-wave rectification is possible using two rectifying paths. This principle is applied in Fig. 26.

mercury vapour from the cathode pool fills this space. Special steps are therefore taken during manufacture to eliminate absorbed gases or other impurities within the vacuum chamber. When rectifying, the mercury vapour emits a characteristic bluish glow which will assume a pinkish tinge should there be loss of vacuum.

As the rectifier heats up due to the energy losses in the rectifying path, the pressure of the mercury vapour rises; for satisfactory operation the temperature of the vacuum chamber must be kept down to about 50 deg. C. by a fan or a water jacket.

Over a part of its cycle, the alternating voltage from the transformer secondary brings the anode to a positive potential relative to the cathode. During this time the anode is able to attract minute electric charges, known as electrons, from the neighbourhood of the mercury pool. The resulting stream of electrons constitutes the flow of current from anode to cathode, and forms a brilliant bluish arc which terminates on one or more bright spots moving to and fro over the mercury pool; these are known as the cathode spots. But as soon as the anode becomes negative to the cathode it repels the electrons, so stopping the flow of current and giving the required rectifying action.

The voltage applied to the anode is not alone enough to initiate the cathode spot, and an ignition anode is provided for this purpose. The ignition anode is held just above the cathode pool, and is pulled down to dip into the mercury by a solenoid outside th vacuum chamber On its release, th ignition anode draw out an arc, so ignit ing the cathode spo and freeing electron from the mercur pool. The free elec trons, attracted t the anodes with resulting flow of cur rent, have the pro perty of freeing many more from th mercury vapour, and the process, know as ionisation, is self-sustained when onc started.

If the load falls to a low value, th cathode spot may become unstable and g out. To prevent this it is usual to provid excitation anodes, continuously carryin a small current sufficient to keep th cathode spot always alight.

The ignition and excitation circuit may be supplied with either direct o alternating current. Fig. 26 shows typical circuit supplied with alternatin current from an auxiliary winding on th main transformer, which becomes aliv as soon as the main windings ar energised. The current at once flow through the ignition magnet coil and pul down the ignition anode into the mercury This short-circuits the magnet coil, an the anode springs back forming an arc The resulting ignition of the cathode spo allows current to flow from the excitatio anodes to the cathode, and this excitatio current operates the ignition contactor t disconnect the ignition magnet coil. Th main load can then be switched straigh on to the rectifier.

The several rectifying paths of a poly phase alternating current system ar generally incorporated in one rectifie unit. This is done by the provision in on vacuum chamber of a suitable number o anodes all firing to a common cathod Where more than six anodes are require it is often found convenient to use two o more rectifier units each containing si anodes and with their cathodes con nected together. Similarly, several units each containing a group of anodes can be used in parallel where the current flowing is too great for the group of anodes in one unit.

The passage of current through the rectifier causes some loss of energy, with a resultant drop from anode to cathode of about 20 volts, which remains roughly constant at all loads. The transformer secondary windings fix the anode potentials, and so the cathode potential must be 20 volts below the most positive anode potential. Thus, because each anode carries current only when positive to the cathode, the current will transfer in phase/sequence from anode to anode with their rise and fall of potential, and each anode will carry current only for a part of the alternating current cycle, the length of which depends on the number of phases.

The direct current output voltage or cathode potential, the anode potential, and the period over which each anode conducts current are shown in Fig. 27 for single-, three- and six-phase rectifiers. An increase in the number of phases gives a smoother output voltage, but a shorter period during which each anode carries current. Thus, for a larger number of phases, the transformer secondary wind-

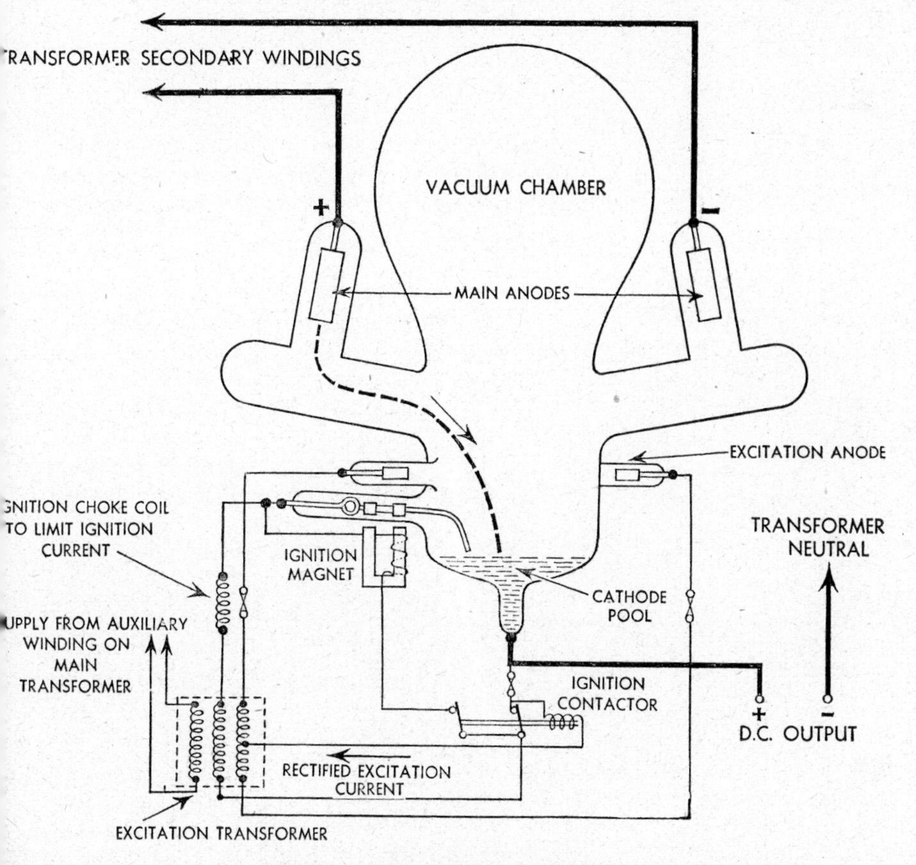

MERCURY ARC RECTIFYING UNIT

Fig. 26. Diagram of rectifier showing method of maintaining the arc. The ignition device to strike the arc and the excitation anodes to maintain it are supplied by the excitation transformer. The contactor disconnects the ignition magnet when excitation current flows in the contactor coil.

ing connected to each anode would carry current for a shorter time, resulting in a poorly used winding and a larger and more expensive transformer. This difficulty is dealt with in the next section.

TRANSFORMER CONNECTIONS

The most general transformer connection is the six-phase double star shown in Fig. 28. The transformer secondary winding consists of two three-phase groups, phases 1, 3, 5 and phases 2, 4, 6 displaced by 180 deg. and with their neutrals connected to the direct current system through a small transformer known as the interphase transformer. The function of the interphase transformer is to absorb the voltage difference between the two groups (shown shaded), so that two anodes, one in each group, always share the load. Thus the equipment operates with a six-phase wave form but with the better transformer utilisation of a three-phase system. It will be seen from the figure that the output voltage is the mean of the voltages of the two separate three-phase groups.

At very low loads, the load current becomes insufficient to allow the magnetising current of the interphase transformer to flow between the two three-phase groups, and operation reverts to that of a simple six-phase connection with only one anode carrying load at a time. There is a consequent voltage rise of 15 per cent. from about 1 per cent. of full load to no load.

This voltage rise is seldom objectionable at so low a load, but when necessary it can be avoided by the six-phase fork connection shown in

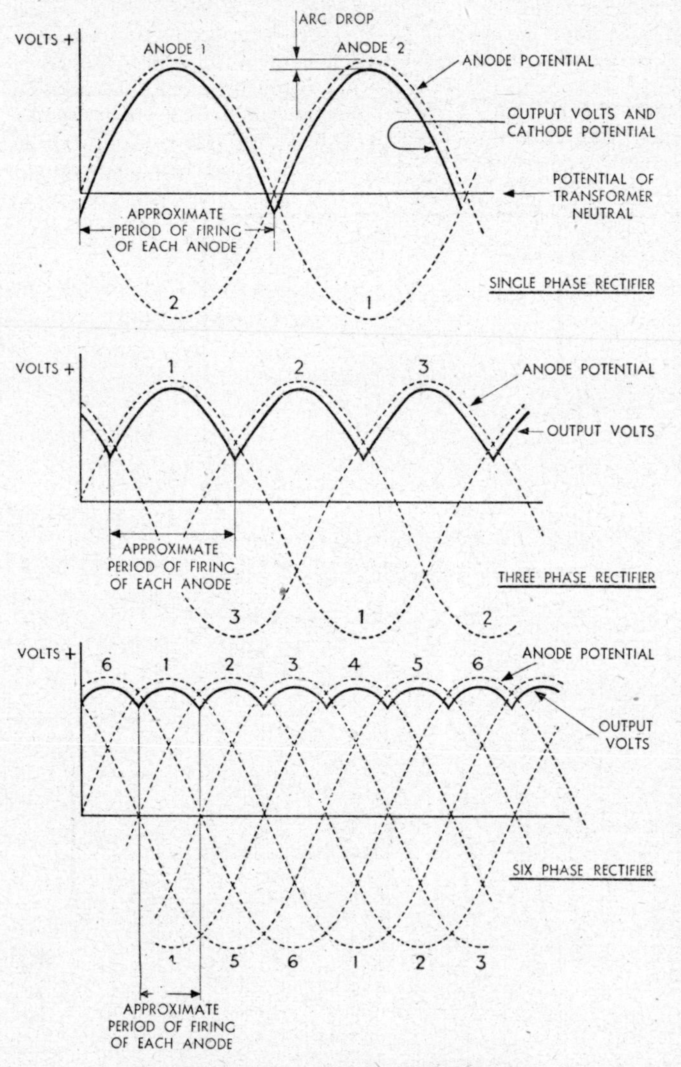

COMPARATIVE WAVE FORMS

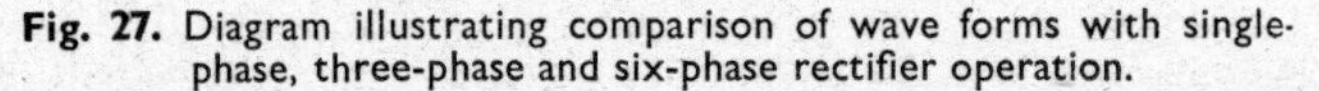
Fig. 27. Diagram illustrating comparison of wave forms with single-phase, three-phase and six-phase rectifier operation.

Fig. 29. The load current is no longer shared between two anodes, so that the rectifier rating is slightly reduced. The windings are not utilised as efficiently as with the double-star connection, but no interphase transformer is required; thus the overall transformer size and efficiency are about the same for the fork and the double-star connections.

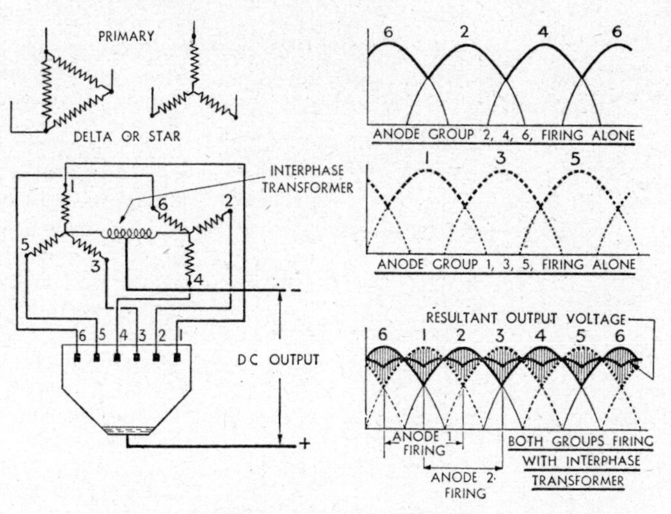

Fig. 28. Six-phase double-star transformer connection. This is the most general method and comprises two 3-phase groups.

Where the ripple in the output voltage may be objectionable, as in electrolytic plant or in certain types of utility traction systems where interference with communication circuits may occur, a twelve-phase winding is used. One of the commonest connections is the quadruple zig-zag shown in Fig. 30, and it will be seen that the transformer is more complicated and so more costly. The interphase transformers result in a voltage rise of 20 per cent. from light load to no load.

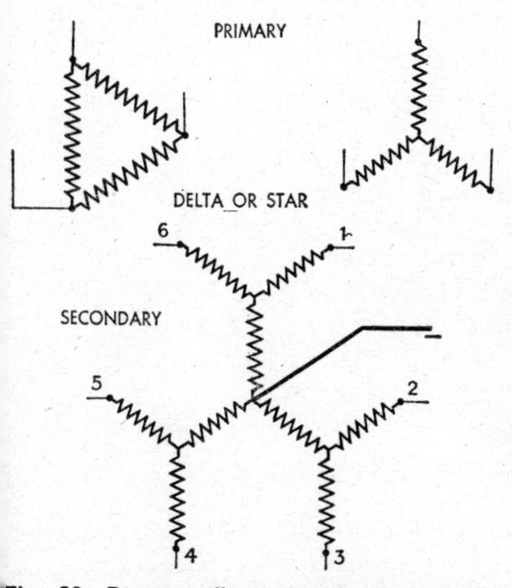

Fig. 29. Diagram illustrating six-phase fork transformer connection. In this type no interphase transformer is needed.

With all these connections, the voltage rise from full load to light load is about 6 per cent. of full load voltage. The voltage rise is entirely due to transformer impedance; smaller values than 6 per cent. would result in the flow of excessive current in the event of short circuits.

Where several rectifiers are used in parallel on heavy currents, variations in arc drop between one rectifier and another tend to cause unequal sharing of the load. Equal sharing is obtained by supplying each rectifier from a separate transformer winding, or by connecting small reactors between each phase of the transformer winding and its corresponding anodes. The smaller current of the lightly-loaded rectifier unit drops fewer volts in the transformer winding or anode reactors than does the more heavily-loaded unit. This resultant extra voltage on the lightly-loaded unit increases its current.

Except for the arrangement of the secondary windings, rectifier transformers are generally similar to power transformers. The high short-circuit currents and insulation stresses which may occur

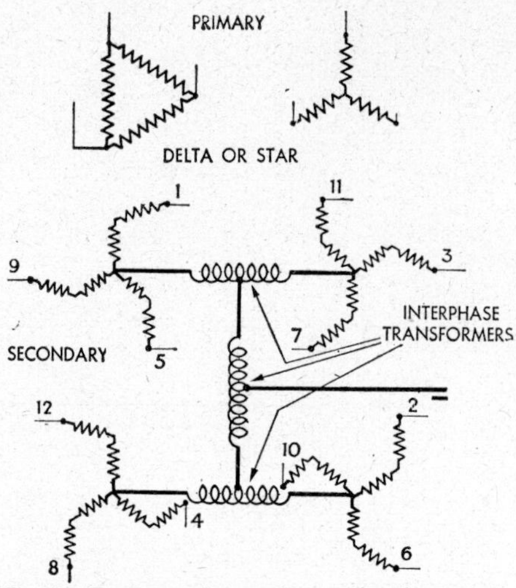

Fig. 30. Diagram illustrating quadruple zig-zag twelve-phase transformer connections, an arrangement that is frequently used.

due to backfiring and surges (see page 136) call for special bracing of the conductors and reinforcement of the insulation. As current flows in each phase of the secondary winding only while the corresponding anode is firing, the incomplete utilisation of the transformer windings calls for a kVA rating in excess of the power output.

For three-wire operation of the direct current system, two rectifier units each fed from a separate transformer winding with a six-phase double-star connection may be used. One unit is connected between each outer and the mid-wire as in Fig. 31.

Where a greater output than can be handled by these two units is required, further units can be connected between the outers to handle the main load, while the two balancing units handle the unbalanced load and the remainder of the balanced load. Alternatively, the rectifier may be connected across the outers, while the unbalanced load is handled by a small rotating balancer set connected between the two outers and the midwire.

VOLTAGE ADJUSTMENT

Control of the rectifier output voltage can be effected by off-load or on-load tap-changing switches on the primary side of the transformer. As with power transformers, this equipment is built into the transformer tank, and can be operated automatically or by hand. Alternatively, induction regulators are used sometimes for boosting and bucking the supply to the transformer.

An alternative method for voltage adjustment is grid control. Just as current is unable to flow when the anode is negative to the cathode, so flow may be prevented by the interposition just below the anode of a conducting screen or "grid" held at a negative potential to the cathode. In this way the start of flow of current can be delayed beyond the point at which the anode becomes positive to the cathode; but once flow of current starts, the grid loses control until the anode again becomes negative to the cathode with a consequent cessation of the current. By altering the delay of firing

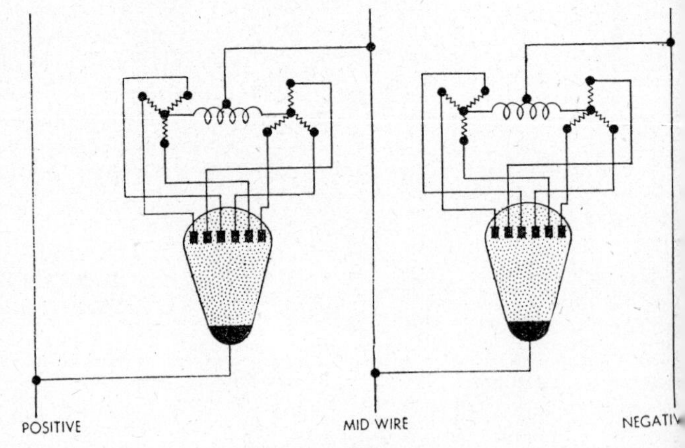

Fig. 31. Two B.T.H. rectifier units arranged for three-wire operation o the direct current system and using separate transformer windings

of the anode by control of the point at which the grid becomes positive, the mean output voltage of the direct current system can be controlled as shown in Fig. 32. Since firing cannot take place unless the anode is positive to the cathode, a positive potentential applied to the grid before the anode becomes positive will not result in earlier firing; thus the voltage of a grid-controlled rectifier equipment cannot be increased above that of a similar uncontrolledequipment.

As can be seen from the figure, the ripple in the output voltage is considerably increased. Further, the power factor of the load drawn from the alternating current supply is reduced, roughly in proportion to the voltage. The application of grid control is therefore limited, but the method is of great value where very rapid or frequent changes of voltage are needed.

For certain applications where the considerable increase in complication and expense can be justified, grid control can be used for inverting direct current power back into the alternating current

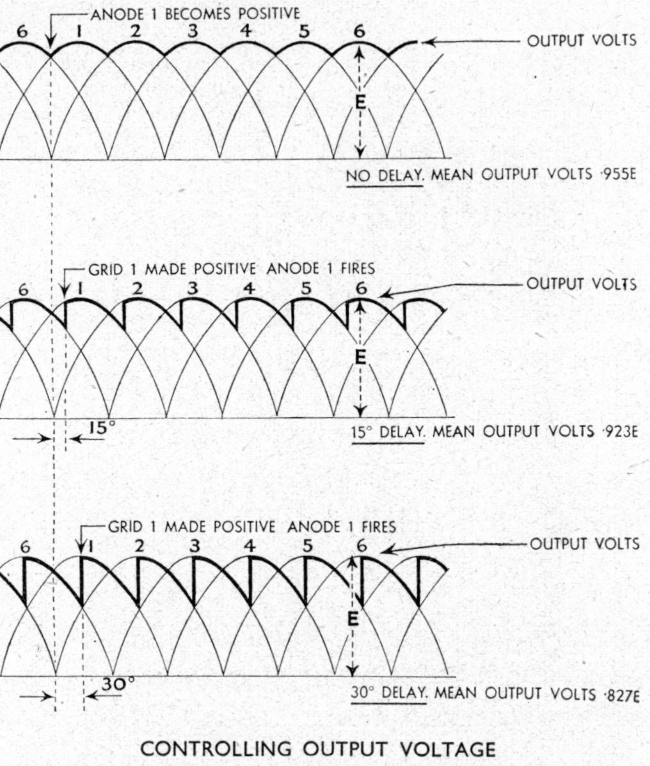

CONTROLLING OUTPUT VOLTAGE

Fig. 32. Illustrating the theory of grid control of the mean direct current output voltage of a six-phase rectifier.

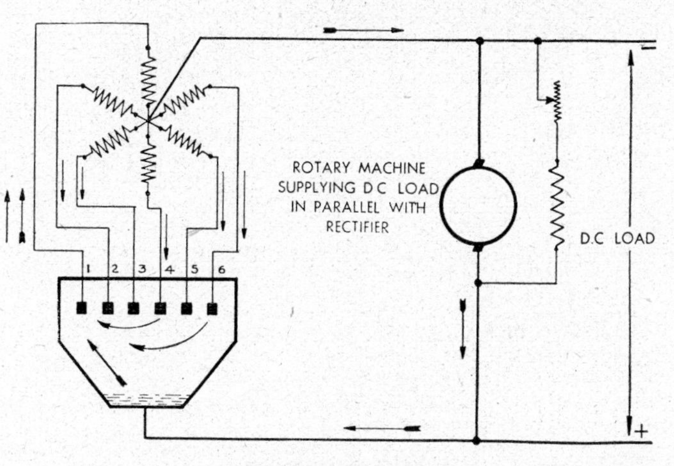

EFFECT OF BACKFIRE

Fig. 33. Anode 1 has backfired owing to failure of its valve action, and current flows into it from the other anodes and from paralleled plant.

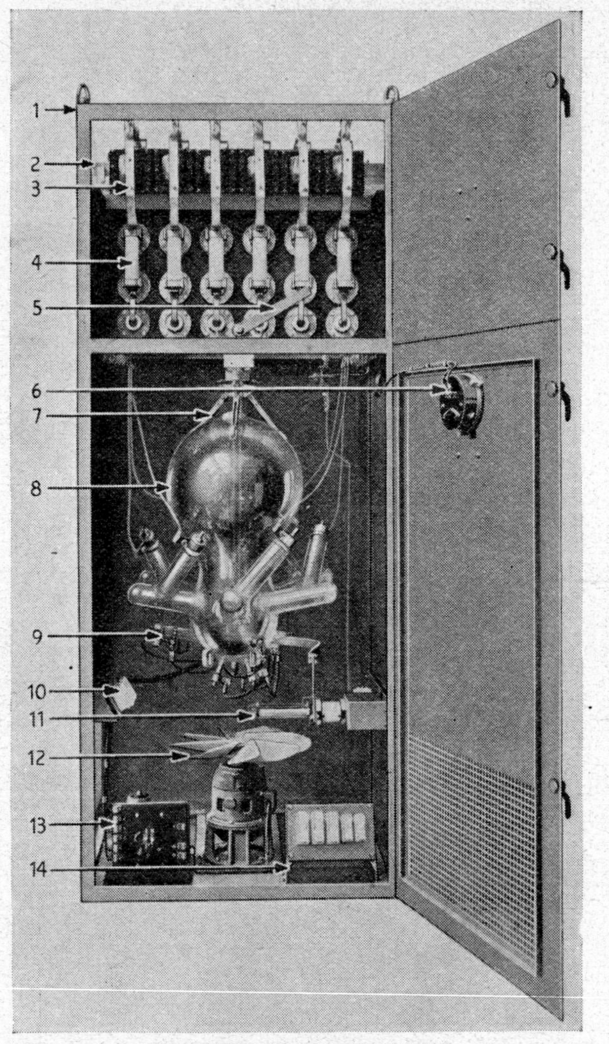

COMPLETE RECTIFIER UNIT

Fig. 34. British Thomson-Houston Company's glass bulb rectifier cubicle, showing main constructional features, these are as follows:—1—Sheet steel cubicle. 2—Busbars for interconnecting cubicles, 3—Anode reactors, 4—Anode fuses, 5—Isolating switch, 6—Voltmeter, 7—Withdrawable bulb carriage, 8—Rectifier bulb, 9—Ignition anode and magnet, 10—Ignition and excitation fuses, 11—Thermal relay for overload protection, 12—Cooling fan, 13—Ignition and excitation transformer and 14—Fan motor fuses.

system. The current in a rectifier cannot reverse as the flow must always be from anode to cathode. Thus, in order to pass energy back from the D.C. circuit to the A.C. system, it is necessary for the D.C. voltage to reverse. Therefore, the grids are arranged to allow firing of the anodes when their phase voltages are in the negative half of their cycle, not the positive half as in rectifying. Except for large amounts of energy, as in traction systems with regenerative braking, this method is rarely used.

BACKFIRING AND SURGES

It has been seen that while the anodes are negative to the cathode, the electrons are repelled and no current flows. Under certain conditions such as prolonged overload, it is possible for this valve action to break down. As shown in Fig. 33, such breakdown, known as backfiring, enables the other anodes of the rectifier and any plant connected in parallel on the direct current system to feed current back into the faulty anode. Very heavy short-circuit currents then flow in the transformer, and suitable protective switchgear must be installed. The design of modern medium- or low-voltage rectifiers makes the chance of backfire remote.

At very low temperatures the mercury vapour density becomes very low, and there may be insufficient electrons in the path of the arc to carry the load. When starting up, therefore, a pulse of current flows which is suddenly stopped by the shortage of electrons. The energy in the transformer secondaries causes voltage surges across the windings which are, therefore, protected by connecting across them current-limiting resistances and spark gaps designed to pass current only at dangerous voltages. These spark gaps may take the same general form as the protective arcing horns which are used across the insulating bushes of high-power circuit breakers as illustrated on page 100.

PROTECTIVE SWITCHGEAR

The rectifier equipment is protected against faults on the direct current system by circuit breakers whose speed of operation is chosen according to the severity of the faults expected. It is usual to install high-speed breakers on traction equipments, and for similar duty. When operating in parallel with other equipment, the rectifier breakers may be connected to trip on the reverse current which would flow during backfire. On glass bulb equipments, anode fuses are generally fitted between the bulb and the transformer secondary. These operate at high speed and afford additional protection to the bulb under adverse conditions. In the case of steel tank rectifiers which are able to stand up to short circuit conditions for a longer time, the fitting of anode fuses can be avoided.

PUMPLESS RECTIFIER

Fig. 35. British Thomson-Houston pumpless steel-tank rectifier (with cover for auxiliaries removed). 1—Cathode lead-in, 2—Anode connections, 3—Main anode insulator, 4—Top plate, 5—Lifting lug, 6—Cooling fins, 7—Vacuum tank, 8—Outer cylinder, 9—Air guide, 10—Fan motor, 11—Rectifier foot, 12—Porcelain insulator, 13—Ignition anode, 14—Ignition solenoid, 15—Vacuum valve for sealing off vacuum chamber during manufacture, 16—Ammeter, 17—Excitation fuses, 18—Excitation relay, 19—Excitation panel, 20—Detachable cover over auxiliaries, 21—Auxiliary transformer for ignition and excitation, 22—Insulating tube for excitation supply leads, 23—Baseplate.

The equipments are also protected by instantaneous overload trips on the oil switch connected between the alternating current system and the transformer.

Where the rectifier is operating under specially severe conditions, as is frequently the case in industrial plants working up to their highest limits of pro-

WATER-COOLED TYPE

Fig. 36. British Thomson-Houston steel-tank rectifier that is water-cooled. 1—Main anode, 2—Control grid, 3—Excitation anode, 4—Thermostat controlling cooling, 5—Main water jacket, 6—Water circulating pump, 7—Auxiliary connections, 8—Cathode cooling connections, 9—Rough vacuum pump, 10—pump motor, 11—Intermediate vacuum chamger, 12—Vacuum gauge, 13—Mercury vacuum pump, 14—Electrical vacuum gauge.

duction, there may be sustained overloads but arrangements can be made for very rapidly making the grids negative should backfire take place. This entirely cuts off the flow of fault current from the A.C. side within about 1 cycle, and the rectifier can be automatically and quickly put on load again.

Interference is a factor which it is necessary to take into consideration for in certain circumstances, notably on traction circuits, the ripple on the direct current output can cause interference with communication circuits. This effect is likely where telephone wires run alongside overhead D.C. feeders, so that the ripple current in the rectifier output causes interference currents in the communication circuit. The risks of interference can be reduced by the use of twelve-phase supply to the rectifier, or, still more effectively, by the use of a reactor in the direct current output line together with tuned condenser circuits connected across the out-going lines to shunt out the ripple current. The chances of interference on industrial installations and on most trolley-bus equipments are very small.

GLASS BULB RECTIFIER

The glass bulb rectifier is usually made with six anodes in each bulb, and is rated up to 400 or 500 amperes per bulb. For larger ratings the required number of bulbs may be used in parallel. Two- or three-anode bulbs are sometimes used on ratings below 250 amperes; and where twelve-phase operation is required, six-anode bulbs are operated in pairs. The bulb is mounted in a sheet steel cubicle together with the cooling fan, ignition and excitation auxiliaries, and anode fuses and reactors, all of which are shown in Fig. 34.

It comprises a complete rectifying unit and provision is made for its connection to other similar units by means of interconnecting busbars.

The unit is also fitted with a full complement of protective devices such as separate fuses for the rectifier and the motor which drives the cooling fan. There is also a thermal relay for protection against overloading.

Study of the illustration will show the essentially practical layout of the unit which provides immediate accessibility to all the components and facilitates not only their inspection and testing, but also their quick replacement when necessary.

HEAVY DUTY TYPES

The pumpless steel-tank rectifier is built for ratings from 250 to 1,000 amperes. Like the glass bulb, the pumpless steel tank is evacuated during manufacture and the vacuum is retained during the life of the tank. The tanks are air cooled, and in the example illustrated in Fig. 35 the ignition and excitation auxiliaries are mounted on the side of the tank. Since the metal tank takes up the potential of the arc, it is necessary to operate the rectifier in a suitable earthed enclosure.

Where specially heavy duty is involved, the continuously evacuated water-cooled steel-tank rectifier as shown in Fig. 36 is used. Closed circuit water-cooled systems with re-coolers are usually employed, and the vacuum is maintained by pumps operating continuously. Outputs up to about 6,000 amperes can be obtained from one tank. The complication of the pumping and water cooling equipment, which is unnecessary with glass bulbs or pumpless tanks, is naturally only justified for large outputs or for high operating voltages.

Since the arc drop in the rectifier is virtually constant, the overall efficiency of complete rectifier equipments remains roughly constant from full load to $\frac{1}{4}$ load, and increased output voltage gives increased efficiency. Typical overall efficiencies are given in the following table, it being noted that the power factor of the current drawn from the alternating current mains remains roughly constant down to $\frac{1}{4}$ load with a value of approximately ·93 for six-phase equipments and approximately ·97 for twelve-phase equipments.

It might be considered unnecessary to include a table giving a number of identical values. But such a table reveals in a most striking manner the high degree of efficiency and constancy in operation which are achieved in modern designs of electrical apparatus.

	4/4 full load	3/4 full load	2/4 full load	1/4 full load
630 Volts ..	93%	93%	93%	91%
550 Volts ..	92%	92%	92%	90%
250 Volts ..	88%	88%	88%	85%
110 Volts ..	80%	80%	80%	75%

TRANSMISSION LINES

The modern system of concentrating the generation of electricity in a relatively small number of large and efficient power stations, situated conveniently as regards supplies of water and fuel, has made the part played by transmission lines of increasing importance. Alternating current is employed for power transmission, because the voltage can be easily transformed up to high pressures so as to reduce the current and thereby enable conductors of small cross-sectional area to be employed. The higher the voltage, however, the better must be the insulation, and voltages ranging from 6,600 to 132,000 are common for British

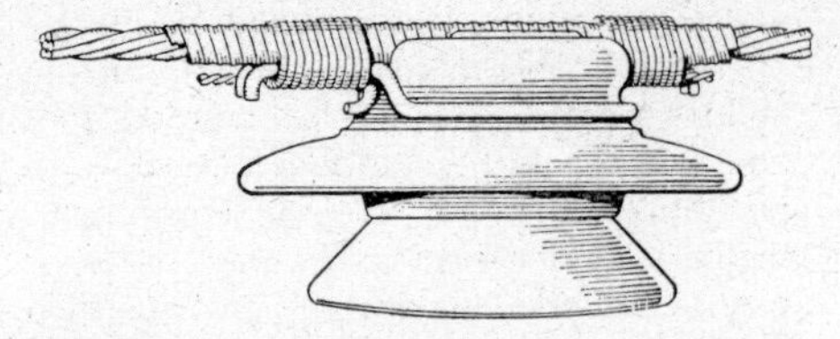

Fig. 37. Typical pin-headed insulator showing the binding of the conductor to the groove at the top. Protecting flanges act as rain shields. For further details see Fig. 38.

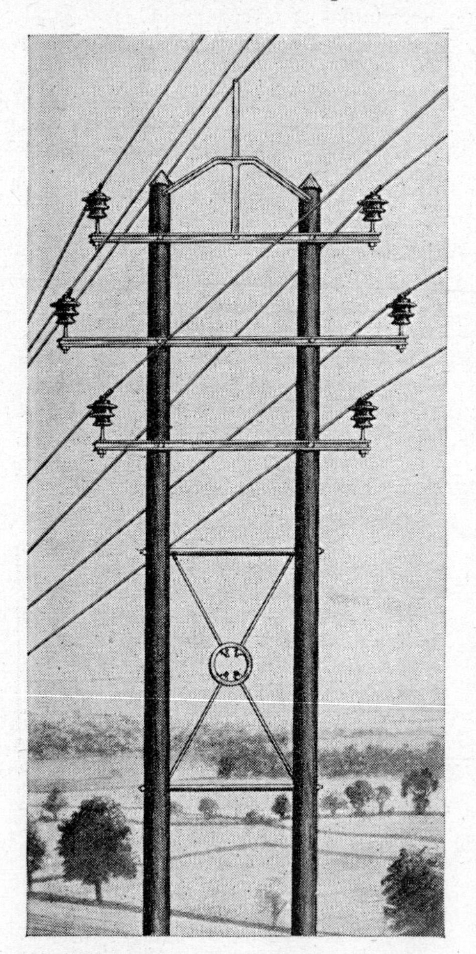

Fig. 38. Double circuit 33,000-volt line with pin-headed insulators and wooden poles of the H type. The non-insulated wire running above the poles is an earth line, bonding together all dead metal, such as cross arms, and connecting it to ground. Long spans are possible with these H supports each of which comprises two poles.

transmission lines, but considerably higher pressures are employed in some countries where large bulks of power have to be transported over great distances.

SUPPORTS

Wooden poles or steel structures of lattice work are the most common types of support, although reinforced concrete is widely employed on the Continent. For voltages up to about 33,000, wooden posts, pickled in creosote to protect the timber against the weather, are much used and a line of this type with double circuits is shown in Fig. 38. To permit the use of long spans, and hence fewer supports, two poles have been tied together in the form of the letter H, by which this type of structure is known.

INSULATORS

The insulators must be capable of withstanding the normal working voltage of the line and any excess pressures which may arise on the system. They must stand up to their duty in all weather conditions and their mechanical strength needs to be adequate. Porcelain is the material mostly employed for the manufacture of insulators, but on low-powered lines glass is sometimes used.

The design of an insulator is such that the underneath side is shielded from the wet and thereby the danger of the high voltage leaking over the surface in bad weather is obviated. When the voltage does not exceed about 33,000, insulators of the pin-headed pattern, as illustrated in Fig. 37, are generally used. The projecting flanges, or petticoats as they are commonly called, act as umbrellas to keep the rain from wetting the whole surface. The conductor is bound to a groove at the top as shown. Another type of insulator is the suspension disc and several of these are joined together in the form of a chain, the number of units depending on the voltage of the line. A clamp attached to the lowest disc serves to hold the conductor.

Good conductivity of electricity, high mechanical strength and immunity from attack by acids in a polluted atmosphere are the requirements of conductors for overhead lines. Copper is largely used, but many lines (notably those of the National Grid) employ aluminium stranded round a central core of steel to give the necessary strength.

DESIGN

Before a line can be erected it is necessary to obtain wayleaves from the property owners concerned and this may take some time. The route has to be surveyed and a profile of the land drawn out so that the positions of the supports can be decided upon. At intervals of about half a mile, but depending on the size of the line, there are special supports, more substantial than the ordinary ones, known as anchorages, and it is at these points that the longitudinal pull of the conductor is taken by tension type insulators as shown in Fig. 39. The anchorage provides a convenient place for joins between adjacent lengths of conductor, connection between the sections being made through jumpers, or the bow-shaped pieces of conductor shown. The horns to be seen, one at the line and the other at the earthed end of the insulators, serve as spark gaps to allow any abnormal voltages to pass to earth without damaging the porcelain.

Fig. 39. Anchor tower on 66,000 volt line. The insulators are in tension because they are taking the longitudinal stresses of the conductors. (By courtesy of the North Wales Power Co., Ltd., and Siemens Bros. & Co., Ltd.)

SPECIAL PRECAUTIONS

At places where overhead wires cross roads, railway lines, telephone lines, etc., special precautions are taken to prevent accidents due to breakage of a conductor. Fig. 40 shows a line crossing post office circuits, a railway, and a canal. It will be noted that the insulators are in duplicate chains to give extra mechanical strength, and that as an additional precaution a cradle guard is slung under the wires to catch them should they happen to break.

OPERATION

Lightning in the vicinity of a line is the chief cause of trouble, due to the setting up of high voltages which cause arcing across the insulators and damage to plant; but to act as a sort of safety valve to relieve high-voltage stresses, some lines are provided with lightning arresters.

A serious cause of trouble, happily not of very frequent occurence in Britain, is due to the wires becoming heavily caked

GUARDS FOR HIGH-TENSION WIRES

Fig. 40. High-tension wires crossing post office lines, railway and canal. At this important crossing a cradle guard is used to catch the wires, should they happen to break, as well as duplicate insulators to give extra mechanical strength. The cradle guard is earthed through the towers and the uninsulated loading wire. (By courtesy of the Corporation of Norwich and Johnson & Phillips, Ltd.)

with frozen snow. Considerable stresses are thereby caused, and owing to their increased area the wires offer a large surface to the wind. Under these conditions a gale may break whole spans.

In certain districts birds are the cause of faults on the overhead transmission system. When pin-headed insulators are used a bird perched on the cross arm may be able to come in contact with the conductor and make a short circuit. This occurrence, unhappy for the mains engineer, the consumer and the bird, can be prevented by designing the cross arms with a steep angle so that it is not easy for wild fowl to use them as perches. Other safeguards include the fitting of fibre sleeves over the cross arms as shown in Fig. 41, insulating the conductor at the places where birds could cause short circuits, or the provision of insulated perches mounted on the cross arms.

Fig. 41. This 11,000 volt line has a steel cross arm between the pole and the insulators. Also it is insulated with a fibre sleeve to prevent short circuits from being caused by birds.

INTERCONNECTION

In order to produce electricity under the most economical conditions the generators must be large and kept as fully loaded as possible at all times, that is to say, run at a high load factor. These conditions can best be fulfilled by generating in a few large stations, rather than running numerous small and independent plants. By means of a system of high-voltage lines, known as a grid, major plants are interconnected so that they can operate together, just like individual machines. The stations supplying the grid must, of course, be synchronised in the same way that an alternator is paralleled on the busbars to which the other machines have already been connected. The linking together of power stations has the further advantage of diminishing the capacity of spare plant required, because the resources of a whole area can be pooled thereby greatly reducing capital costs.

BRITISH GRID

In Britain the Central Electricity Board is responsible for the operation of the majority of the power stations, and they have been interconnected by the Board's 132,000 volt grid lines. The system acts as if it were a great busbar common to all the generating plant in the area. The power houses which come under the jurisdiction of the Board are known as selected stations and, depending on the conditions under which they are run, are termed base load, or peak load plants. The former class includes the largest and most efficient stations which are kept at all times as fully loaded as possible, while the peak plants are connected to the grid only at times of maximum demand for power. The grid, for convenience of operation, has been divided into areas, normally working independently of one another, but they can be coupled together for mutual assistance if required.

Every area is operated from a central control room where are housed instruments showing the loads on the various stations, and equipment to indicate the open or closed positions of all 132,000 volt switches. Indication of any operation of these switches is immediately automatically transmitted to the control room where the conditions are shown on a mimic diagram of the system. The control room has direct communication with all power stations and key points in the area. With these facilities at their command the engineers on duty in the control room are able to issue all instructions as to the operation of plant and switchgear in the whole area. Fig. 42 shows erection operations on a 132,000 volts grid line constructed with galvanised steel lattice work towers, on an average 70 feet high and spaced 900 feet apart. The conductors are built with a number of aluminium strands wound spirally on a central core of steel wires to give strength, and they are to be seen passing over snatch blocks before being pulled up taut. A length corresponding to several spans is drawn tight, and then the conductors are transferred from the snatch blocks to the clamps at the ends of the insulator strings.

ERECTION OPERATIONS

Fig. 42. Stringing up the conductors on a 132,000 volt grid line. The towers have an average height of 70 feet. (By courtesy of the Grampian Electricity Supply Co., Ltd., and Balfour Beatty & Co., Ltd.)

At generating stations and places where supplies of power are taken from the grid, there are sub-stations where the line insulators are attached to strong terminal towers, and connections taken to the switches and transformers which are designed to be operated in the open air in order to save building costs.

The National grid has been in service for a number of years; it has given

Britain a highly efficient generating system and made the power available over wide areas, thanks to the use of overhead lines. These circuits are of particular value in time of war, because if damaged they can be repaired speedily, and even if a whole power station be put out of action supply of current can be obtained quickly via the overhead lines from distant plants. The grid is, therefore, a very important national asset and one that distributes power on the most economical basis with a very high degree of reliability. It carries electricity to the remotest country districts.

CONSTRUCTION AND JOINTING OF UNDERGROUND CABLES

The method of conveying power via overhead transmission lines has already been discussed, and it is now proposed to deal with the method of conveying power via underground cables whether it be from the power station to the transmission lines or sub-station; or whether it be from the sub-station to the consumers' premises.

There are three main systems in use, these are:—

(1) *Super Tension* where power is conveyed over long distances at high voltage, i.e., 33,000, 66,000 or 132,000 volts.

(2) *Extra High Tension* for the conveyance of power in the region of 11,000 volts, or 22,000 volts also over long distances.

(3) *Low Tension* which conveys power at a pressure in the region of 230 volts for lighting and 400 volts for heating and electric motors. In this system owing to the close proximity of the consumers' premises and the large consumption of electricity, cable runs are usually short.

Each of these systems requires the use of a different type of cable, and although laying in each case is, in some respects, similar, jointing differs considerably. Before discussing the jointing of cables however, it is essential to know something about the requirements and construction of the various types of underground cables which are in general use for the distribution of power.

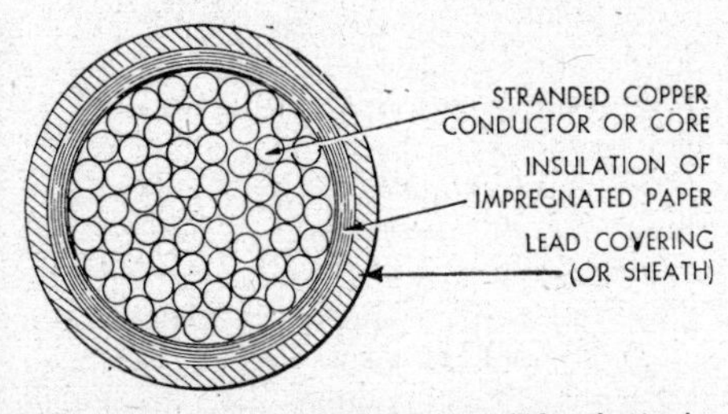

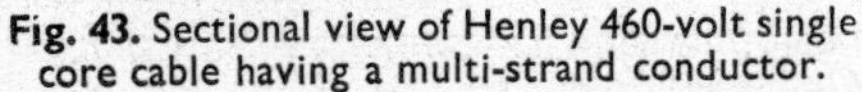
Fig. 43. Sectional view of Henley 460-volt single core cable having a multi-strand conductor.

UNDERGROUND CABLES

An underground cable must be a good conductor of electricity and, for this purpose, stranded copper wire has been found to be the best and possibly most economical. For convenience short cable runs have proved the most satisfactory method of conveying power. As has already been explained, this is achieved by erecting sub-stations at convenient points throughout the area where current is required.

It must be insulated sufficiently to withstand the normal working voltage and any sudden pressure rises which may result from trouble on the system, there must be adequate protection against mechanical damage. The cross-sectional area of the conductor has to be sufficient to carry the maximum current of the circuit without becoming unduly hot, or causing excessive drop of voltage.

LOW-VOLTAGE CABLES

It has already been stated that a cable for power supplies must be a good conductor. For this purpose pure copper is used; copper being the most economical of metals with "first class" conducting capabilities. If, however, a single strand of copper wire were used the cable would not be flexible owing to the large cross-sectional area required to carry the load. To overcome this difficulty the conductor is made up of a number of small wires. One of these forms a centre and runs straight throughout its length, and it is round this wire that the others are wound spirally. The cross-sectional view of a single-core cable is shown in Fig. 43.

As most systems of supply require at least three conductors, the relatively high cost of laying three or more separate single-core cables has been overcome by the introduction of the multicore type of cable. This type encloses the conductors in one sheath of armouring as well as insulating each conductor. The end of a partly unwrapped three-core cable is shown in Fig. 45B, the disposition of the cores being clearly visible.

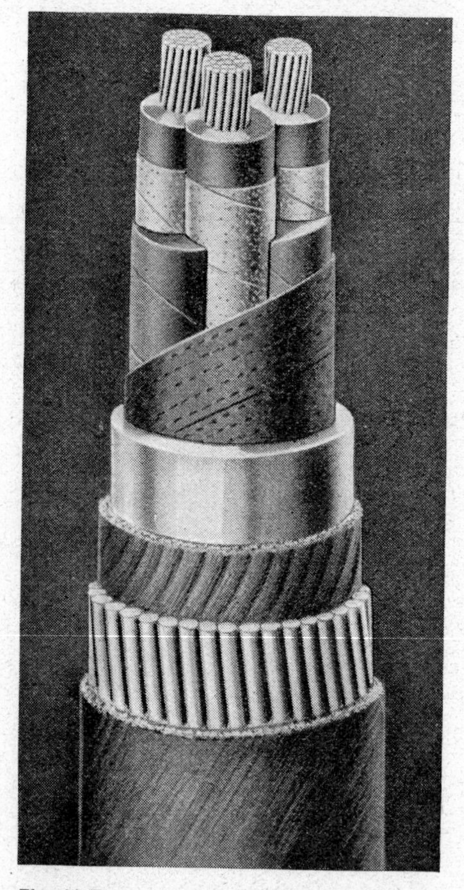

Fig. 44. Three-core H-type cable for extra high-tension. The three conductors are insulated with paper wound into cylindrical form and bound with metal foil wrappings. The whole is enclosed in a tube of lead protected by steel wire armouring and hessian tape.

The number of conductors that are employed depends upon the system in use and also upon the requirements of that system. For instance, a three-wire direct current system would require three cores and a four-wire alternating current system would require four cores. In many cases, however, extra cores are provided for street lighting. The assembly of the insulated cores is given a definite lay similar to that given to the strands which form individual conductors. This ensures a circular contour for the completed cable. A study of Fig. 45 will reveal the construction of (A) a four-core cable, and (B) a three-core cable.

HIGH-VOLTAGE CABLES

The "Belted Type Cable" illustrated in Fig. 44 is unsuitable for very high working pressures, i.e., above 22,000 volts, for the following reason:—When the cable is working on load its temperature rises, causing expansion, particularly with the impregnating oil. This expansion causes the lead sheath to expand; on cooling off, the oil, insulation, and conductors contract but, as the lead sheath is plastic, it does not contract to its original dimensions. This results in the formation of voids between the lead sheath and the insulation.

The formation and existence of voids eventually reduces the insulation properties of the paper insulation, with the result that faults develop in the cable. The "Oil-Filled Cable" which has a hollow conductor (see Fig. 46) eliminates the formation of voids by having maintained throughout its length a pressure of oil under all conditions.

Outside insulation is achieved by wrapping the conductor in wood pulp and manilla fibre paper which has been impregnated in resinous oil to obtain high insulating qualities, this being far

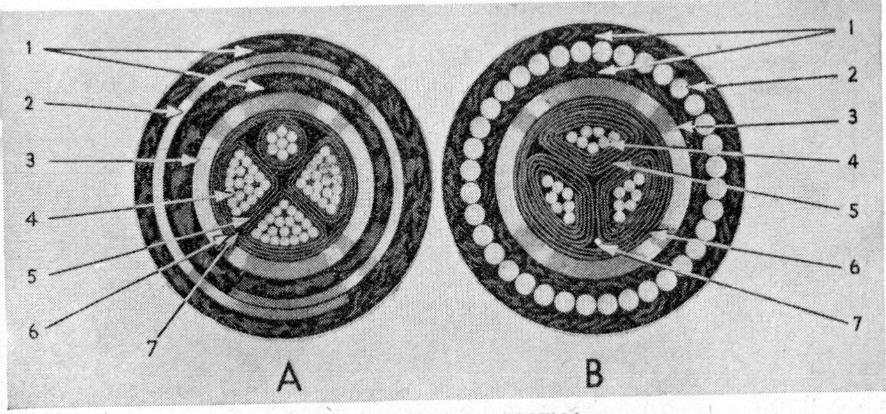

HENLEY CABLES IN SECTION

Fig. 45. Section "A" shows section through 4-core, low tension, paper-insulated, lead-covered and steel-tape armoured cable. 1—Tarred jute servings, inner and outer. 2—Steel-tape armour, about half width overlap. 3—Lead sheathing. 4—Stranded copper conductors or cores. 5—Impregnated paper insulation for cores, each core separately insulated. 6—Impregnated belt paper or binder enclosing the arrangement of insulated cores. 7—Impregnated jute to fill in gaps between insulation of individual cores and belt paper.

Section "B". Section through 3-core, extra high-tension, paper insulated, lead-covered and steel wire armoured cable. With the exception of the following, the construction is identical to Section A:—2—Steel-wire armour, single layer instead of steel-tape armour as with the 4-core cable.

superior to any other type of insulation. Its greatest disadvantage, however, is that it is easily effected by damp, but this is overcome by wrapping the paper in a lead sheath. The outer sheath, in turn, is protected from external damage by an armoured covering of steel tape or steel wire. This, in turn, is covered by a serving of tarred jute or hessian.

The Theory of Operation of the Oil-Filled Cable, put very simply, is as follows: The cable run is divided up into a number of convenient sections, usually about 2,000 yards per section, with a special type of joint known as a "stop joint" at each end of a section.

In excavating the cable run for a section it is arranged that there is a gradual fall along the whole length. Connected to the stop joint at the high-level end by means of a pipe is an oil reservoir which operates under gravity feed, while at the lower end of the section an oil pressure tank is connected to the stop joint.

When the temperature of the cable rises the brass reinforcing tape wound over the inner lead sheath tends to limit the expansion of the sheath. As the oil expands considerable pressure is set up which results in a movement of oil along the cable into the reservoir and pressure tank. The pressure tank is constructed to exert a back pressure on the oil from the cable, tending to maintain a constant pressure of oil along the cable under all operating conditions throughout the section, and offsetting formation of voids.

LAYING AN UNDERGROUND CABLE

Long runs in low-tension underground cables (as mentioned previously) are seldom possible owing to the large number of consumers in most supply areas. Joints, therefore, have to be made at frequent intervals and for this purpose a joint hole is dug at the end of each trench of the cable run. Good work cannot be accomplished without the necessary room to do the job, therefore the hole should be excavated to allow plenty of freedom of movement. Further, the hole should be excavated to at least eighteen inches below the level at which it is proposed to make the joint.

It is also essential that a good covering be arranged over the hole with the

Fig. 46. Single-core oil-filled cable for 220,000 volts. The conductor is made tubular to permit the passage of insulating oil.

opening in the same direction as the wind is blowing. This removes any possibility of the joint being exposed to dust and grit which may be blown about by the wind during assembly.

JOINTING MATERIALS

Because reliability is so essential especially with E.H.T. jointing, much research has, in recent years, been carried out by the cable makers in designing E.H.T. joints. Several excellent types of E.H.T. joints can be obtained in kit form. These contain lead sleeves of correct size, insulating materials specially prepared, ferrules or connectors for jointing the cores together, and high-grade solders for both sweating the ferrules on to the cores and wiping the sleeve on to the cable sheath. All these are kept ready for assembly by the supply authorities jointer.

As there is a variety of joints for the various types of cables in use, a few representative ones will be given as typical examples. These are as follows:—

STRAIGHT JOINTS

Owing to lack of space it is impossible to describe this type of joint separately but the correct method of accomplishing a good straight joint can readily be understood by a close study of the section on joints given below.

TEE JOINTS

(1) *L.T. Service 2-Core Cable.* The type of joint to be described is used to provide a consumer with a single-phase A.C. supply, in which the service cable to the consumer's premises has two cores, and is to be connected to a four-core main or distributor cable as a "branch" or "tee" joint; the joint is enclosed in an iron tee box. When used for D.C. supply the main has only three cores and is bonded with fittings to both armour and lead sheath. With all L.T. cables individual cores have coloured insulation, a four-core cable having red, blue, green and white cores. With this type of work the colour scheme is adhered to wherever possible by connecting the cores of the service cable to corresponding coloured cores on the main. One of the cores of the main is known as the neutral and is usually the white core. It is necessary to connect the white core of the service to the white core of the main, the jointer receiving instructions as to which core of the main the other core of the service must be connected.

Preparations and Jointing. During laying of the service cable to the consumer's premises it should be arranged that the service overlaps the main by about one foot to provide ample length for jointing. Jute serving and armour are removed from both cables to conform to the dimensions of the box, and lead sheath is then cut off both cables again to box dimensions, and belt paper removed

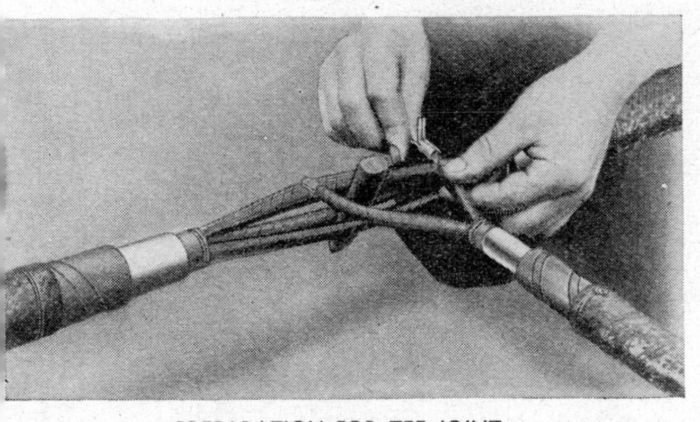

PREPARATION FOR TEE JOINT

Fig. 47. Showing bottom-core of Henley cable separated by means of wood wedge. The service cores are laid over main ready for teeing on.

to within one inch of the lead at each end exposing the insulated cores. When making a tee joint it is easier to work from the bottom core on the main to the top one, each core being jointed and insulated before starting the next.

Set the cores of the service in position about 2 ins. apart and lay over the main marking off the teeing-on positions. Assuming that the white is the first to be jointed, separate the white of the main by inserting one hardwood wedge between it and the others, the wedge being one side of the teeing-on position and remove about $1\frac{1}{2}$ in. of insulation exposing the stranded copper core (Fig. 47). As this type of joint is usually made without interrupting the supply, it will be very necessary for the jointer to stand on a mat or wear a pair of rubber galoshes.

Next, remove the insulation to the required length from the white core of the service exposing the stranded core. Untwist one of the strands and take two turns round the core; this will provide a good "butt" against the main. Untwist the remaining strands and divide into two groups binding one group in one direction

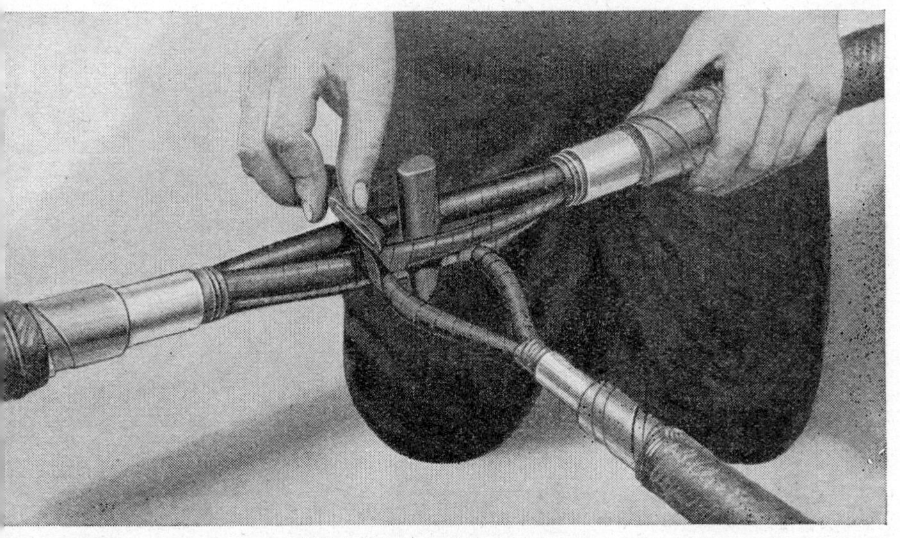

PROTECTIVE CORE COVERING

Fig. 48. One core is finished and the second core is shown being insulated on Henley cable. Lead tape is used over the insulation of the core. Note the wedge used to separate the cores while working.

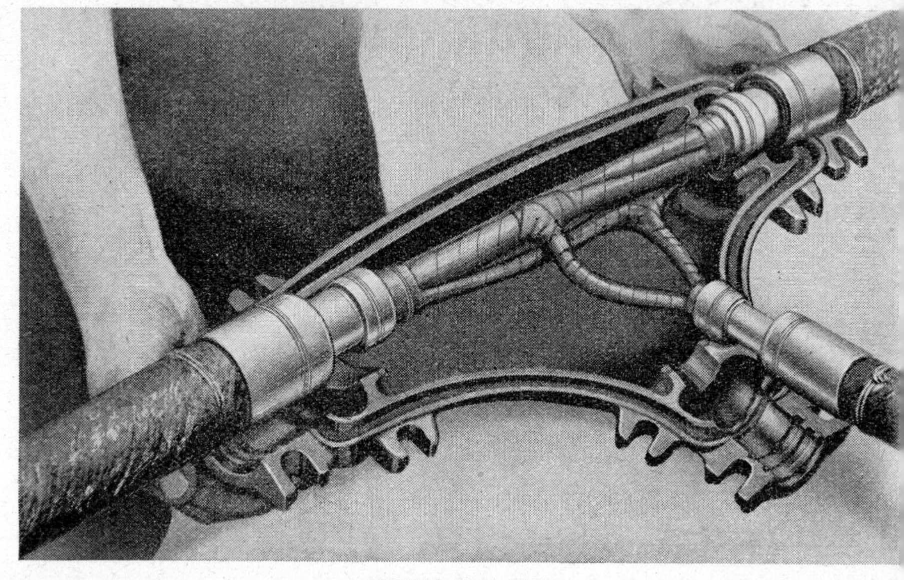

FITTING THE BOX

Fig. 49. Showing lead tape wrapped round armours and lead on Henley cable. The bottom half of the box is then fitted. The fittings should drop snugly into their grooves.

round the main and the other group the reverse way round, this will ensure a tight joint.

Place a paper chute between the core to be sweated and the others to direct the flow of hot metal, and sweat the joint, wipe clean, remove the paper chute and insulate, repeating the operation from the other service core. Lead tape, two inches wide, is then bound round each of the armours and three-quarters inch wide round each end of the lead to the required diameters as fixed by the fittings, making off the lead tape with wire binders (Fig. 48).

Place bottom half of box in position (Fig. 49) bolt on armour clamps and remove binders from the lead tape, remove the cover plates from the top half of the box and slacken off the shuttle screws and bridges that are used to bond the lead to the box. Warm the bottom half of the box with a blow lamp and fill the groove with hot compound, placing on the top half and bolting down also tightening shuttle screws to effect good bonds. The box is then filled with compound and topped up in the usual way, after which the cover plates are fixed in position and flooded with compound, thus completing the joint, as shown in Fig. 50.

(2) *L.T. Service 4-Core Cable.* This type of joint is one that would be used to give a consumer what is known as a "three-phase four-wire, low-tension alternating-current supply", in which the service cable to the consumers' premises has four cores and is to be connected to a four-core main cable as a "branch" or "tee" joint. It is enclosed in a lead tee sleeve, which is wiped on to the lead sheath of both cables, and then enclosed in an iron tee-box. As previously stated, in all L.T. cables the individual cores have coloured insulation, usually red, blue, green and white, and in this type of work the colour scheme should be adhered to wherever possible, by connecting the cores of the service cable to corresponding coloured cores on the main.

Preparation for Jointing. During the laying of the service cable to the consumers' premises, it should be arranged

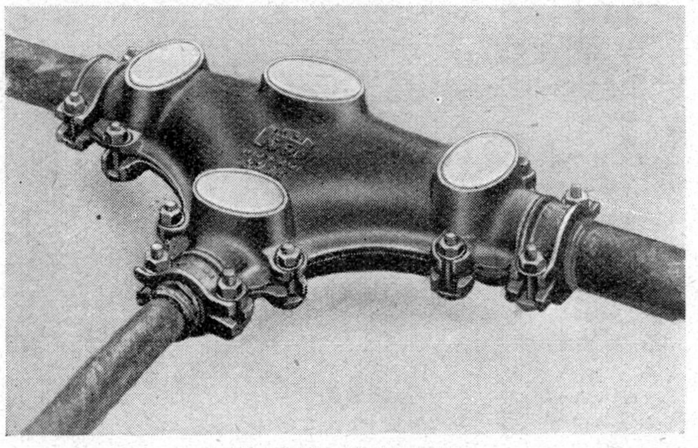

TEE JOINT COMPLETED

Fig. 50. Showing completed joint on Henley cable, the cover plate is flooded with bituminous compound as a protection against moisture

that the service cable approximately overlaps the main by one foot, to provide enough length for jointing purposes. Jute serving and armour are removed from both cables to conform to the dimensions of the iron box. The lead sheath is then cut off from both cables, arranging for one inch to protrude inside each end of the lead sleeve, following which, the belt paper may be removed to within an inch of the sheath at each end, exposing the insulated cores.

Jointing. When making a "tee" joint, it is easier to work from the bottom core on the main, to the top core. Assume that the bottom core on the main is the white one. A hard wood wedge is inserted between it and the others, thus separating it. About two inches of insulation are now removed at the point where the joint is to be made, exposing the copper conductor.

The white core of the service cable is now laid over the exposed conductor of the main, and the insulation removed to expose the stranded core. One of the strands is untwisted down to the insulation and twisted round the core, thus providing a good "butt" against the main. The remainder of the strands are now untwisted and divided into two groups. One group is bound round the main in one direction, and the other group in the other direction thus ensuring a tight joint. The joint is sweated in the usual way and insulated, the operation being repeated with each of the remaining cores. At least one inch clearance should be allowed between the centres of each pair of joints. As a number of faults which occur in L.T. multi-core cables are due to burning of one of the cores of the service cable at the teeing-on point, it is a good plan to place a wad of impregnated tape between the teeing-on point of each core and the adjacent core over which each service core passes.

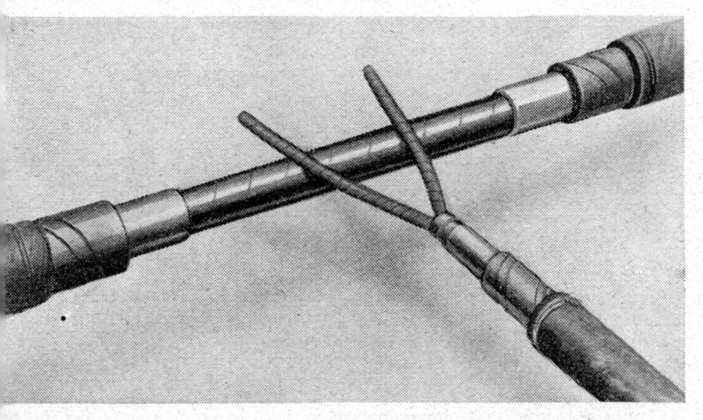

JOINTING SERVICE CABLE

Fig. 51. Showing the main stripped down to the belt paper and the Henley service cable to the insulated cores as a first step in jointing.

Lead Sleeve. The sleeve having been suitably dressed and

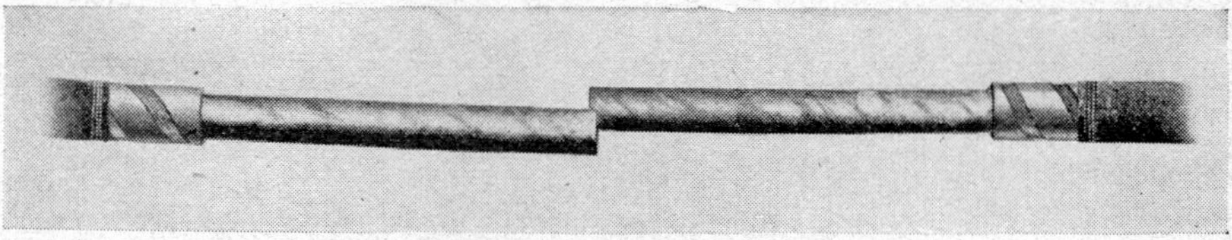

JOINTING THREE-CORE CABLES

Fig. 52. Showing Henley cable ends prepared and cut to length; note overlap at centre to give correct spacing of cores and correct alighnment. Approximately, one-eighth of an inch will suffice.

blacked, should then be wiped on to the lead sheath of both cables and filled with compound, resorting to topping up until the sleeve is cool, when it may be sealed down. This leaves only the iron box to be fitted, making certain that the armour is properly bonded. It is then filled with compound and, when cool, the plugs are replaced in the filling holes.

(3) *E.H.T.* (11,000 *Volt*) 3-*Core Straight Joint.* The jute serving and steel tape armour should be removed to the desired length off both cable ends, to accommodate the cast iron shell, which fits over and affords protection to the lead sleeve, and also provides an efficient electrical bond or connection between the armour of both lengths of cable.

Insulating Materials. Insulating materials supplied with the jointing kit, should be removed from the sealed container in which they arrive, and placed in a wire basket in a covered pail of hot compound, with which the sleeve will finally be filled, until they are required. It is important to ensure that no particles of grit or dust be allowed to settle on the insulating materials.

These materials, in this type of joint, will consist of:—(1) insulation for the individual cores in the form of rolls of impregnated paper, about one inch wide, wrapped round a length of one-half inch impregnated linen tape, and made up into rolls about one inch in diameter, (2) impregnated paper spider with three grooves, used for keeping the cores correctly spaced, and (3) impregnated paper binder or belt to keep the whole assembly in position.

Lead sleeve. This should be suitably dressed and painted with plumber's black to facilitate plumbing.

Ferrules. Three "weak back" ferrules or connectors are used for jointing the cores together.

Cast Iron Shell. This should be kept clean and warm.

Jointing. The cable ends having been prepared, the jointing should proceed as follows: The cable ends are put into

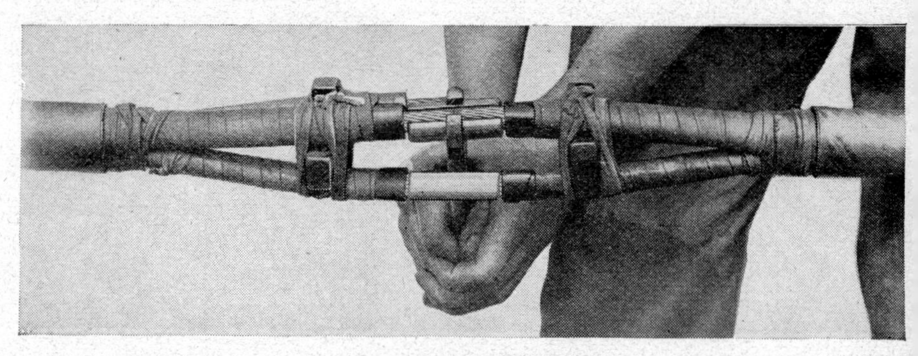

FITTING THE FERRULES

Fig. 53. Henley cables showing arrangement of the crutches, cores, and spreaders, these being bound with boiled tape, and ferrules fitted. The ferrules are closed down tightly with pliers.

correct alignment, and are cut at a position corresponding to the centre of the joint (Fig. 52), allowing about $\frac{1}{8}$ in. overlap, this being necessary to give the correct spacing between the cores. A hacksaw must be used for this operation, and care taken to ensure a straight cut, otherwise all the cores will not be the same length.

The length of lead sleeve will decide the amount of lead sheath to be removed from the cable, it being usual to allow one inch of sheath to protrude inside each end of the sleeve when fitted, the sheath being cut off the cable with a "hacking" knife. Sheath ends should now be "belled out" by means of a special "belling" tool.

These operations completed, the lead sleeve should be slid over one of the cable ends, so that it may be brought up and over the joint when made. The "belt" paper or covering which encloses the cores should be taken off to within one inch of the sheath on either end, and the cores exposed.

The point where the cores emerge from the belt paper is known as the "crutch", and before jointing can be effected, this must be correctly formed, by bringing the cores into correct alignment for jointing and inserting a spreader into each crutch. The cores and spreader are now all bound up together with impregnated linen tape to prevent further movement.

Sweating the Cores. Before fitting the ferrules it should be noted that there are no sharp bends in the cores, gradual curves being necessary. Enough straight should be arranged on either side of the ferrule position to enable the insulation to be applied evenly, since if this is not done before sweating, it will be very difficult afterwards. Sufficient core insulation should now be cut off each core end to accommodate just over half a length of ferrule. This being carried out the ferrules may now be fitted by placing each ferrule over the correct pair of cores to be jointed, and then closing the ferrule by means of a pair of pliers (Fig. 53).

After fitting, each ferrule is sweated by pouring hot tinman's solder over each joint in turn, care being taken to carry on the sweating long enough to make the solder run freely inside the ferrule, when it may be filled up with the metal and

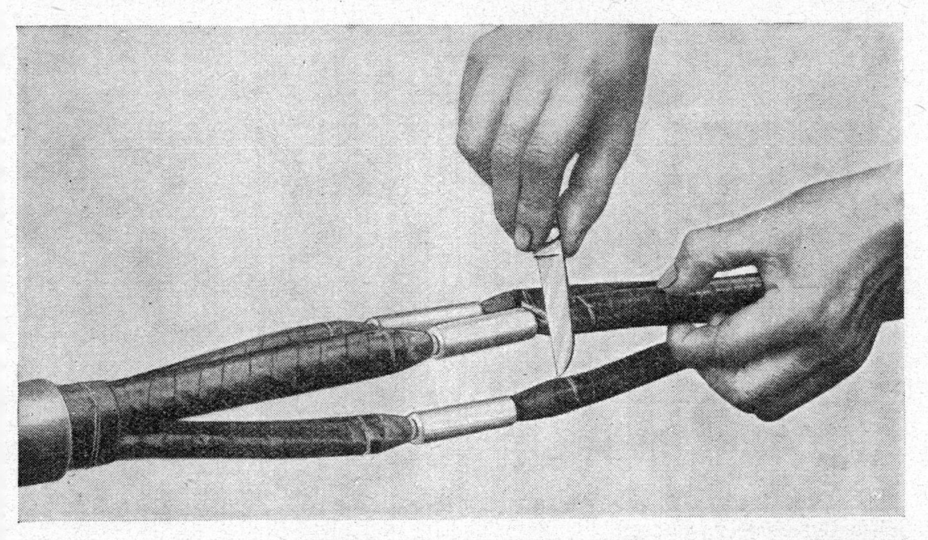

CHAMFERING THE CORE INSULATION

Fig. 54. Showing sweating of Henley cable completed and core insulation being chamfered down. It is vital that any irregularities shall be removed. Impregnated thread is used to make a smooth surface between the cores and the ends of the ferrules before the paper insulation is applied.

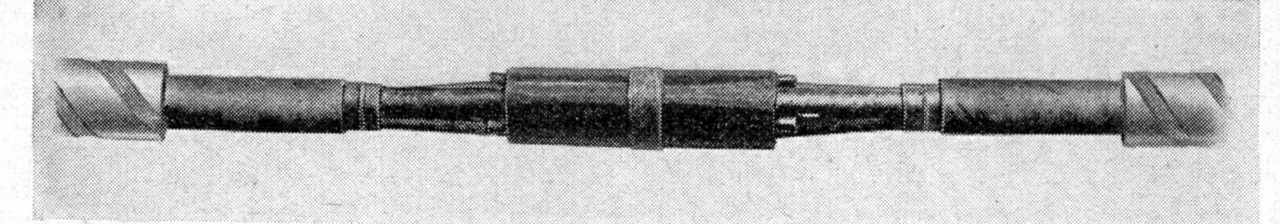

INSULATION COMPLETED

Fig. 55. Henley 11,000 volt cable joint with insulation completed. The sleeve has been brought into position for wiping on after it has been dressed down on the lead sheath. This part of the jointing needs to be done with great care so that a workmanlike finish is imparted.

gradually cooled off and wiped, leaving a clean, smooth surface.

Insulating the Joint. Before applying the narrow rolls of paper insulation to the cores, the boiled tape which was used to bind the cores and spreaders should be removed (Fig. 54), and any irregularities in size between cores and ferrules made good by thread, which has been properly impregnated. It is important that the paper insulation should be applied to an even surface, the same amount of insulation being placed on each core.

The paper spider should now be inserted between the cores, taking care to see that the ferrule is in the centre of the groove. This completed, the paper binder is applied over cores and spider to keep them in position.

Fitting Lead Sleeve. The insulating being completed (Fig. 55), the sleeve is brought up over the joint, dressed down on to the lead sheath, and wiped on with plumber's solder.

Filling the Sleeve. Bituminous compound, at a temperature usually about 250 deg. Fahrenheit is poured into the sleeve in such a manner that all the air inside the sleeve is excluded (Fig. 56). It will be found that as the compound cools off, its level inside the sleeve falls. It must therefore be frequently topped up until it is cool, when the sleeve may be sealed by wiping on the lead caps provided for the filling holes.

Fitting the Iron Shell. In fitting the iron shell the steel-tape armour must be bonded or connected to the shell by means of the clamps provided. The filling plugs in the top of the box should be removed, and the shell filled with

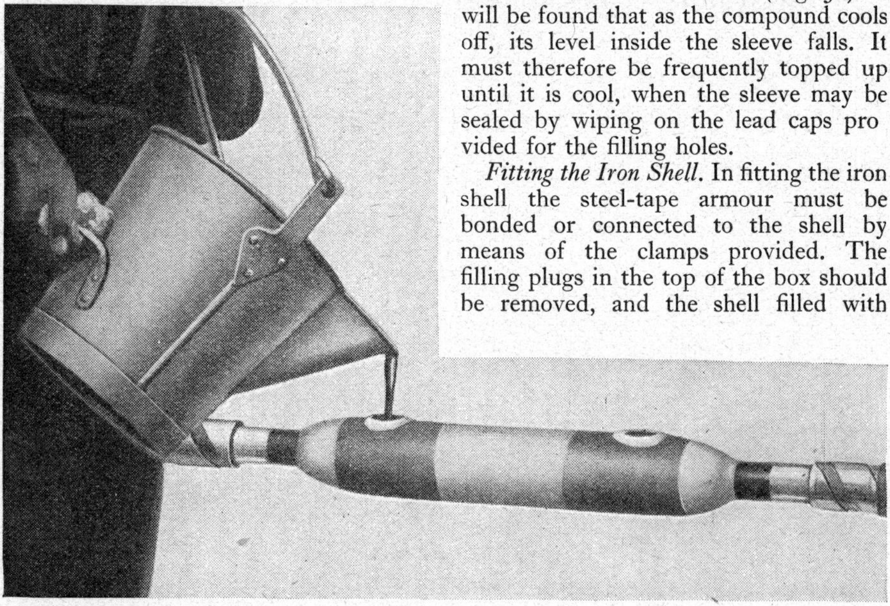

FILLING THE SLEEVE

Fig. 56. Wiped on lead joint of Henley cable being filled with bituminous compound at 250 deg. F. Topping up after the compound has cooled is necessary owing to its shrinkage. Lead caps close the filling holes and completes the jointing operation except for the fitting of the cast iron shell

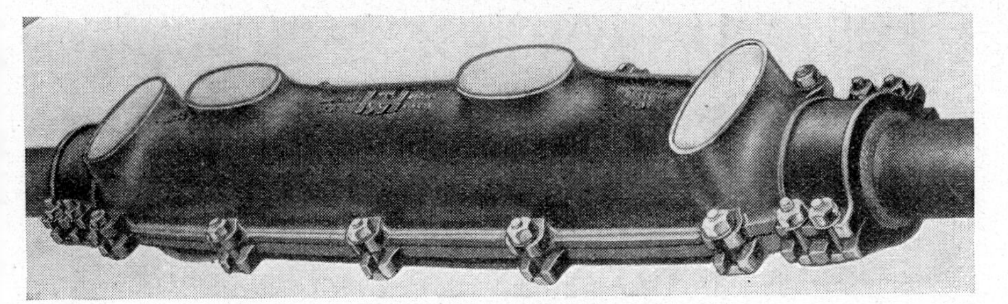

FITTING THE IRON SHELL

Fig. 57. Finally the iron shell is fitted and this too, filled with bituminous compound. As in the case of the sleeve, topping up will be necessary to make good the shrinkage of the compound as it cools.

bituminous compound. Again, as the compound in the shell cools off its level will fall, so that topping up should be resorted to as in the case of the sleeve. Replacing the plugs in the top of the shell when the compound has finally cooled off completes the joint (Fig. 57). Very great care must be exercised in filling in the joint hole. The joint should be supported at both ends and the earth used for filling well rammed up to the level of the top of the box. If this is not done and the cables and joint sag, there is a possibility of the joint pulling out, causing a breakdown. Tiles are placed over cable and joint, and the filling in should then be completed.

JOINTING OIL-FILLED CABLES

A 2,000 yards run between two stop joints requires several drums of cable and, as these have to be joined together, a special type of "straight through joint" is necessary to allow the movement of oil along the section. A cable section requires two stop and several straight through joints. With both types of joint, special ferrules are necessary to give mechanical strength, maximum conductivity, and allow free movement of oil. As the job of making either type is very detailed only the essentials can be given, the joints described are designed by Messrs. Pirelli-General Cable Works Coy., and have been very successful in operation on working pressures of 132,000 volts.

STOP JOINT

The stop joint for a single core "Oil-Filled Cable" consists essentially of a cylindrical copper tank filled with oil, and containing two inserted porcelain insulators fitted with gunmetal terminal caps which are connected together electrically by a flexible coupling. The bases of the insulators are supported on gunmetal castings, one at each end of the tank. At such high pressures a very intense electric field is set up between the terminal caps and the tank, and to ensure an even distribution of the electric field a metal shell and rings suitably insulated with impregnated paper are located over the terminal caps.

The tank portion of the joint, with insulators mounted and terminal caps connected, and correctly insulated, is sent to the jointing site hermetically sealed. The actual jointing process is the preparation of the cable ends, fitting the special contact plugs, insulating the cable ends, and insertion into the insulators.

The contact plugs may be described as being in two sections, one being the plug portion which makes contact with the terminal cap, the other being the ferrule portion. The ferrule portion is placed over

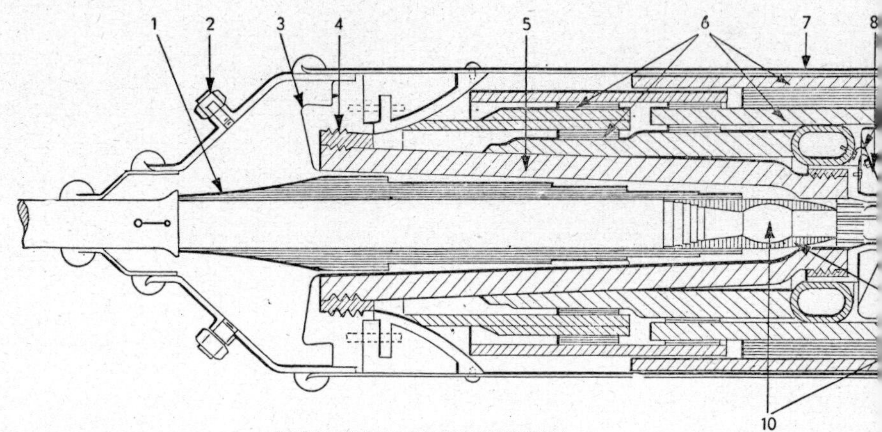

Fig. 58. Cross-section of stop joint for 132 kV oil-filled single-core cable showing details of construction. 1—Lead wire stress control, 2—Bronze unions, 3—Gun-metal casting, 4—Cement, 5—Porcelain insulator, 6—Paper roll insulation, 7—Copper casing, 8—Copper screen, 9—Copper bond, 10—Bronze ferrule, 11—Flexible coupling, 12—Paper tape, 13—Paper tubes, 14—Paper tube insulation, 15—Varnished silk tape. Three completed stop-joints are illustrated in Fig. 64.

the hollow core of the cable into which a steel pin is first inserted. Hydraulic pressure is then applied to press the ferrule and the hollow stranded core on to the pin (Fig. 58 shows a section through a stop joint).

Jointing Preparations. As with other types of jointing a joint hole of adequate dimensions is necessary, in this case the hole should be about two and a half times the length of the joint. A three-phase transmission system will require three single-core cables, and three stop joints will have to be made in the same joint hole. The joints must be laid out to give ample clearance round each joint to carry out the work. Suitable coverings are necessary over the hole with the opening on the leeside.

It is also necessary that a log of weather and temperature conditions be kept during jointing. Suitable thermometers must be hung both inside and outside the jointing tent and readings taken at prescribed intervals.

In order to facilitate the entry of the finished cable ends into the porcelain insulators the trench on either side of the hole should be left open for about 15 feet.

Jointing. The cable ends are now set up to the joint, allowing about 6 ins. of slack, and with the ends overlapping by about 6 ins., and the centre line of the joint marked off on each cable end. From the centre line of each end the outer sheath and reinforcing tape should be removed to the required distance. From the centre line another mark is made to allow for the plug portion of the ferrule, it is at this point the cable must be cut.

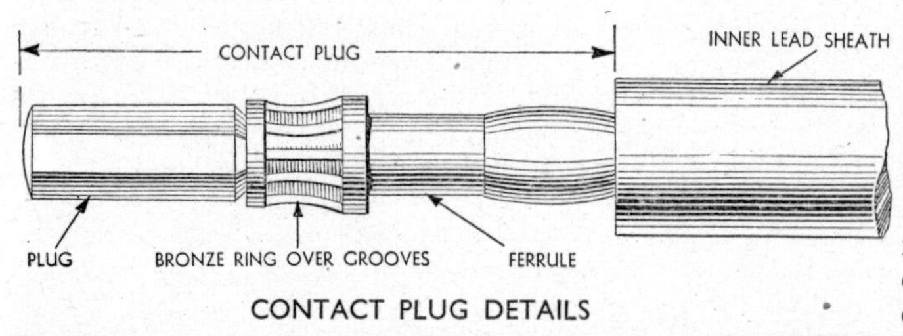

Fig. 59. Diagram showing plug ready for removal of first section of lead.

Before cutting, the oil engineer will make sure that the oil connections between the oil-feeding points and cables are in order and that no obstruction to the oil flow is present during jointing. The cables are now

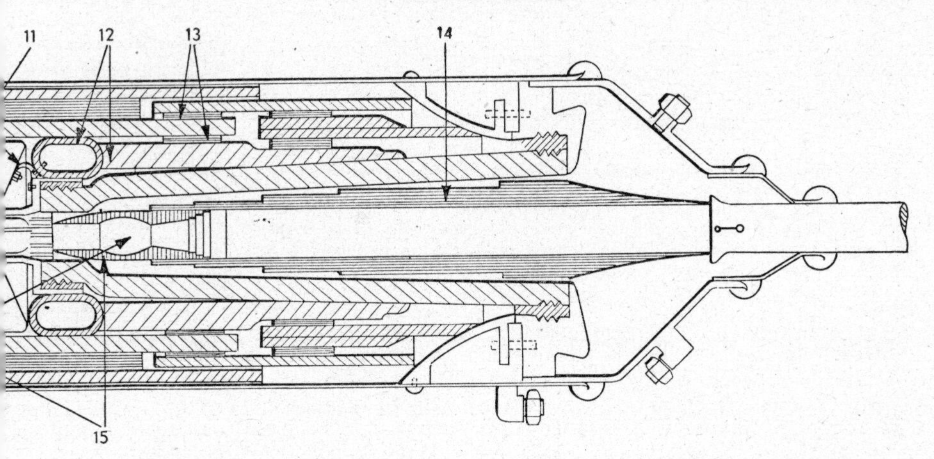

placed on special trestles with their ends pointing up at an angle of not less than 30 degs. to the horizontal. A basting pan should be placed under the ends to catch any surplus oil from the cores after the cables are cut.

One cable is now cut, and the mouth of the oil duct cleaned out to remove metal dust. The spiral inside the duct is pushed back and, when full oil flow is obtained, the steel pin is inserted into the hollow core, these operations being repeated for the other cable end.

The inner sheath is now removed from each end for sufficient distance to accommodate the ferrule bore of the contact plug, this measurement being taken from the head of the steel pin. The insulation is removed and a wire binder placed round the core to prevent it splaying out.

The copper end bells of the joint are now slid along the cable ends beyond the cut in the outer sheath, and the ferrule ends of each contact plug placed on the cores, the binders being taken off. The cables should then be lowered on the trestles into a horizontal position and the hydraulic pump placed in position. Pressure is applied by the pump to press the ferrule and conductors on to the steel pin. The pump is then removed and any edges left by the press dies filed off, the phosphor-bronze rings are brought up over the grooves made by the dies. Fig. 59 shows the contact plug on a cable end.

Insulating the Joint. In order to insulate the cable ends the inner sheath is removed in sections. The first section is cut off and the paper insulation is stepped down to the correct diameters; silk tape is applied to build up the insulation to the largest diameter exposed, this tape insulation being carried over the ferrule and phosphor-bronze clip. A further section of sheath is removed and the paper stepped down, silk tape being applied as previously. Fig. 60 shows the ferrule and stepped insulation after application of the silk tape. The last section is now removed and the end of the lead carefully "belled" out, the exposed insulation being basted with oil at 230° F. Two layers of silk tape are applied over the whole length of insulation, and basting again repeated (see Fig. 61). The cable is

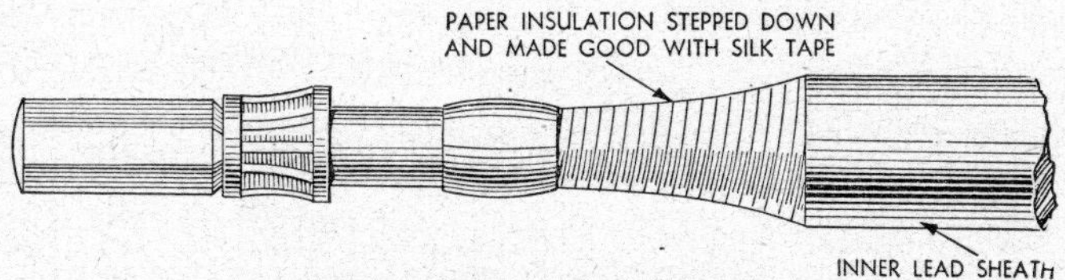

Fig. 60. Joint ready for removal of first section of inner lead. Note the ferrule and stepped insulation that has been made good with silk tape

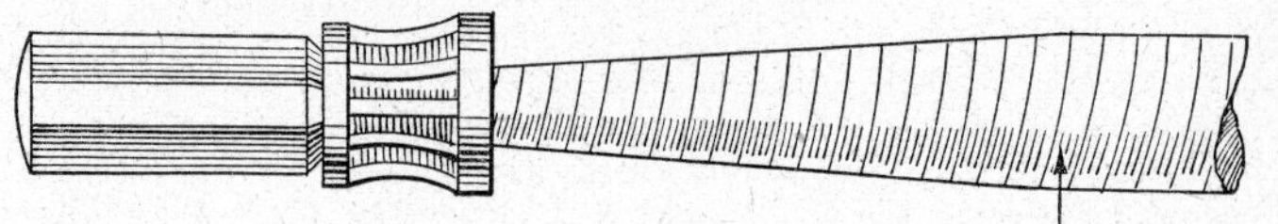

APPLYING PAPER TUBES

Fig. 61. Core ready for application of paper tubes. Two layers of silk tape are applied over the whole length of insulation and basting is again completed as before.

now insulated with five paper tubes of different lengths, the longest being put on first, and each tube put on in its correct position, the last tube being made off with silk tape.

The paper tube insulation adjacent to the lead sheath should be carefully chamfered, an even surface being obtained by the use of clean glass paper, the insulation being again basted with oil at 230° F.

What are known as "stress controls" are fitted over the chamfered insulation. This is done by winding lead wire over the insulation from the lead sheath to within a short distance of the top of the chamfer, care being taken to see that adjacent turns of the lead wire lie close together. The free end of the lead wire at the sheath end may be taken through a small hole drilled in the bell of the sheath and soldered on the outside, the belled out part of the lead being carefully laid down on the lead wire. The other end of wire is made off by bringing the free end under the last turn and then soldering (see Fig. 62). These operations complete the ends are ready for insertion into the porcelain insulators. Fig. 63 shows a cable end ready for insertion.

When inserting the ends into the porcelains the slack should be taken up by easy horizontal bends, also care must be exercised in making certain that the contact plug enters the gunmetal terminal cap to its limit.

The ends in position the copper end bells are brought up to their correct positions and the two joints at each end wiped on, stick wiping must be resorted to in order to avoid general heating up of the joint.

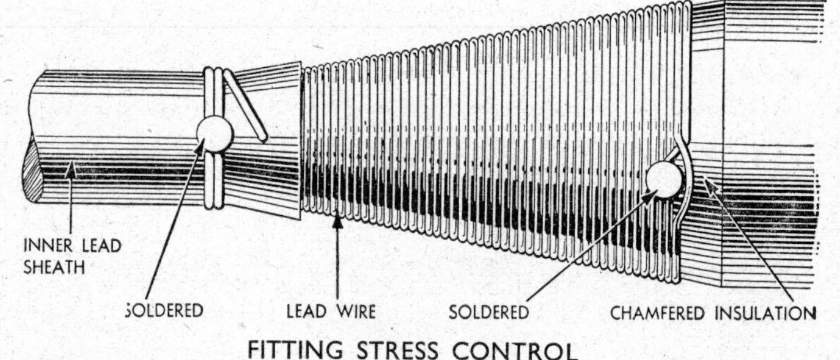

FITTING STRESS CONTROL

Fig. 62. Diagram showing method of fitting stress control. Lead wire is wound over the insulation, the ends being securely soldered as shown.

The outer lead sheath and reinforcing tape are made off by binding to the inner lead sheath with 16-gauge tinned copper wire and then plumbed together.

Over the inner edge of this wipe, and

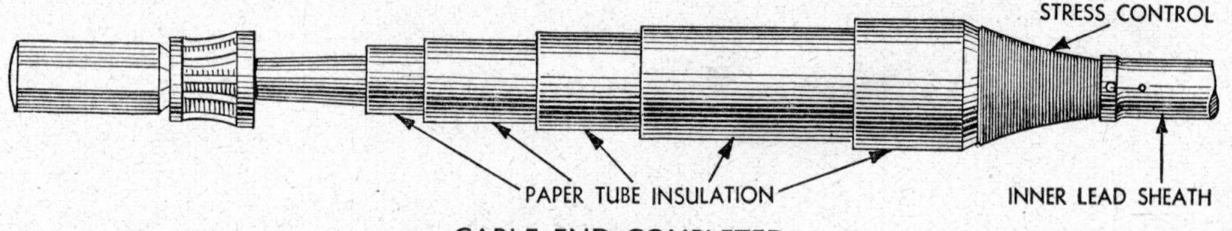

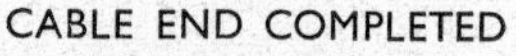

CABLE END COMPLETED

Fig. 63. Cable end completed and ready for insertion into porcelain insulator. The slack must be taken up by easy bends and the contact plug inserted to its limit into the terminal cap.

extending over the small wipe on the copper end bell, is placed a close wound layer of 16-gauge wire for reinforcing purposes, this being lightly wiped over and then covered with compounded tape for protection.

An earth plate is buried in the trench just outside the joint hole. The outer lead sheaths of the cables are bonded across the joints, adjacent cables also being bonded together, and connected to the earth plate by means of copper strip.

Upon completion the impregnation of the joint is carried out by the oil engineer. Three stop joints showing oil connections are illustrated in Fig. 64.

The straight through joint consists mainly of a special type ferrule which is fitted over the hollow conductors of both cable ends, a hollow steel pin having been first inserted into each conductor. Hydraulic pressure is applied to compress the ferrule and hollow conductors on to the pins, resulting in a connection between the conductors which, while being mechanically strong, allows the free passage of oil through the joint. The insulation on the cable ends having been suitably prepared, the joint is insulated in stages, by the application of varnished silk tape, paper tape, paper rolls and tubes.

Screening is accomplished by a light gauge copper screen, which is placed over the insulation, and bonded to the inner lead sheath on both cable ends. Stress controls are fitted as in the stop joint, the whole assembly being housed in a copper sleeve which is wiped on to the inner sheaths. Fig. 65 shows a section through a straight through joint.

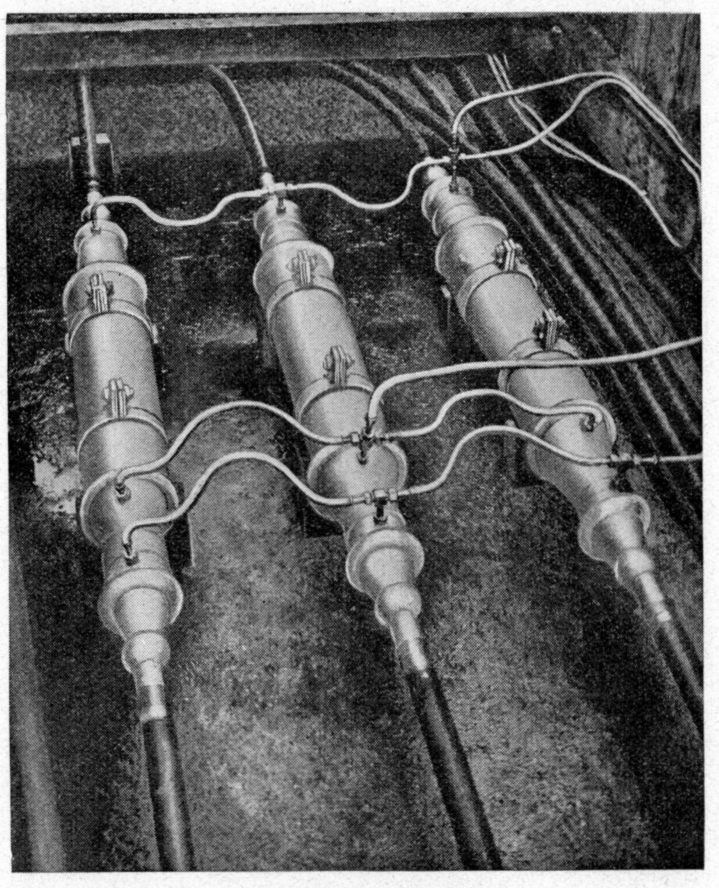

TYPICAL STOP JOINTS

Fig. 64. Showing three typical stop joints complete with oil connections. Copper strips and a buried plate are used for earthing. See also Fig. 58.

Jointing Preparations. The remarks applying to joint hole, jointing tent,

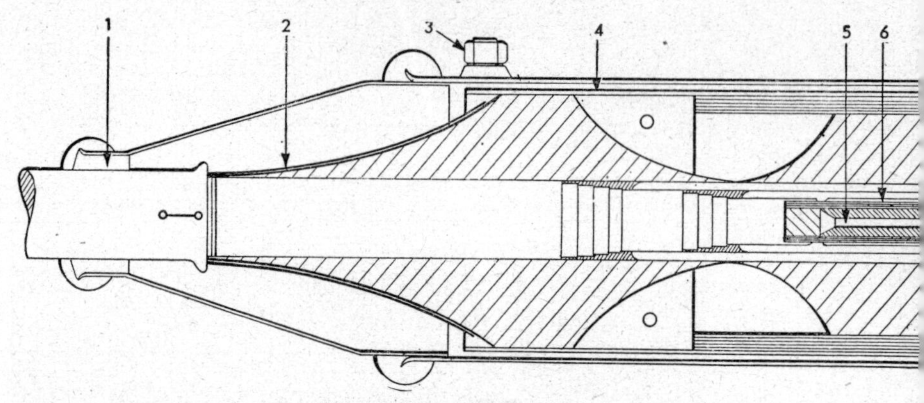

STRAIGHT THROUGH JOINT

Fig. 65. Cross-section of straight through joint for oil-filled single core cable. 1—Lead bush, 2—Lead wire stress control. 3—Bronze unions, 4—Copper screen, 5—Hollow steel plug, 6—Bronze ferrule, 7—Paper roll insulation, 8—Varnished silk tape, 9—Copper casing, 10—Copper bond.

weather and temperature log, apply as in the case of the stop joint.

Jointing. The cables are set up correctly on the supports and lined up with the concrete base of the pit, the centre of the concrete base fixing the centre line of the joint which is marked off on both cables.

Both cables are now placed on the jointing trestles and the centre marks brought into line. The correct amount of outer sheath to be removed is marked off on both cables from the centre line, the outer sheaths and reinforcing tapes being removed. The cables should now be lifted up on the trestles so that the ends are pointing upwards at an angle no less than 30 degs. to the horizontal, a basting pan being placed under the ends to catch any oil which emerges from the cables when cut.

Again, before cutting, the oil engineer will make sure that all oil connections are in order as in the case of the stop joint. The ends are now cut through at the centre line in each case, the oil ducts cleaned out and the hollow steel pin inserted in both hollow conductors, making certain that all air is ejected from the pins.

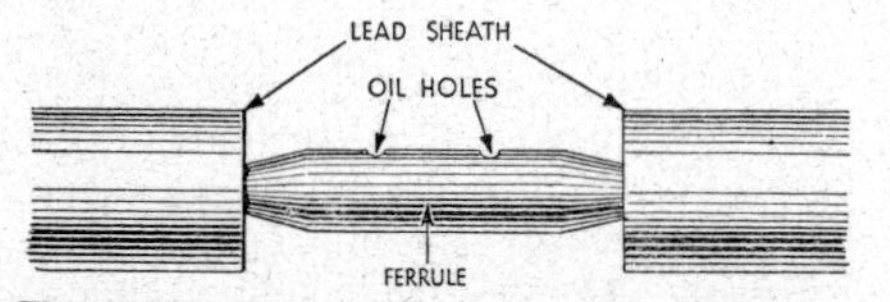

Fig. 66. Ferrule fitted and ready for removal of first sections of lead sheath and final insulation.

The end bells of the copper sleeve are placed on the cables and the sleeve slipped along one cable, paper having been first wrapped round the cable to prevent dust entering the sleeve. The inner sheath is cut off each end equal to the distance of one-half of the ferrule as measured from the head of the steel pin. Paper insulation is removed to accommodate the ferrule, a wire binder being placed round each conductor to prevent the strands from splaying out.

The ferrule is now fitted over one conductor and the wire binder removed. Both cables are now lowered and the conductor without the ferrule is inserted into the ferrule on the other conductor, making sure that the two small holes are uppermost, and that oil is flowing freely from them. The phosphor-bronze rings are placed over the tapered ends of the ferrule, and a silk binder wound round the ferrule to check the flow of oil.

The hydraulic press is set up and pressure applied to compress the ferrule and conductors on to the steel pins. This operation satisfactorily completed the press is removed, all edges left by the press dies are carefully filed off, and the phosphor-bronze rings are brought up to fit over the grooves where pressure was

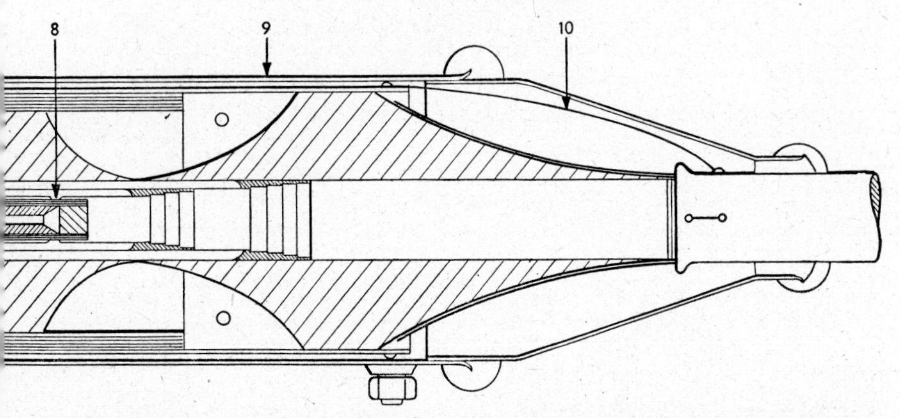

pplied. Fig. 66 shows the ferrule fitted.

Insulating the Joint. When insulating he joint the inner sheath of each cable is emoved in three stages, corresponding engths on each cable being removed at he same time. The first section of sheath s cut off and the insulation correctly tepped down, then basted with oil at 30° F. Silk tape is applied over the tepped insulation and built up to the argest diameter exposed, then two layers re applied over the remainder of the xposed insulation and ferrule.

The second section of sheath is emoved, the insulation stepped down, nd silk tape applied as previously, after- vards basting. The cavities at the ends of he ferrule are built up with narrow paper ape in order that a uniform surface be rovided for the paper tube insulation see Fig. 67).

The first paper tube is applied by otating the tube round the core, it being ocated central to the ferrule. The tube is ghtened by gripping it with a strip of lean glass paper and applying a steady otary pressure until all superfluous oil is queezed out, the ends of the tube are hen chamfered and the cavities filled with paper tape to the diameter of the tube, the whole then being basted.

A second paper tube longer than the previous one is now put on, being wound in the same direction as the first, the ends chamfered, cavities made good with paper tape and basted as previously; Fig. 68 shows the second tube applied.

Five more paper tubes of different lengths are applied, the longest first and in the same direction as the previous tubes, the whole being basted.

The third section of sheath is removed from each cable the ends of the sheath being belled out. Over the insulation exposed by the removal of the sheath from each cable six paper tubes of different lengths are applied, the longest first, and each tube in its correct position. Fig. 69 shows the paper tubes in position. The whole of the stepped paper tube insulation is chamfered as in Fig. 70.

Stress controls are fitted in the same manner as those on the stop joint. Two further paper tubes are now applied over the centre portion of the chamfered paper tube insulation, and to the same diameter as the insulation at the ends of the joint. Fig. 71 shows the insulation completed.

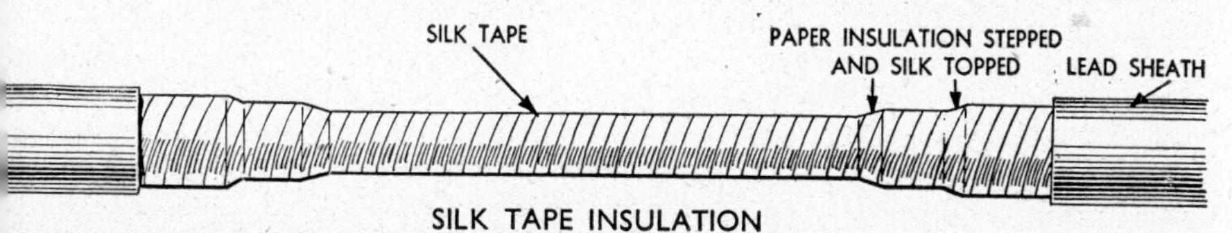

g. 67. Showing the silk tape insulation to provide uniform surface for the tube ends. End cavities f the ferrules are built up with narrow paper tape. The first paper tube can now be put on.

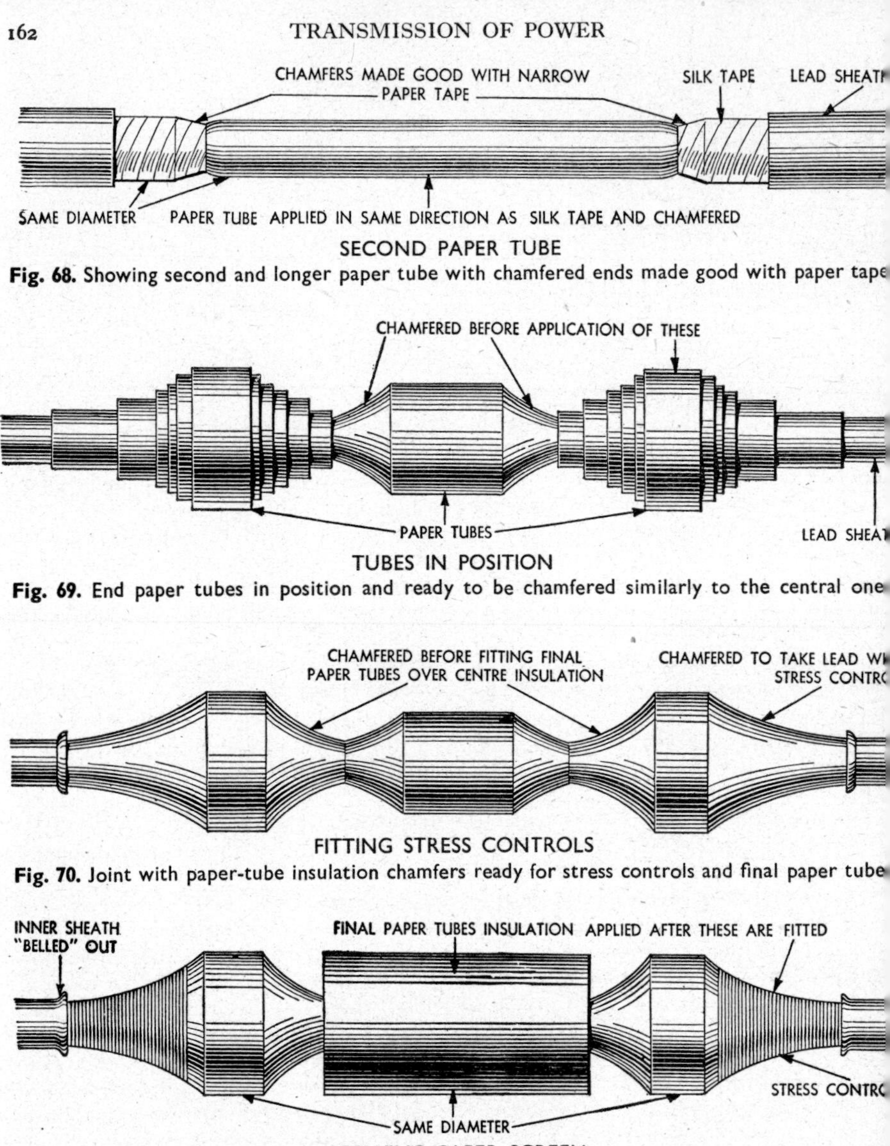

Fig. 68. Showing second and longer paper tube with chamfered ends made good with paper tape

Fig. 69. End paper tubes in position and ready to be chamfered similarly to the central one

Fig. 70. Joint with paper-tube insulation chamfers ready for stress controls and final paper tube

Fig. 71. Showing the joint ready for the application of the paper screen which completes insulatio

The whole insulation is now finally basted, and the copper screen after being first washed in oil, is fitted, with its joint 45 degs. from the vertical, and is bonded by soldering the copper braids on to the inner sheath.

The copper sleeve and end bells are brought up into position and correctly aligned, the end bells then being wiped on. The outer lead sheath and reinforcin tape are made off and plumbed, an tinned copper wire reinforcing applie over the inner sheath as on the stop join

After the joint has been impregnated is taped over with hessian tape an painted with hot black compound. Fig. shows three straight-through joints.

When connecting cables to tran

ɔrmers and switchgear the connection is sually made in what is known as a "cable ıd box" or "dividing box", this is a ıst-iron box attached to the connecting oint on the equipment, the cable entry eing usually through a brass socket or wiping gland" which is wiped on to the ıble sheath, the armour being bonded on the wiping gland above the wiped int by means of a clamp. The connecons are then made inside the box, which, hen completed, is filled with compound. ividing boxes of special types are used ı E.H.T. overhead transmission systems ıd in unit form for L.T. distribution.

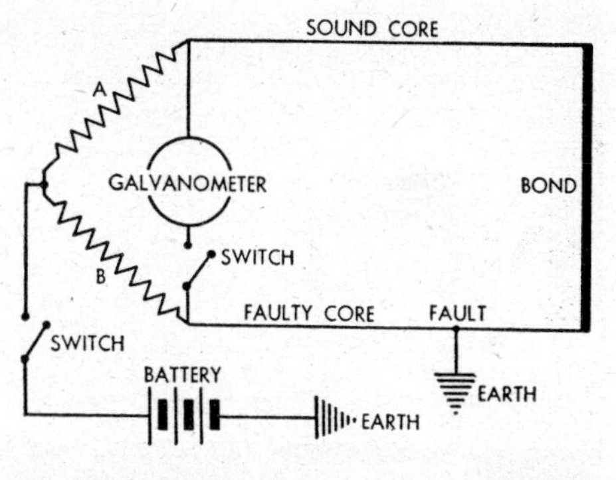

Fig. 73. Circuit illustrating the Murray loop test for locating short circuits to earth in a cable.

TESTING AND OPERATION

On completion of the installation of a ıble, the resistance of the insulation is sted with a "Megger" tester and then voltage, considerably higher than ɔrmal, is applied for some time in order detect any weaknesses.

Properly constructed and installed ıbles can be counted on to give reliable rvice; they are not subjected to the fects of lightning or storms to the tent that overhead lines suffer. If ults do occur they are not usually so ısy to locate as on an overhead system. o avoid unnecessary excavating there e various methods of testing to find the act spot where the trouble lies. If a conductor is short circuiting to earth the point may be determined by means of a test which is based on the original Murray loop test which is illustrated in Fig. 73. Two variable resistances A and B are connected across two cores of the cable which at the far end are bonded together by a low resistance connection piece. The galvanometer and battery are coupled as shown in the diagram. The arrangement forms a Wheatstone bridge, A and B, the ratio arms, being adjusted until they balance the two resistances formed by the two lengths of cable, one on either side of the fault. Balance is obtained when the galvanometer pointer shows no deflection when the circuit is made. If L is total effective length of route the distance of fault from the testing point is:—

$$\frac{BL}{A + B}$$

Much research has been devoted to the study of cable insulating materials and methods of applying them with the result that the modern cable is a first-class engineering production.

TYPICAL STRAIGHT JOINTS

g. 72. Three typical straight joints completed. Many of their details of ıtallation are similar to the stop joints which are illustrated in Fig. 64.

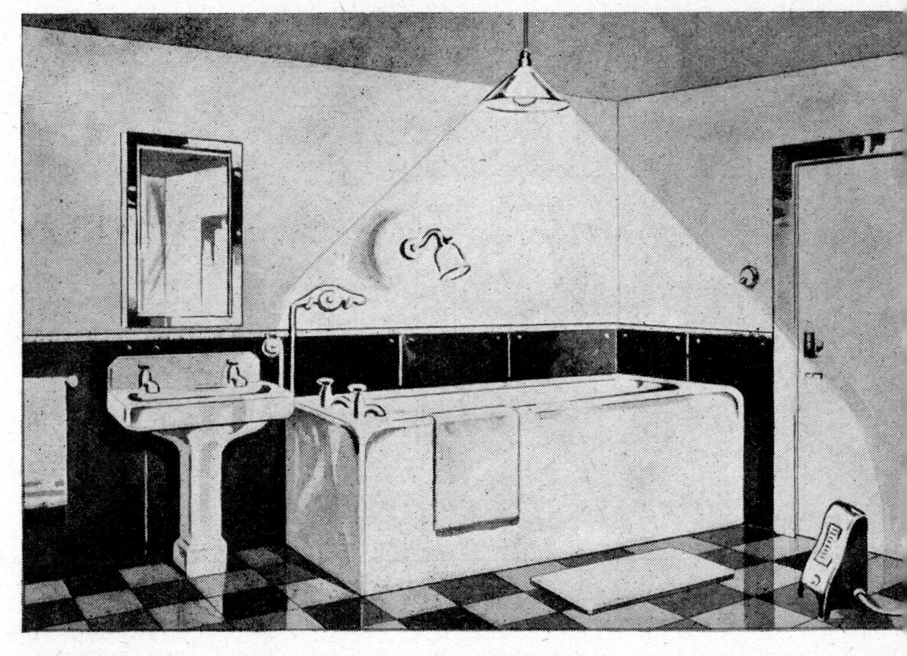

LAYOUT OF A BATHROOM

Fig. 1 (above). Incorrect placing of radiator, switches, etc., and **Fig. 2** (below) the correct metho

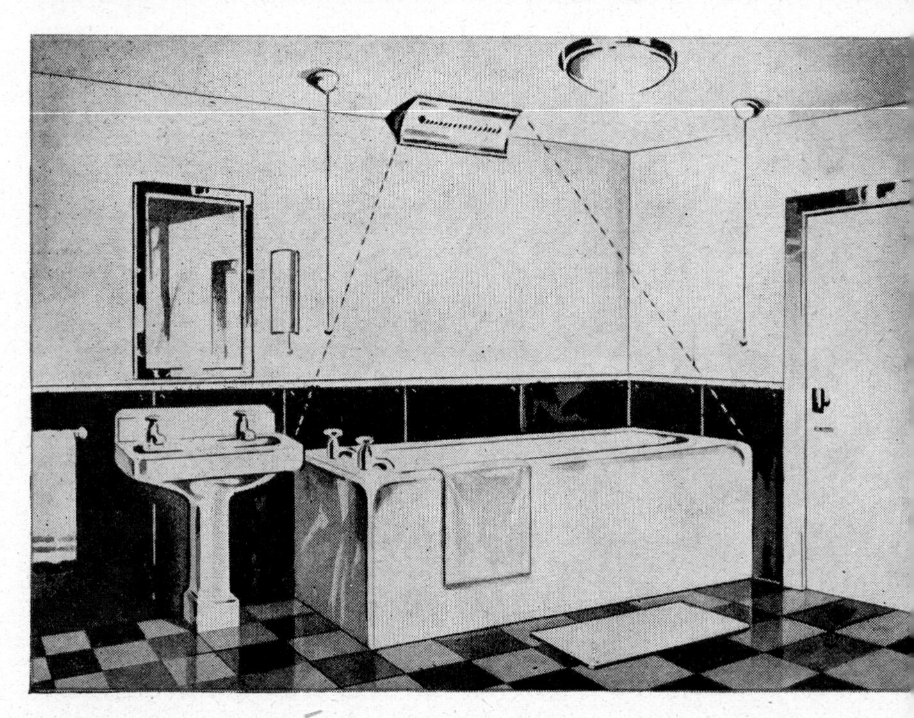

CHAPTER 5

INSTALLATION WORK

Electrical Installations. Mechanical Protection. Layout Requirements. Heating Appliances. Planning Schemes. Metal-Clad Systems. Light-Gauge Conduit Systems. Cleat Wiring. Joints and Jointing. Solders and Soldering. Lead-Covered Wiring Systems. Insulated Wiring Systems. Under-Floor Duct Systems. Erection of Equipment. Erection of External Overhead Lines. Switches and Switching. Fault Localisation and Testing. Subdividing Circuits. Intermittent Faults.

IT is obviously impossible within the scope of this work to treat adequately all the many processes of electrical wiring, switching, fitting and testing, or to describe the endless calls made upon the ingenuity of the electrical operative in connection with his work under the widely differing conditions met in modern buildings. The electrician's skill is daily exhibited in the small domestic installation as well as in the modern factory or public building; the proper connection of a wall socket and plug may be of equal importance from the safety point of view as the installation and connection of complicated industrial equipment (Figs. 1 and 2).

Regulation No. 1 of the I.E.E. Wiring Regulations states: "Good workmanship is an essential requirement for compliance with these Regulations." Without good workmanship all else is valueless; the skilled wireman or fitter will make a safer job with inferior material than the incompetent and half-trained will do with the very best equipment that can be obtained. More than mere hand skill is to-day demanded from the electrical operative; the widespread use of A.C. supplies requires complete knowledge of regulations, and, more important even, of the principles underlying them.

The practical points and hints dealt with in this section are designed to assist the practical electrician to appreciate the fundamental principles of good practice, leaving him to apply these principles to the different types of installations upon which he will be employed.

ELECTRICAL INSTALLATIONS

THE layout of an installation suitable for industrial or business purposes will be described as illustrative of the points it is wished to emphasise. For work of this class, screwed conduit is the only suitable system because it must provide the following requirements:—

(1) Complete protection from fire risk, shock and mechanical damage, and,

(2) Permanence, coupled with the necessary facilities for inspection and replacement of conductors, without undue disturbance to the installation after it has once been completed.

A screwed conduit system when installed properly will answer all these requirements, but, in the first place, much forethought must be given to planning. This is a long term policy which must decide beforehand how the installation shall give the greatest convenience, with a view to providing facilities for easy extension at a later date.

MECHANICAL PROTECTION

This is secured adequately by a screwed conduit system, because all joints can be made efficiently, and the conduit is robust and able to withstand great mechanical strain. It must be seen, however, that some system of assembly must be adopted which will provide a means for easy wiring when the conduit is installed. Many types of junction boxes are available for the various requirements met with, also backing-off boxes for all types of accessories.

The important point to note here is that continuous protection is necessary over all parts of the installation, and that no part, however small, is without some form of conduit or box protection. Incidentally, the above system automatically gives protection from fire, can be made watertight, and gives "continuity", which is the basis of efficient protection from shock. This protection is secured by "bonding" the conduit to earth by connecting a strong copper clamp to some part of the main system and running a cable to a main cold water supply pipe. As all conduits or exposed metal work are liable to become live, they form an electrically and mechanically continuous sheathing throughout the whole system, protection is secured because the system must remain at "zero" potential. Therefore, even if leakages exist, providing that the system is in order, leakage current is conveyed to earth in safety. As "continuity and bonding" are of supreme importance, a special part of the Electricity Regulations is devoted to the subject. In brief, it specifies that the overall resistance of an earthing and earth conductor system may not exceed one ohm, and that periodic tests should be taken to maintain it in that state.

GENERAL LAY-OUT

While no two installations can be identical, the foregoing will give a guide to the principles involved. Object to be obtained is:—

(1) General control of the main supply system to secure safety with regard to the heaviest current carried,

(2) Distribution to a number of localised feeding points, by means of cables which will carry the load without undue drop in supply pressure, and,

(3) Sub-division into final circuits of not more than ten points, so that possible faults may be confined to a small area, and not interfere with the installation as a whole, and also to allow of feeding wire of smaller section to be used in the actua wiring of the circuits.

These points (shown diagrammaticall in Fig. 3) are secured by:—

(1) An efficient main control switc and fuses, capable of handling the entir load carried, must be placed within thre feet of the supply company's servic cable.

(2) An adjacent main distributio board from which radiate suitable dis tributing cables to the localised distribu tion boards in various parts of th building. The cables will be of fair heavy cross section and the points a which they terminate must be decided b the conditions met with. Experienc proves that, generally, economy is be secured by termination about the centr of the area served, as it reduces th amount of smaller wiring required an gives more even voltage drop, and,

(3) Local distribution boards with th required number of fuse-ways; fuse generally, at five amperes and loaded to maximum of three amperes, or not greate than ten lighting points (whichever ma apply). From these distribution board radiate the circuits to the actual points.

LARGE INSTALLATIONS

In installations where the deman exceeds 20 kilowatts, it is sometim required that the supply be taken a 3-phase A.C. or 3-wire D.C. accordin to circumstances. This ruling is laid dow by supply authorities in order to enabl them to balance the demand on the supply cables. The installation then mu be divided into two or three sections, eac section taking an approximately equ load. As it is possible to obtain voltag from various parts of such systems co siderably in excess of the normal lightin supply voltage (approximately double the following precautions must b observed:—

Main switches and distribution boar must be at least six feet apart. Lightin points and small power consumin devices fed from different sides of th supply system may not be brought in the same room, office or workshop, but in the case of very large places they may exist together, providing the distance apart and lay-out of installation absolutely precludes the possibility of accidental inter-connection. This applies particularly to the range covered by appliances using flexible "wandering" leads. In the case of large spaces, such as multiple stores and large workshops, it is very convenient to be able to introduce alternative sources of supply to safeguard against possible failure, but it can be seen that extreme care and forethought is needed in the planning of such an installation, to secure the safety of personnel who cannot be expected to know anything about the numerous problems which are involved.

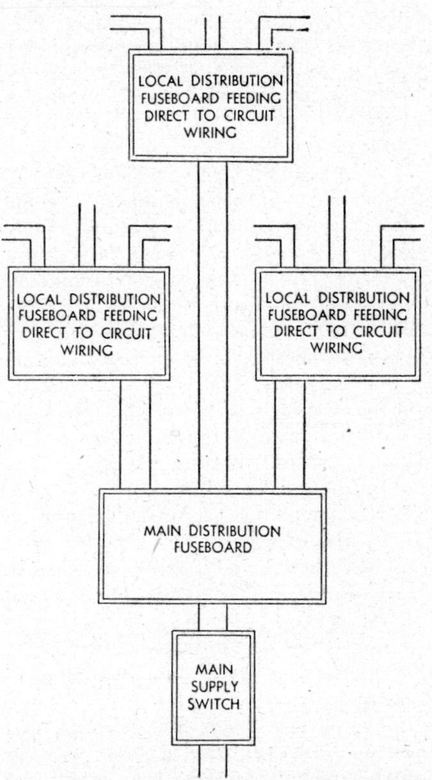

Fig. 3. Simple diagrammatic layout showing systematic distribution of supply to feeding points. The main board must be capable of handling the total load of the whole system.

HEATING AND SMALL POWER

Heating appliances may under no circumstances be connected to the lighting system, and no small power device exceeding 100 watts consumption is allowed either. It is, therefore, necessary to provide an entirely separate system to supply these devices.

Currents carried are very much heavier and it must be quite obvious cables of much heavier section are required, and the mechanical construction of switches, plugs and fuseboards, etc. must be more robust. General lay-out of the main distribution scheme is much the same, except that main switches, fuseboards and cables must be capable of carrying very heavy currents, consistent with the total possible maximum load. Final circuits from the local fuseboards must consist of cables not less than 7/029 gauge, wired with only one plug to each circuit, and terminated in a three-pin fifteen-ampere switch-plug, the third pin being bonded to the conduit system and providing an earth connection (generally terminating in a connection to a cold water pipe) which is attached to the frame of the apparatus by means of a three-way flexible cord as shown in Fig. 4.

Fixed heating apparatus of greater capacity than this must be supplied by a separate circuit, specially adapted to the required load. Cables entering hot enclosures must be covered with asbestos or porcelain beads for at least 12 ins. from the hot terminals.

Smaller consuming devices are provided for by "Utility Plugs" capable of supplying 1,000 watts, fitted with a five-ampere type three-pin switch-plug. These must be wired separately and controlled by five-ampere fuses, two plugs being allowed to each circuit, and wired with 3/036 cable.

Large electric cookers and water heaters are treated as separate circuits, specially wired and controlled with due regard to the maximum load, and frequently special arrangements have to be made for separate metering. No attempt should be made to supply these from a plug point, but wiring must enter the apparatus directly, completely covered with flexible metallic tubing, or other durable protection. Frames of apparatus must be efficiently earthed.

ILLUMINATION SCHEMES

Brief mention will be made of some important points to be considered. Electrical illumination is adaptable and flexible, also amenable to instant control. Full advantage must be taken of these facts, if full benefit is to be derived from them. Switches must be placed at points of convenience. The value of instantaneous illumination is lost if a room has to be crossed in darkness to reach the switch position. Rooms having alternative entrances should be provided with two-way switching. Stairs and corridors can be provided with two, three or even four-way switching control, and delay-action switches can be obtained, which can be set to operate for a period of seconds to allow for passage through a corridor, landing, etc., then switching off automatically.

In installations such as large shops, it is most convenient for general lighting switches to be grouped at one point, but subsidiary lighting subject to local control, should be provided for separate use for caretakers and staff to operate when the general scheme is shut down for the night. In all cases where failure of lighting would cause extreme inconvenience or confusion, alternative lighting should be provided from a separate distribution board or, better still, an independent system. Automatically controlled systems which run from batteries are available on the market, these are suitable for hospitals, banks, etc. They come into operation immediately main current fails. Every location should be provided with both general and localised lighting.

Even in a well planned installation where the lighting intensity is high, it is found necessary to augment this by local lighting for close or intricate work, but in cases where localised lighting of a high value is employed, such as work-bench,

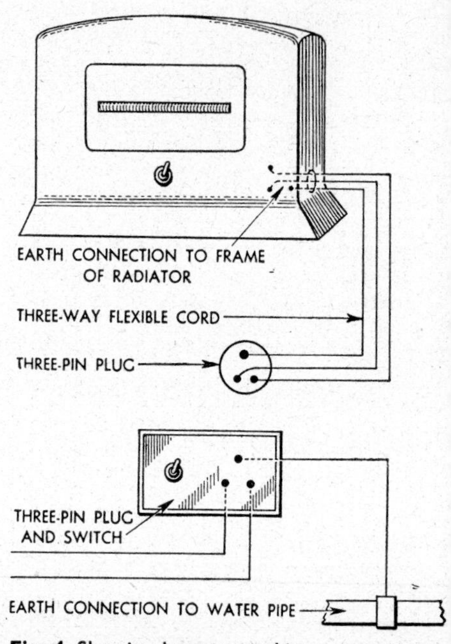

Fig. 4. Showing how an earthing connection is carried from frame of radiator to plug by means of three-way flexible cord and 3-pin plug head.

desk or drawing table, it is important that a fairly high standard of general illumination is maintained also, otherwise there will be a sharp transition from light to shadow which causes severe eyestrain. For further information on this subject see Chapter 7 (section entitled "Electric Lamps and Lighting").

DOMESTIC INSTALLATIONS

Domestic installations are much simpler than industrial ones owing to the smaller number of lighting and power points involved, but they have their own particular problems. Foremost of these are:—Necessity of concealing wiring, or at least rendering it inconspicuous; minimum disturbance to existing decorations and structure of the building.

As the employment of screwed conduits involves much cutting and making good in finished houses, lighter systems of wiring have been developed, chief of which are:—Lead-covered wiring and tough-rubber-sheathed cables. These are completely reliable if installed in the manner intended by their manufacturers, that is to say, with all the complete accessories for continuity and protection.

As electric wiring is dealt with later on in this Chapter, it is only intended to mention certain points about general safety in the home. Chance of electric shock in a well planned installation is very small, but there are risks in certain situations, and, owing to the fact that human actions cannot be controlled by regulations, every attempt is made to minimise the risks by insisting on rigid adherence to certain carefully planned lay-outs, which are designed to remove those risks as far as is humanly possible.

Bathrooms can be mentioned as an ideal example of this. Owing to the presence of water, steam and earthed metal-work in the form of taps, basin and bath, and also that the body when immersed provides excellent contact with earth, the following precautions are taken to avoid non-contact:—Ceiling lights must be at a height exceeding eight feet, provided with a Home Office type insulated and skirted holder, pendant cord of tough flexible rubber or, as an alternative, a totally enclosed fixture mounted directly on the ceiling. Lighting control switch fitted in a position impossible to reach from the bath (Fig. 2) or, if not feasible, controlled by switch mounted on ceiling with mechanical pull cord. Electric fires must be permanently fixed, not portable, at a distance beyond reach of a person in the bath. A good alternative is provided by fixing a reflector type radiator at eight feet above floor level focused downwards, controlled by ceiling switch with pull cord. All exposed metal work including bath must be bonded to earth by means of heavy copper conductors.

SAFETY PRECAUTIONS

No utility five-ampere plug is allowed to be installed in a bathroom to which any portable apparatus can be attached, such as hair-driers, additional lights or portable fire (Fig. 1). Presence of steam is conducive to rapid corrosion of electrical connections. Highly ornamental bracket fixtures wired with flexible cord are prohibited unless they can be adapted to comply with regulations as for ceiling fittings.

To sum up, it should be noted that special precautions are taken in places having hygroscopic flooring, such as concrete or tiles, etc. A general rule to follow is that all apparatus must be enclosed in a metal protective covering and earthed, or if this is not feasible, it must be totally enshrouded in some form of highly insulating material, and arranged so that it is impossible for accidental contact to be made with live points.

THE ERECTION OF WIRING SYSTEMS

STEEL and copper conduits, lead and copper-sheathed cables, have been the most popular methods of installing electrical conductors in the past, and the former has almost reached the status of a national institution. A high grade of workmanship is required to produce a sound and efficient system with heavy gauge screwed-steel conduits, whilst scarcely less in the case of the light gauge conduits; on the other hand, the ease of installation associated with lead-covered cables has led to their indiscriminate use, but experience has now shown that this system, in particular, requires careful and expert installation if a safe and reliable job is to result.

The rules for efficient installation of metal-clad wiring systems are few, and might be condensed into two main requirements:—the necessity to preserve the protective covering of the conduit as far as possible, and the ensuring of complete and certain continuity throughout the whole installation. Without these simple precautions metal-clad systems may represent a menace rather than a protection, and the following paragraphs are mainly concerned with these points. Screwed steel conduits are formed from heavy gauge mild-steel tubes, varying in thickness from ·06 to ·064 in. in the $\frac{5}{8}$ in. tube, to ·088 in. in the $2\frac{1}{2}$ in. tube. Steel conduits are measured externally, as distinct from gas and water pipes, which are graded on their internal diameters. The tubes are connected to fittings and their various accessories by means of screw threads cut on the tubes by means of fixed dies, the number of threads varying from 18 to the inch in the case of the $\frac{5}{8}$ in. tube to 14 threads to the inch on the $2\frac{1}{2}$ in. tube; these threads are finer than the standard gas and water tube threads, and the walls of steel conduits are much thinner than equivalent sizes of iron pipes.

The highest grade of steel conduit is known as solid-drawn, and is used only on the highest class of work; the most popular grade is known as welded, and is made up from strip steel, with the butt joint welded. There is another grade, also constructed from strip steel, but the joint is brazed; some engineers prefer this, but it is true to say that the great majority of screwed-steel conduit installations are carried out with welded tubes. Provided that care is taken during the threading process not to "spring" the welded joint, perfectly satisfactory work can be done with this grade of conduit. Finishes vary from black enamel to high-grade galvanising or sherardising, these latter being used in exposed or wet situations.

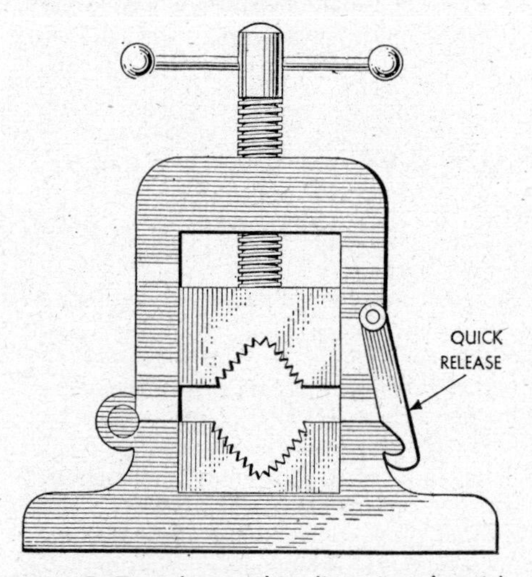

Fig. 5. Typical pipe threading vice. A quick release ratchet is fitted to facilitate the handling of very long tubes and permit their quick removal with having to draw them right through.

CUTTING

Screwed steel tubes are usually cut by means of a hack-saw, whilst firmly fixed in a pipe vice. The most convenient form of vice is shown in Fig. 5, and it will be noted that this has a quick release action whereby a long length of tube may be quickly removed from the vice without having to be drawn through it for the whole length. The use of pipe cutters, as employed for water and gas pipes, is not possible, as these produce a bad cut on the lighter conduits, which requires considerable time and labour to clear. In emergency, a file may be used to cut a channel round the conduit, care being taken to keep this at right angles to the tube's axis; when this cut is sufficiently deep the tube may be broken off at the point of cutting.

The hack-saw, however, provides the most suitable means of cutting, but the cut must be kept straight, or difficulty in threading will arise by reason of the crooked end of the tube.

THREADING

This most important operation requires considerable care if the joint is to be efficient and sound. The first requirement is that the tube shall be firmly fixed in the vice; if pressure is too heavy the thin tube will be flattened, whilst if it is too light the tube will tend to turn under the action of the rotating die and a very unsightly burr will result. A vice with badly worn teeth that will not grip the tube without excessive pressure should be scrapped, as it will waste more time in repairing damage to the tubes than it is worth. After threading, a tube should leave the vice with no more marking on the external finish than the slight cuts due to the vice jaws; unsightly burrs extending round the tube indicate either a worn-out vice or careless workmanship. With the tube fixed in the vice, the cut end may now be prepared for threading. The first operation is to remove any burr left from cutting, but it should not be necessary to file down the whole end of the tube for a distance of an inch or so; the ordinary die, if in good condition, does not require this drastic preparation of the tube, however favoured it may be by water and gas fitters. The filing of the actual cut edge of the conduit to form a slope to the cutting edge of the die is all that is necessary.

Before threading actually commences some form of lubricant for the dies will be required; this may range from old engine oil to tallow, and the latter has advantages. This is smeared on the tube in generous quantities, and the application should be sufficient for the complete cutting of the thread; where long threads are necessary, as for "running joints", it may be advantageous to run the die off the thread and apply further lubricant.

CUTTING DIE

The cutting die is held in a stock of the correct size; one stock will usually accommodate several sizes of die, in the smaller sizes from $\frac{5}{8}$ in. to 1 in. In front of the die is fixed a guide, and under no circumstances should the die ever be applied to the tube without this guide in position. If any thread required is so short that the presence of the guide offers an obstacle to the completion of the thread, then the design of the joint is wrong, and should be altered. The function of the guide is to keep the die straight during the process of cutting, and without it a perfect thread can hardly

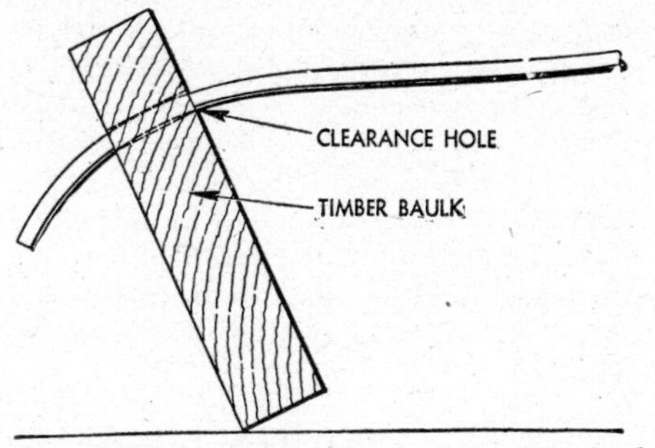

Fig. 7. Diagram showing correct method of bending conduit using a bending block.

result. Guides are marked with the sizes of die they are to accompany, and usually fit fairly closely over the outer surface of the conduit tube.

The guide is placed over the end of the tube and gradually pushed forward whilst the stock is rotated in a clock-wise direction; if the tube has been properly prepared the die will soon be felt to "bite" the tube, and from then on no forward urging is required from the mechanic. The die will take itself forward with the thread, and only the rotating motion is necessary to complete the operation.

LENGTH OF THREAD

A very common fault amongst operatives is the cutting of far too long a thread, with the result that when the joint is completed or the accessory attached there are several unused threads exposed beyond the socket. About 4 full threads are all that are necessary for a perfectly sound joint, and this enables the tube to be screwed tightly into its socket with all threads concealed. This is especially

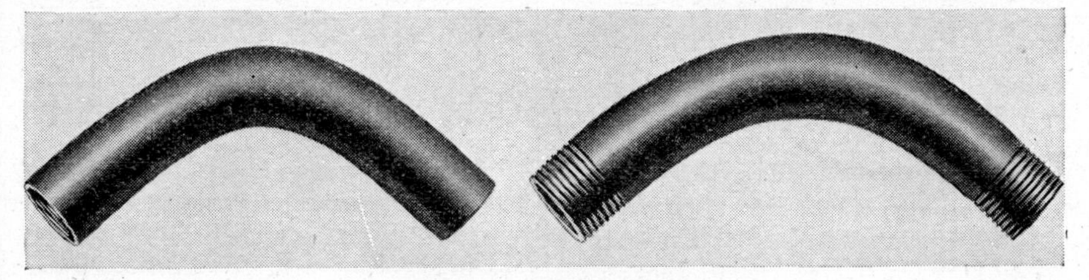

NORMAL CONDUIT BENDS

Fig. 6. Fittings which enable the run of conduits to be changed. The one on the left is internally threaded and the other externally threaded. For "easy" bends the conduit itself may be bent.

important with galvanised tubes, which are used in positions where damp and rusting may be expected; the exposed threads will invite trouble from rusting and the continuity of the system may be destroyed from this cause. The mark of a well-executed job is the absence of excess threading at all points and, as mentioned above, 4 complete threads will meet all normal requirements.

CLEARING THE DIE

These four complete turns having been decided upon, they should be taken without rotating the die back upon itself; go straight ahead for four turns, as with a properly designed die and guide, the metal cut from the threads should be easily cleared without taking the die backwards; on the other hand, reversing the rotation during the cutting of the thread may result in damaged threads due to the cuttings being forced into the threads; when the cut has been completed this risk may be obviated by giving the stock a sharp blow, when the cuttings held by the lubricant should fall out of the clearing spaces.

When the stock and die have been removed they should be given a slight blow

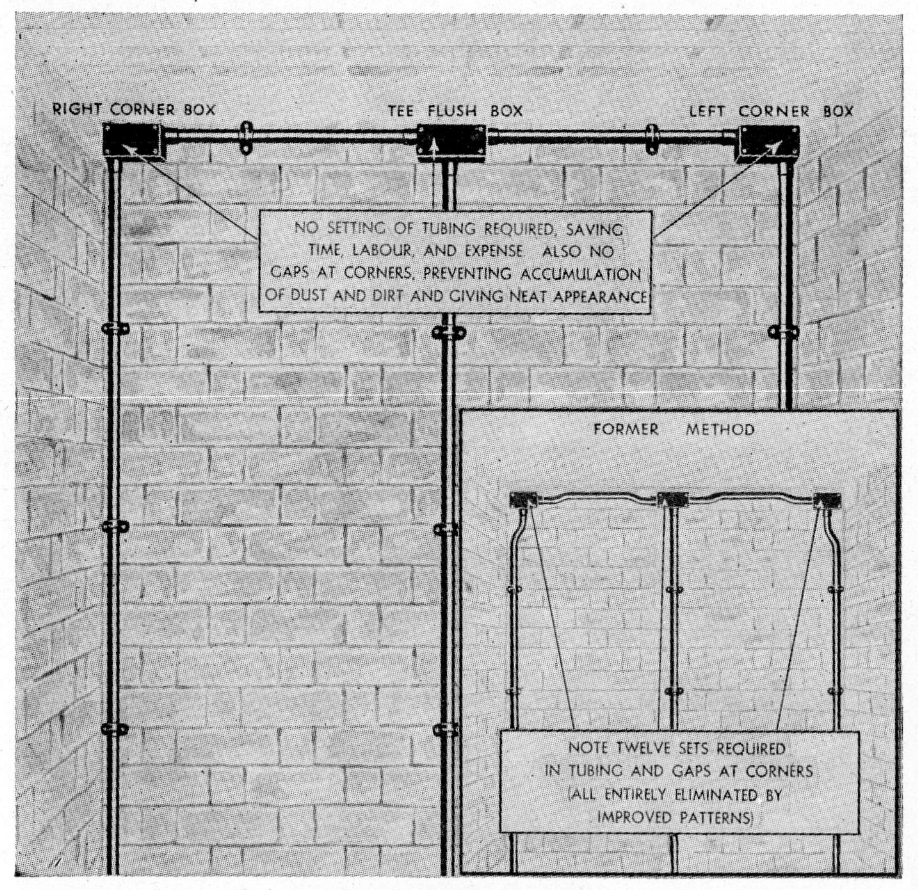

Fig. 8. Showing how the modern method of fixing suitable conduit fittings eliminates unnecessary bending and setting and contributes a neat appearance. Note the former method shown inset.

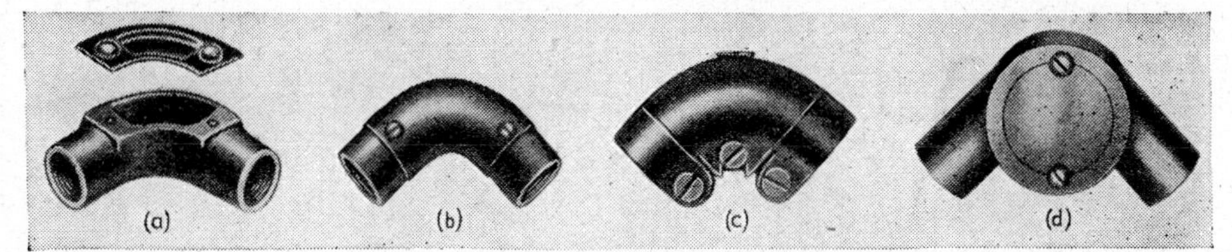

TYPICAL INSPECTION ELBOWS

Fig. 9. Screwed channel types of inspection elbows which permit conductors to be drawn in are shown at (a) and (b), while at (c) is a lug grip inspection elbow and at (d) a circular pattern.

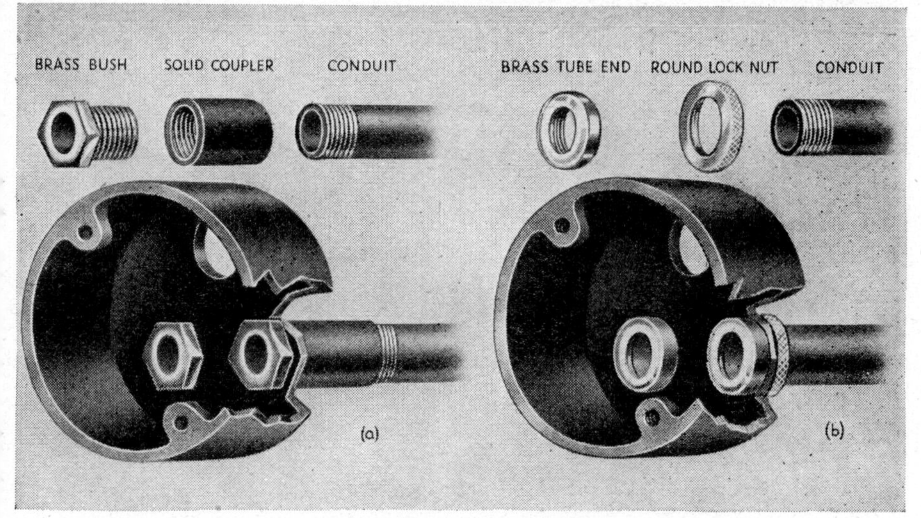

CONNECTING LOOP BOXES

Fig. 10. Method of connecting loop boxes with (a) tapped holes using brass bushes and (b) clearance holes using brass tube ends and round lock nuts to fix the conduit firmly in position.

against the bench for the purpose of removing any metal still adhering in the cutters, and which might damage a subsequent thread. The new thread is then wiped clean of lubricant and attention given to the inside of the tube; during cutting a small burr may have been formed, and this can be removed with the special reamer supplied by conduit makers. If this is not available, the tang of a large file may be used, or a small round file used actually to file clean the interior of the tube. After this has been done it is, of course, necessary to remove every trace of the filings which are adhering either to the interior or exterior of the conduit.

If a fitting is required to be screwed to this tube it should be done whilst the tube is still in the vice and undisturbed; if taken out and reclamped this will result in a fresh set of markings on the protective covering of the tube, usually enamel, and the risk of rusting at that point becomes likely. It must be remembered that one golden rule is the preservation of this protective coating. It is normally very efficient but it is easily damaged by mishandling. Incidentally, remember, an electrician's work will be judged by its appearance as well as its technical efficiency.

BENDING

When conduits are required to change direction of run, bends, as shown in Fig. 6, and screwed internally or externally, may be used; often changes of direction do not amount to a full 90 deg., however, and then the mild steel tube may itself be bent to the required angle. This may be safely accomplished by means of a "bending block", Fig. 7, which consists merely of a block of wood of sufficient

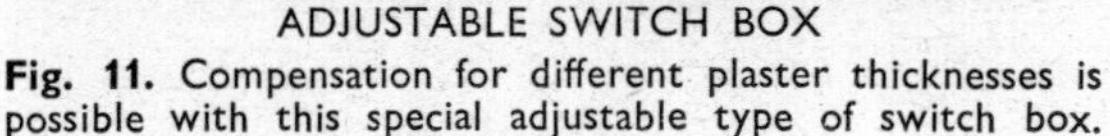
ADJUSTABLE SWITCH BOX

Fig. 11. Compensation for different plaster thicknesses is possible with this special adjustable type of switch box.

length to permit reasonable leverage on the tube, through which a clearance hole is bored. Tubes up to 1 in. diameter may be "set" by this means, the conduit being placed in the hole, a slight bend given, and followed by further slight angles as the tube is pushed further through the wood block. Where several sets on a multiple run of tubes are required to follow the same contour of the building a bending machine is advisable, as this permits the production of many bends to exactly the same angle.

CONDUIT FITTINGS

With the judicious use of conduit fittings, however, a great deal of setting and bending work can be avoided, as shown in Fig. 8. On the other hand, in concealed work, the wide sweeps made possible by self-set angles makes for ease in the drawing-in of cables. Attempts should not be made to form very sharp sets on conduits, as this will almost invariably result in flattened tubes.

As the screwed steel conduit system is essentially a "draw-in" system, the regulations require that sections of tubing shall be made complete before cables are drawn into position. This means that all angles, tees, and other fittings must be of the "inspection" type, that is, fitted with covers to permit the drawing-in of the conductors after the conduits have been erected. These fittings are of two main types, channel and circular, as shown in Fig. 9; in addition, the standard B.S.I. box may be employed at all points, if required.

BUSHED CONDUIT JOINT

Switch, socket-outlet, and ceiling point boxes often require the making of a "bushed" conduit joint, and this may be formed in two ways. One, the end of the tube is threaded and fitted with a lock nut; this is passed through the clearance hole in the box and clamped tight by means of a brass ring bush, designed with a rounded edge to prevent damage to cables during the drawing-in process. Further grip on the iron box may be ensured by tightening the lock nut at the back. This method is illustrated in Fig. 10b which shows the separate items used as well as one conduit clamped in position.

An improved method is to use a

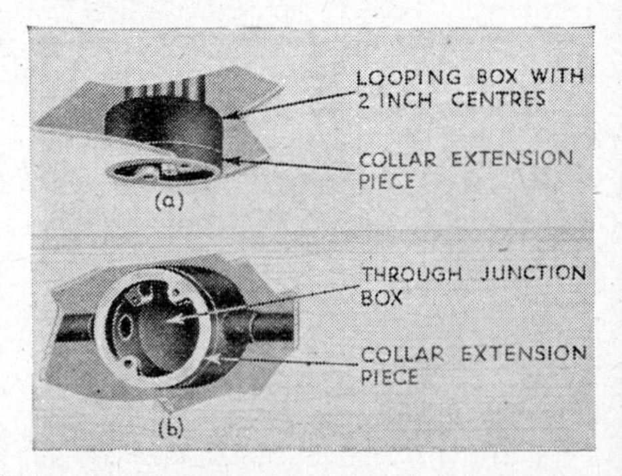

Fig. 12. Collar extensions for adjusting depth of looping box (a), and (b), through junction box.

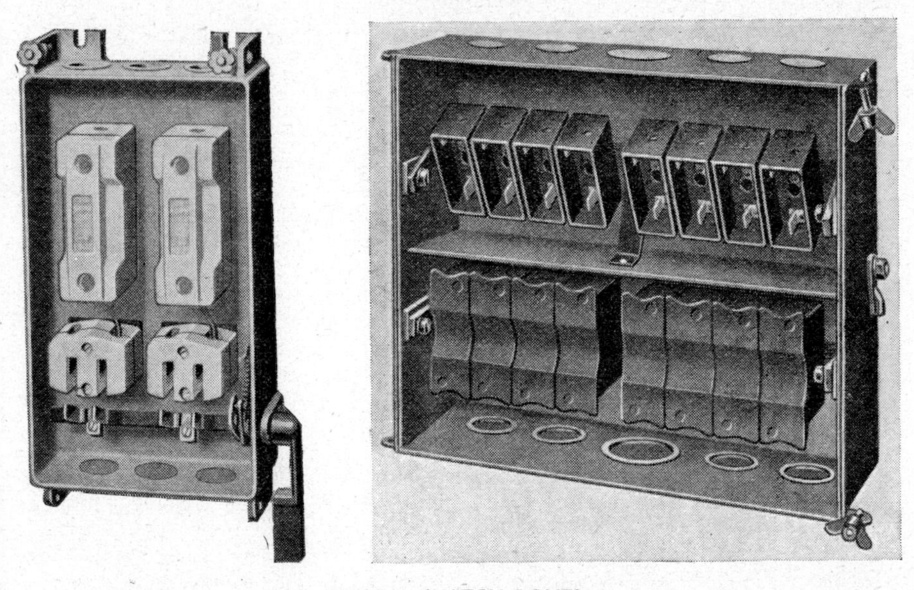

TYPICAL SWITCH BOXES

Fig. 13. On the left is a main switch box which has three "knock-outs" for conduit entry. On the right is shown a distribution board in which there are five "knock-outs".

socket behind the box, with an internal brass bush with hexagon flange fitted inside the box; this enables all necessary tightening to be carried out from the front of the fitting, by means of a box spanner, and is usually more convenient and certain. This method is illustrated in Fig. 10a.

To level up the mounting distance for flush switches, and to compensate for differing thicknesses of plaster, adjustable switch boxes are employed, one pattern being shown in Fig. 11. In the same way, the ceiling box may be built up to fill the space between mounting and plaster level by means of collar extensions, which are shown in Fig. 12. The fixing lugs in these boxes are placed at the standard distance of 2 in. centres, and will thus accommodate standard ceiling roses and other fittings.

Main switch fuses and distribution boards also employ the bushed type of conduit entry, Fig. 13, being filled by means of "knock-outs", which, as the name implies, may be knocked out as required; unwanted entries are left filled. The essential features of a good-class distribution board are given in this illustration which shows two types that are often used in modern installations.

FIXING

Concealed conduits are normally secured in position by means of saddles or crampets, and present no problem. For surface work, however, the popular "spacer-bar" saddle is used, illustrated in Fig. 14, which avoids the necessity for frequent setting of the conduit where it enters conduit fittings or accessories. The $\frac{1}{8}$ in. bar behind the saddle is the same depth as the base of the standard conduit fitting, so that tubes may be kept perfectly straight and run directly into the fittings, which back on the wall. A further advantage is that the tubes may be placed in position, and the saddles adjusted to take up for any slight deviation in the run.

Special girder clips enable runs across or along girders to be firmly held in position, see Fig. 15.

Now we come to light-gauge conduit systems which are also known as "grip-

Fig. 14. Showing method of fixing one-way spacer-bar saddle which is widely employed for surface conduit runs. They can be adjusted to take up slight deviations in conduit directions.

continuity" systems, owing to the fact that the tubes are joined to fittings, etc., by means of a grip, instead of a screwed thread. This permits the use of a lighter gauge steel tube, which although vulnerable to damage, provides a useful and cheap alternative to the more expensive screwed system.

The tubes are made up of strip steel, with open or brazed seam, the former being known as "close-joint", and enjoying considerable popularity. There are many types of grip fittings available for use with these light gauge tubes, some of which are illustrated in Fig. 16. The tube is cut by means of a file, a deep groove being made all round the tube, which may then be broken off at this point, and the sharp edge cleaned off. The protective enamel should *not* be cleaned off where the tube enters the fitting, or serious rusting will result; any efficient type of grip fitting will cut its own contact into the tube wall without this drastic treatment.

As in the case of heavy gauge screwed systems, light gauge tubes and fittings must be erected complete before any conductors are drawn into position. It therefore follows that only inspection type fittings are permissible with light gauge, or grip, conduit systems, if they are to comply with the regulations. The practice of erecting conduits simultaneously with the insertion of cables is definitely contrary to regulations, and should not be contemplated; with a system constructed in this manner the withdrawal of conductors is next to impossible, and repairs or extensions are rendered very difficult. Light gauge tubes are liable to damage from nails, etc., and if cables are in the tubes they are often damaged beyond repair; a nail penetrating an empty tube may be drawn out and the section of tube replaced without serious difficulty.

The erection and fixing of light gauge tubes follow very closely upon the methods already described for heavy gauge tubes, but they will not generally be found amenable to bending by means of blocks or other methods. Slight sets may be formed, if of wide radius, but otherwise serious flattening of the tube, with opening of the seam, will result.

DRAWING IN CABLES

The numbers and sizes of cables that may be safely drawn into screwed steel conduits are set out in Table 18 of the I.E.E. Wiring Regulations, and in general these allowances should not be exceeded. Much depends upon the distance between draw-in points, and it will be noted that the regulations recognise this; where distances between such points are likely to be long, advantage should be taken of inspection couplers, shown in Fig. 17, especially at points where the conduit changes direction.

Where distances between draw boxes are short, the cables may often be pushed in by hand; longer runs may necessitate the use of a steel spring passed through the conduit between draw boxes, the cables being bound to the end of this spring and drawn in after it. With intricate runs, containing several bends, it is good practice to leave a small galvanised steel wire in the conduits during erection, and this is later used as a means of drawing the conductors into the conduits.

Cables should never need the application of french chalk, or other evidences of bad conduit design, in order to get them into the conduits. With an adequate number of draw boxes, properly placed, the cables should go in with ease, although in hot weather cable braiding is liable to get sticky and may need the application of chalk. Far too often this material is used to force more cables into a conduit than it should properly hold, and this can only lead to deterioration of the cable with early breakdown. In vertical runs, cables should be fed into the conduit from above, so that the weight of the cables assists the drawing in rather than otherwise; drawing cables *up* tubes means that the conductor has to be pulled against the force of gravity in addition to overcoming friction of the tube walls; the conductor will probably stretch and the rubber insulation be placed under tension, factors making for early breakdown.

Without adequate bonding and earthing steel tube systems become more of a menace than a safeguard against fire and shock. The I.E.E. Regulations devote considerable space and emphasis to this important point, and require that the resistance of any conduit run, measured from a point near the main switch to the furthest point in the installation, shall not exceed one ohm. In addition, the conduit joints must be sufficiently sound to carry heavy fault currents without overheating or deteriorating in any way.

EFFICIENT JOINTS

Provided that tubes are tightly screwed into the spouts of the various fittings and accessories, low conduit continuity resistances can be secured and maintained during the life of the installation. In cases where conduit resistances have been known to increase, the fault is almost invariably due to joints of the bushed type, by reason of imperfect cleaning of the faces in contact or negligence in tightening up lock nuts, brass bushes, etc. In all cases where bushed joints are employed it is essential that the greatest care be taken to ensure that the joint is adequate and permanent, or under conditions of damp and vibration the joint is bound to deteriorate. The result is that fault currents are restricted by the resistance offered, and fail to reach the magnitude necessary for the blowing of the circuit fuses or the opening of the overload circuit breaker; it follows that the whole conduit system becomes alive and remains so indefinitely. Many fires have had their origins traced back to inefficient conduit joints, and the Home Office records contain many instances of this neglect.

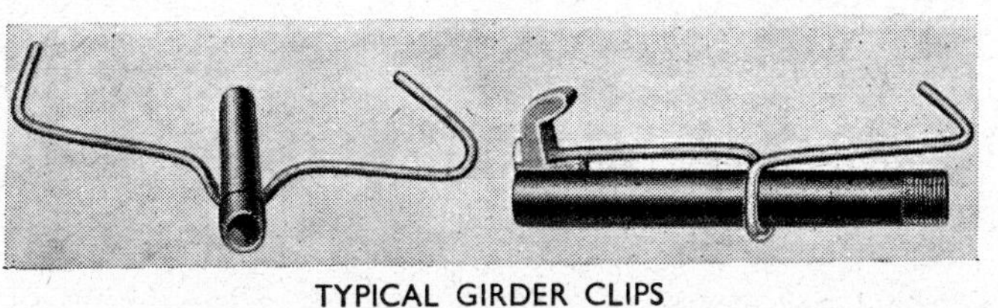

TYPICAL GIRDER CLIPS

Fig. 15. Left, typical girder clip for holding conduit in position along girders and, right, clip for conduit crossing a girder.

The whole of Section 10 of the I.E.E. Wiring Regulations should be carefully studied by all electrical operatives, as it is impossible to over-state the importance of adequate bonding and earthing. There are

LUG GRIP FITTINGS

Fig. 16. Lug grip inspection type conduit fittings for use with light gauge tubes, an inexpensive alternative to screwed conduit which is perfectly satisfactory for many purposes.

simple commercial instruments designed for the testing of conduit continuity, and there is no excuse whatever for neglect of this most important factor in the safety of all steel conduit installations.

The final earthing connection between the completed conduit installation and a suitable earthing electrode, usually a main water pipe, must be made by means of a copper conductor of adequate cross-sectional area for the heaviest fault currents likely to be encountered, and protected against mechanical damage and corrosion. The actual connection to the water pipe must be made by means of suitable earthing clips, typical examples of which are shown in Fig. 18, and on the incoming side of any stop cocks, water meters, or other apparatus associated with the water supply and which may have either red-leaded joints, or by their nature are liable to periodic disconnection for inspection or repair.

ADEQUATE BONDING

So important is this question of adequate bonding and earthing that if it is not possible to earth directly to a main water system in an urban district, then it is advisable to employ an insulated form of wiring system; this applies to metal under-floor duct systems and to lead and copper sheathed systems as well as to steel conduits. All metal-clad equipment or apparatus associated with the installation may, however, be adequately protected with

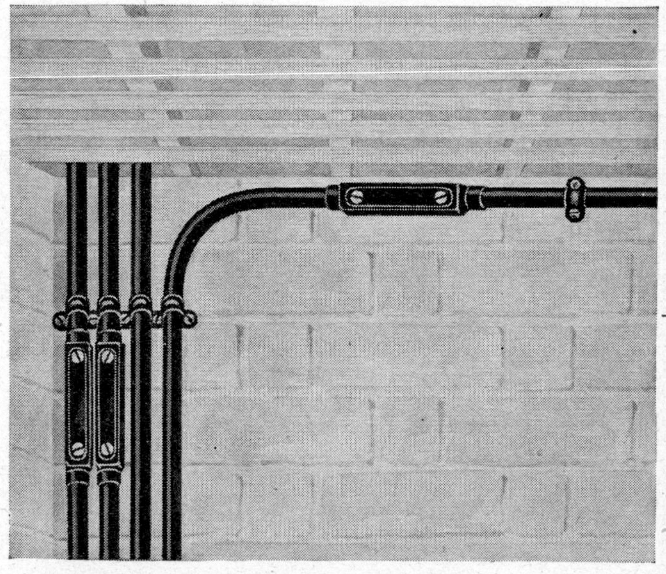

FITTINGS FOR LONG RUNS

Fig. 17. Inspection couplers with removable front covers facilitating the easing of cable round bends and long runs during drawing-in operations.

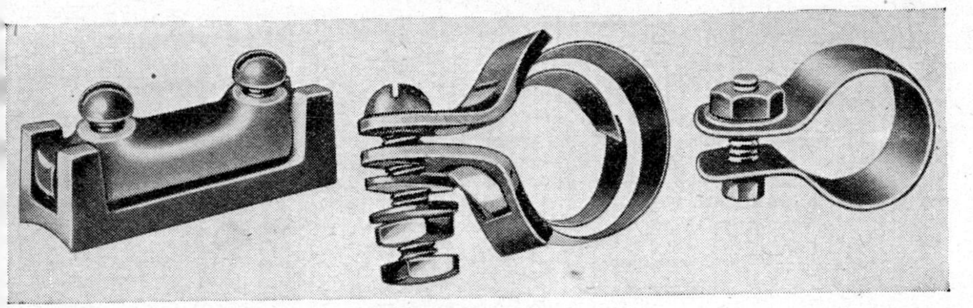

EARTHING CLIPS

Fig. 18. Typical examples of earthing clips, sockets, and clamps for use in making earth connections.

an assurance of safety by means of earth-leakage circuit breakers, as required under Section 10 of the I.E.E. Wiring Regulations. This matter is further dealt with under "Insulated Wiring Systems."

CLEAT WIRING

Cleat wiring consists of supporting bare V.I.R., or rubber-insulated and taped, cables on porcelain or wood cleats, these being spaced to suit conditions. Contrary to general opinion, cleat wiring is not simple to install, but demands a high standard of workmanship unless it is to look an untidy mess. Provided that care is taken in selecting runs which will naturally provide a certain amount of protection for the exposed cables, that runs are straight, and that sufficient tension is imparted to the conductors to prevent sag, then usually a cleat system will provide a useful, economical system, suited to most situations.

All installations, from the smallest to the largest, may be in part carried out by cleat wiring; it is utilised in farmhouses and farm buildings, with the types of cleats shown in Fig. 19. In mines, and similar installations, heavy cables are supported on cleats as shown in Fig. 20, whilst large numbers of heavy electricity supply feeders and distributors are carried in underground tunnels on cable racks, or multiple cleats, as in Fig. 21. The major problem in large installations is to find adequate fixings for the cleats carrying heavy cables, and this is often done by means of bolts grouted into walls and ceilings; mechanical means are sometimes employed to impart the necessary tension to the heavier cables, without which very unsightly installations result.

The use of junction boxes is to be deprecated in connection with cleat systems, as difficulties will be found in taking cables in or out, whilst at the same time keeping the run unobtrusive, and the cables tight. It is better to make all

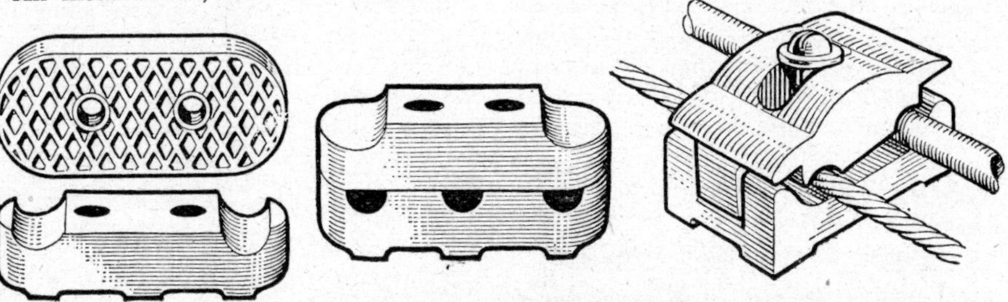

CLEATS FOR DOMESTIC WIRING

Fig. 19. Types of porcelain cleats as used for the smaller or domestic installations and in farms and farmhouses. Cleat wiring is not simple to install and demands skilled workmanship.

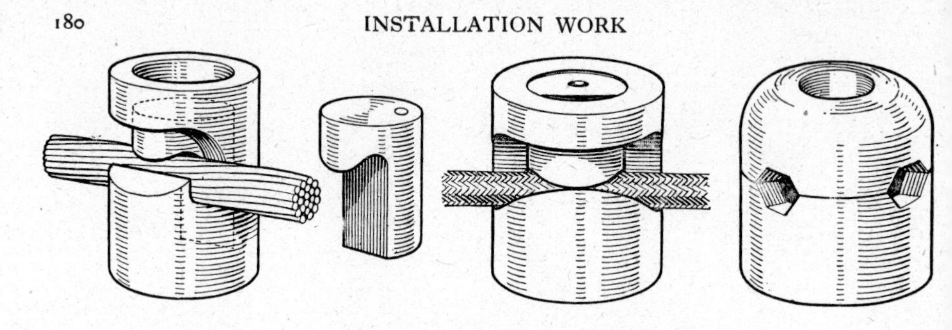

CLEATS FOR HEAVY CONDUCTORS

Fig. 20. Cleats used for heavy conductors carrying considerable currents such as in mine and similar installations. A special hard quality of porcelain is used in their manufacture.

junctions in the run between cleats, by means of simple tee joints, as described later. In damp situations no damage appears to accrue to cables by reason of water running down them, but every endeavour must be made to prevent moisture entering accessories. The liberal use of drip-loops, described elsewhere, provides the answer, and means that in running down to switches and sockets the cables are taken below the accessory, and bent upwards to make the necessary connections. The loops thus formed provide traps for moisture, which drips off at the lowest point. This precaution is equally important in runs down slanting roofs to ceiling roses; the loops should be placed a few inches from the ceiling rose, with equally effective results.

EARTHING CONDUCTORS

The provision of earthing conductors with cleat wiring is not easy, but in general bare conductors may be run in one groove of a line of cleats, or if these are all occupied, be supported under the screw holding the cleat. Cleats may be built up, one above the other, the top sections being held by the one set of screws passing through the whole bank of cleats, to provide extra accommodation for cables where required; multiple cleats of this type are made up of many bases, utilising one cover cleat only on the top.

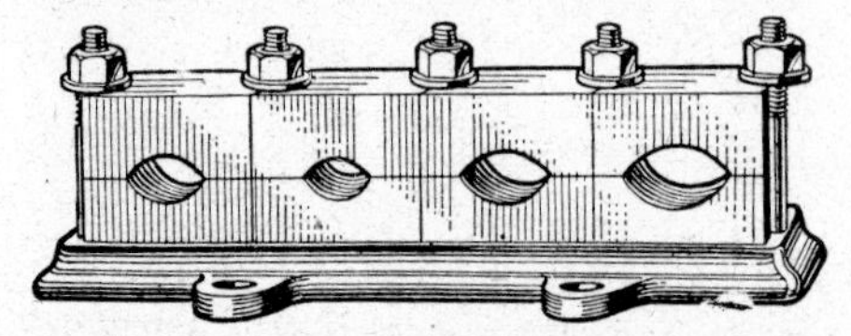

Fig. 21. Multiple cable rack or cleat to suit varying diameters of cable as used in tunnels.

It is important that the correct size of cleat be selected for the job, as if too large, effective grip on the cables will not be made, resulting in loss of tension and unsightly sagging; if too small, some risk of damage to the cable insulation will result. The packing of grooves, or the wrapping of cables, with black adhesive tape to secure tight fixings is ineffective, as sooner or later the cables will draw away through the tape.

JOINTS AND JOINTING

With concentration upon cleat wiring, consequent upon the issue of Emergency Wiring Regulations which in a large measure cover the employment of vulcanised india-rubber cables, the jointing of these cables takes on a fresh importance. It is usually more efficient and convenient to joint a V.I.R. cable in the run between cleats than to attempt the fixing and connection of a junction box for this purpose. The simpler types of joint, preparation of cables, and insulation are, therefore, briefly dealt with, together with simple joints for bell, alarm and telephone work.

To remove the taped insulation of the conductor, including the braid, if present in the system employed, a sharp knife is the best means. Care must be taken that the copper conductor is not nicked in the process, and the careful cutting of two rings round the cable insulation at the points of greatest extent of the joint will assist the removal of the rubber and tape in between. Joints should always be made as small as possible (it is surprising how much current may be safely carried by a well-soldered joint only half an inch in length) in order to ensure the conservation of solder and rubber insulation; all rubber removed has to be replaced later. The tape and/or braid should then be pared off for a short distance from the exposed rubber coating of the cable, as will be noted in the illustrations of typical joints.

In modern practice it is not considered essential to scrape the copper conductors thereby removing the tinned surface to expose the copper beneath. Cables usually strip very clean, and should any of the vulcanised rubber insulation still adhere to the conductor or conductors this may be easily removed by means of a rag soaked in petrol or benzine. It is essential that the tinned surface of the conductor be preserved, both as a preventative against corrosion (the reason it was placed there in the first instance) and to assist the quick and easy soldering of the joint. It cannot be ensured that the subsequent soldering of a joint will replace the full coating of tin on the conductors, and without it a risk of chemical action from even the best of insulating materials, or from the mechanic's handling, must remain. Do not, therefore, scrape or sandpaper the copper wires comprising the conductor, but remove traces of rubber insulation by the means mentioned above.

TWIST JOINTS

There are many types of joint, but in most cases a simple close twist, well soldered, will provide the connection necessary. On the smaller conductors a very few amperes are carried, and for the larger cables sleeve or machined-faced coupler joints will be employed as a rule. It is doubtful if any advantage accrues from the making of such complicated joints as the "married" joint, and similar types, although examples of these are

Fig. 22. Straight joint of the simple twisted type. It should be noted that rather too much cable has been bared and this should be avoided.

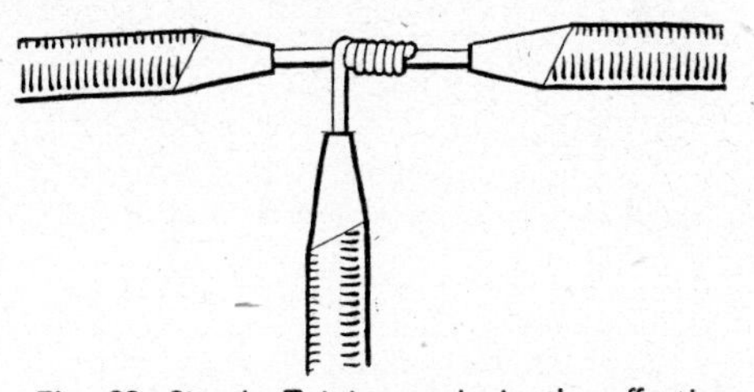

Fig. 23. Simple T joint made in the effective twist manner. This method is frequently used and is quite satisfactory given efficient soldering.

Fig. 24. Too much cable has also been bared in making this T joint. Nothing is to be gained by taking the insulation back in such a manner.

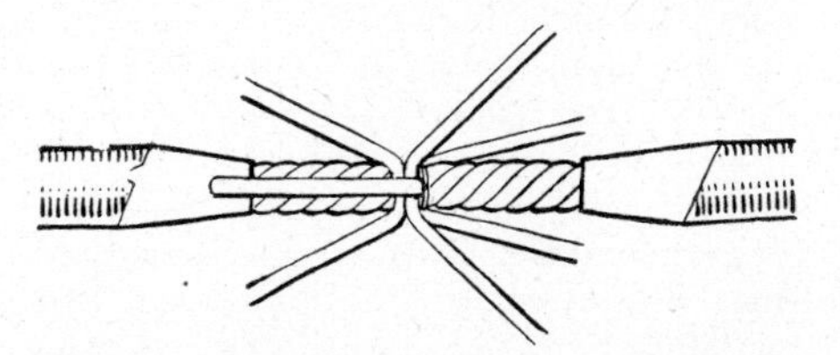

Fig. 25. First step in making a straight joint of the more difficult "married" type. It can be very effective in experienced hands.

Fig. 26. Married joint completed; six conductors have been twisted on each side. The centre one in each case is cut out.

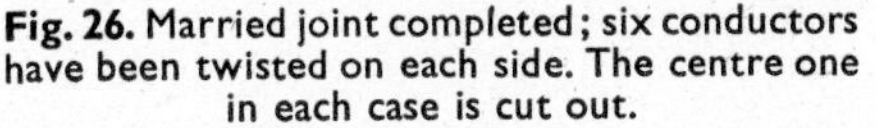

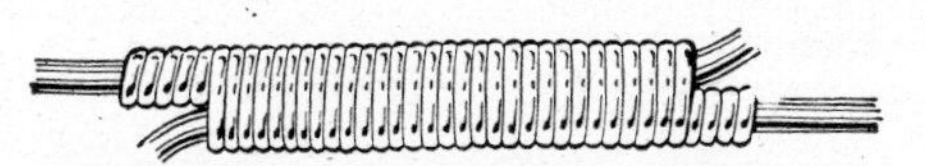

Fig. 27. Britannia joint as often used in the jointing of aerial telephone lines. Tinned binding wire is used and the whole is then soldered.

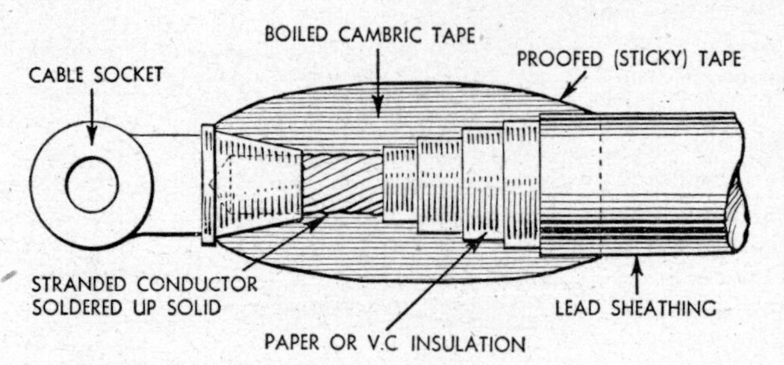

SIMPLE CABLE SEAL

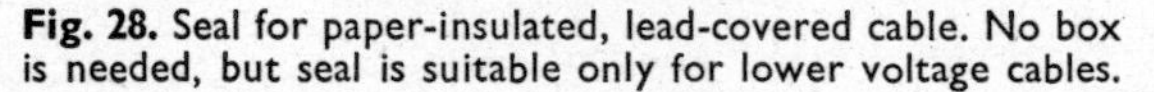

Fig. 28. Seal for paper-insulated, lead-covered cable. No box is needed, but seal is suitable only for lower voltage cables.

given. A close twist with efficient soldering (too much emphasis cannot be placed upon the last requirement) will usually provide an efficient and sound connection.

Simple twist joints are shown in Figs. 22, 23 and 24, for single and stranded conductors. In all three illustrations far too much of the cable has been bared, and it will be noted that there is no useful purpose served in the lengths of bare conductor existing beyond the actual wrap of the joint; half the length would suffice. The usual form of "married" joint is shown in Fig. 25, with the completed twist in Fig. 26; the centre strand of the conductor is cut out, leaving only 6 conductors to be twisted on each side. This can be a very effective joint in experienced hands, but otherwise is not recommended. Similar simple twist joints may be utilised for the jointing of bare aerial telephone lines, although the "Britannia" type, Fig. 27, is popular for this purpose. The two ends of the conductor are overlapped for about two inches, after having been carefully cleaned, laid together and tightly bound with tinned binding wire of smaller gauge; this binding being continued for a few turns over the single wire at either end, as shown. The whole is then soldered, the excess flux afterwards being carefully cleaned off.

INSULATING THE JOINT

For V.I.R. cables pure rubber strips are used for covering joints. The strip is usually in coils, paper interleaved, and before being used is slightly stretched; the strip is wound round the joint under slight tension, with subsequent turns overlapping their predecessors by about half. The first layer or two are placed on the conductor only, but the third and fourth may be taken up on to the rubber insulation of the cable that is left at the ends of the joint; if all layers are taken on to this insulation an unsightly bulge results, whereas all that is required is to replace the rubber removed in the process of jointing. There is obviously no advantage to be gained from continuing to build up the insulation beyond that point and to do so can only result in making the work look amateurish and untidy.

No solution or other fixing material is necessary, as if under sufficient tension the rubber will remain in place, the warmth of the hand being sufficient to cause it to adhere to itself in the progressive lappings and layers. When the covering of the bare conductor by the rubber strip has been carried to the length that the new insulation is about the same thickness as the removed insulation, this is sufficient, there is no need to pile on rubber to form greater thickness. For mechanical protection a layer or two of black adhesive tape may be used, carried over the ends of the cut tape or braid; black adhesive tape should never be used for the insulation of the joint.

SEALING CABLES

The jointing and insulating of large lead-covered cables, or concentric cables, is a matter for the expert, and is dealt with in a separate section. At the same

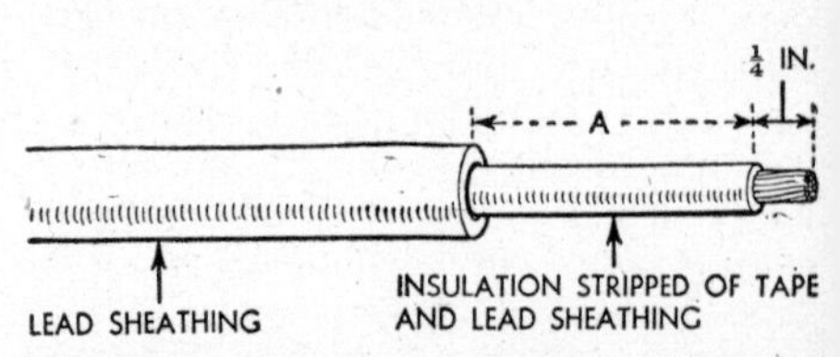

Fig. 29. Length of A is governed by special regulations and varies with voltage as shown by the measurement table appearing on page 183.

time, the electrical wireman may be called upon to deal with the ends of such cables where they actually enter or are connected to his equipment. For instance, in factory and other work the use of paper-insulated, oil-impregnated cables, lead sheathed and sometimes armoured, is increasing, and it is necessary that the ends of all such cables are effectively sealed against loss of oil; in addition, oil "bleeding" into electrical equipment may be very objectionable for many reasons.

It is not always necessary to provide sealing boxes for this purpose, as a simple seal may be ensured as shown in Fig. 28. In this, the strand is exposed by an amount slightly greater than that necessary to fill the cable lug, and this conductor, usually untinned copper, should be sweated solid by means of a blow lamp or pot and ladle. The cable insulation is then trimmed in not less than four steps about ½ in. long, and upon the conductor, close to the trimmed insulation, a lapping of cambric tape boiled in oil, from ½ in. to 1 in. wide, should be applied, the width depending upon the size of the cable.

This tape should then be tightly wrapped between the cable lug and the first step in the insulation, successive layers of tape being applied to break joint until the whole space between the lug and the lead sheathing has been filled; a further lapping should then be applied over the cable lug and the lead sheathing, as shown. A final layer of black adhesive tape may be employed to provide a mechanical protection. The complete seal should then be given three coats of insulating varnish or compound, the latter being applied hot. This provides a simple means of sealing paper cables, and is perfectly satisfactory at low voltages.

Another type of cable that the electrical operative may be required to seal is that used for the connections between transformers and tube electrodes on neon and similar high-tension connections. Bell glasses must be used for this purpose, and a simple method is described below.

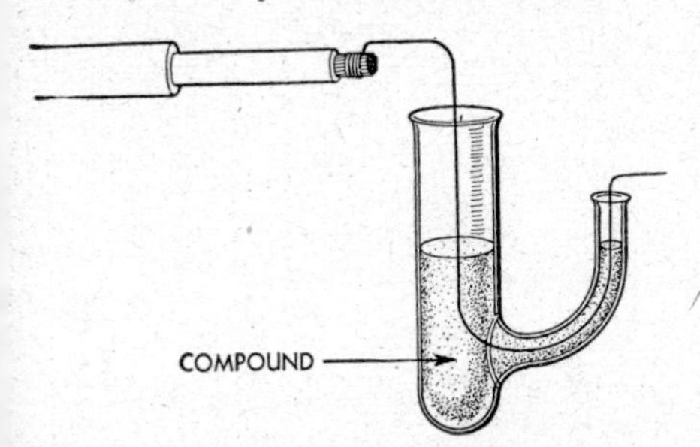

Fig. 30. Sealing a cable with the aid of a bell glass when making connections between transformers and the electrodes of a neon tube.

LEAD SHEATHING

A length should be marked off at the end of the cable, shown at A in Fig. 29; strip off the lead sheathing to this mark, care being taken that the insulation is not damaged. The tape must also be removed for the same length, and finally the conductor bared for about ¼ in., as shown. The I.E.E. Regulations govern this process, and No. 812 (A) gives the appropriate lengths of A, as under:—

Working Voltage	Length of Lead Sheathing to be Stripped Back
2,000	1·5 inches
4,000	2·0 ,,
6,000	3·0 ,,
8,000	4·0 ,,
10,000	5·0 ,,
14,000	7·0 ,,

A simple means of memorising these lengths is to take one inch for every 2 kV.

A short length of binding wire is then soldered to the conductor, and threaded through the bell glass, Fig. 30; melted Chatterton or other suitable sealing compound is then poured into the glass tube, sufficient to cover the exposed surface of the insulation. The glass tube must be kept warmed to prevent the compound hardening before the operation is complete.

The cable is then pushed down into the bell glass and the binding wire pulled taut. The final seal should be as shown in

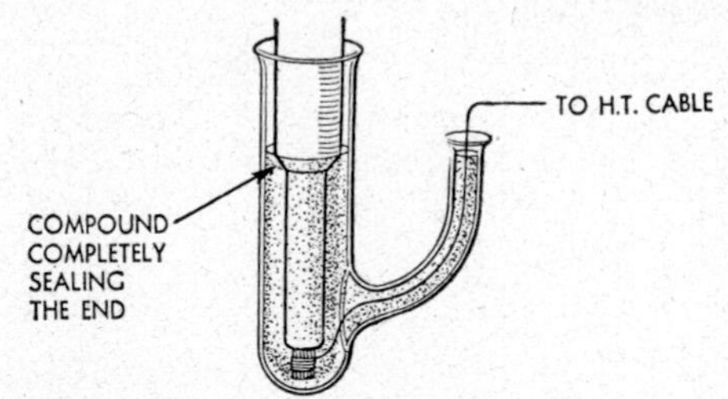

Fig. 31. Completed bell-glass seal of H.T. cable.

Fig. 31, and the bell glass is permanently mounted with the open mouth downwards so as to afford as much protection from weather or dampness as possible.

PRINCIPLES OF SOLDERING

In spite of the widespread use of mechanical connectors for electrical conductors, soldering enters largely into the electrical operative's requirements, especially for the efficient jointing of the larger conductors and the fixing of cable sockets and lugs. It is said that practice only can afford any sort of proficiency in the art of making a satisfactory soldered connection, but a knowledge of solders, their melting points, and the use of suitable fluxes will provide a basis upon which sound practice may be built.

The art of soldering consists of providing an alloy which will, under certain circumstances, unite with two similar or dissimilar metals which it is required to join. Such alloys are usually made to function with the application of heat, and in electrical soldering the matter is complicated by the fact that the application of heat is likely to damage the insulation of conductors. It is, therefore, very important that the correct types of solder are selected and used, not only to secure the junction of the copper cables and/or brass cable lugs, but to effect this with the application of a minimum amount of heat.

Practically all metals when exposed to the air take on a coating of oxygen, which forms an oxide of the metal, and this oxide seriously interferes with the action of any jointing alloy, such as solder. It is, therefore, necessary to clean thoroughly the surfaces of metals to be joined, in order to remove this film of oxide, but it is equally important that its re-formation during the process of soldering is prevented. The cleaning of the metals prior to soldering is a simple matter, but the application of heat for the purpose of soldering immediately replaces the coating of oxide; a substance known as a flux is therefore employed, having the property of melting very easily and immediately flowing over the cleaned metal surface, thus preventing the access of air and the formation of fresh oxide.

The alloying metal, or solder, usually consists of a mixture of tin and lead, in varying proportions, depending upon the type of joint or work required, and upon the permissible amount of heat that may be applied. Some of the common alloys, with their melting points, are given in the table below:—

Tin	Lead	Melting point	Type
1 part	10 parts	290° C.	Poor quality solders, with high melting points.
1 ,,	5 ,,	260° C.	
1 ,,	2 ,,	230° C.	Plumber's jointing solder.
1 ,,	1 part	180° C.	General purpose tinman's solder.
2 parts	1 ,,	170° C.	
4 ,,	1 ,,	160° C.	
4 ,,	8 parts (with 15 parts bismuth)	70° C.	Fine solder.

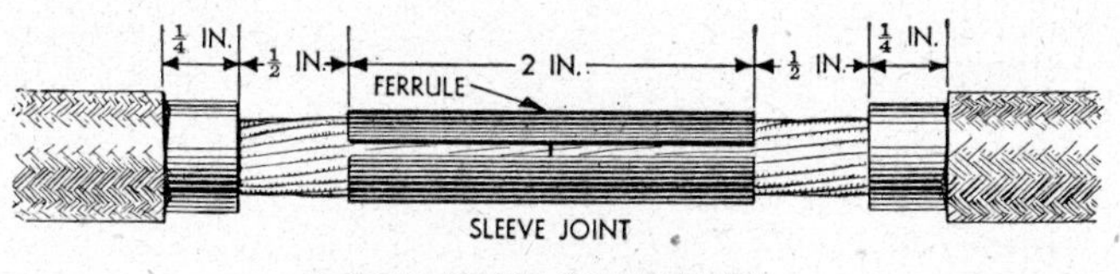

SLEEVE JOINT SOLDERING

Fig. 32. Typical sleeve joint with cable ends bared and ferrule fitted for the application of solder, this making a strong, efficient joint.

The softer solders are generally used for electrical joints, and for metals with low melting points, such as tin and lead. Copper can also be soldered with soft solder, and usually is, for electrical joints at least, and as the temperature at which electrical apparatus is run is well below the melting points of such solders there is little risk of unreliability. In the case of commutator connections, where much higher temperatures may be expected, a hard silver solder is used, melting at 296° C., and for which non-corrosive fluxes are suitable.

There are many fluxes in common use, but very few are suitable for electrical use, owing to their corrosive nature. Although every care may be taken in cleaning off surplus flux from a joint, yet it is certain that sooner or later evidence of chemical action will appear, and the joint will be rapidly destroyed. Only one of the following fluxes (namely resin) is really suitable for electrical purposes:—

(1) *Hydrochloric acid, or spirits of salt.* Useful when an article is very dirty or greasy, and commonly used on irons and the heavier metals.

(2) *Zinc chloride* (also called "killed spirits", being formed by the placing of strips of zinc in hydrochloric acid) is less potent than (1) but its corrosive properties are sufficient to bar it from all forms of electrical work.

(3) *Borax.* Often used with the hard solders, and in brazing, but its insulating properties make it unsuitable for electrical joints and similar kind of work.

(4) *Sal ammoniac.* Should never be used on copper cables.

(5) *Resin* (which may be used by itself or dissolved in methylated spirits) is most suitable for electrical work, as it is non-corrosive. It has a low melting point, enabling it to be used with the softer solders, and it is also suitable for the harder silver solder used for the connection of armature conductors to commutator lugs. There are several patent preparations on the market, such as "Fluxite", which also form safe fluxes for electrical solders, but as a general rule the use of resin is to be recommended. There remain one or two other low-melting-point fluxes, chiefly tallow, olive oil and sweet oil, and which, although useful for some plumbing purposes, are of too oily a nature to be brought into contact with the rubber insulation of cables.

METHODS OF APPLYING HEAT

There are three ways of applying the heat necessary to melt the flux and the solder (1) By means of a soldering iron, which is a bolt of copper fixed to a handle, and heated by being placed in a flame; (2) By blow lamp, which includes the small blow-pipe; and (3) by means of solder pot and ladles. The joint having been prepared, is covered with powdered resin, and the heated soldering iron is brought into contact with it. The transference of heat to the copper cable will cause the resin to melt at once, and the cleaned metal surfaces should be thus protected against further oxidisation. A stick of fine solder is then applied to the joint, and this will also melt and run through the twisted wires. The copper bit should be kept in contact only so long as is necessary to fill completely the spaces in the joint with solder, as prolonged heating will damage the rubber insulation of the cable.

Although this sounds a very simple operation, considerable skill is required to make a satisfactory joint. Firstly, the iron must be heated to the required temperature and no more, or the cleaned face of the bit will become oxidised and no transference of heat will take place. It is usual to "tin" the face of the copper bit before making a joint, and this consists of filing the flat face of the bit, covering with flux, heating the bit, again covering with flux, and rubbing the stick of solder on to the bit until a "tinned" surface is obtained. This surface consists of melted solder, and it will be easy to transfer the heat to the joint, the liquid solder making closer contact with the cable strands than would be possible with the copper bit alone. Skill is also necessary to know just when the soldering operation has been completed, and when the iron can be removed; too little heat will result in an incomplete joint, whilst too much, as mentioned above, will result in damaged insulation. When the joint is complete it may be cooled by blowing, or by the application of a damp rag, in order to prevent the conduction of the accumulated heat into the conductor of the cable.

Method (2), the use of blow-lamp or blow-pipe, is usually confined to the fixing of cable sockets and lugs, although many cable jointers use this method for all cables above about $\frac{3}{8}$ in. in diameter. It provides an effective means of transferring heat to the joint or cable socket, but as this method will be further dealt with under the section describing the fixing of lugs, it will be left for the time being. In the meantime it can be said that a fair amount of experience is needed before a blow-lamp can be used properly.

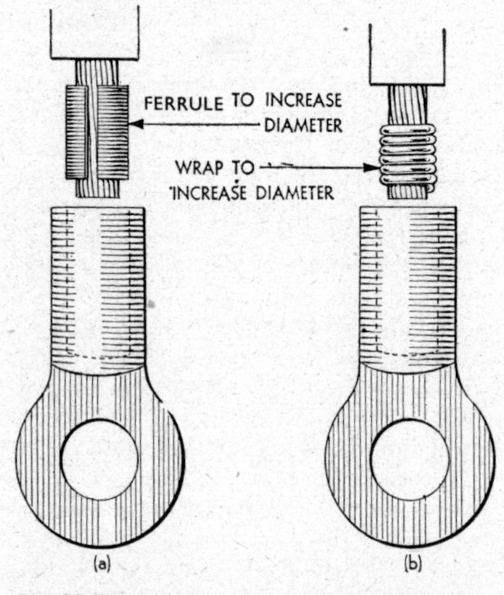

Fig. 33. Two methods of increasing the diameter of cable ends so that they fit thimbles snugly

The third method may be used for all types of joints and lugs, and with all sizes of cables. Provided that care is taken it affords probably the most effective way of soldering joints, and the method consists of melting the solder in an iron pot, taking a small portion of this in an iron ladle (that is provided with a spout) and pouring the molten solder over the joint into a second ladle held underneath. The precautions to be observed are as follows:—

The molten solder must be constantly stirred in the pot, or the tin, having a lower melting point than the lead, will rise to the top, and consequently the top layer of solder will be richer than the lower layer. The ladles must be kept hot, or the solder will be cooled in passing from one to the other; usually constant dipping of the ladles into the molten solder will maintain heat, but it is essential that the ladles are pre-heated also. It is inadvisable to use one ladle and hold the pot containing the molten solder under the joint, as some jointers do on paper insulated cables, as the intense heat rising from the pot is liable to damage the rubber insulation of cables. For the fixing of cable lugs the pot and one ladle may be used, provided that care is again taken to avoid injury to rubber insulation.

Should the lower layer of solder lose an undue amount of tin, the deficiency can be made good by the addition of phosphor tin.

SLEEVE JOINT

The sleeve, or ferrule, joint is a particularly good one for the employment of the pot and ladle method; this consists of a split brass or copper ferrule placed over the conductors to be jointed, Fig. 32. The tinning of the conductors before inserting in the ferrule is optional but will be further referred to in the section which

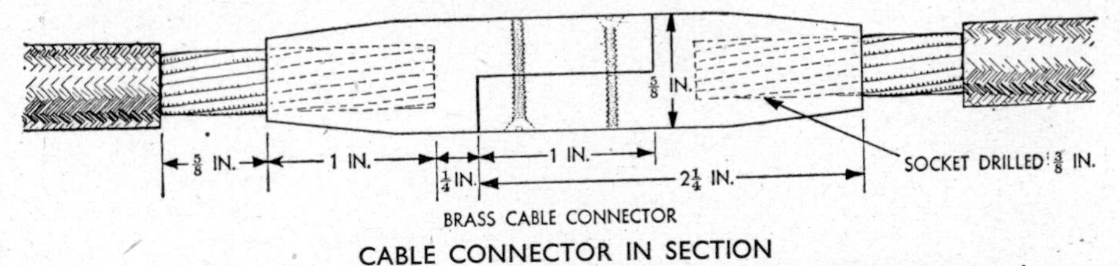

Fig. 34. Brass cable connector in section showing details of construction. This connection does not lend itself to pot and ladle soldering method, owing to the danger of excess solder getting into the machined faces and, therefore, it is necessary instead to use a blow-lamp carefully.

deals with the preparation of joints for soldering.

If the molten solder is too cold when poured, it is liable to form sharp-pointed projections on the underside of the ferrule, which leads to a great deal of unnecessary work in filing clean; if the points are left, they are liable to penetrate the insulation of the joint. The best way to remove such points is to pour further solder of the correct temperature over the joint; a very clean joint will result from the use of solder of the correct temperature.

FIXING CABLE LUGS

The cable end is prepared as described, and the lug should be set up in two projecting pieces of wood firmly held in a vice; the lug cannot be placed in the vice jaws, as the transfer of heat to the vice is too great. The blow-lamp flame is played on the upper open end of the lug, which has previously been treated with flux, until it is hot enough to melt a stick of solder. The solder is allowed to run into the lug until it is about two-thirds full, when the cable is introduced slowly, the blow-lamp flame still being kept on the lug. When it is seen that the solder is taking round the strands of the cable, and it is felt that the cable has reached the bottom of the lug, then the flame can be withdrawn; the cable must be held steady until the solder is set, and the cooling process may be assisted by the application of a damp rag.

The same procedure may be followed when the pot and ladle method is used, but considerably greater skill is required for a satisfactory result. In the hands of the amateur the solder tends to run over the outside of the lug, not in itself objectionable, but at the conclusion of the work it will be found that several blobs of hardened solder are projecting from the faces of the lugs intended for clamping under the terminal nuts; these have to be cleaned off, and the straight machined face of the lug is gone. Some workers soak the lug in the molten solder before setting it up for fixing; this results in quick heating and shortens the time necessary to make the fitting.

As solder has a comparatively high resistance it is necessary to use lugs that fit fairly closely to the cable, in order to prevent the existence of a thick wall of solder surrounding the cable. Where the conditions demand a lug of a certain size, and the cable is on the small side, then it is advisable to increase the cable diameter. This may be done by means of a ferrule, Fig. 33 (a), or a strand of the cable itself, Fig. 33 (b), care being taken that the finished cable is not too large to enter the lug easily during any part of the soldering process.

PRECAUTIONS

The type of connection shown in Fig. 34 does not lend itself to the pot and ladle method, owing to the danger of getting solder on the two machined faces making the butt joint. Once these have been filed for cleaning off excess solder it is very difficult to make an efficient joint; careful work with the blow-lamp is, therefore, called for, and if the wood clamps previously described can be made to cover the faces of the joint then this is usually sufficient to protect them against

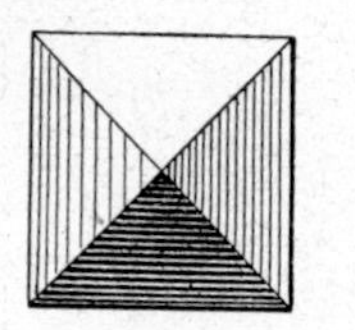
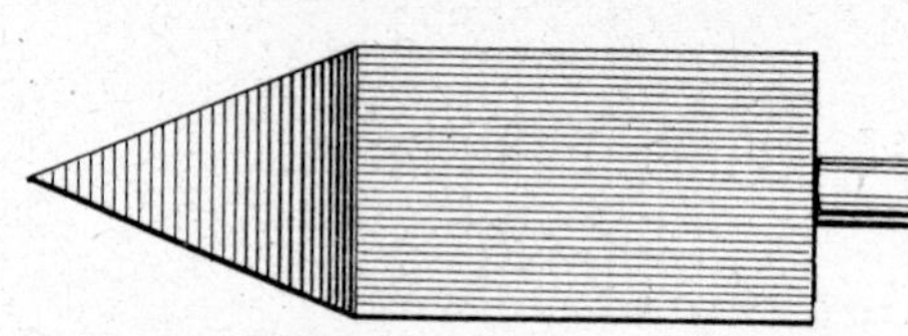

PYRAMID SOLDERING BIT

Fig. 35. End and side views of pyramid soldering bit, a pattern often used for fine work. Soldering bits are available in a variety of weights.

accidental overflow of solder from the lug.

Typical copper bits are shown in Figs. 35 and 36; the flat faces should always be kept well "tinned" and perfectly clean.

Soldering bits are available in a number of different weights and, in general, it can be said that a fairly heavy one will be the best one for general work. It will distribute its heat better than a lighter one. This applies to plain or electrically-heated types.

LEAD-COVERED WIRING

Lead-covered wiring systems are fundamentally surface systems, although they are sometimes installed so as to be concealed. Under such circumstances considerable precaution must be taken to guard the vulnerable cables against mechanical damage, the methods differing widely in various types of buildings. For this reason concealed systems will not be considered, but the main points associated with a satisfactory surface installation dealt with alone. In concealed systems the main precautions are to keep cables clear of old oak, from iron and steel work, and especially from the deleterious action of patent plasters; these points apply also to surface installations.

Lead-covered cables may be run on practically any surface, subject to the points mentioned above, and owing to their flexibility are able to follow the contours of walls, etc., with greater facility than steel conduits, resulting in a less objectionable appearance. At the same time, care must be taken to prevent sagging, usually from insufficient support, and crooked runs, or the result will be decidedly objectionable.

Runs should be marked beforehand by

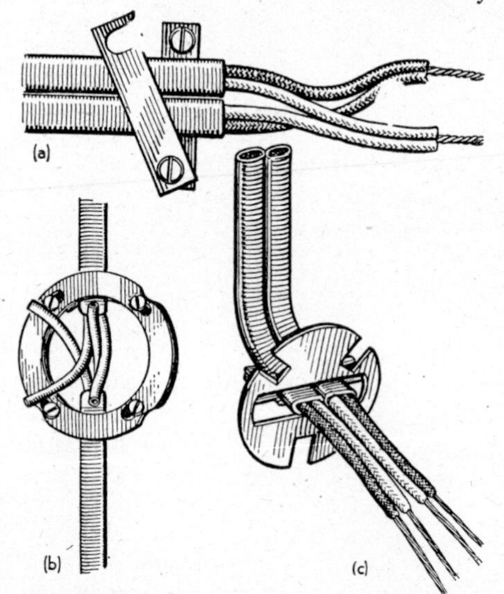

Fig. 37. Three types of bonding clamp used with lead-covered cables, (a) for continuity at switch and socket points, (b) ring type, (c) for cables emerging from skirtings and walls, etc.

means of a line obtained from a chalked string, whether vertical or horizontal, and the clips fixed in position on this line. The Regulations give the distances apart for fixings for different sizes of cable, and to which reference should be made. Working from the top of a run to the bottom will prevent unnecessary bending of the cable during erection, and cables should always be

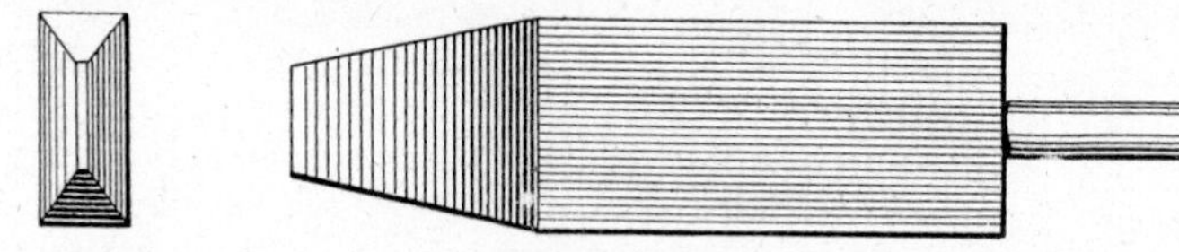

CHISEL SOLDERING BIT

Fig. 36. End and side views of chisel soldering bit, a popular pattern for general work. The flat faces should always be kept clean and "tinned".

straightened by running a cloth along them before being placed in position. Irregularities will be difficult to remove at a later stage.

BONDING AND EARTHING

What has previously been said concerning the importance of good bonding and earthing in connection with steel conduits applies with even greater force to lead-covered cables. This is more difficult in connection with lead-covered cables owing to the non-mechanical nature of the covering, which does not lend itself to tight gripping. For this reason two types of cables are marketed, one containing a small bonding wire placed immediately below the lead sheath, and which is relied upon to maintain continuity, and the ordinary type relying upon connection to the lead sheath by means of clamps. The former is by far the most efficient, and can be connected into earthing terminals of accessories, etc., with greater facility than connections can be made from the sheath to such terminals. The bonding wire is connected into terminals in junction boxes, or soldered, as preferred, the main point is to connect it and ensure continuity.

Regarding the ordinary type of cable without bonding wire, there are many types of clamps to suit various positions in the installation. Fig. 37 shows three types; (a) for continuity at switch and socket points; (b) a ring type for use under wood blocks, etc., and which will be referred to later; and (c) for use where cables come through skirtings, walls, etc., as, for instance, behind wall sockets. The whole art of successful installation of lead covered cables depends upon the proper selection and use of these clamps, and with care a reasonably efficient bond can be obtained; pressure of the clamp must be sufficient to maintain this without damaging the insulation of the conductors.

METHODS OF WIRING

These are two in number, and may be described as installation with junction boxes and installation without. In the first method standard junction boxes are used, resulting in considerable economy in cable; the bonding is obtained by the use of special clamps now incorporated in the junction box, as shown in Fig. 38, electrical connections being made by means of porcelain connectors, or even soldered joints. Junction boxes should be accessible, and not concealed under floors, etc., although in certain situations concealment is resorted to.

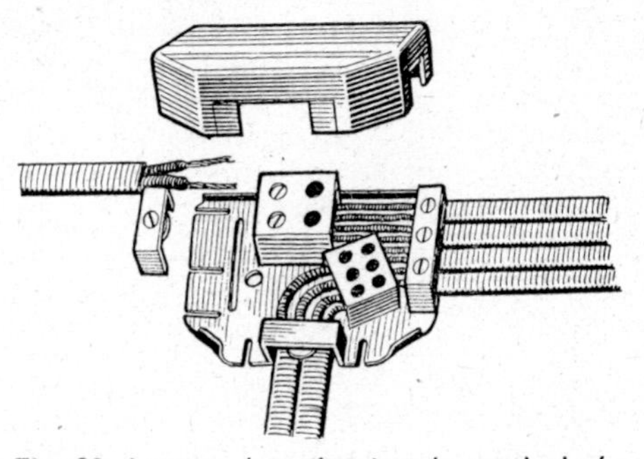

Fig. 38. Junction box showing the method of bonding lead sheath with the aid of special clamps to ensure efficient earthing continuity.

BONDING RINGS

The second system relies upon the use of the bonding ring shown in Fig. 37, twin cables being run from point to point, as indicated in Fig. 39. This has the advantage that every lighting point becomes a potential junction box, from

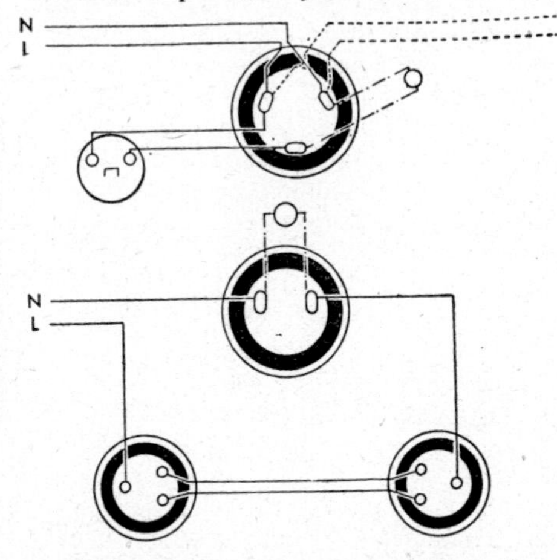

Fig. 39. Wiring without junction boxes by the use of bonding rings which are shown darker.

which further points can be extended with ease; on the other hand, the method absorbs greater quantities of cable than the junction box method. The choice of methods must be decided by the type of installation, and no general rules can be laid down.

SPECIAL GLAND METHOD

A third method is sometimes used where lead-covered cables are to be erected in exposed or damp situations, when a special gland, carefully soldered to the cable sheathing, is employed, this being shown in Fig. 40. The use of this gland enables standard conduit boxes to be utilised in connection with lead-covered wiring systems, and also steel accessories, shown in Fig. 41. The continuity of the system is usually beyond question with this method, but care must be taken in soldering the gland that excessive heat is not applied,

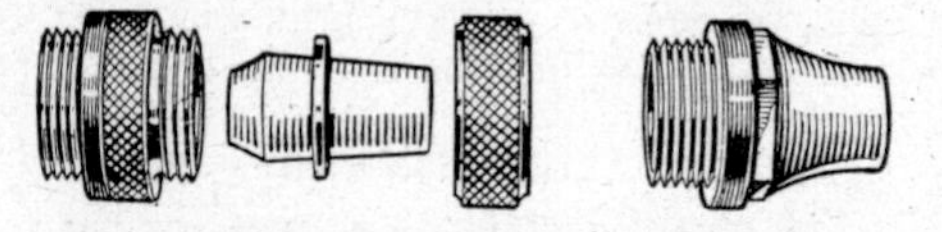

Fig. 40. Soldered continuity gland for damp or exposed positions. Careful soldering is needed.

or the insulation of the cables will be damaged. Used in this manner, lead-covered wiring systems form a reliable external system, provided that protection against mechanical damage is amply provided.

Rubber insulated lead-covered cables do not require sealing at ends, except in damp situations employing the ordinary methods; paper-insulated cables must always be sealed.

INSULATED WIRING SYSTEMS

The standard insulated wiring system is now that employing tough rubber, or cab-tyre-sheathed cables, and in general these cables are superior from a mechanical point of view to lead-covered cables. In addition, they may be concealed without danger, being impervious to the corrosive influences associated with lead sheaths, and even vermin-proof types of

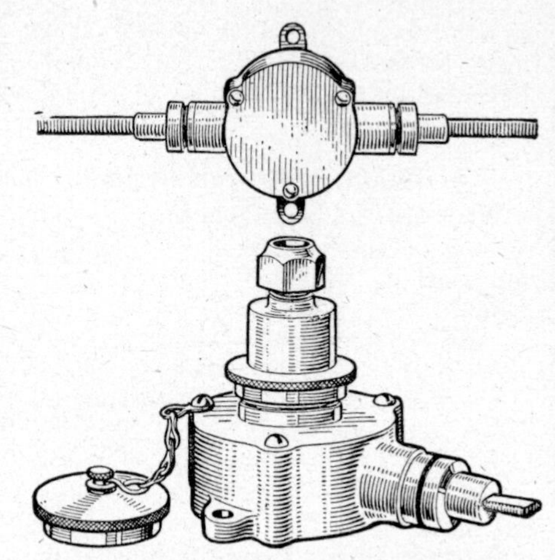

Fig. 41. Standard conduit accessories used with lead-covered cables in conjunction with the soldering gland which is illustrated in Fig. 40.

cables are now available. The methods of neat installation follow those previously described for lead-covered cables but, of course, the bugbear of sheathing continuity on longer runs arises.

Where an earthing conductor is required for use with three-pin sockets, etc., a type of T.R.S. cable is available incorporating a conductor placed immediately beneath the tough rubber covering. This is connected into earthing

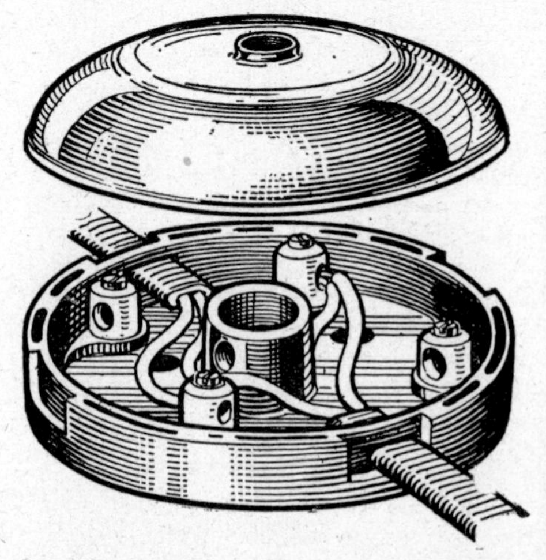

Fig. 42. Plastic junction box for use with T.R.S. cables contribute to a most effective system.

terminals, and jointed or teed at junctions as required, forming a very effective method; the earthing conductor being covered with the semi-insulating sheath it is protected against all forms of corrosion or mechanical damage, and is usually perfectly reliable. Insulated wiring systems employing this type of cable and with careful attention to jointing and earthing of the bonding wire probably form the most efficient system, electrically, of any. The cost is usually much below that of steel conduit or lead-covered cable, whilst the flexibility of the system makes it especially suitable for small or domestic installations. The main precaution to be taken is in connection with external work, when the cables must be protected against direct sun rays; this may be provided by means of wooden channelling, which also forms a neat covering for internal use.

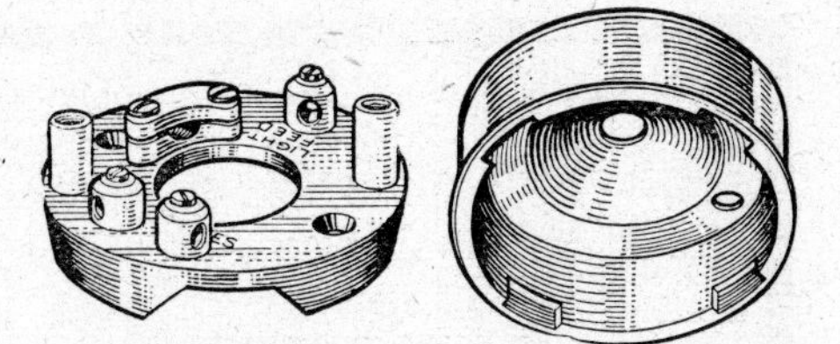

Fig. 43. Junction box which has been specially designed for loop connections. This type may also be utilised as a ceiling rose.

JUNCTION BOXES

Types of junction boxes used with the system are shown in Figs. 42 and 43; looping the twin cables from point to point, with the use of three-plate ceiling roses makes a simple and effective system. It is one which compares most favourably with the tee-ing in method which was at one time in almost universal use and which rendered repair work considerably more difficult.

Where insulated wiring systems are used it is advisable to keep the installation all-insulated throughout, with the use of plastic accessories, main switch fuses, etc., all of which are now readily available. The use of metal accessories with insulated wiring systems often leads to difficulty associated with the proper earthing of such accessories, unless the special bonding cable be used, and is to be deprecated. There is a decided trend towards the all-insulated installation, where applicable, consequent upon the efficient service and freedom from faults of such systems. They are in all cases to be recommended against any form of metal-clad installation, although all installations do not lend themselves to the use of such systems. In some instances first cost of installation is of primary importance.

UNDER-FLOOR DUCT SYSTEMS

The distribution of electrical energy in modern buildings presents problems arising from the nature of the building structure, and the varying requirements

Fig. 44. Sections of non-metallic under-floor ducts for use in distribution systems which allow for future additions and extensions in buildings in which concrete and iron are largely employed.

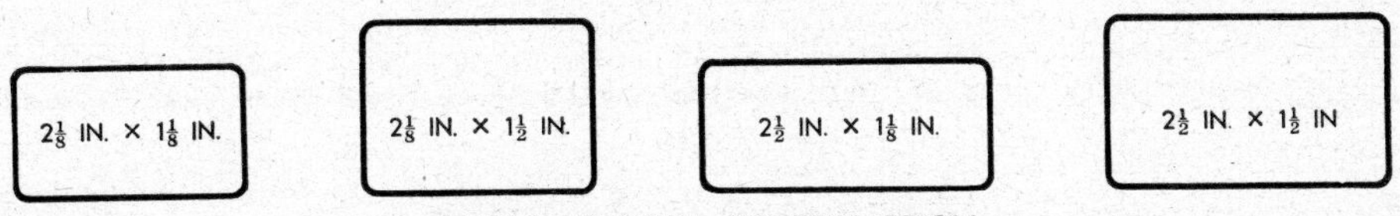

DUCTS OF STEEL CONSTRUCTION

Fig. 45. Sections of steel under-floor ducts; the dimensions are in accordance with B.S.I. recommendations. Ducts of this type are also frequently used for Post Office telephone wiring.

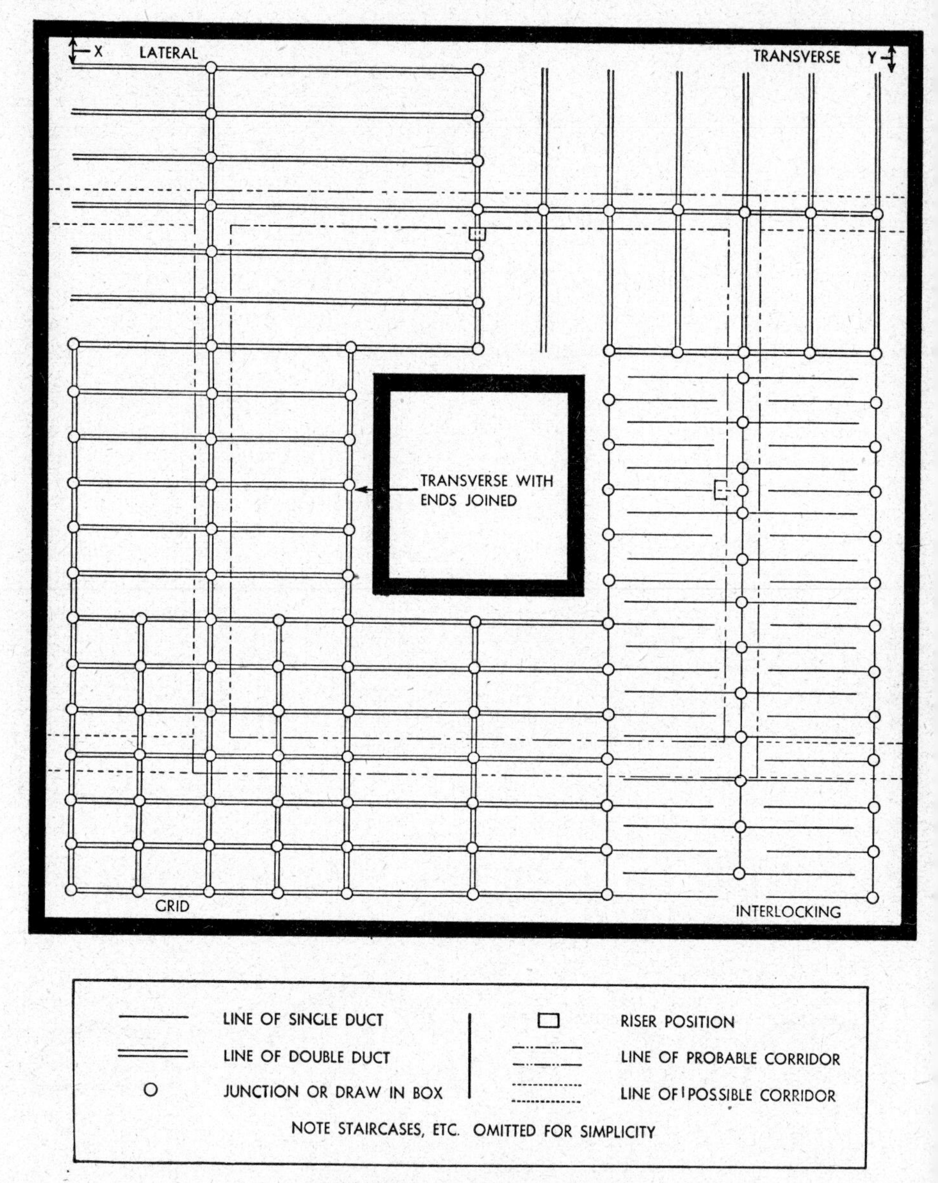

METHODS OF DUCT LAYOUT

Fig. 46. Five systems are interconnected to show flexibility of duct arrangement to suit conditions. X and Y are distances equivalent to 3 ft. max. All details of a purely structural nature have been omitted so that the duct lines can clearly be seen. Note the placing of junction and draw-in boxes.

in such buildings. The amount of wood and similar material that can easily be cut or chased to receive electrical conduits or ducts is becoming progressively less; it is true to say that the modern building is composed almost entirely of concrete and metal. Consequently, extensions and alterations can be made only with diffi-

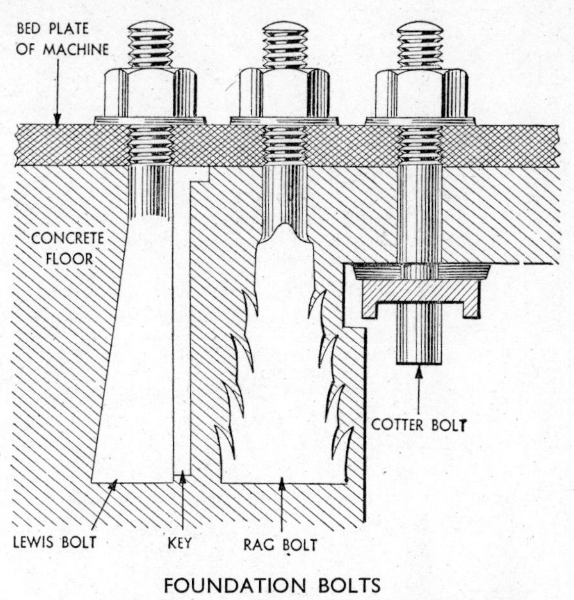

Fig. 47. Three types of foundation bolts for motors.

culty, and produce unsightly results. The object of a duct system is to make provision in the building structure itself for any extensions or additions that may be required in the future.

Under-floor ducts may be of metallic or non-metallic construction, common sections being shown in Figs. 44 and 45. The methods of making outlets into these ducts, and of providing draw-in and junction points vary with different manufacturers, and reference should be made to the specialists' publications for this information. The form of lay-out will vary with different buildings used for different purposes, but typical arrangements are shown in Fig. 46 with its accompanying notes.

In addition to lighting and power wiring, under-floor duct systems are utilised to convey telephone wiring to various points; often the several services run side-by-side; the Post Office requires that telephone wiring shall be in separate ducts from power wiring.

ERECTION OF EQUIPMENT

The large number of types and sizes of electrical equipment requiring installation precludes any detailed treatment of the subject, but in many cases the straightforward nature of the job entails no problems. However, it is important to remember that in many cases there will be mechanical as well as electrical considerations. An installation that is sound in every aspect from a purely electrical point of view may still be open to criticism if it has not been efficiently mounted. It will very often be the case that the electrician will need to co-operate and even obtain the active assistance of other specialists in order to carry out his work. In the case of control switchgear, all that is necessary is to ensure adequate fixing, with completely level placing of the gear, especially if contactor equipment is incorporated. This type of gear should never be installed on walls subject to extreme vibration, or to slamming doors; it is preferably housed in floor-mounting cabinets and firmly grouted to solid foundations. The installation of motors, especially in connection with belt drives, calls for attention, however, and this will be briefly dealt with.

INSTALLATION OF MOTORS

Electric motors have the great advantage that they may be installed and used in practically any position, but simple means must be taken to ensure that good service results. For instance, if motors are mounted on walls, then stronger rails are necessary than if they were mounted on the floor, and most manufacturers will supply these. If a motor is installed with its shaft upwards, the wall-mounting type should be used.

For all normal drives, slide rails should be used, these being fixed to the floor by means of special bolts, types of which are shown in Fig. 47. The slide rail adjusting screws must be placed between the motor and the driven machine, and allowance

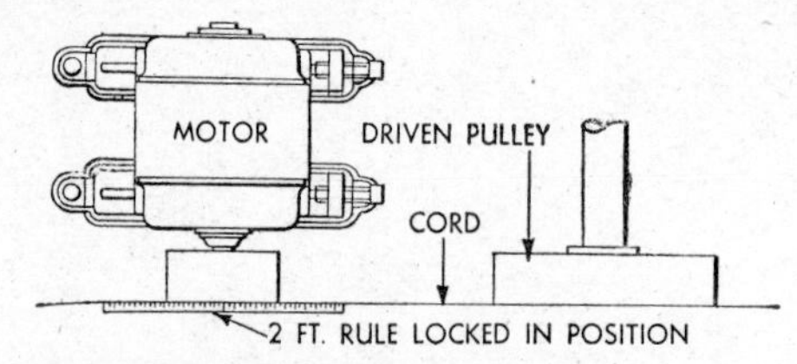

Fig. 48. Method of lining up pulleys using a standard two-foot steel rule and a cord.

must be made, when wiring, by means of flexible conduits or otherwise, for the motor to be moved along the rails for belt adjustment. The standard terminal box position is on the right-hand side when looking at the pulley end; make sure that there is room for this. The placing of the terminal box on the opposite side entails extra cost.

With flat belt drives slide rails must always be used, and the drive arranged so that the slack side of the belt is uppermost; all vertical drives should be avoided, if possible. The minimum distance between the driving and the driven pulleys should be four times the diameter of the larger pulley, and the maximum belt speed should not exceed four hundred feet per minute. For exceptionally wide belts a third bearing should be provided, and when fast and loose driven pulleys are used always arrange for the drive to the fast pulley to be taken from the end nearest to the motor bearing. It is most important that driving and driven pulleys should be in line. When lining up a belt drive place a cord along the face of the large driven pulley and fix the far end to the floor; then move the motor itself on its slide rails roughly into position. The pulley on the motor being relatively small it is sometimes difficult to ensure that the shaft of the motor is parallel with the driven shaft, and this is important on chain and vee-belt drives also.

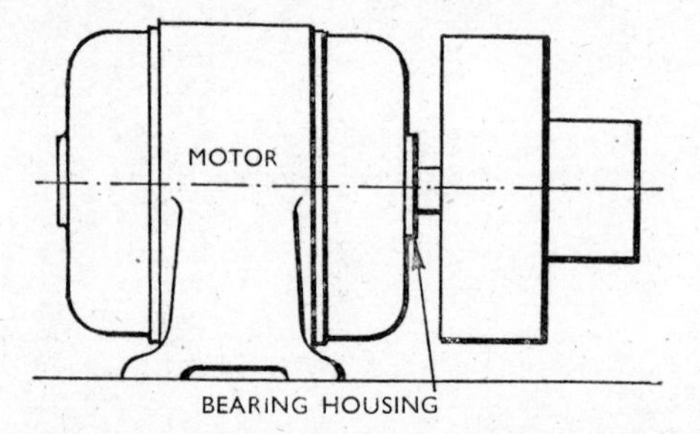

Fig. 49. Showing arrangement of two-speed pulleys. Note, the larger diameter pulley must always be placed nearer the motor bearing.

A standard two-foot steel rule, locked in position, may be placed across the end of the pulley, as shown in Fig. 48, and the motor can be lined up by checking the position of the cord with the ends of the steel rule. When two-speed pulleys are used, keep the larger diameter pulley nearer the motor bearing, as in Fig. 49.

It must be noted that all these remarks apply to the smaller and medium-sized machines such that it is usual for the installation engineer to put in on prepared foundations.

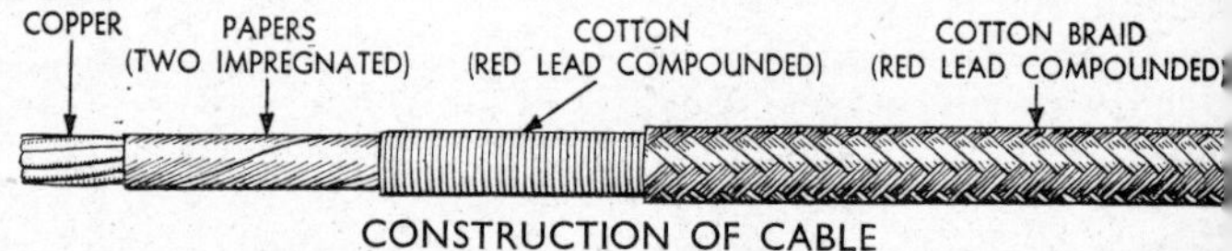

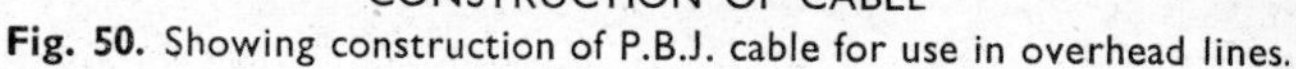

Fig. 50. Showing construction of P.B.J. cable for use in overhead lines.

With the larger motors it is normal practice for the manufacturers to carry out all the installation work and also to undertake tests of the wiring and of the performances of the motors before handing them over. A special staff is normally maintained by most big firms for this type of work.

Other simple points to remember are:

Vee belts. Ensure that all belts are of the same length; otherwise the shorter belts will carry all the load. Slight variation is permissible, as this will work itself out in a short time.

Chain drive. Accurate alignment of driving and driven sprocket wheels is essential, and the former should be fixed close to the motor bearing.

Direct coupling. A flexible coupling should always be used, as this will com-

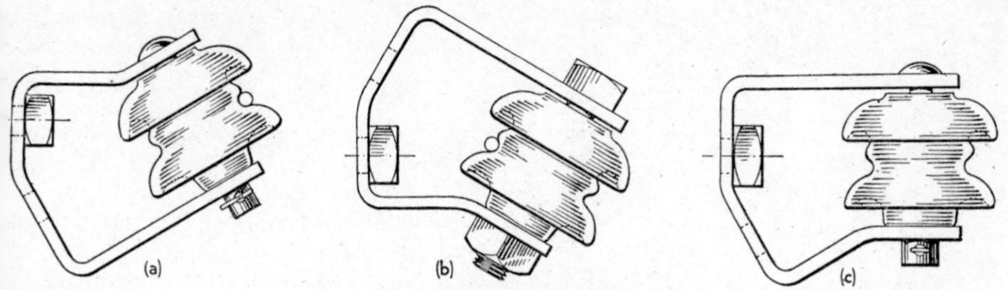

Fig. 51. Insulators for medium and low pressure lines. (a) As used for straight line position or left-hand deviation; (b) straight line position or right-hand deviation; (c) as used on straining pole.

pensate for small inaccuracies in mounting which are liable to occur. If solid couplings are used, accurate alignment is absolutely essential.

OVERHEAD LINES

Overhead lines provide the cheapest method of conveying power over longish distances, but objections have been raised to this form of distribution owing to unsightliness. Provided that a line is perfectly straight, and suitably stayed where unavoidable changes of direction take place, and there is a proper spacing of the poles so that undue sagging of the conductors does not take place, many of these objections may be overcome. The following notes deal with the erection of low- and medium-pressure lines, the erection of high-tension lines being dealt with in Chapter 4.

Poles may be red fir, larch or spruce; B.S.S. 139/1921 covers fir poles and B.S.S. 513/1933 larch poles. Rough poles should be barked and creosoted, and the portion buried in the ground coated with Stockholm tar, extended about 2 feet above the ground line. Holes should be dug in steps, and the final foot in depth should be barely large enough to receive the butt of the pole. Normal working conditions may be ascertained from the table that appears on this page.

The heights of the poles are based on the conductors being placed in vertical formation, Fig. 52, and where two circuits are erected, placed on opposite sides of the pole. Where lines cross roads 19 ft. clearance is necessary, and where running along roads 17 ft., and in positions inaccessible to vehicular traffic 15 ft. The tops of poles must be protected against the weather by tarring or other means.

STAYS

Stays must be fixed at the angle of resultant pull where a line changes direction, and consist of base plate and rod and bow with tightening screw. Galvanised steel-stranded wire of a size dependent upon the load is necessary, $\frac{7}{12}$ is a good average size, but B.S.S. 183 states $\frac{7}{8}$. Stay wires must be insulated by means of a barrel insulator placed in the wire at a height of not less than 10 feet from the ground. It is also necessary that

Load	Ground clearance, ft.	Length	Class of pole (B.S.S. 139)	Depth in ground, ft.
One 4-wire circuit	15	26	Light	5
with conductors up	17	28	,,	5
to 0·1 sq. in. ..	19	30	,,	5
Two 4-wire circuits	15	26	Medium	5
with conductors up	17	28	,,	5
to 0·1 sq. in. ..	19	30	,,	5

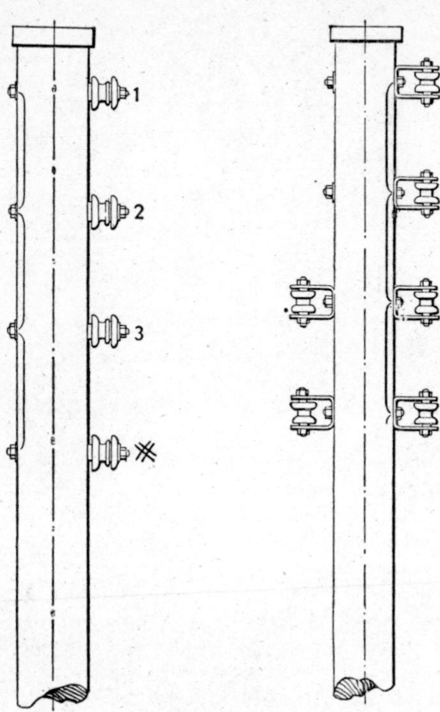

Fig. 52. Vertical arrangement of lines, with bonding conductor connecting insulator ironwork. The neutral is at the bottom.

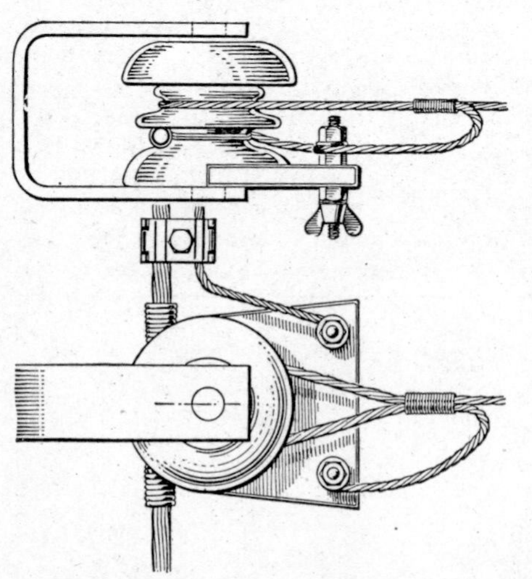

Fig. 53. Showing arrangement of fuses and method of binding conductors to the insulator.

the stay anchor should comprise a creosoted timber baulk, not less than 4 ft. long, and located in undisturbed ground by means of undercutting from the excavation. Where traffic or other considerations prevent the use of stays, struts for the angle pole may be provided, of similar timber to the poles and similarly treated. Stays are required at the ends of all runs, and in the case of heavy lines may require duplication.

CONDUCTORS

For low and medium pressure lines conductors are usually of hard-drawn copper, preferably stranded and to B.S.S. 125. No joints are permitted in these conductors except at pole positions, all junctions being made at the insulators. Conductors may be bare, except for service lines to buildings, when the phase conductor should be of the P.B.J. type; all conductors crossing over Post Office lines must also be of this construction, as shown in Fig. 50. The red lead compound, hardened through oxidisation under the action of the atmosphere, provides a highly resistant and reliable covering, which, although its insulation value is not high, is sufficient to prevent danger to telephone operators should a telephone wire come into contact with it.

INSULATORS

For low and medium pressure lines insulators are usually of the shackle type, a reel type insulator held in a "D" iron, Fig. 51. The arrangement for vertical construction is shown in Fig. 52, the neutral line being placed at the bottom. The bolts are connected together by means of copper wire of fairly heavy gauge, terminating at the lowest insulator; it is undesirable to earth the pole ironwork for low and medium pressure lines.

STRAINING OF CONDUCTORS

The conductors should be bound to the insulators with soft copper wire, as shown in Fig. 53.

After the conductors have been loosely strung through the "D" irons they are strained up to the requisite tension by

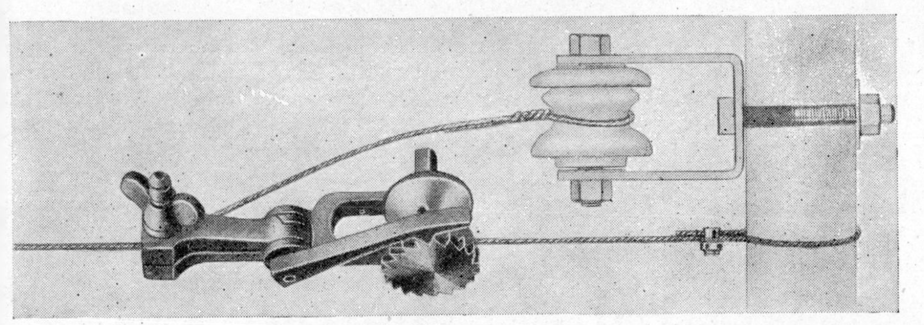

REDUCING SAG IN LINE

Fig. 54. Line conductor is gripped in the jaws of the draw vice, whilst flexible steel conductor is drawn on to ratchet by means of a key until the necessary tension of conductor is obtained.

means of draw vices and straining ratchets, as described in Fig. 54. After tensioning and making off, copper bindings are applied to all the intermediate insulators; little pull should fall on these bindings, their main function being to sustain the conductor on the insulator. Connections to overhead lines are usually made by means of special clamps, typical examples being shown in Fig. 55; the arrangement of a clamp in position is shown in Fig. 53.

These connections are, of course, made at pole positions and should not be placed otherwise, even though an alternative would seem to be advantageous in certain cases.

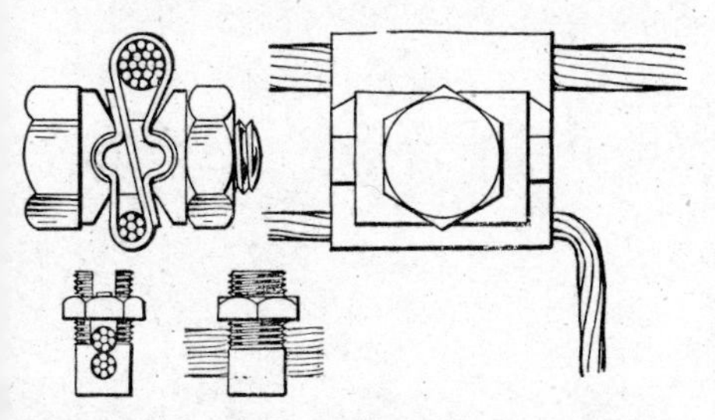

Fig. 55. Patterns of line taps and clamps in common use for connections to overhead lines.

USE OF FUSES

Fuses are sometimes required at the point of junction, and one form of line fuse is shown connected in Fig. 53. They have the great disadvantage that they are not readily accessible for replacement, but their low cost is a matter requiring consideration.

Although ordinary lead-covered and tough-rubber sheathed cables may be used externally if desired, subject to precautions with the latter type regarding shielding from direct sunlight, it is usual to employ one of the special systems designed for the purpose. The special cables

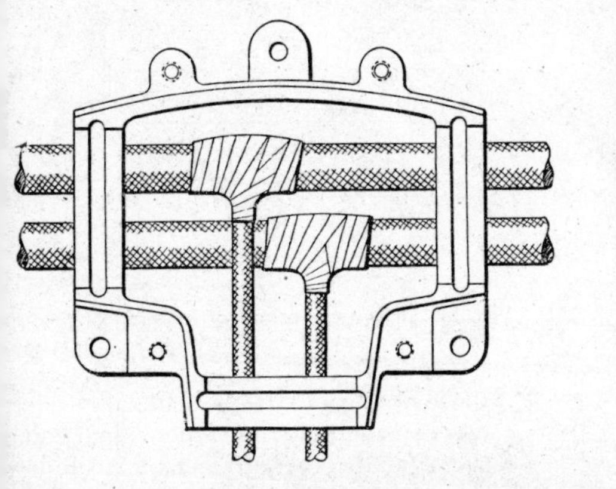

EXTERNAL DISTRIBUTION SYSTEM

Fig. 56. Method of making junctions in boxes by means of ordinary joints

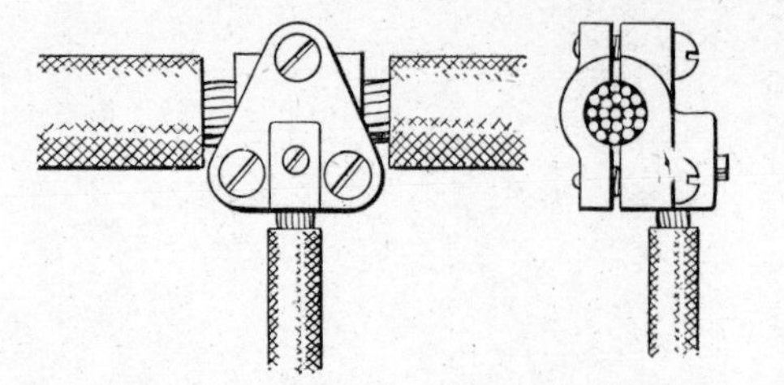

Fig. 57. External distribution systems; method of making junction by means of clamps.

are available in twin or single pattern, and for ease in jointing and erection the latter is to be preferred. These systems are often used for distribution to rows of houses, from mains carried on poles, and for which they are eminently suitable.

A junction box for an external system is shown in Fig. 56, with wooden glands fitted to the cast iron body. Ordinary joints may be made in these boxes, or special clamps may be employed, Fig. 57; it will be noted that the box has a removable plug at the top, to permit filling with hot sealing compound. In other patterns the box is filled with plastic compound, this being pressed into position round the cables and the cover screwed into position. The cables are supported on porcelain cleats, a common pattern being shown in Fig. 58.

Entries through brick walls, etc., are made by lead-in tubes, the straight pattern being shown in Fig. 59; it is necessary to form a drip-loop on the incoming cable to prevent rain passing down the cable and into the building. With the lead-in tube provided with a downward spout this formation is automatic, and the latter type is generally used.

Fig. 58. Usual form of cleat used for supporting cables in various external distribution systems.

Sometimes a sealing compound is used with lead-in tubes, but this is obviously not so essential when the type having the downward spout is employed.

CABLES BETWEEN BUILDINGS

External cables may be carried between buildings with the provision of a taut catenary wire, usually made up of stranded-steel cable with thimbles, and a turnbuckle at one end to provide the necessary tension. If the catenary is left slack considerable movement may take place, and the cables be liable to injury where taken from the wall on to the suspension wire. The cables may either

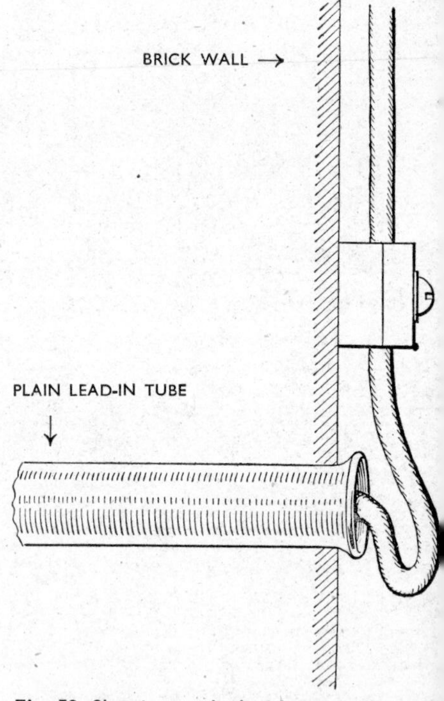

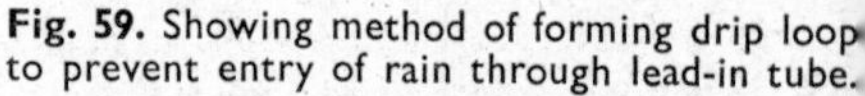

Fig. 59. Showing method of forming drip loop to prevent entry of rain through lead-in tube.

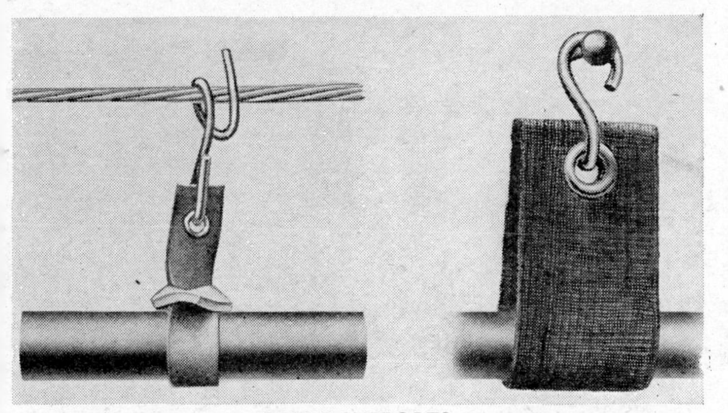

CABLE SUPPORTS

Fig. 60. Usual forms of slings or supports for cables suspended on catenary wires. Alternatively, they can be tightly taped.

be tightly taped to the catenary or suspended therefrom by means of cable slings, two forms of which are shown in Fig. 60. All types of cables may be suspended by this means, whether power and lighting, or telephone circuits in lead-covered cable.

PREVENTING CABLE MOVEMENT

In the case of lead-covered cables considerable care must be taken to prevent injury to the lead sheath due to cable movement. In most forms of sling heavy cables tend to move towards the point of lowest sag, and to overcome this a special type has been devised, known as the "Elder" suspender, Fig. 61. In this the suspended cable is kept close to the catenary wire, the individual slings are secured to the catenary by means of wire clips, and on sloping suspension wires a thumb clip is provided which still further restricts any tendency of the cable to move. Care must be taken with all types of cable, but especially with lead-covered cables, where they pass from the rigid fixing on walls, etc., to the comparatively flexible suspension of the catenary. An angle piece is sometimes provided to which the cables may be clipped, one form being shown in Fig. 62. With heavy lead-covered cables a double catenary may be necessary, one steel wire being placed above the other, and used to take up excessive sag on the lower wire.

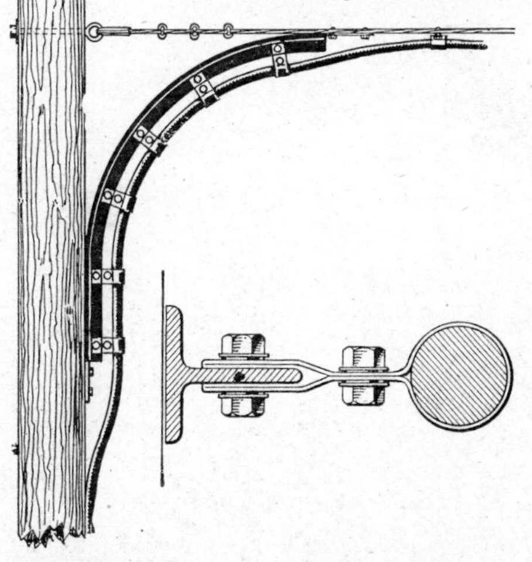

Fig. 62. Method of taking cable from a catenary wire to a vertical support using an angle piece.

This will impose considerable strain on the end supports and these will clearly need to be of a construction appropriate to the weight and the stresses that they will be called upon to bear.

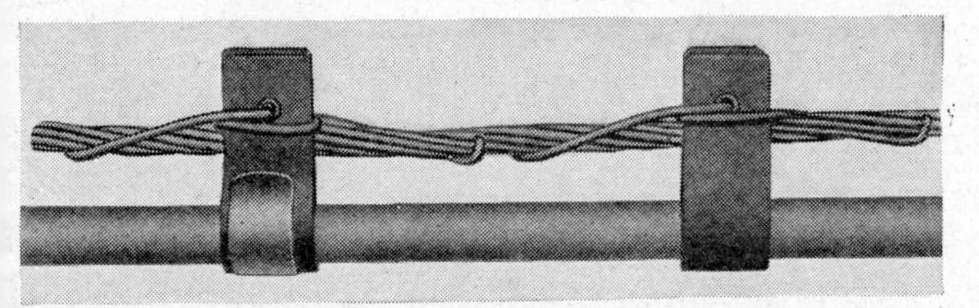

ELDER CABLE SUSPENDER

Fig. 61. Note the wire clips that are placed over the cable and secured to the individual slings so as to assist prevention of cable movement.

SWITCHES AND SWITCHING

A GREAT variety of local control switches is available, but it is only possible here to show representative types, with explanations of the salient features. The constructional requirements of these switches are: (1) Sound base of vitreous porcelain, (2) Proof against surface leakage, (3) Great mechanical strength, (4) Snap action, controlled by robust spring able to stand up to repeated action, (5) Lever action mechanically strong, (6) Ample insulation between live parts and "dolly". A surface pattern switch, of the "all-insulated" type which combines the above requirements, is now often employed, while Fig. 63 shows details of a simple type of switch action still extensively in use. The principle is employed in less expensive switches.

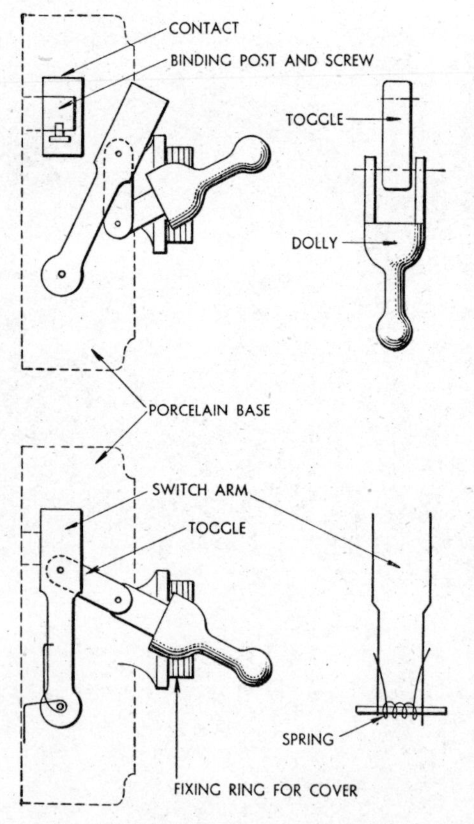

Fig. 63. Diagram showing simple link, or "toggle" action, of a less expensive type of switch mainly used in domestic installations.

For use on concealed wiring systems the flush types are available; these may be obtained as "all-insulated" types in brown, white and most colours, also with metal surface plates finished in oxidised copper, oxidised silver, bronze, and other pleasing effects.

FLUSH SWITCHES

Cast iron boxes must be provided for use with flush switches (Fig. 64). These are fitted with screwed entry and can be used direct for attachment to screwed conduit, or with split screwed bush for use with plain conduit.

Boxes fitted with lug-grip fittings are provided for direct connection with plain conduits. Good cast boxes also provide adequate fire protection, and are fitted with threaded fixing screws which give a sound mechanical attachment for the switch. Deep boxes with adjustable alignment grids are provided for some situations. These are designed for use in building work where the conduit is erected before plastering is finished. They allow for adjustment to the finished plaster level.

PENDANT SWITCHES

These are designed for control of single lights only, usually as "bed-point" switches. Owing to their ornamental nature they are inclined to be somewhat "flimsy" in construction. Care should be taken to use only those made by reputable manufacturers, to ensure getting sound mechanical construction. A more durable form is the ceiling-pull switch (Fig. 65), operated by a hanging cord; these being larger, have more scope for mechanical strength and also the advantage that live cords (always a source of minor troubles) are dispensed with.

A form of two-, three- or four-point switching is available which gives great

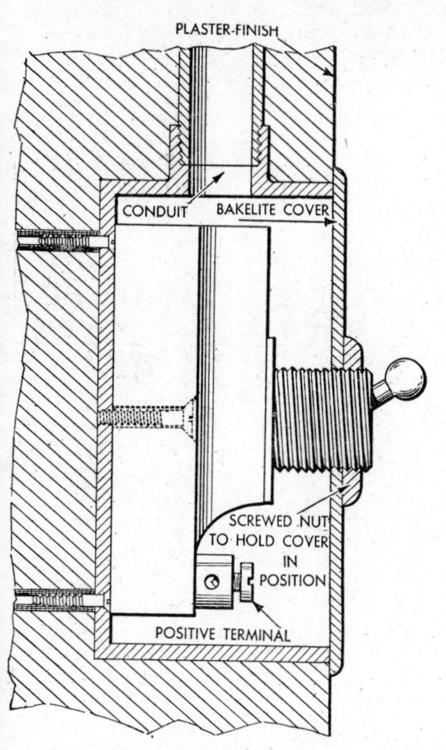

Fig. 64. Sectional side view of a typical flush switch sunk below the finished plaster level.

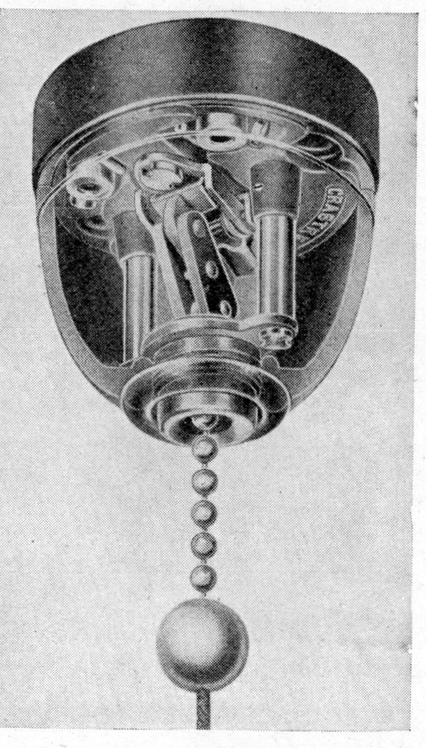

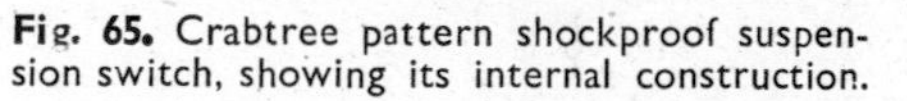

Fig. 65. Crabtree pattern shockproof suspension switch, showing its internal construction.

MULTI-POINT SWITCHES

Fig. 66 (Left). Crabtree two-way switch and (right) intermediate switch, showing details of interiors. The two-way switches occupy the outer positions or extreme ends of wiring. (See Fig. 67).

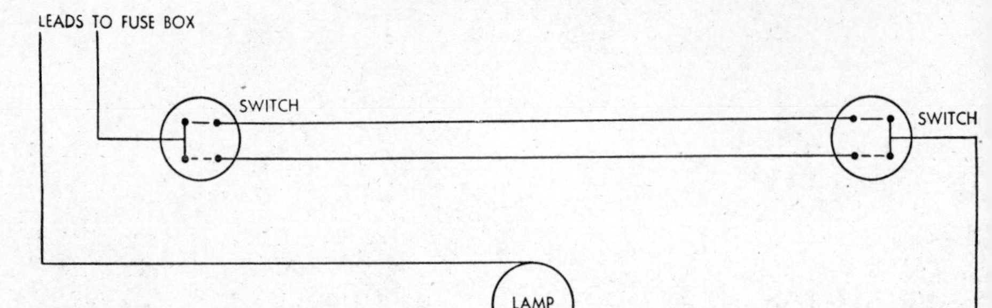

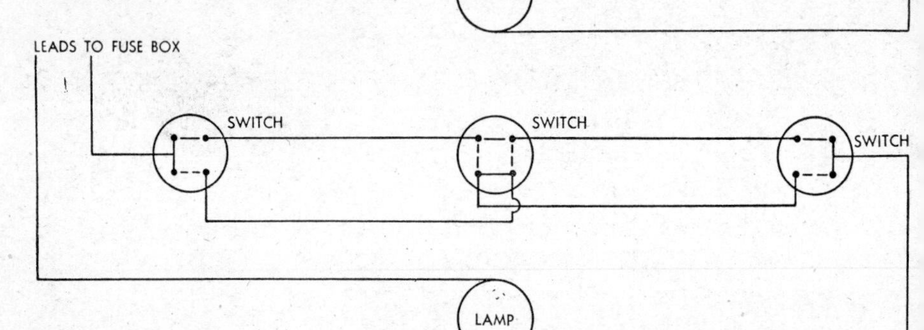

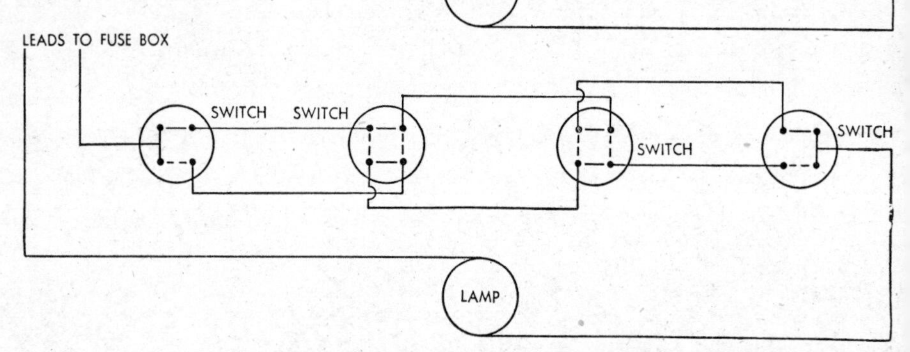

MULTI-POINT SWITCHING CIRCUITS

Fig. 67. Convenient control for stairway and corridor lighting can be arranged with specially constructed switches. Two- three- and four-way switching schemes are shown in these diagrams.

convenience for lighting control on stairways and in corridors. This demands specially constructed switches (Fig. 66), and complicated wiring. Fig. 67 illustrates the wiring for two-, three- and four-point control. Switching can be obtained by reversing the switch knob position at any point.

Cooker and Heater switches are usually of the rotary type and must handle heavy current up to twelve and fifteen amperes; having double-pole contacts, strong snap action, capable of breaking the circuit without arcing they are usually arranged for high, medium, low and off positions, as they are used in conjunction with heating elements which are arranged for this form of control. They provide what is known as series-parallel control (Fig. 68), a very useful means of securing temperature variations of hotplates and ovens. Similar rotary type switches are

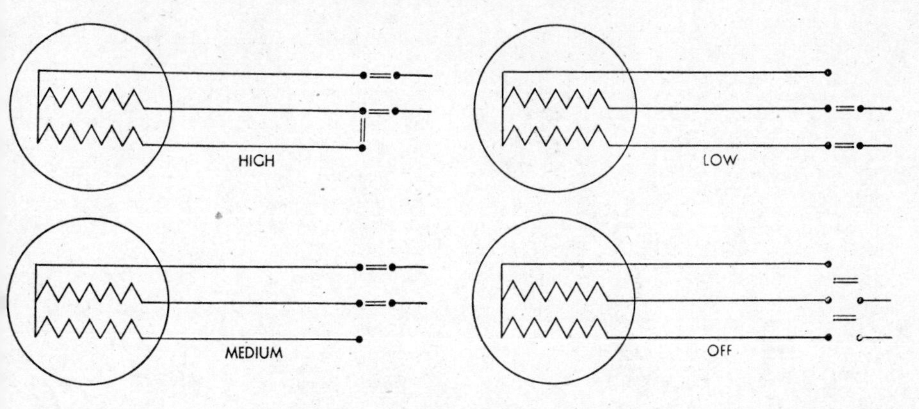

CONTROL FOR HEATING ELEMENTS

Fig. 68. Theoretical representation of the functioning of a type of switch which provides for the series-parallel connection of heating elements and thus gives temperature variations for hotplates and ovens. Only the one element is used in the "medium" position.

used for electric radiators, but arranged for one-, two- or three-bar control. The series-parallel system is not suitable for radiators, as the bars always burn at their maximum red heat, and temperature control is adjusted by switching individual bars in or out.

The cooker cables are taken from a cooker switch control panel. It consists of a double-pole switch capable of carrying thirty amperes, mounted in a cast-iron box, and with it one separate five-ampere circuit fitted with 3-pin plug and fuse to provide a convenient connection for kettle or iron.

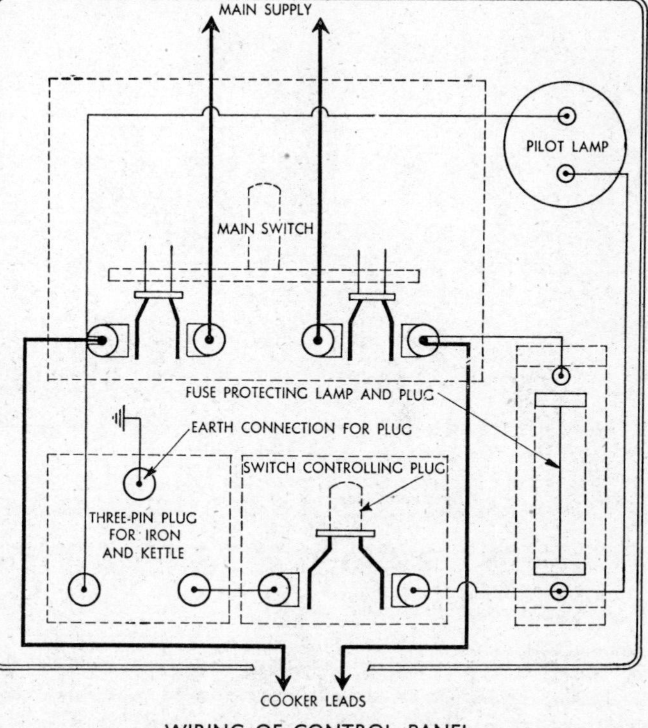

WIRING OF CONTROL PANEL

Fig. 69. Circuit of the control panel of a cooker. Main fuses are not generally fitted in these panels and section fuses are usually fitted inside cooker's outer casing. The pilot lamp is in circuit the whole time that the main switch of the cooker is closed. In some designs a mechanical indicator is used instead of a lamp to show whether the current is "on" or "off".

Automatic interlock exists between switch and plug to prevent withdrawal while plug is "live". A red pilot lamp or mechanical indicator gives warning whether current is *On* or *Off*. Main fuses are not generally fitted in these control panels, but section fuses guarding the various elements are fitted inside the outer casing of the cooker. A theoretical circuit for one such panel is shown in Fig. 69.

DOMESTIC TYPES

For domestic installations there is a large variety of suitable switches, ranging in capacity from five to thirty amperes, both in ironclad and all-insulated types. These are of the double-pole variety for use on low voltages, and in the ironclad type (Fig. 70) are provided with "bushed" entry, that is to say, conduits do not enter the switch directly, but cables enter without protection, a small amount of slack cable being allowed before it enters the insulating bush (Fig. 71b). Every ironclad switch must be provided with a strong earthing screw to give electrical continuity on to the switch case. Alternatively, as shown in Fig. 71a, the conduit itself is joined to the switch casing by a coupler.

"All-insulated" switches generally have a solid base of porcelain with a cover of bakelite, and arrangements are made in both types of switches by an interlocking device, to ensure that the switch is in the

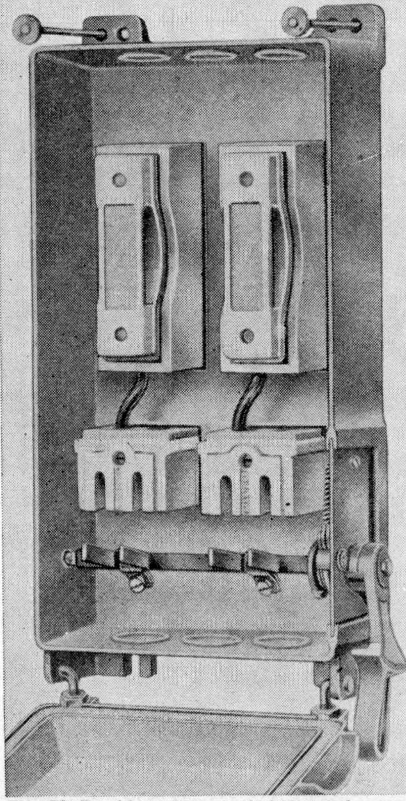

Fig. 70. Double-pole iron-clad switch for use on low voltages. It may be provided with a "bushed" type of cable entry as at Fig. 71b.

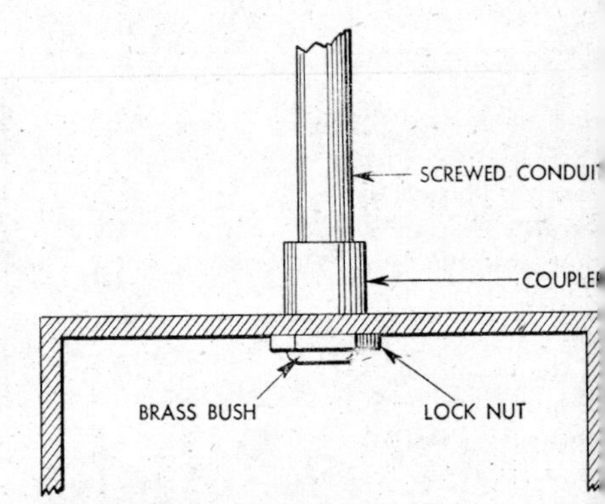

Fig. 71a. Diagram showing entry to switch case by screwed coupler with lock-nut. An alternative method of cable entry applicable to switch on left is shown in the diagram below

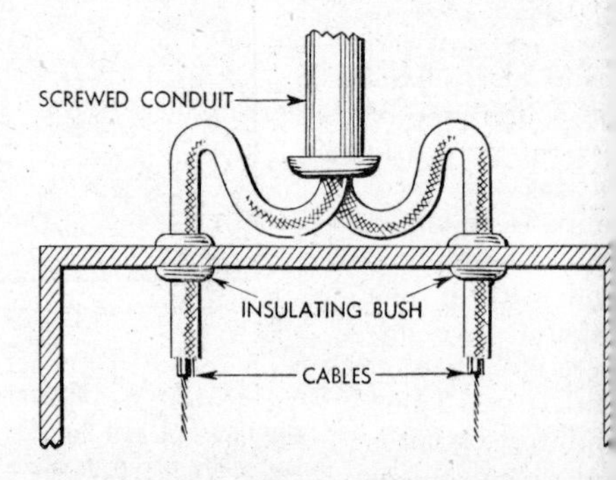

Fig. 71b. Slack cables and insulated bushes are used for this method of entry into a switch casing which requires to be bonded to earth

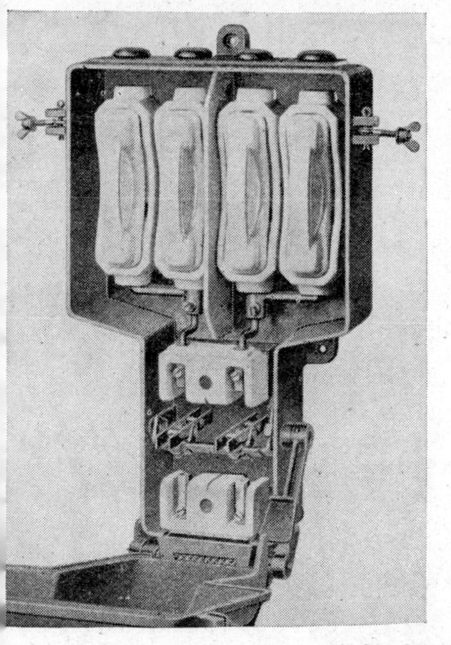

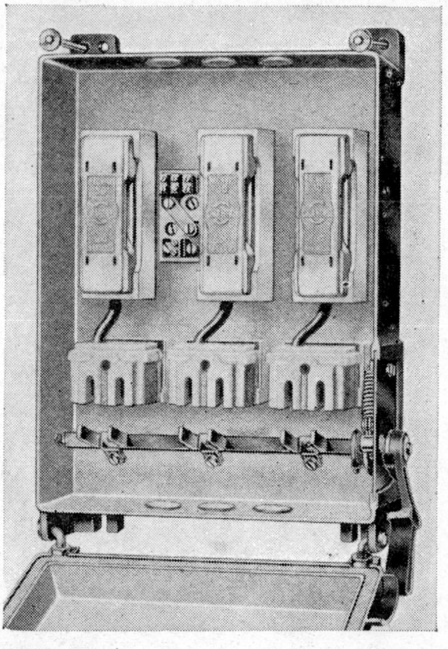

IRON-CLAD SWITCHES

Fig. 72. Main switch and small distribution board combined for small installations. It is known as a splitter switch and permits an economy in use of fuses. Connections are made by bushed entry of the type shown in Fig. 71b.

Fig. 73. Crabtree three-phase industrial power switch for alternating current with neutral link and fuses. The case is provided with "knock-outs" removable at will. Modern industrial power switches are always iron-clad.

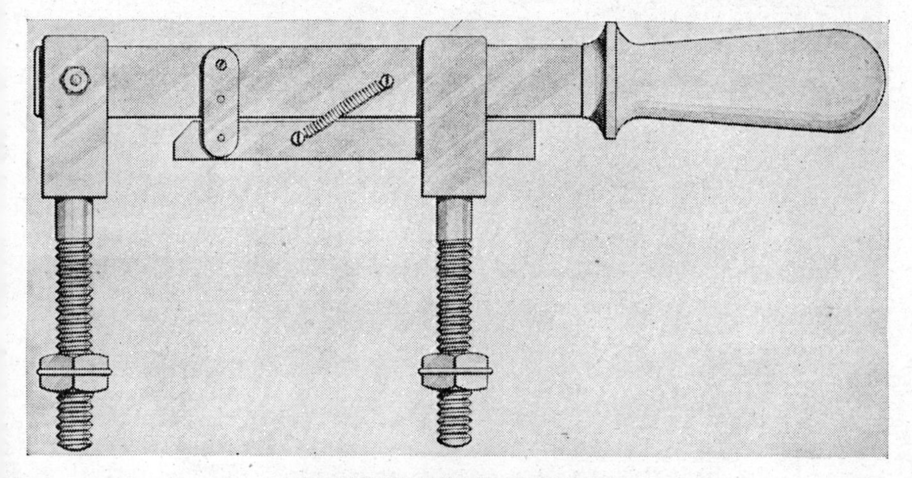

SINGLE-POLE KNIFE SWITCH

Fig. 74. Quick-break action is obtained by means of a spring. When the main blade disengages from the contacts, the auxiliary blade remains until the spring pulls it out with a snap thus accelerating the breaking of the circuit. In this way the arc formed by the heavy current is broken. It is impossible to break this type of switch slowly, a very strong spring is used to couple the front and rear blades. This type of switch is designed for mounting on a panel.

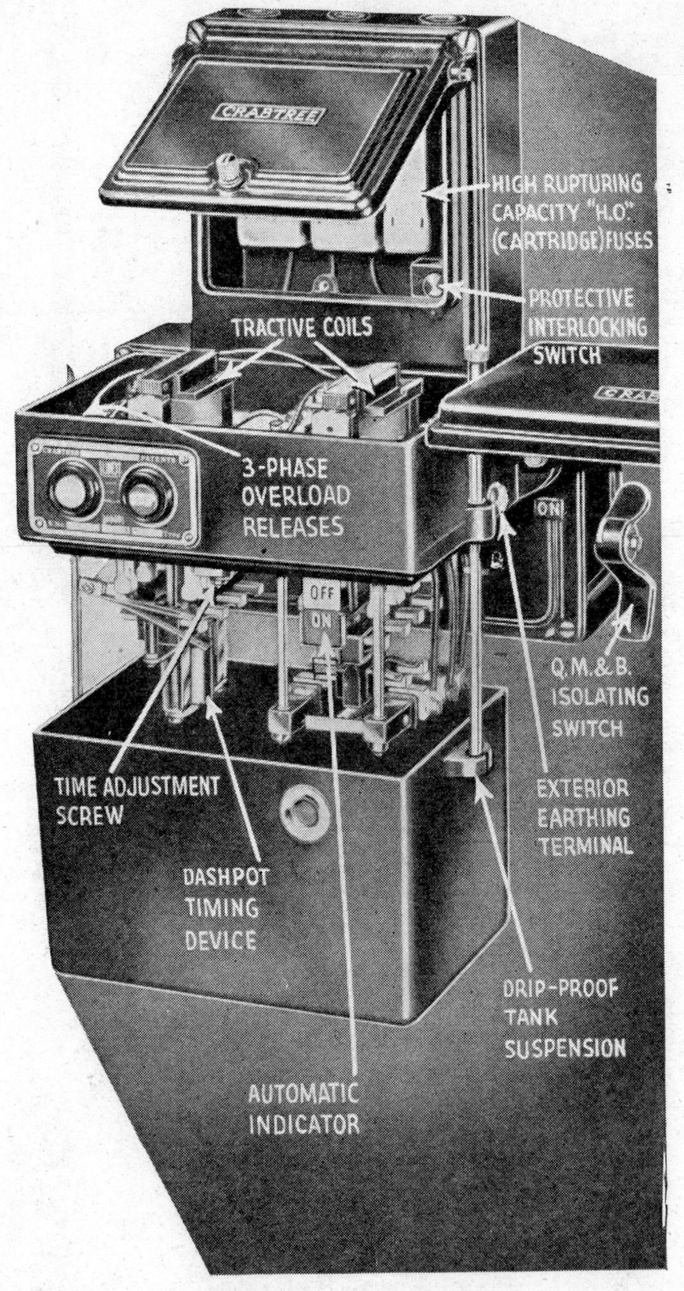

OIL-IMMERSED POWER SWITCH

Fig. 75. Crabtree oil-immersed power switch for alternating current, in the form of a 3-phase automatic motor starter with automatic indicator. The current-carrying switch parts are immersed within the tank.

Off position before the cover can be removed.

All main switches must be double-pole pattern to give simultaneous operation on both poles with the switch movement, and detachable fuses of the porcelain bridge type are included. These types of switches are not intended for industrial or power use.

The useful splitter switch (Fig. 72) for small installations combines the functions of the main switch and small distribution board. The circuits numbering two or three are directly "split" at the main switch, thus doing away with one pair of control fuses. Electricity Regulations, however, limit the loading for which these switches may be used.

The maximum number of fuseways in a splitter must not exceed three and this type of switch is not permissible if the connected lighting load exceeds five amperes and the total connected load exceeds thirty amperes.

Industrial and power main-switches (Fig. 73) are always iron-clad and while resembling the previously mentioned ironclad switches, are generally more robust in construction and provided with larger spacing between live parts. Such switches belong to the medium voltage or 500-volt class, and are provided with arrangements for screwed conduit entry direct into switch. Bush entry with slack cables is not allowed in the 500-volt class. The switches can also be obtained in watertight patterns, designed to close on a carefully machined facing, with packing gland, which will prevent entrance of water. As heavier cables are used, considerably more space must be allowed for manipulation inside the switch. Power switches are also made with triple-pole main switches and triple-fuses. These are for control on three-phase A.C. systems.

KNIFE SWITCH

Switchboard "knife" switches are designed for panel mounting and are essentially of "quick-break" action in addition to being capable of handling heavy currents. The blades of the switch are divided into two parts, the front one of which is mounted rigidly with the ebonite handle (Fig. 74); the back half is attached to the front piece by a strong spring. Laminated jaws of strong springy copper are mounted on the panel, with bolt connection through and terminal nuts behind. On moving the ebonite handle, the front piece is withdrawn to an angle of approximately 60 degrees, while the spring is placed in tension to the full extent; the spring then overcomes the friction holding rear piece in position causing this to fly out with great rapidity, breaking arc formed by heavy current. It is impossible to break this switch slowly. A heavy switch is constructed so that no current is carried by the hinged parts, as this would be liable to set up serious heating owing to the slight freedom of the parts where the hinge joins the supporting bolts. Sizes are available from 10 to 1,000 amperes for Direct Current use and are also made as double-throw types suitable for "change-over" from one supply to another.

OIL-IMMERSED POWER SWITCHES

Switches for use with A.C. which have to carry heavy loads, are of the oil immersed type in which the "breaking" points of the switches are surrounded by an insulating and non-combustible oil in a tank (Fig. 75). The oil provides a means for rapidly quenching the arc which forms when heavy currents are interrupted. These switches are of the three-phase type, which have three switches operating simultaneously one in each phase line. Owing to this method of construction, A.C. switches follow quite different lines from their D.C. counter parts. Frequently, too, switches of this class are operated by remote push-button control by means of a magnetic solenoid. This is found especially convenient where large switchboards are concerned. Some of these switches having large capacities, require a large amount of force to operate, and are frequently beyond the limit of manual operation; they also require considerable floor space. It has been found necessary, therefore, in large power stations, to operate these switches from a central control desk, from which small

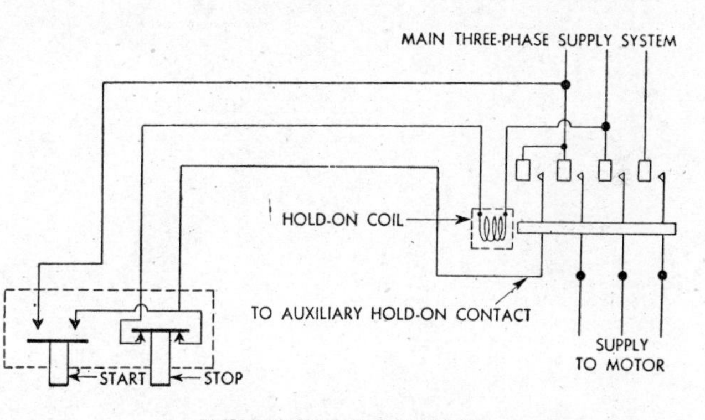

Fig. 76. Theoretical circuit for push-button control switch, using a hold-on coil, which gives remote control of main control panel.

TEN-AMPERE TIME SWITCH

Fig. 77. Venner time switch suitable for the control of current up to 10 amperes. The switch contact is of the air-break type. Switching is sometimes carried out by a mercury dipper switch.

cables run carrying comparatively small currents. These, in turn, operate large magnetic solenoids or motors for opening and closing switches sometimes at very considerable distances from the control point.

PUSH-BUTTON SWITCH

A switching device that will be frequently met with in industrial systems is the push-button control type. This is a form of remote control and operates in conjunction with some form of relay or holding-on coil fitted in the main control panel. The use of the switch allows the control of power at a distant point without the necessity of diverting heavy cables to the control position. The controlling wires which may be run in conjunction with several other "stations" are of small gauge, as only the magnetising current for the holding-on coil has to be carried. Fig. 76 is a theoretical diagram showing the general principle of the switch.

There is no limit to the distance over which a remote control of this kind can be operated. For short distances the simple hold-on coil is quite effective and more elaborate relays are seldom needed.

TIME SWITCHES

Time switches are a form of automatic switching suitable for the control of shop window lighting, street lighting, etc. The mechanism takes the form of the usual clockwork construction but has to be mechanically very robust, as it is called upon to operate the switching mechanism as well (Fig. 77). The familiar clock face is absent, and is replaced by a 24-hour brass disc, usually painted black in one section to indicate the approximate hours of darkness. Two indicating pointers, which are sliding arms, are provided, each of different lengths, which can be set to indicate "switch-on" and "switch-off" positions. These can be locked in place. An ingenious mechanical arrangement ensures the arms engaging with a pivoted lever to secure the necessary on-off movement. The end of the lever terminates in a dipper switch and mercury cup, which makes and breaks the electrical circuit (Fig. 78). By this means fairly heavy currents can be carried by the switches. The movement is usually 8-day, but clocks can be obtained to give alternative switching so that arrangements can be made to avoid switching on for certain days, for example, Sundays, early closing days, etc., or to any specified requirements. Maintenance, other than winding and an occasional inspection is nil.

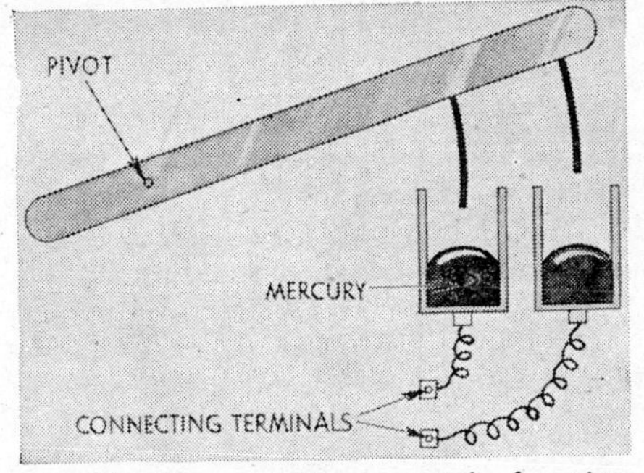

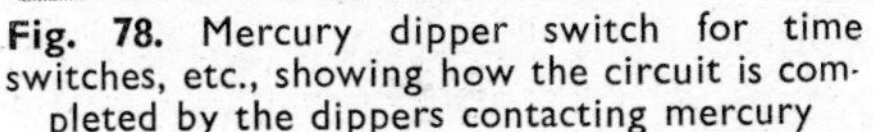
Fig. 78. Mercury dipper switch for time switches, etc., showing how the circuit is completed by the dippers contacting mercury

MERCURY SWITCHES

A form of switch which has come into use increasingly during the last few years is the mercury switch. This is employed in apparatus of an automatic nature such as water heaters, time clocks, etc., where control of reasonable amounts of current can be secured without very heavy mechanical parts. The construction is as follows:—A glass tube about two and a half inches long forms an enclosure into one end of which is fused two electrical contact pieces, separated by about half an inch spacing. The contacts are supplied with flexible connections protected by porcelain bead insulation by which they can be joined to the circuit terminals. A quantity of mercury lies in the tube, but the tube is balanced by a rocking lever in such a way that in one position the mercury remains at one end of the tube out of range of the contacts. On the control lever being operated (usually by thermo-action) the tube is tilted sufficiently for the mercury to run to the other end where it rests, covering the two lead-in contacts. An electrical contact capable of making and breaking the current in safety is secured by this means with very little mechanical effort. A typical enclosed type is illustrated in Fig. 79. A representative use for a switch of identically this construction is in a refrigerator which, by means of a thermo-action device as mentioned above, is automatically switched off and on at predetermined temperatures in order to maintain constant refrigeration and to prevent the unnecessary use of electrical current.

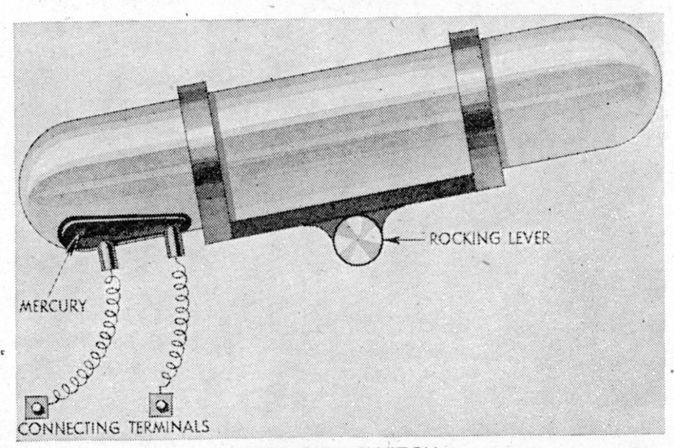

MERCURY SWITCH

Fig. 79. Enclosed mercury control switch, as used in refrigerators, showing how contact is made and the circuit closed by tilting the tube.

FAULT LOCALISATION

To provide a high standard of safety and reliability it is necessary that an electrical installation is subjected to exacting tests with regard to its insulating properties. These are laid down in "The Regulations for the Electrical Equipment of Buildings", issued by the Institution of Electrical Engineers and are recognised by electrical authorities generally, as providing the necessary standard of perfection. A consumer can be legally compelled to keep his installation in the necessary state of repair under penalty of disconnection of service supply.

What then, are the requirements of this insulation test of an electrical installation? Very briefly they are these:—

For a general lighting installation test, the total outlets are counted (by "outlet" is meant any lighting point, switch or plug at which a supply is given) and the total is divided into the number "50", the resultant giving a number which expresses the minimum insulation resistance required in megohms. An example will make this clearer. A small lighting installation has 10 lighting points, 10 switch points and 5 lighting plugs—total outlets 25. The number 50 divided by 25 then gives 2 megohms as the insulation resistance required for such an installation. Larger installations have generally a much lower insulation resistance than smaller ones, owing to the larger amount of possible leakage points, and this method of deciding the testing standard takes this fact into account, as a consideration of the above will show.

Fig. 80. Evershed and Vignoles "Wee" Megger insulation and continuity tester in case.

There is also a proviso in the regulations that no complete installation in which the insulation leakage is evenly distributed, need exceed 1 megohm, this figure being found quite satisfactory by experience.

For power appliances such as motors, dynamos, arc lamp resistances, etc., which consist of some form of mechanical construction, the minimum value is half a megohm for each piece of apparatus, tested separately. It is also stated by the regulations that a D.C. source of not less than twice the working potential must be used for these tests.

INSULATION TESTING APPARATUS

The standard portable instruments for Insulation Testing are those sold by Evershed & Vignoles, Ltd., under their Registered Trade Mark, "MEGGER". These include the Wee-Megger Tester, Fig. 80, the "Meg" Insulation Tester, Fig. 82, and the high range "Megger" Insulation Tester, the choice of instrument depending on the desired testing pressure and range of insulation required. The actual instrument shown in Fig. 80 has two ranges enabling both insulation and continuity tests to be made. Every type of "Megger" Insulation Tester

STANDARD PORTABLE INSTRUMENT

Fig. 82. Evershed and Vignoles' "Meg" insulation and continuity tester. It comprises a hand-driven generator, and direct reading ohmmeter.

consists of a hand-driven generator and a direct reading ohmmeter combined in one case, the principle of operation being shown in Fig. 81. The ohmmeter movement consists of two coils, the control coil and the deflecting coil, which are connected in parallel across the generator, the deflecting coil being in series with the insulation resistance under test. The two coils oppose one another, and the ultimate position of the pointer on the scale will vary with the ratio of the currents in the two coils, this ratio depending only on the value of the insulation resistance under test, since variations in voltage affect both coils in the same proportion.

In order to make a test it is merely necessary to connect two wires to the terminals on the instrument, turn the generator handle at about 160 r.p.m., and read the position of the pointer on the scale of the ohmmeter. In extensive wiring systems there will be considerable electrostatic capacity between the conductors and earth which renders advisable the use of a constant speed model of the Megger having a slipping clutch which slips at a certain speed. In this way direct readings of resistance are given without the necessity of using batteries or any other independent source of current for testing.

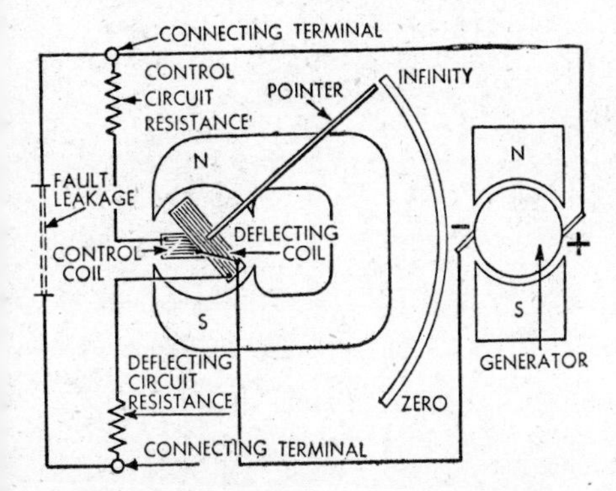

Fig. 81. Diagram showing principle of Evershed and Vignoles' "Wee Megger" tester.

METHOD OF FAULT LOCALISATION

It should be realised that the testing instrument is really a "tool", capable of giving only a particular reading when connected to a circuit. It, therefore, demands intelligent use if it is to aid in the localisation of a fault. Successful fault-finding is the result of years of

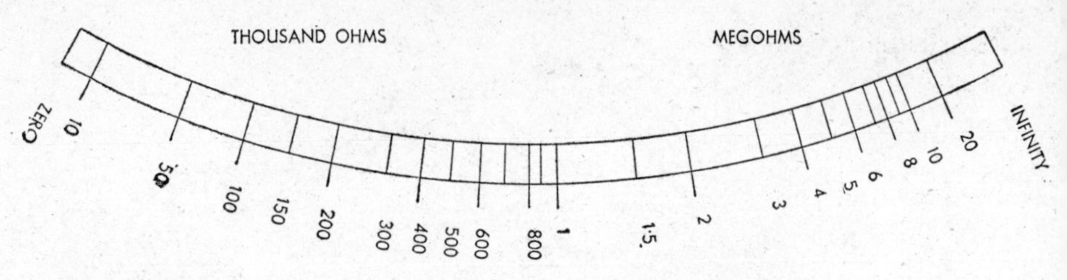

Fig. 83. Enlarged scale of the "Wee Megger" tester. Actual size is $2\frac{5}{8}$ ins. approx. The scale covers both continuity and insulation tests for which direct readings in ohms and megohms are given.

practice and, in time, an electrician will develop a "flair" for looking in those places which his experience tells him are likely sources of trouble; but *method* must always be the keynote of successful fault localisation.

A reference to the section on Electrical Installations will give the reader an idea of the general planning of an installation, and the general method of localisation will be described. The installation will be presumed to be one of moderate size, consisting of lighting only. Two types of test must be carried out. The first is known as "between poles" (Fig. 84) and is the measure of the insulation resistance between the "live" and return wires of each separate circuit, and the second is an "earth" test (Fig. 85) to measure the insulation resistance between each wire and "earth". By "earth" is meant any body of conducting material such as water pipes, steel girders, etc., which would provide a leakage path directly down to the main body of the earth. All lamps must first be removed from their sockets, and all switches left in the "on" position. This is very necessary, as it ensures bringing the testing voltage right across the lighting points. If this were not done, possible faults across the ceiling cords and adjacent wires, would be concealed by the presence of the lamp in the socket (Figs. 86, 87 and 88). Great care must be taken to see that the main control switch is open, thus safeguarding the operator and preserving the testing instrument from damage.

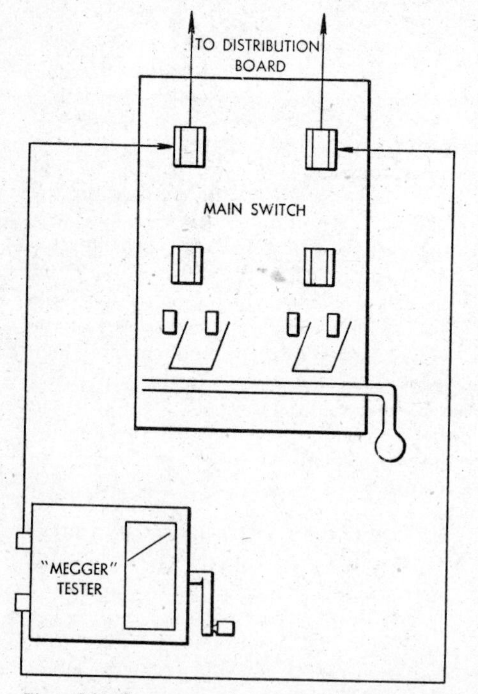

Fig. 84. Between-poles test of insulation using a Megger between live and return wires.

MAKING THE TEST

Take a general test of the whole of the installation between poles and earth. This is done as follows:—Provide the testing instrument with two "tails", consisting of thoroughly sound cable, about two yards long, fitted to earth and line terminals provided; place on a rigid base, in a thoroughly comfortable and well-lit position. These points are very important because, as a testing job may be of a somewhat protracted nature, discomfort and strain on the part of the operator, may lead to slovenly, unmethodical work, and as difficulties are sure to be encountered, the operator's frame of mind is not likely to be improved by working in uncomfortable conditions. Make methodical notes of each test. This is also important, as reference back is sometimes needed, and also a change in the value of a particular test may provide a clue leading in the right direction.

To make the earth test, the testing wire from the instrument which is connected to the terminal marked "earth" must now be connected to earth. This is usually done by making a firm connection to a main cold water supply pipe which, by its nature, makes an efficient contact with the main body of earth. This may involve running out a length of connecting cable to some convenient position, but it is very necessary for a successful test. On no account should gas pipes or other earthed metal be used, as there is no guarantee of continuity to earth. This also applies to a water pipe which runs from a tank or from some fitting and not direct from the main supply.

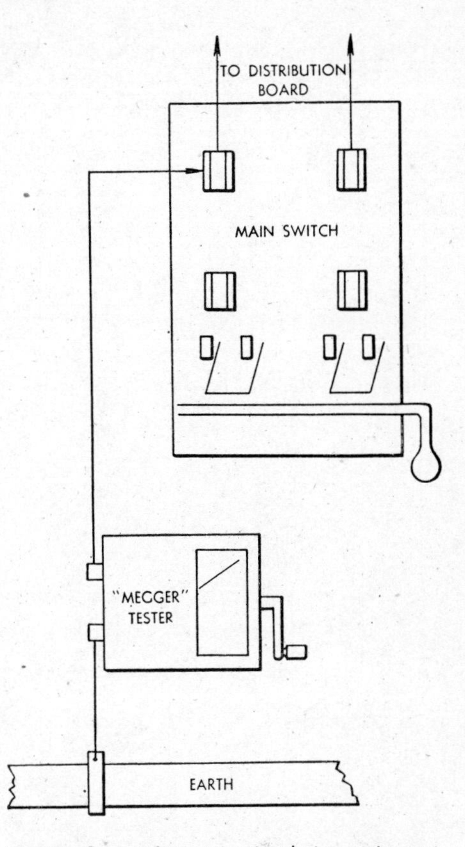

Fig. 85. Circuit for testing insulation resistance to earth. All the lamps must be removed.

SUB-DIVISION OF CIRCUITS

It will be assumed for the purpose of illustration, that an earth leakage reading "zero" has been indicated on the live main. The next step in location is a methodical sub-division of the wiring into groups, and a process of gradual elimination of the good circuits. The pair of main cables will feed into a distribution fuse-board at which all the circuit sections should meet. An assistant is stationed at the board and fuses are withdrawn in pairs, tests being made after each disconnection.

Assuming one of the circuits contains the fault, it will immediately be indicated on the withdrawal of the fuses concerned by the needle moving from zero to some much higher position. A re-check should be made of the remaining part of the installation, minus the defective circuit, to see if it gives a satisfactory test or otherwise. Attention is now turned to the circuit which is definitely indicated as faulty. This circuit may consist of from five to ten points, so further sub-division is necessary. It must be borne in mind that successful localisation aims at the minimum disturbance of the installation or building, and that anything undone or moved unnecessarily is wasted time, as it must subsequently be replaced. A little forethought, then, may well repay in time eventually saved. An examination of the wiring should be made, as far as possible, before disconnection is made. It is essential to know the extent of the circuit; which points belong to a particular circuit and, if possible, the order in which it proceeds from one point to another. This, of course, is where experience plays a large part; also an examination may reveal a helpful clue to

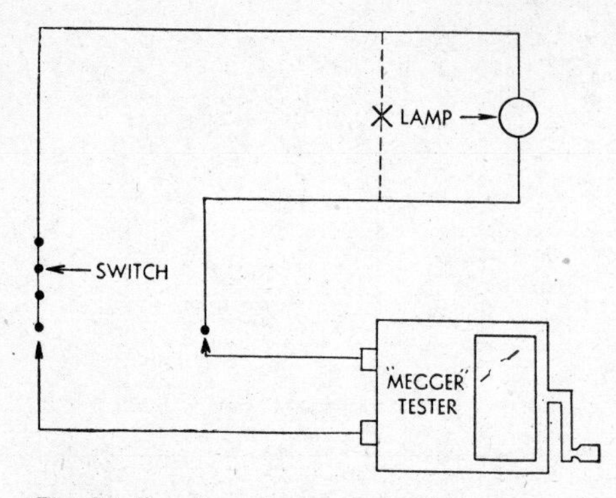

Fig. 86. Showing why lamps should be removed when making insulation test. Fault at "X" would be hard to locate with lamp left on.

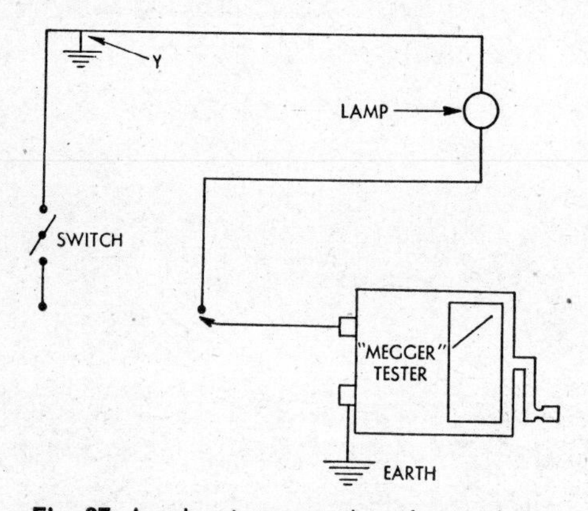

Fig. 87. Another instance where leaving lamps could cause a confusion in testing. Fault at "Y" would seem on wrong main with lamp left in.

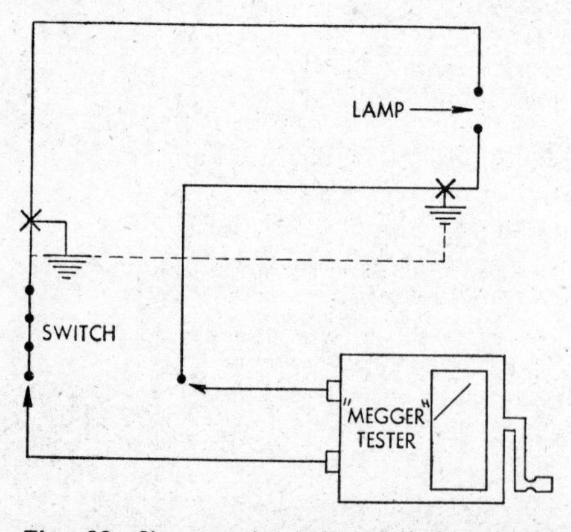

Fig. 88. Showing how "earth" fault might register as low test between poles. This is the type of fault that dampness could originate.

the source of the trouble. Note should be taken, for example, of possible dampness, the evidence of leaking water pipes, structural alterations to the building or any other factor which may provide a clue to possible damage to the installation at any point.

SUB-DIVISION OF WIRING

In a correctly wired installation, sub-division should be easy, as all modern wiring is done on the "loop-in" system (see Figs. 89 and 90). Reference should be made here to the section on electrical wiring for an explanation of "looping-in".

The circuit should now be divided into two parts. This is done by removing a switch and ceiling fixture at a point approximately half-way along the circuit, and opening out the loops at each. This will leave the first half joined to the testing set, the second half being disconnected temporarily.

A further test to earth should now be made. If the fault is now cleared, it can be presumed to lie in the remaining part of the circuit. If the fault still shows, it obviously occurs on that portion being tested. Proceed by this method of sub-division by trial and test until finally one loop only remains which cannot be further sub-divided without cutting. Careful inspection may reveal the actual point of earth fault, or, if the wiring is encased in tubing, it will be necessary to dismantle that section for repair. Remember, the object of localisation is to find the approximate location of the fault before any dismantling or cutting is done, thus saving the cost of reinstatement of work which has proved not to be faulty.

Tests must be taken at each additional movement. This is very important because faults, or at least low tests, may exist on the bases of any accessories removed, and this will provide an indication immediately on their removal. Also, in work which has been installed some years, wires become dry and the movement involved in disconnecting the accessories may either cause more faults to develop or the reverse effect. By moving the point of contact through which the current is leaking it may render it difficult to locate. This leads us to a class of fault which is very difficult to locate.

INTERMITTENT FAULTS

Faults sometimes occur in which the contact with "earth" is of a varying nature. Owing to the fact that at the actual moment of testing the fault remains temporarily clear, it provides an electrical "will-o'-the-wisp", which is the bane of the electrician and calls upon every ounce of his skill and experience.

This explains why extreme care and method should be used in carrying out and recording the various tests. Under such circumstances, recourse has to be made sometimes to various subterfuges to attempt to bring the fault "on", such as vibration of floorboards by stamping, disturbance of the suspected parts by gentle hammering, etc.

This accounts for the need of the high voltage used on the testing set. Regulations specify that the testing voltage shall be at least twice the normal voltage, and this high voltage helps to break down across intermittent faults or places of poor insulation which might not be revealed by a lower testing voltage.

GENERAL LOW TESTS

A class of test is frequently called for in which no actual fault occurs at one specific point but, nevertheless, a general low insulation test exists over the installation as a whole. On sub-dividing and testing the various circuits individually, it is found that the test is much higher, which is really due to the fact that a lesser amount is being tested and the insulation appears relatively higher at each subdivision. The point is really that in such an installation it can be presumed that, while no direct fault of low value exists, there are many thousands of contact points at which small amounts of leakage occurs and which are cumulative. One such case would occur in an installation that had been in service many years, where the insulation has become poor in condition, combined with the effects of dirt and damp in the bases of accessories generally. When such a state is indicated, no attempt should be made to repair small portions, because from practical experience it has been proved cheaper to re-wire the system and replace the accessories (or, at least, those not proved entirely above suspicion), than to waste time in many hours of fruitless testing which, under the circumstances, cannot improve the state of the insulation.

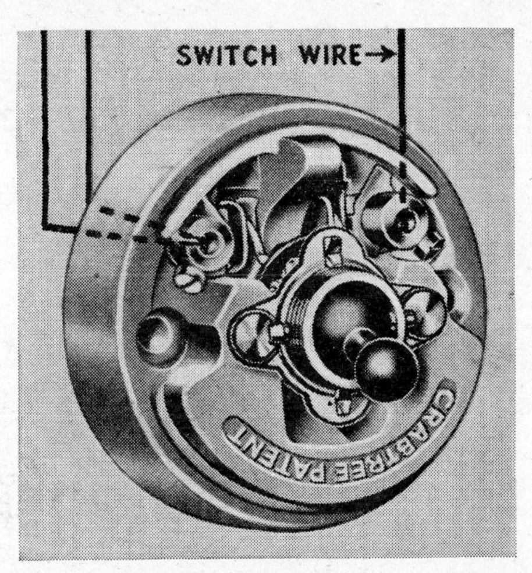

Fig. 90. This is a switch wired in accordance with the loop-in principle which is shown theoretically in Fig. 89.

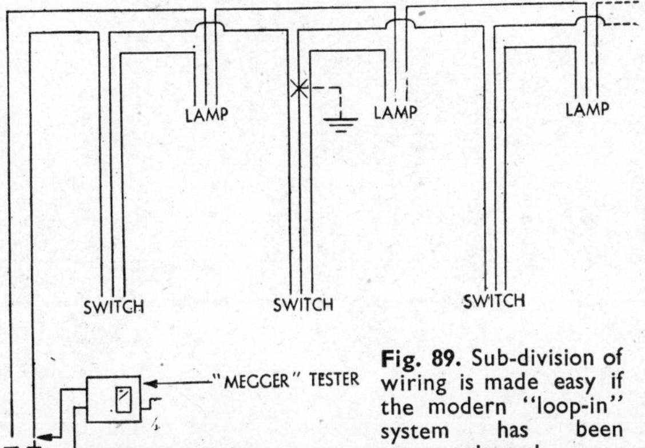

Fig. 89. Sub-division of wiring is made easy if the modern "loop-in" system has been adopted.

CHAPTER 6

ELECTRIC MOTORS

Direct Current Motors. Principles of Operation. Details of Construction. Alternating Current Motors. Induction Motors. Synchronous Motors. Synchronous Induction Motors. Variable Speed Commutator Motors. Single-Phase Motors. A.C. Series Motors. Induction Motor Construction. Bearings. Performance of Electric Motors. Rotating Temperature Rise. Losses and Efficiency. Power Factor. Cooling and Types of Enclosure. Uses of Different Kinds of Motor. Load Speed Characteristics. Analysis of Industrial Drives. Recent Developments in Design and Construction. A.C. and D.C. Armature Windings. Connection of Phases. Materials.

BEFORE discussing motors in detail it would be wise for us first to decide what we mean by an "electric motor". In simple terms, it could be described as a box into which is lead a supply of electricity and out of which protrudes a steel shaft, which can be made to rotate. In more scientific parlance it is a piece of apparatus for converting electrical energy to mechanical energy in the form of rotary motion. It is in fact the most convenient and compact source of mechanical energy so far discovered.

Here then we have in the motor the most important link between the electricity suppliers and the consumers, where the energy, produced by the generators and handled by switchgear, transformers, and converters, is turned into useful work.

Proceeding from this general survey, we might next seek an answer to the question "How does a motor operate". Briefly, this could be answered by the statement that rotation of the "armature", as the moving part is termed in a D.C. machine, or "rotor" in the A.C. case, is brought about by the forces exerted on its conductors (when they are carrying current) by the magnetic field which is produced in the stationary system.

In the following pages it is intended to describe in detail the various forms of motor first from a theoretical, then from a constructional standpoint. For this purpose the simplest classification will be into direct and alternating current motors.

DIRECT CURRENT MOTORS

REFERENCE has already been made in an earlier chapter to two main principles which govern the functioning of all electric motors, namely, first:—

The fact that a force is exerted on any electrical conductor or wire situated in a magnetic field, whenever a current is made to pass along the wire. (See Fig.1), and complementary to this:—

The fact that a voltage is generated in a conductor whenever it is made to move through or across a magnetic field.

(It is in fact to this latter simple phenomenon discovered by Faraday that the electrical engineering industry owes its existence.)

It should be mentioned here in passing, that although we are interested primarily in motors, there is no real difference between a D.C. motor and a D.C. generator, both represent the same machine employed in different ways. Each machine develops both a torque, that is a turning effect and a voltage (or e.m.f.). In the motor the generated voltage is less than the supply volts so that the current is forced in the opposing direction. Conversely, in a generator the developed torque is less than the driving torque applied and the armature rotates in the opposite direction to that of the opposing torque developed by the output current that is generated.

Keeping an eye on the basic principles outlined, let us now consider what we require in a D.C. motor. In the first place we must have:—

(a) A magnetic field of considerable strength. For this a "field system" is employed.

Secondly there must be:—

(b) A conductor or conductors on which the driving forces are to be exerted. These conductors form part of the "armature", that is to say, they comprise the armature winding.

Finally it is necessary for there to be:—

(c) Some arrangement for conveying current to the armature conductors and for causing this to flow in the correct direction at any instant. This requirement is fulfilled jointly by the "brushes" and the "commutator".

The field system consists of the main frame or "yoke", the main poles, interpoles and field coils, and forms the greater part of the magnetic circuit as shown in Fig. 2. The position of the magnetic lines of force or "magnetic flux" as they are termed collectively, is indicated by the dotted lines, the flux itself being established by the field coils when current is passing through them. As will be seen from Fig. 2 the armature core forms the flux path between X and Y. With the exception of the short distance where the flux passes from the pole shoe to the armature, which is known as the "airgap", the whole of the magnetic circuit consists of iron or steel on account of the high permeability of these metals compared with that of air and other media; actually it is about five hundred times greater than that of air. The field coils are so connected that alternate poles all produce flux in the same direction, each being of opposite polarity to its neighbour, as indicated by the arrowheads representing the direction of the flux. The region where the magnetic flux is of most interest to us is between the pole shoe and the armature

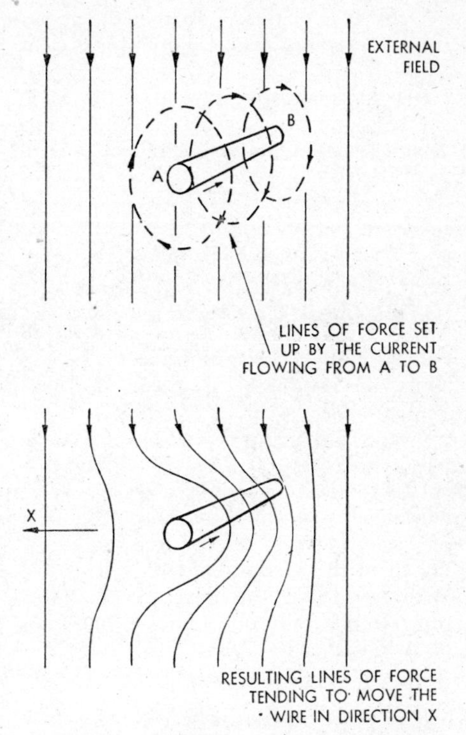

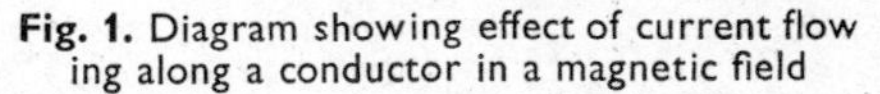
Fig. 1. Diagram showing effect of current flowing along a conductor in a magnetic field

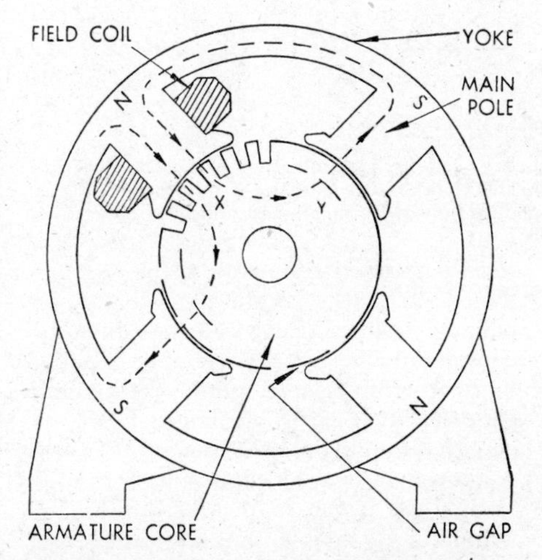

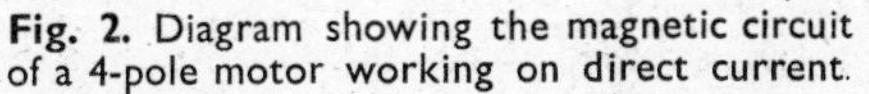
Fig. 2. Diagram showing the magnetic circuit of a 4-pole motor working on direct current.

because it is at this point that the armature conductors are actually able to cut through it.

We have already spoken of the force exerted on any current-carrying conductor situated in a magnetic field as well as of the voltage generated in a conductor moving through it. It must be realised however, that these quantities for a single wire are relatively small and both are proportional to the field strength in the region of the wire at any instant, i.e., Force per conductor is proportional to field strength × current in wire.
Volts per conductor are proportional to field strength × velocity of wire.

Now the armature winding of a D.C. motor consists of a large number of conductors connected in pairs by "end windings" to form coils. Specific details of various types of winding are contained in the section entitled "Armature Windings". Fig. 3, however, illustrates (diagrammatically only) how in one type of winding, the "start" of one coil

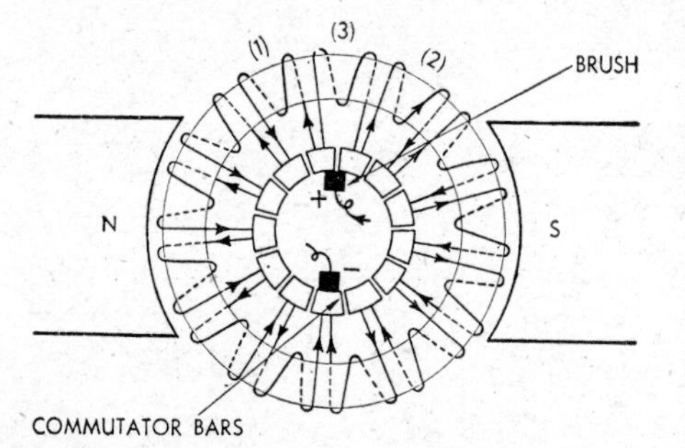

Fig. 3. Simplified diagram of 2-pole armature and commutator showing winding connections, direction of current being indicated by arrows.

together with the "finish" of the next are joined to one "commutator bar". In passing it should be noted here that the commutator is virtually a copper cylinder built up from a large number of tapered copper bars each insulated from its neighbour by thin segments of mica. A typical industrial commutator can be seen on the armature illustrated in Fig. 4.

Sliding on the commutator surface are two or more blocks of graphite or "brushes". These are mounted, one, two or more abreast, on brush arms, the number of arms corresponding with the number of main poles in the machine. From Fig. 3 it will be seen that as each coil passes from position (1) to position (2) the direction of the current indicated by the arrows in that particular coil is reversed or "commuted", hence the use of the name commutator. During this period the coil is said to be undergoing commutation. The brush arms are so positioned circumferentially that the coils being commutated are always those which, at the instant in question, are situated midway between the main poles, e.g., coil (3). This systematic reversing of the current ensures that when coils are under poles of north polarity, the current flow is always in a certain direction, while when they are under poles of south polarity it is always in the opposite direction. The resulting individual torques in the wires therefore, though pulsating, never actually reverse with respect to the motor shaft. Similarly, the generated e.m.f.'s though alternating in each particular conductor, are always in the same direction with respect to the motor terminals. A glance at Fig. 3 will show that there is always the same group of coils between the two brushes relative to the main poles, although the actual coils forming the group are changing constantly. As long as the magnetic flux, produced by the "field" coils is maintained constant, the total effect on the armature conductors will also remain constant, producing a steady torque at the shaft and causing a steady voltage to be generated between the brushes. *This occurs whether or not the machine is operating as a motor or as a generator.* For the machine to operate as a motor the supply voltage must:—

(a) Force the armature current through the resistance of the armature windings.

(b) Counteract, i.e., overcome the e.m.f. generated in the armature winding by its rotation in the main field, i.e., the "back e.m.f."

If we interpret these requirements in the form of an equation, we obtain the fundamental relationship for a motor,

ARMATURE OF D.C. MOTOR

Fig. 4. D.C. Armature complete with typical industrial commutator and cartridge-type bearings. A fan is provided for purposes of cooling. Note the ventilating ducts along core (see page 236).

and this can be expressed as follows:—
Supply volts = generated volts + volts drop in the armature resistance, or using symbols:— $V = E + IR$.

SPEED OF ROTATION

What determines the speed at which the armature of a D.C. motor rotates? Let us assume that we have a D.C. motor in which a constant current is passing through the field coils, thus producing a fixed amount of magnetic flux. Suppose now that we switch a 220 volt supply, for example, across the brushes of our motor, which is in effect across the armature. A heavy current will immediately flow through the armature conductors since the total winding has only a low resistance; the motor will then begin to accelerate on account of the turning effect produced by the forces exerted on the conductors by the magnetic field as described previously. The armature will go faster and faster until the gradually increasing voltage generated in the armature winding (back e.m.f.) is just less than that of the supply voltage, the difference being the volt drop in the armature resistance, as already discussed; let us assume this occurs at 500 r.p.m.

Suppose now that the amount of flux had been half what it actually was, and that we had switched on to the armature the same 220 volt supply, then it would have been necessary for the armature to reach a speed approximately twice that reached under the previous conditions, before the back e.m.f. generated would be high enough to bring about the voltage balance again; in other words, by halving the magnetic flux we can raise the speed from 500 r.p.m. to roughly 1,000 r.p.m. This fact leads us to what is probably the most important property of a D.C. motor, namely, the ease with which the speed of rotation can be varied. The following simple rule summarises our point.

(a) Field strength reduced : speed increased.

(b) Field strength increased : speed reduced.

The strength of the field is, of course,

determined by the number of "ampere turns" present in the field coils or, for a given motor, merely by the number of amps. flowing through the turns of the coils. Thus to control the speed of a D.C. motor, all we require is some means of varying the field current; this is normally effected by connecting a rheostat (variable resistance) in series with the field coils as shown in Fig. 5(a) and 5(c).

FIELD WINDINGS

Industrial D.C. motors fall into three main groups which theoretically differ only in the way in which the field coils are connected, but their working characteristics differ considerably. They are known as "shunt-wound", "series-wound" and "compound-wound" motors. Fig. 5 indicates diagrammatically the three arrangements. The field winding of a shunt motor consists of coils wound with a large number of turns of fine wire and is connected directly across the main supply circuit all the time that the motor is working; it is in parallel with, i.e., "shunted" across, the armature winding. The series motor, on the other hand, has field coils wound with a few turns of heavy wire through which the armature current passes because the field winding is in "series" with the armature. The compound motor, as its name implies, possesses both shunt and series windings, the series coils usually being the smaller.

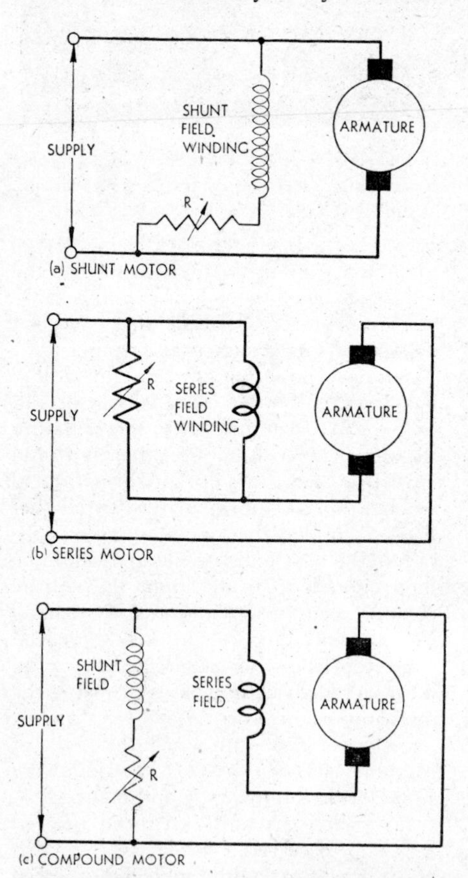

Fig. 5. Diagrammatic arrangement of the field windings of D.C. motors showing field rheostats (i.e., variable resistances), for speed control at R.

INTERPOLES

On any modern motor of moderate size the reader will no doubt have noticed that between each pair or each alternate pair of main poles is a smaller pole, an interpole, visible in Fig. 6. The sole task of the interpoles is to ensure that satisfactory commutation can be obtained at all loads, particularly on overload, without the need for "rocking" the brushes as was done in the old days. In other words they prevent sparking at the brushes; the reason for them being referred to as commutating poles will now be apparent. The action of the interpole is twofold, in the first place it neutralises the effect of the magnetic field set up by the current in the armature winding, i.e., "armature reaction", whose axis is at the neutral plane between the main poles. This prevents a voltage being generated in the coil being commutated which is short-circuited by the brush. It also causes a small reverse voltage to be generated in this coil just sufficient to ensure that the current in it has been completely reversed before its commutator bar has moved from under the brush.

CONSTRUCTION OF D.C. MOTORS

We have discussed how a D.C. machine operates; it is now intended to give some idea of how the theoretical requirements are embodied in the manufacture of present-day industrial machines. First, we will consider the magnetic system of a motor.

The yoke of a modern D.C. motor complete with the main poles and interpoles is illustrated in Fig. 6. For this main ring-shaped frame, rolled steel billets have now greatly displaced the former cast-steel construction, because of their better magnetic qualities, that is, the ability to carry more flux, and their increased mechanical strength. The use of cast iron has, for similar reasons, now practically ceased altogether. This development has resulted in considerable reductions in the size and weight of modern machines compared with the older ones. In the larger D.C. machines a split yoke like the one illustrated is frequently adopted to facilitate erection and dismantling operations.

D.C. MOTOR YOKE

Fig. 6. Field system of 6-pole D.C. motor showing main poles and interpoles complete with field coils. Note the split yoke.

The number of main poles is determined largely by practical considerations commencing with 2 in the case of small motors, 4 and 6 being usual in the 5 to 250-h.p. range, while much greater numbers of poles are encountered in very large machines. Main poles can be either machined from solid steel or, as is now customary, built up from heavy steel laminations about one sixteenth of an inch thick and held together by long rivets. The practice of using built up poles favours the commercial policy of employing more than one length of core in the same diameter of machine. In addition the use of laminated poles (or pole shoes only) minimises the eddy currents set up in the pole face by the flux "swinging" from tooth to tooth as the armature rotates. The earlier method of casting poles solid with the yoke is now seldom followed.

Normally, interpoles are made from solid steel bar and on larger machines are usually tapered towards the inner end. At this end an interpole tip is bolted on to the body section, the tip usually being longer than the interpole acts as a support for the interpole coil.

The poles are secured to machined seatings inside the yoke by bolts screwed through from outside into holes tapped in the pole bodies. It is customary to insert between a pole and its seating one or two thin sheets of steel known as "liners" so that variation of the airgap can be effected by adding or removing one.

FIELD COILS

Shunt coils which, normally, are of fine wire are usually wound with single cotton covered wire (s.c.c. wire), double cotton covering being employed often for diameters over 0·032 in. In special machines for operating at high temperature, asbestos covered wire, and during the last year or two, wire covered with glass fibres, have been employed. The coils can be wound either on wooden formers afterwards removed, or as some manufacturers now do, directly on to metal spools, which have been first insulated with pressboard or mica wrap and washers. Metal spools tend to avoid high internal temperatures, give a more solid coil and also reduce the danger of damage during assembly.

Series and interpole coils which like shunt coils are often found on spools, are wound with square or rectangular covered wire in the small sizes, while on larger machines and for heavier currents they are generally made from bare copper strap, sometimes wound flat, sometimes on edge.

It is now practically a universal practice for completed field coils to be impregnated with some insulating compound or varnish after drying them out to remove all moisture in order to prevent any loss of insulation value through hygroscopic action, i.e., absorption of moisture. Reference to one highly successful process in which the complete coil is impregnated solid with bitumen is made in the section on "Armature Windings".

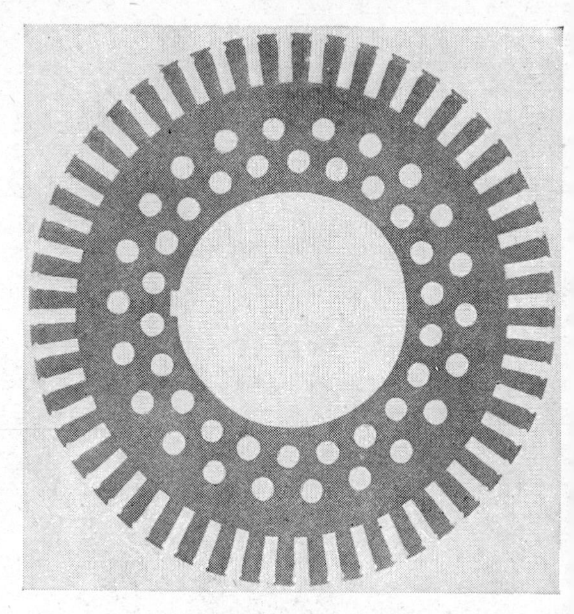

ARMATURE LAMINATION

Fig. 7. D.C. motor armature punching, showing keyway and axial ventilating holes, stamped from thin sheet steel.

ARMATURE COMPONENTS

The complete armature of a D.C. motor besides including the winding and core to which we have referred comprises also the shaft, commutator, bearings and, for a ventilated machine, the fan. All these items are clearly visible in Fig. 4.

The shaft is made from a solid bar and machined in steps corresponding to the bores of the core, fan, commutator bush and is usually ground to size where these members are actually located. The largest diameter occurs usually in the middle, that is at the core.

For the armature core, which forms part of the magnetic circuit, a solid piece of steel would be desirable for many reasons, but unfortunately this is not practicable on account of the eddy currents which would be induced in the solid metal just as the currents are caused to flow in the windings of a generator. It has, therefore, been found necessary to build up the core from thin steel sheets about ·016 in. thick insulated from each other by thin layers of paper pasted on. The sheets are punched out (except in large diameter armatures) in complete rings like the one in Fig. 7. The punchings, or laminations as they are termed, are held compressed between two end plates. The tightness of the core is obtained by squeezing the punchings together in a hydraulic press during building. One endplate rests against a shoulder on the shaft while the other is locked in place by a keyring slipped into position when the core is still in the press. A long piece of rectangular steel, or "key", which fits half into an axial groove in the shaft and half into the punchings, prevents the core rotating on the shaft and hence transmits the torque from the one to the other. In larger machines, and usually where the number of poles exceeds six, the core laminations are built up, not directly on the shaft, but are carried by a "spider" much as the rim of a wheel is carried by the spokes. This avoids the need for a solid core where only a small depth of iron is necessary.

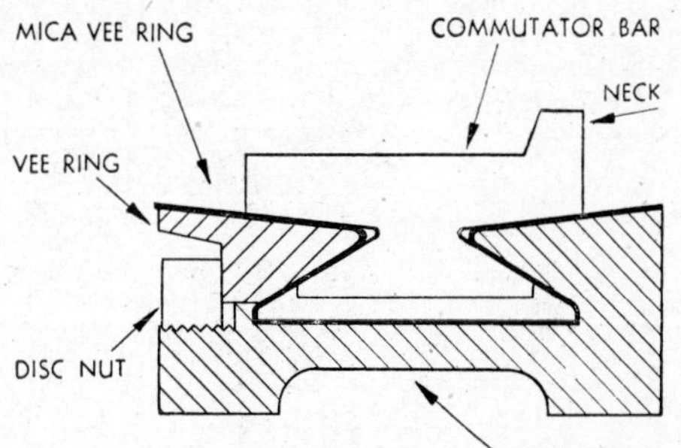

Fig. 8. Sectional drawing of a typical commutator showing method of retaining segments.

COMMUTATOR

We have already referred briefly to the commutator, but the reader will now see from the sectional drawing, Fig. 8, more of how the copper and mica segments are held in position. The principal feature is that the segments have vee-shaped portions cut away from either end enabling the whole assembly of bars and micas to be clamped between two correspondingly shaped steel rings. Separating the bars electrically from these rings, i.e., the "vee-ring" and "commutator bush" are two mica rings of vee-section. A final forcing of the vee-ring along the bush forces the tapered bars inwards thereby producing a finished commutator which is extremely robust.

The detailed features of the brushgear on a normal industrial machine will be fairly obvious from Fig. 9, it is not intended, therefore, to take up further space by describing its construction in detail

ALTERNATING CURRENT MOTORS

THERE are several fundamentally different types of A.C. motor in industrial use at the present time, but by far the most widely employed machine is the three-phase induction motor. It has become so universally popular for normal steady speed drives, by reason of its relatively low cost and simple construction, that speaking of the range of motors from 5 h.p. to 5,000 h.p. at 1,000 r.p.m. there are now more machines of this design in service than of all other types put together, including both D.C. as well as A.C. machines. Usually, when an A.C. motor is referred to without any other indication of its type being made, it is an induction motor which is meant.

INDUCTION MOTORS

The first practical induction motor was designed as far back as 1888 by Tesla, although it was not until the standardisation in relatively recent years of three-phase alternating current in this country for power supply, that the induction motor really came into prominence. The principle on which an induction motor operates is briefly this; a "closed" i.e., a short-circuited coil is placed in a magnetic field, the axis of which is rotating, and the coil begins to rotate also in an attempt to follow the field. In order to understand this fully, some conception must be obtained of what is meant by a "rotating field" and how it is produced.

Rotating Magnetic Field. Let us consider the essential parts of an induction motor. First we have an outer-ring-shaped mass of iron known as the "stator core", shown diagrammatically in Fig. 10(a). Inside this there is a circular core, the "rotor core" mounted on its shaft and separated from the stator by a small air-gap all the way round. In actual practice there are axial slots along the inner surface of the stator and on the outer surface of the rotor, but these have been omitted from the diagram in order to reduce it to the theoretical form required and thus to avoid any confusion.

Supposing now there are three coils placed in stator slots in the position shown in Fig. 10(a), and that they are connected respectively to the three phases of an A.C. supply. The end windings are not shown since the diagram is intended to imply that we are looking on to the ends of the embedded portions of the coil ; the significance of the dot and cross to indicate the current direction will no doubt be familiar to the reader. The time relationship between the phase currents flowing in the corresponding three coils will be as in Fig. 10(b). At the instant "p" the current in phase A is at a maximum. Therefore, neglecting the phase currents B and C which at this moment are small, the field axis will be in a direction P, the general direction of the flux being shown by the dotted line. Now consider the position $\frac{1}{3}$ of a cycle later when B is maximum, i.e., the instant "q", then the resultant field is along Q. Similarly, another $\frac{1}{3}$ of a cycle later, the field is at R. It will be seen in this arrangement, that is a 2-pole system, that the flux axis makes one complete revolution every cycle. The reader will no doubt have time to trace out the intermediate positions and also to prove for himself that when, for example, A is a maximum, both the other two phase currents B and C increase the effect due to current A to a small extent and vice versa.

Voltage Induced in the Rotor Circuit. Let us now examine the effect produced by the rotating field on the rotor. In principle we are visualising the rotor winding as being a single short-circuited coil. As soon as the stator supply is switched on, a voltage is generated in the rotor coil, due to the lines of force cutting the coil as the field rotates, or it can be viewed, by reason of the persistent changing of the number of magnetic lines passing through the coil. It is this phenomenon of the voltage being "induced" in the rotor coil, which gives the motor its name. *There is no electrical connection between the supply and the rotor winding.* The induced voltage causes a current to flow which tries to oppose the effect of the rotating field. The interaction of this current and the rotating magnetic field make the coil begin to rotate and follow the field round, taking with it the rotor core in which it is embedded. The speed of the coil can never actually catch up with that of the field, because in such an eventuality, i.e., at "synchronism", there would be no relative movement between the coil and the field axis. This would mean

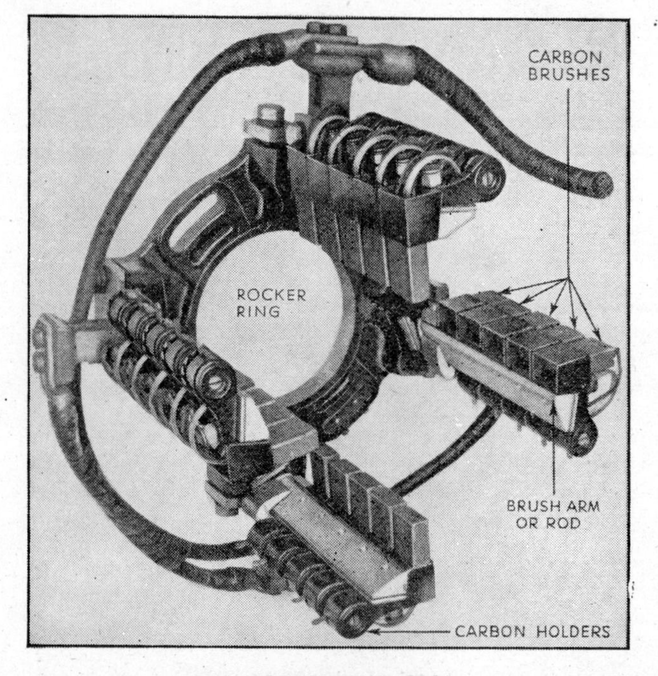

D.C. MOTOR BRUSHGEAR

Fig. 9. Details of the brushgear construction for a 4-pole D.C. machine showing the rocker-ring, brush arms and carbon brushes.

no alteration in the flux linking the coil and hence no induced voltage to produce the driving current. The difference in speed between the frequency of rotation of the field and that of the rotor itself is known as the "slip", and is usually expressed as a percentage of the synchronous speed.

The synchronous speed in revs, per minute of an induction motor is given by the following formula:—

$$\frac{\text{Supply Frequency} \times 60}{\text{pairs of poles}}$$

or in the case of a 4-pole machine,

$$\text{r.p.m.} = \frac{50 \times 60}{2} = 1{,}500 \text{ r.p.m.}$$

(50 is the standard frequency in cycles per second of A.C. supplies).

It should be noted that the speed is not greatly influenced by the supply voltage.

TYPES OF ROTOR

Induction motors can be divided into two main groups:—

(a) Squirrel cage motors,

(b) Slipring motors,

which in principle are identical. In the squirrel cage machine the rotor winding consists of bare copper bars joined to two heavy copper end rings at either end of the rotor core, as in Fig. 11a. The bars are therefore permanently short-circuited. (The name is derived from the fact that an assembly of the bars and rings without the core rather resembles a squirrel cage.) A slipring rotor, Fig. 11b, on the other hand, possesses coils wound in slots and constituting three separate phase-windings. The three-phase leads are lead out to three brass or bronze sliprings mounted on the shaft. Whereas a squirrel cage rotor is virtually a low voltage heavy current winding, the slipring rotor carries a much smaller current per wire and uses a correspondingly smaller copper section, but has at the same time a greater number of conductors, with the result that a rotor voltage on open circuit of several hundred volts is quite common. When running normally, the slipring motor has its rotor

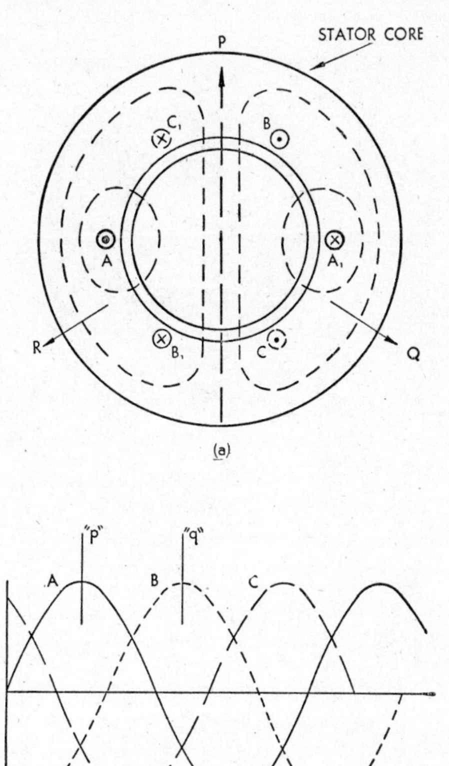

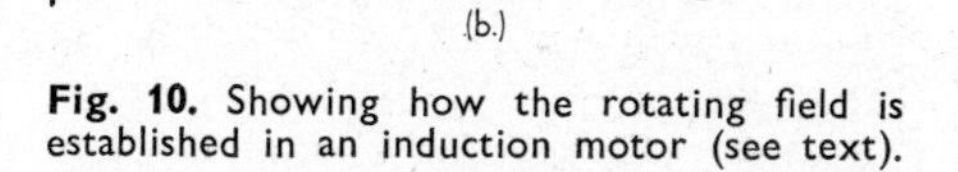

Fig. 10. Showing how the rotating field is established in an induction motor (see text).

winding short-circuited at the brushes.

Surveying the relative merits of the two types, the squirrel cage motor besides having a slightly better efficiency and power factor, has two main advantages over the slipring machine, in that

(a) It costs only about 75 per cent. of the price of the slipring motor and in fact is the least expensive of all types of electric motor for a given h.p.

(b) It requires considerably less maintenance in that there are no brushes and sliprings to keep in order, and it possesses a simpler and more robust construction resulting in great reliability.

The fundamental reason for the slipring design being employed at all is merely to enable the resistance of the rotor circuit to be varied, that is, increased. To

SQUIRREL CAGE ROTOR

Fig. 11a. Squirrel cage rotor complete with fan and bearings. The winding comprises bare copper bars joined to heavy copper end rings.

explain the need for this it will be necessary to consider for a moment the one serious drawback of the squirrel cage motor, namely, that of its high current at starting.

STARTING CHARACTERISTICS

If a normal squirrel cage motor of, for example, 100 h.p. be switched directly on to the three-phase supply it will exert probably a little more than its full load torque represented by point A in Fig. 12, but the current it will take initially before reaching top speed may be anything up to five or six times the normal current when running on full load. Except in the case of small motors, supply authorities are strongly opposed to such a practice. The only simple way to avoid the high starting current is to apply a reduced voltage to the stator; this, it should be remembered, does not appreciably affect the speed to which the motor will run up. The normal method by which this reduction in voltage is brought about is either by means of:—

(a) A "star-delta" starter which, as its name implies, involves connecting the stator winding first in "star" and then in "delta", or

(b) an "auto transformer" of the starter type.

The starting current is reduced in proportion to the value of the voltage, but the starting torque unfortunately also falls as the voltage squared. In case (a) therefore, while the starting current is reduced from 5 times to $5 \div \sqrt{3}$, i.e., 2·9 times normal, the starting torque instead of being just over the normal full load value at A is down to about one third of this value, i.e., Point B. The interdependence of torque on initial voltage is the same in case (b) only there the voltage tapping may be 50 per cent., 60 per cent. or 75 per cent. of normal. It is interesting to note that when something like full load torque is required with star/delta starting, or where, perhaps, twice full load torque is required with direct starting, a special "high torque" rotor

ROTOR FOR SLIPRING MOTOR

Fig. 11b. Wound rotor complete with sliprings. This method of construction enables a better starting characteristic to be secured by varying the resistance of the rotor circuit. Note the coils wound in slots.

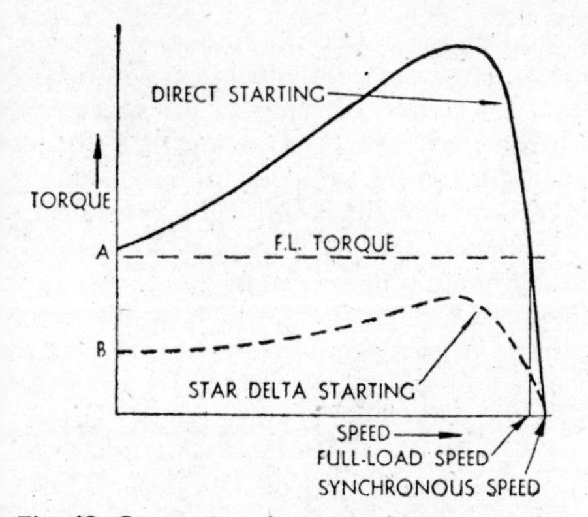

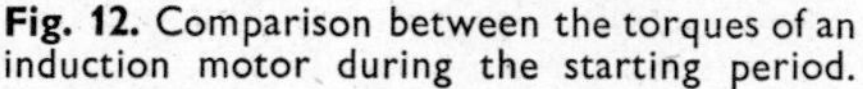
Fig. 12. Comparison between the torques of an induction motor during the starting period.

is frequently used. This has the starting characteristic shown in Fig. 13. In this case the starting currents differ little from those for the straightforward design, but the efficiency is usually lower due to increased losses in the rotor which frequently make it necessary to increase the size of the motor compared with the standard design. Such a rotor usually possesses a high resistance cage as well as one of low resistance, and is thus frequently referred to as a "double-cage" rotor. It is only when the current torque figures of even the high torque motor are unacceptable, and also where it is necessary to start up the load gently thereby avoiding the sudden application of torque which occurs when starting squirrel cage machines, that the real need for the slipring machine arises.

Earlier in this section we mentioned the

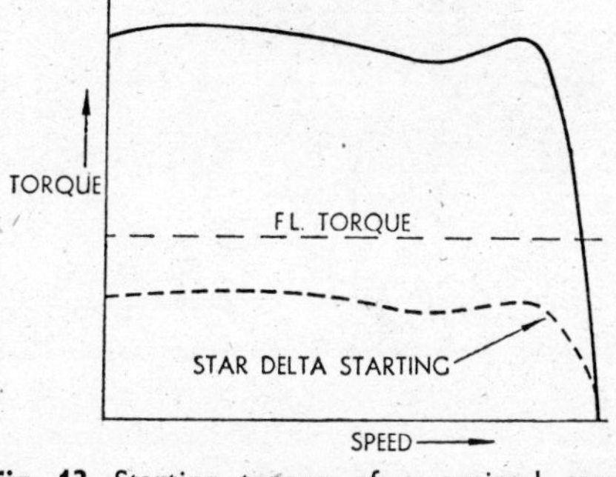

Fig. 13. Starting torque of a squirrel cage induction motor employing a "high torque" type of rotor.

"slip", that is the percentage by which the actual rotor speed on load is below that of the rotating field, i.e., below "synchronism"; in a 100 h.p. 4-pole motor this might be 3 per cent. meaning that its synchronous speed would be 1,500 r.p.m., but that it would run at 1,455 r.p.m. on load. The slight relative movement between the field and the rotor winding causes a voltage to be induced which in turn forces the normal rotor current through the rotor resistance. For the same full load torque, therefore, and hence the same rotor current if the total resistance of the rotor circuit be increased, it is necessary for the rotor voltage to rise, and hence the slip increases. Pursuing

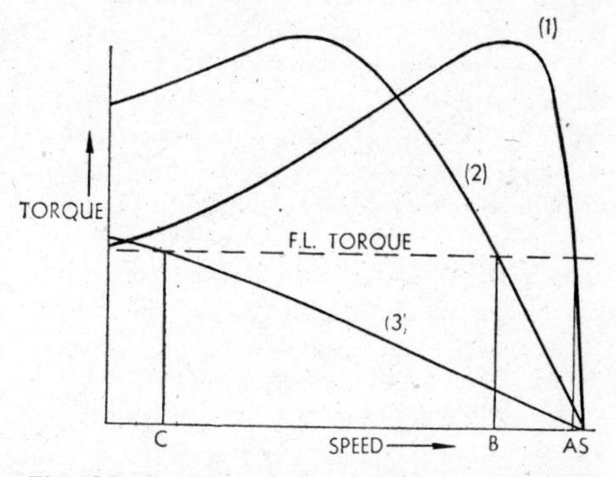

Fig. 14. Torque curves of slipring motor for different rotor resistances.

this we can so raise the rotor resistance that the slip at normal torque approaches 100 per cent. or, in other words, the speed is almost zero. Here, then, is where the sliprings play their part in allowing us to connect variable or fixed resistance units in each rotor phase winding via the brushes and rings. By this means we can obtain full load torque at starting with little more than full load current and, in addition, the speed will rise slowly depending on how quickly we bring back the rotor controller to zero resistance. Fig. 14 shows first in curve (1) the normal torque characteristic, indicating the normal speed at A. Curves (2) and (3) show how the characteristic changes when first a little resistance (2) and then a high value (3) are added, the speeds at full load torque being represented by B and C respectively.

In practice a special star-delta, three-phase type of starter resistance is connected across the slip rings of the motor for starting purposes, this resistance being gently reduced as the motor increases its speed.

SYNCHRONOUS MOTOR

Elsewhere in this work a description is given of a simple A.C. generator, or alternator as it is usually called, from which it will be apparent that in its simplest form an alternator is identical with a D.C. generator except that the commutator has been replaced by slip-rings connected to two or three fixed points in the armature winding, according to whether the machine is for single- or three-phase use. Just as a D.C. motor and generator are one and the same machine, likewise a synchronous motor and an alternator are also fundamentally the same. It will be appreciated, therefore, that a supply of direct current must be available for exciting the field coils.

There is a physical difference between the A.C. and D.C. cases in that it is now more usual for the armature winding to be on the stator so that the rotor then carries the "field system", the field current being led in via two sliprings. This is particularly advantageous in high voltage machines, where it avoids the use of high tension on the rotor and brushgear. Comparing the synchronous motor with the induction motor, in the latter case the magnetising current, which is the zero power factor component of the main current, is drawn from the mains, resulting in the lagging power factor, while with the synchronous motor this is furnished from the D.C. source. Thus, depending on the degree of D.C. excitation, the synchronous motor can be made to have a lagging, unity or even leading power factor. It is to the latter property that the machine owes its employment as a means of power factor improvement.

The machine has two limitations and these are as follows:—

(a) It can run only at synchronous speed, i.e. with the field system "in step" with the rotating field of the stator.

(b) It is not normally self-starting.

The latter difficulty is usually overcome by providing a cage winding mounted in the face of the field system. This operates as a squirrel cage winding

SYNCHRONOUS INDUCTION MOTOR

Fig. 15. Motor of this type needs a source of D.C. for exciting the rotor, which in this case is provided by a D.C. exciter overhung from the main machine. Typical connections are shown in Fig. 16.

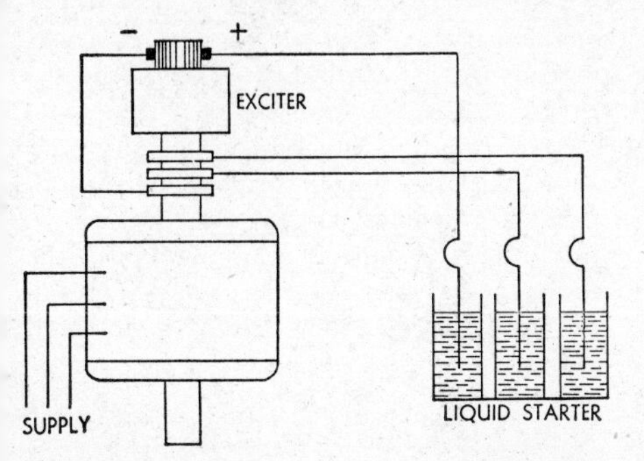

Fig. 16. Connections from synchronous induction motor to exciter and liquid starter.

until the speed of the rotor is just below synchronism, when the D.C. supply is switched in and the rotor pulls "into step". Alternatively, a small "pony" motor is necessary for starting purposes.

SYNCHRONOUS INDUCTION MOTOR

On medium-sized machines the S.I.M. is more frequently encountered than the pure synchronous motor. In construction it is identical with the slipring induction motor and during the starting period it actually functions as such, but when once up to speed it pulls into synchronism and operates as a synchronous machine. Like the latter it requires a source of direct current, which usually takes the form of an exciter coupled to the main motor. Fig. 15 illustrates an S.I.M. with an exciter overhung from the main machine while in Fig. 16 is shown a typical arrangement of connections.

VARIABLE SPEED MOTOR

This motor which has a definite, even if a limited field of application, operates on the principle of an induction motor; at the same time, however, it also makes use of a commutator. Electrically it consists basically of:—

(a) A 3-phase induction motor wound stator, referred to as the "secondary" winding in Fig. 17.

(b) A normal slipring rotor winding, i.e., the "primary" winding.

(c) A second winding on the rotor similar to a D.C. winding and connected to a commutator. A transformer action takes place between these two windings and tappings are taken from the second rotor winding to the commutator.

On the commutator of this machine are two distinct sets of brushes which can be moved independently in a circumferential direction, each set consisting of 3 equally spaced brushes. Each stator phase is connected to one brush of each set, so that by increasing or reducing the distance between brushes in one pair, differing voltages can be taken from the commutator and injected into the stator winding. The supply is to the rotor so that the stator winding behaves like the rotor winding of a normal machine. Appropriate relative movement of the brush sets by a suitable handwheel enables a wide range of speeds to be obtained on either side of the normal synchronous speed.

So far only three-phase motors have been considered, although large numbers of single-phase machines are in use chiefly for the smaller horse-power ratings. Space will not permit of a

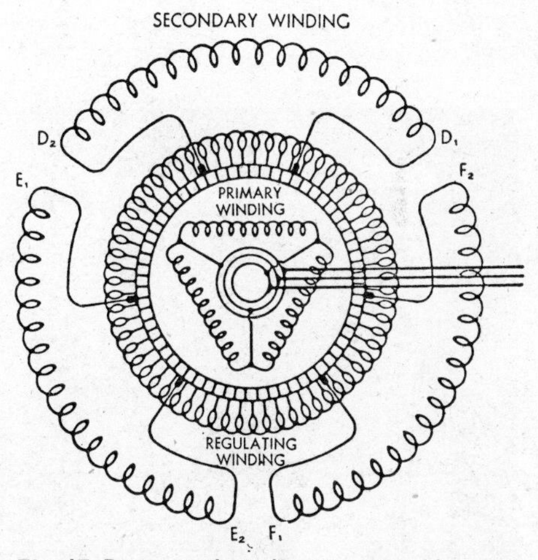

Fig. 17. Diagram of windings in a variable speed commutator motor using two rotor windings.

detailed description of these various kinds, but of the induction type there are split-phase, capacitor motors, shaded-pole motors, etc., which depend for starting at least on the production of a phase difference between the currents flowing in two parts of the stator windings to establish the rotating field effect.

Leaving for the moment the induction and exclusively A.C. types of machine, the series commutator motor is a machine finding regular if not extensive application for A.C. work. In principle it is identical with the D.C. series motor and possesses similar operating characteristics. It is hardly necessary, therefore, to extend this brief reference beyond mentioning that because the main flux is alternating it is necessary for the whole of the field system to be of laminated construction in order to reduce eddy current losses. As far as physical size goes this machine has a lower rating than its D.C. counterpart and possesses the additional disadvantage of a poor power factor.

INDUCTION MOTORS

Since from a constructional standpoint, much of what has been said of D.C. motors is applicable to A.C. machines, it is proposed to confine the present remarks to aspects of construction not so far dealt with.

Usually in induction motors, the main frame or yoke is made from cast iron and performs the purely mechanical function of transmitting the reaction of the motor torque through the feet to the solid foundation on which the machine is standing. The trend, therefore, in modern scientific designs is to concentrate as much of the yoke metal as possible in the plane of the feet, that is, at either end; this tendency can very clearly be detected in Fig. 18.

STATOR AND ROTOR CORES

The stator core consists of a pile of steel laminations assembled under pressure in the yoke. The laminations as they are called, are ·016 in. thick and are insulated with a thin layer of paper on one side, like those in the armature of a D.C. machine.

If the core were solid, heavy currents would be induced in it which would flow axially through the iron just as in the rotor conductors, causing excessive "eddy" loss and consequent overheating. The slot shape and the winding details are discussed later in the section on "Armature Windings". A similar procedure is adopted in the case of the rotor core, the core being built between end-plates on to the shaft itself or on to a "spider", as in a D.C. armature. The rotor punchings, like those of the stator, have slots in their periphery to receive the rotor coils in the case of a slipring machine or to accommodate the cage windings in the case of a squirrel cage machine.

SLIPRING INDUCTION MOTOR

Fig. 18. Metrovick screen-protected slipring induction motor. Note the modern feature of concentration of yoke metal in the plane of the feet.

The practice in the case of medium-sized squirrel cage motors is for the rotor winding to consist of lightly insulated copper bars driven into the slots, the bars being brazed

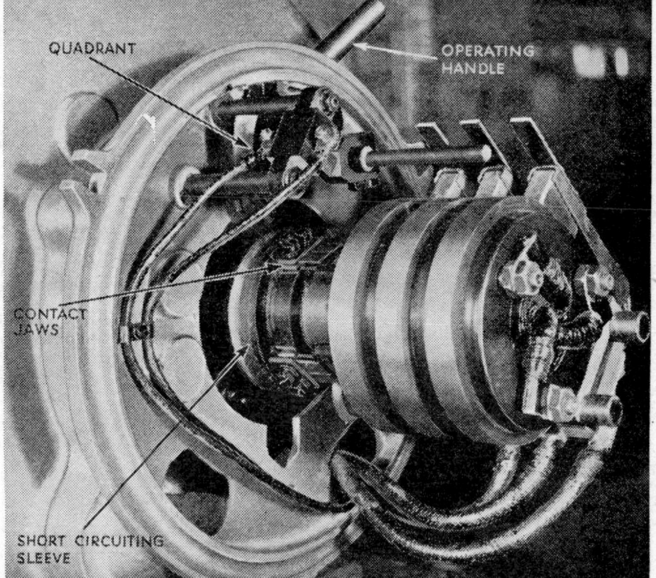

A.C. MOTOR BRUSHGEAR

Fig. 19. Showing brush-lifting and short-circuiting gear of an A.C. motor slipring assembly. Note the sliding short-circuiting sleeve.

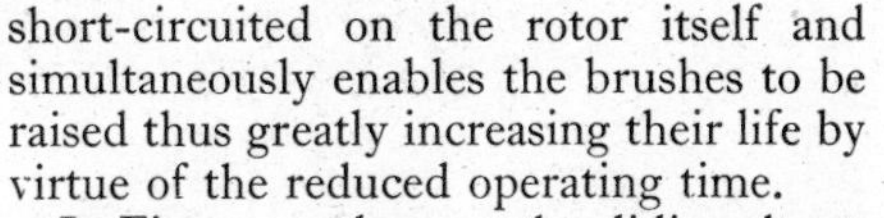

into slotted end rings at either end of the core. In the smaller sizes of squirrel cage motors, a practice now very much in favour is for the squirrel cage to be made of aluminium cast into the rotor slots under pressure and of course rendering the bars integral with the end-rings. This enables speed of production to be increased and also results in a robust construction.

The sliprings or collector as the complete assembly is sometimes called, are usually mounted externally in British design, that is, mounted on a shaft extension at the non-driving end of the motor, the cables from the winding to the rings passing along a hole up the centre of the shaft. The collector is frequently made by moulding the rings into a solid bakelite bush. An alternative construction employed particularly on large machines is for the separate sliprings to be shrunk on to a mica-insulated steel bush. For slipring machines which have to run for long periods without stopping, brush-lifting and short-circuiting gear is often specified. This enables the rings to be short-circuited on the rotor itself and simultaneously enables the brushes to be raised thus greatly increasing their life by virtue of the reduced operating time.

In Fig. 19 can be seen the sliding short-circuiting sleeve complete with contact jaws which in the running position engage with corresponding blades at the inner end of the slipring assembly. In the picture can also be seen the inclined quadrant which is caused to engage the V-groove in the sleeve when the operating handle is moved over to raise the brushes.

A.C. AND D.C. MOTOR DETAILS

CERTAIN features such as bearings, performance, cooling and types of enclosures, etc., are more or less common to both A.C. and D.C. motors. These items are now discussed in the light of their importance in modern practice.

It might seem a little out of place in what is primarily an electrical study to discuss the subject of bearings, but in view of the vital contribution they make to the reliable operation of a machine and the way they have influenced electrical design in the past, a brief word or two may not be amiss.

First of all, how many bearings must a motor have? This may vary on the one hand between none in one or two cases where a motor is overhung from the driven shaft as in the case of some machine tools and, at the other extreme four, depending on the nature of the transmission from the motor to the driven machine. Most motors of course have two bearings particularly when they transmit their power through a flexible or solid coupling, but when the drive is by means of ropes, vee-belts, chains or ordinary flat belts the load on the driving end bearings arising from the belt pull is so high that frequently an "outboard" or third bearing is necessary. On even heavier drives using many ropes and therefore a wide pulley, or with several steel belts in one transmission as is sometimes the practice in America, two pedestal bearings are employed with a "jackshaft" flexibly coupled to the motor, making four bearings in all.

Bearings on medium-sized machines are now usually mounted in the endshields, instead of on pedestals as in most earlier types of construction and as still employed on large machines.

Bearings can be divided into two distinct classes:—

(i) " Sleeve " bearings.

(ii) Anti-friction or ball and roller bearings.

Until about 1925 practically all electric motors except those having shafts smaller than 1 in. diameter had bearings of the first type. After that time ball and roller bearings began to acquire more and more popularity as their reliability came to be established, until now they are the standard type of bearings used by most motor manufacturers for machines up to about 1,000 h.p.

Thrust bearings have also been considerably developed for special purposes and, as a matter of interest, 36,000 h.p. has been transmitted through a single collar thrust.

It is not proposed to dwell on sleeve bearings beyond saying that the shaft revolves in bushes made either of bronze or from iron lined with white metal, the bushes being carried in "bearing housings." Lubrication is effected usually by means of oil rings which dip into an oil well below the shaft. A sectional view of a modern sleeve bearing is given in Fig. 20.

Ball and roller bearings consist of four components, an inner and outer race accurately ground to size, a number of hard steel balls or rollers and a "cage" which keeps the balls in their correct circumferential position. The only points really requiring lubrication are those where

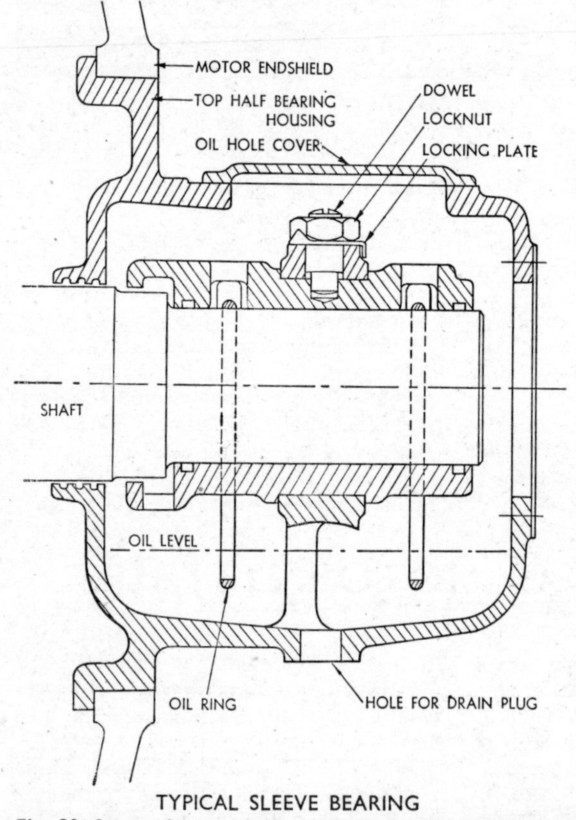

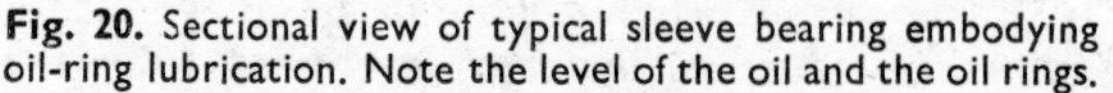
TYPICAL SLEEVE BEARING

Fig. 20. Sectional view of typical sleeve bearing embodying oil-ring lubrication. Note the level of the oil and the oil rings.

the rollers slide against the cage, all other motion can be regarded as pure rolling motion.

The relative advantages of the two types are set out below:—

BALL AND ROLLER BEARINGS.

(1) Require little maintenance.
(2) Unaffected by tilting of the motor.
(3) Permit the use of a small air gap since no radial wear occurs.
(4) Small axial length.
(5) Very low friction.
(6) Obtainable from many suppliers all over the world.

SLEEVE BEARINGS.

(1) Usually split enabling removal without withdrawing the coupling.
(2) Usually give more warning of impending failure.

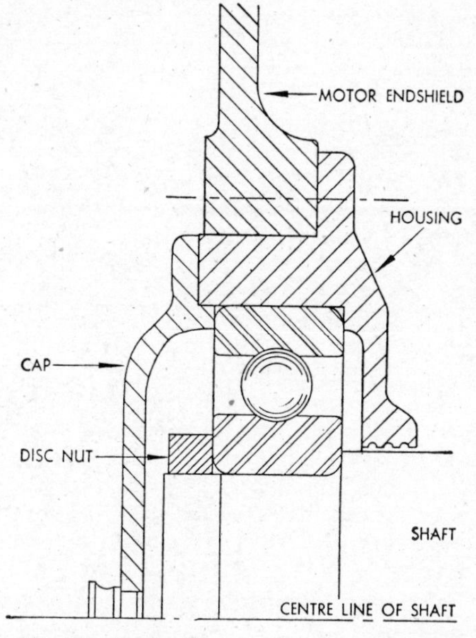

Fig. 21. Sectional view of a modern type of ball bearing in a cartridge form of housing.

Grease is usually the medium employed to lubricate ball and roller bearings, the grease acting as a carrier or sponge which slowly releases a slight amount of oil over very long periods. It is a very serious error to imagine that the grease itself should be "churned" round between the rollers, as occurs when an excess of grease is put into a bearing initially; such conditions produce excessive heat and a rapid decomposition of the grease. It should only be necessary to inject a little extra grease perhaps twice a year in ordinary circumstances.

In assembling ball bearings in machines it is a good practice to employ a so-called "cartridge" type of housing. A bearing assembly incorporating this feature is shown in section in Fig. 21. With this arrangement the bearing remains enclosed even when the armature or rotor complete with bearings are withdrawn from its stator. This enables a motor to be dismantled without disturbing the grease and at the same time prevents the dirt entering the bearing. The cartridge type bearings can be seen still fitted to the shafts in Figs. 4 and 11.

Of the two main bearings in a motor it is desirable only to locate the shaft axially at one end. This is frequently achieved by employing a ball bearing at one end and a plain roller bearing (which is free axially) at the other. Where two ball bearings are utilised as in smaller motors, the outer race of one is generally not "nipped".

PERFORMANCE OF MOTORS

Although there are many kinds of motor and types of construction, there is nevertheless a certain degree of uniformity about motors manufactured in this country; it arises in this way. In 1901 a body then known as the Engineering Standards Committee and now known as the British Standards Institution was formed to further the progress of standardisation in all branches of engineering. With this aim in view the Institution, after wide investigations and consultations throughout industry, issues so-called British Standard Specifications relating to particular classes of engineering equipment such as the sizes of cable for particular currents, the dimensions of lamp fittings, and so on.

In the motor field, there is a British Standard Specification Number 168/1936 which very adequately covers the "Electrical Performance of Industrial Electric Motors and Generators" and is now the common basis of design for all motors manufactured in this country ranging from 1 h.p. to 2,500 h.p. at 1,000 r.p.m. This means merely that the specification establishes common values or interpretations for such quantities as:—

(1) The standard voltages of machines.

(2) The methods of "rating" motors.

(3) The temperature rise permissible in the parts of a motor which is operating under normal load.

(4) The permissible divergence of the actual efficiency and power factor from the guaranteed figures.

(5) The minimum overloads a motor must be capable of withstanding safely.

(6) The testing procedure to be adopted.

(7) The types of motor enclosure available.

At the same time it allows each manufacturer complete freedom with regard to the methods he employs and the designs he produces to fulfil these requirements.

RATING

So far we have said little about the power which can be developed by any particular motor. When a maker produces a motor, he assigns to it a "rating". This is really a statement saying what output can be obtained from it and specifying under what conditions it applies. Motors can be rated in either of two ways depending on their intended service:—

(a) Continuous Rating.

(b) Short-time Rating.

The first rating means that a machine may be allowed to run for an unlimited period under the conditions of load, voltage, etc., specified on its nameplate, i.e., "rated" conditions. When testing continuously rated machines a six-hour run is now officially accepted as the standard equivalent of continuous operation, since it is extremely rare for the various parts of a motor not to have reached a steady temperature within a period of six hours.

The short time rating states the load at which a machine may be allowed to run for a given limited period. The usual periods recognised are either 1 hour or ½ hour.

The short-time ratings do not mean that the machines concerned will operate for only 1 hour or ½ hour at a time, but merely represent the accepted British Standards used in testing motors on intermittent service such as crane drives or lifts, without the inconvenience of repeating over a long period the actual duty cycle.

TEMPERATURE RISE

One is perhaps tempted to ask next how it is that a particular machine comes to be rated by the maker as a 50 h.p. motor and not, for example, as a 55 h.p. or 60 h.p. motor when, as is probable, there would be little difficulty in obtaining such outputs from it. The answer to this lies in the matter of "temperature rise", by far the most important factor governing the design of present-day machines. It will be realised that for a given type of insulation there must be some limit to the temperature at which this may be kept continuously, if deterioration is to be avoided. It has been found that for class "A" insulation a rise in temperature of 40° C. for ventilated type machines as measured by a thermometer placed on the windings, and 50° C. for totally enclosed types, allows a sufficient margin to prevent the hottest parts of the windings reaching a dangerous value when the motor is operating under "rated" conditions. These figures assume a maximum air temperature or "ambient" of 35° C. The reader will surmise, therefore, that as long as a manufacturer ensures that the winding temperature of, for example, a 50 h.p. motor, does not exceed 40° C. above that of the surrounding air he can aim at using as little material as possible, consistent with mechanical strength, thus striving towards a smaller and more economical motor. Such is in fact one of the principal aims of the motor designer.

It will now be seen why the rating of continuously rated motor is specified usually as 50 h.p. 6 hours 40° C., or that of a totally enclosed short-time rated machine as 50 h.p. 1 hour 50° C.

Let us now consider why the temperature of a machine rises at all, when it is in operation, instead of remaining the same as the surrounding air.

LOSSES AND EFFICIENCY

When we switch on the supply to a motor and thereby cause it to drive some other machine such as a pump or a lathe, we are putting into it electrical power. A large proportion of this power, but not all, is given out as mechanical power which drives the pump. The remainder, however, is wasted and represents the "losses" in the motor. The relationship between the output of a motor and its input give us its "efficiency", i.e.,

$$100 \times \frac{\text{Output}}{\text{Input}} = \text{Efficiency per cent.}$$

Since it is customary to express the output of a motor in horse power and the input in watts, we could say, Efficiency

$$\text{per cent.} = \frac{(\text{Output in h.p.} \times 746)}{\text{Input in watts}} \times 100$$

It is the losses which are responsible for the heating of an electric motor; theoretically a machine with an efficiency of 100 per cent. would have no temperature rise no matter what output were being taken from it. Detailing the losses they are:—

(1) Losses in the windings—"copper losses."

(2) Losses in the magnetic circuits—"iron losses."

(3) Mechanical losses—friction and "windage."

The copper losses represent the energy expended in forcing current through the resistance of the various windings; this energy is converted into heat and tends to raise the temperature of the copper conductors. For a current of I amps. and a winding resistance of R ohms, the loss is I^2R watts.

The iron losses can be separated into two parts, namely the "hysteresis" losses and the eddy-current losses. Hysteresis loss represents the energy actually lost by the repeated reversing of the magnetic flux in the various parts of the iron circuit, as described in the section on "Magnetism". The eddy current losses can be likened to the copper losses, except that they arise from currents flowing through the resistance of the iron laminations, instead of the copper. These are the losses we seek to minimise by using a laminated core. Even so, small eddy currents do circulate in each of the separate punchings. As in the case of the windings the energy lost in the iron is converted into heat, thus raising its temperature.

MECHANICAL LOSSES

The friction losses, as their name implies, represent the power wasted in overcoming the friction of both the bearings and the brushes on the commutator or sliprings. Windage loss is the power consumed in the mechanical process of drawing the cooling air through the various ducts in the cores, but both this and the friction loss contribute little if anything to the heating of the windings or core of the motor.

The following table will perhaps serve to convey a general impression of the efficiency figures encountered in typical industrial machines of two different types.

TYPICAL EFFICIENCY FIGURES

Power Rating as Specified by the Manufacturer	3-ph. Induction Motor Squirrel Cage				D.C. Shunt Motor			
	Full load	3/4	1/2	1/4	Full load	3/4	1/2	1/4
50 h.p. 750 r.p.m.	89%	88%	87%	70%	88%	87·5%	86%	73%
100 h.p. 750 r.p.m.	91%	91%	89%	72%	89%	88·5%	87·5%	74%

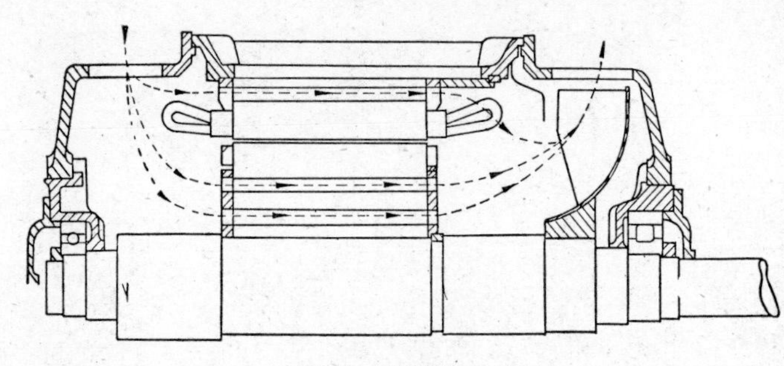

Fig. 22. Sectional view of A.C. motor with axial ventilation which permits the use of a large, efficient fan for practically any air quantity.

In an earlier chapter we have seen how the power factor of an inductive load, such as that represented by an A.C. motor in an A.C. circuit can be expressed as:—

$$\frac{\text{watts}}{\text{volt amps.}} \text{ or } \frac{\text{useful current}}{\text{total current}}$$

Typical values of power factor for a 100 h.p., 750 r.p.m. induction motor are:—

Full load	.. ..	0·89
$\frac{3}{4}$,,	.. ..	0·86
$\frac{1}{2}$,,	.. ..	0·77
$\frac{1}{4}$,,	.. ..	0·55

These figures together with those of efficiency emphasise the need for ensuring that a motor is made to operate somewhere near its rated load if the minimum of power is to be wasted and particularly if supply companies penalise consumers for low power factor.

We have seen how the horse-power which can be obtained from a motor is limited usually by the temperature rise permissible on the windings and not by the mechanical strength of the component parts. We have discussed also how the heating results from the energy losses which occur in all types of electrical machines.

VENTILATION

In endeavouring to obtain the most, therefore, from a given size of motor, the policy of the designer has been first to keep down the losses prevailing for a certain horse-power output and, secondly, to get rid of the greatest amount of heat from the particular size of machine. The first course is a matter of pure design and somewhat beyond the scope of this article. The second aspect brings us to the subject of ventilation; it is in this direction that the greatest strides have been made in recent years. In the very

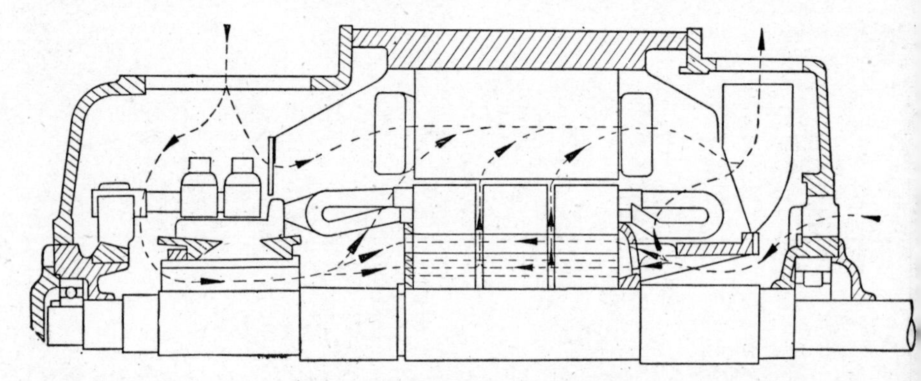

Fig. 23. D.C. motor with mixed type ventilation and double air inlet which combines both the axial and radial principles. This system is widely used for modern D.C. motors and many A.C. motors.

early machines which were of completely open construction, there was little to prevent the surrounding air from coming into contact with the main parts of the machine. On the other hand, there was nothing to cause a steady current of air to pass over the various hot surfaces, other than the normal convection currents caused by warm air rising above the motor and thereby causing cool air to replace it from beneath, together with the general fanning action of the rotating armature or rotor which caused the air in the neighbourhood of the end windings to be flung radially outwards. This latter effect was subsequently increased by fixing small radial blades to the ends of the core; in this simple way emerged the system of "radial" ventilation which was at one time standard practice. Unfortunately, this early arrangement possessed the drawback of providing cooling only for the end windings while still permitting the winding and iron in the centre of the core to attain high temperatures. The next step, therefore, was to provide radial ventilating ducts at positions along the length of the core, like those visible in Fig. 4. They have remained a standard feature in most D.C. machines and many A.C. motors right up to the present day.

PIPE VENTILATION

Fig. 24. Slipring induction motor of a normally ventilated type arranged for pipe ventilation at the inlet end.

AXIAL VENTILATION

A later development, particularly for A.C. motors, where the coinciding radial ducts of stator and rotor tend to produce air noise, has been the introduction of "axial ventilation", an example of which is to be seen in Fig. 22. Axial ventilation has the important advantage of permitting the use of a large efficient fan capable of being designed for practically any air quantity. The holes constituting the axial ventilation ducts can be seen in the picture of a stator and rotor punching in Fig. 38. The fans which on medium-sized motors are normally of the centrifugal type are very much in evidence in the photographs of Figs. 4, 11a and 11b.

ENCLOSURE

It is now quite common for modern D.C. motors and many A.C. motors to employ a combination of both axial and radial ventilation, as illustrated in Fig. 23, which is a sectional drawing of a D.C. motor.

While striving therefore to ensure as efficient ventilation as possible it is necessary to take into account the site conditions under which a motor will be called upon to operate. In many installations these are anything but favourable. It is because of this that over a period of years a series of standard forms of enclosure have been developed to meet the differing service conditions. Briefly they are:—

(a) *Open.* This enclosure was employed in the very early machines but is now confined to large machines in localities where untrained personnel cannot approach them.

(b) *Screen-protected.* From a ventila-

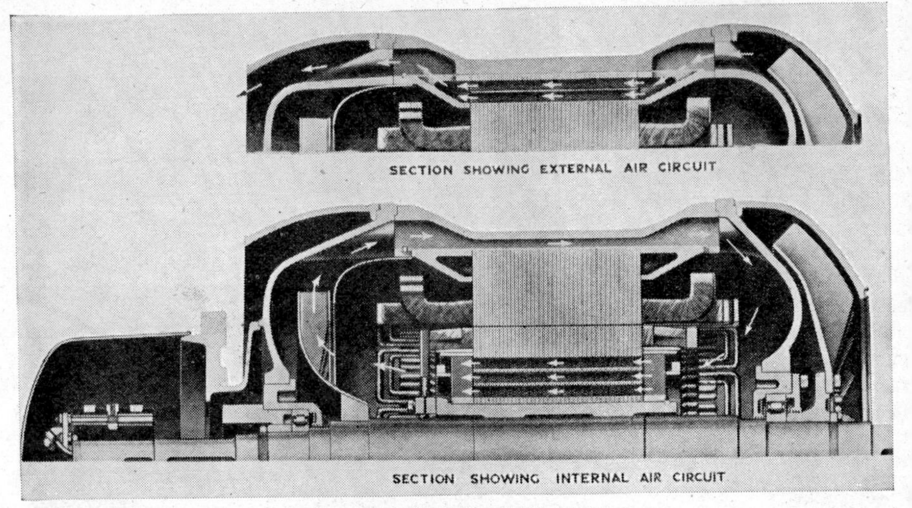

TOTALLY ENCLOSED A.C. MOTOR

Fig. 25. Section through totally enclosed fan-cooled A.C. motor, having ducts through the stator core, showing internal and external air circuits. Another view of this motor is given in Fig. 26.

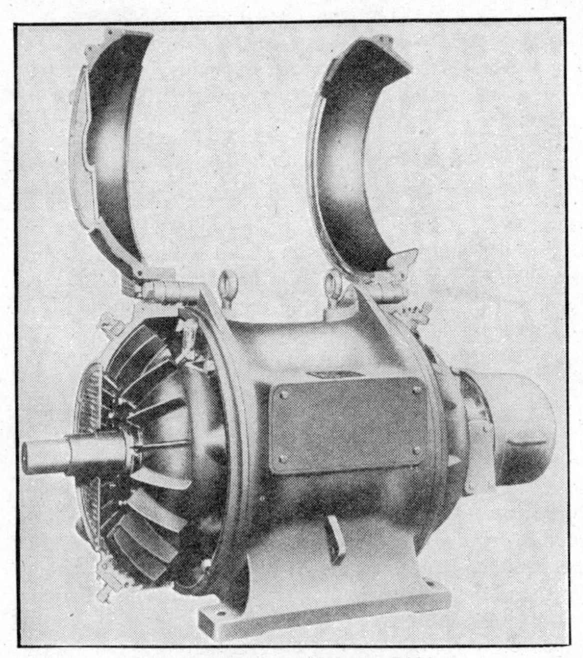

SHOWING EXTERNAL FAN

Fig. 26. A Metrovick totally enclosed fan-cooled motor with cowls raised to show external fan. See also Fig. 25. A motor of this type is generally used in places where persistent fumes and dust are present which would prove injurious to the windings and tend to clog up the rotor ventilating ducts.

tion standpoint this is the same as (a), but all openings are covered with some form of mesh screen to prevent anyone touching the moving parts. It is the most common type of enclosure encountered in industrial motors in clean surroundings, i.e., the type shown in Fig. 18.

(c) *Drip-proof*. This enclosure is similar to (b) except that additional protection is afforded from falling water by the provision of cowls and louvres on the upper and side openings respectively.

(d) *Pipe-ventilated*. For this type of enclosure a normal ventilated motor is employed, provided with a single inlet opening to enable an air trunking to be connected to it. Along this the motor draws a supply of clean air from outside the building in which it is working. Such a system is frequently used for motors operating in cotton mills. It is not usually necessary to pipe the outlet opening, seen towards the left of Fig. 24.

(e) *Totally Enclosed Fan-cooled.* This is a design in which the windings are completely enclosed inside the machine, but which employs one or more fans on the shaft to pass cooling air through or over the motor. In some designs this consists merely in blowing air over the exterior of the motor carcase. Fig. 25, however, is a section of an induction motor having both internal and external air circuits. In the former the hot internal air carries heat from the rotor to cooling ducts located near the outer surface of the carcase, while at the same time outside air is blown by the external fan through ducts actually situated in the stator core itself. The same motor can be seen in Fig. 26. It is normally employed in situations where the presence of fumes and foreign matter in the atmosphere would be injurious to the insulation of the windings or would tend to clog up the rotor ventilating ducts and impede ventilation.

From the foregoing it will be seen that ventilation is a vital aspect of machine design, and that attention must be paid to its application to suit the various different conditions under which machines operate.

USES OF VARIOUS MOTORS

A CHAPTER discussing, amongst other items, the principles of operation of the various kinds of electric motor would be incomplete without some mention being made of when and where each type can be most suitably employed. Leaving aside for the moment questions of enclosure and mechanical construction, three factors to be considered in selecting a motor for a particular service are:—

(a) Load characteristic required.
(b) Speed requirements.
(c) Type of supply available.

LOAD CHARACTERISTIC

By the load characteristic of a motor is meant the graph or curve showing the way in which the speed or torque of a motor varies with the load on it. The various load/speed requirements of most industrial drives fall roughly into three groups and are represented by the characteristics of the three main types of D.C. motors shown in Fig. 27.

It will be seen that the speed of the shunt motor is practically independent of the load; it falls only slightly as the latter increases. As the reader will no doubt be aware, this is the most common characteristic since it is the one required for all those drives where the speed must remain roughly constant despite any load fluctuations. This is desirable, to mention only a few cases, in machine tool drives, conveyors, cotton spinning machinery, air compressors and for most pumps.

In the case of the series motor, on the other hand, the speed varies very widely, as indicated by curve (b), depending on the load on the motor. This is explained by the fact that on light loads the field is weakened by reason of the main current being also the field current; we have seen earlier how field weakening causes an increase in speed. Conversely, with the application of heavy loads or overloads the motor speed falls considerably. Series motors possess the important property of being able to exert an enormous torque or turning effort for short periods, enabling them to withstand heavy momentary overloads. Because of its high no-load speed the series motor is normally used on direct coupled drives where it is impossible for all the load to be removed, as would occur for instance with a belt drive if the belt were to break. In view of its high starting torque, it finds employment in those drives where frequent starting against a heavy load occurs and where a "series characteristic" is desirable to avoid the more severe supply peaks associated with a motor which attempts to maintain a steady speed under overloads. It is widely utilised for traction work, i.e., as train or railway motors, on cranes, for the heavy auxiliary drives in rolling mills and for other applications of

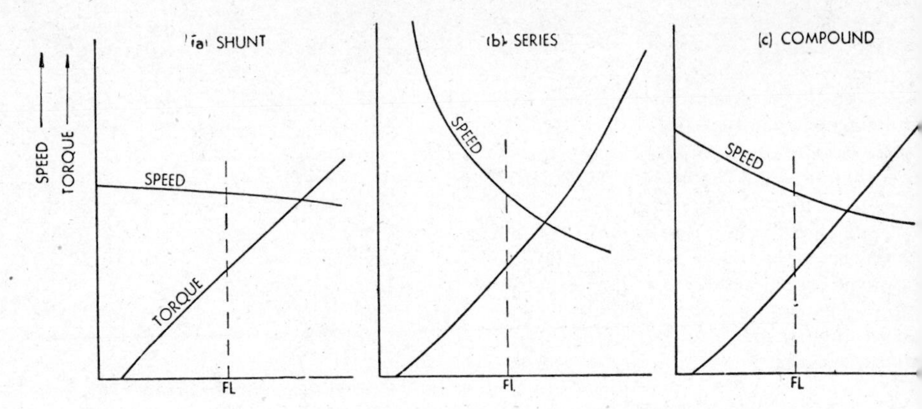

D.C. MOTOR LOAD CHARACTERISTICS

Fig. 27. Load characteristics of the three main types of direct current motors are shown in these graphs. Point of full load is indicated in each case by a vertical dotted line.

a similar nature. Series motors are obviously suitable where the load is constant as in the driving of small fans and pumps.

The compound motor, as its name implies, has a characteristic which is really a compromise between those of the shunt and series machines, in that the motor suffers a greater speed variation from zero to full load and can withstand greater momentary overloads than the shunt motor, in spite of being regarded as an approximately steady speed machine. These properties are very desirable for the driving of individual machines such as winches, where a series characteristic is desirable but where it is necessary to limit the no load speed to a safe value. Further, they are particularly suited to drive presses and allied equipment, in conjunction with flywheels, where frequent heavy load-peaks arise. The falling motor speed enables some of the energy stored in the flywheel to be given up during each overload period, thus levelling out the load.

Turning to the A.C. machines, the induction motor and A.C. commutator motor can be regarded as having "shunt characteristics", in other words, the percentage fall in speed up to full load is very small. It is represented in Fig. 14 by the distance AS. The synchronous motor and the S.I.M. as we have already discovered rotate in synchronism with the three-phase supply and, therefore, have a horizontal speed/load characteristic with no variation, though sudden changes in load would cause a synchronous motor's speed to fluctuate if appropriate damping were not included in its design.

SPEED REQUIREMENTS

Leaving aside the question of speed variations arising purely from changes in the load, from the point of view of the nominal speeds required at full load, industrial drives can be grouped into three classes, namely those demanding:—

(a) A single speed.

(b) Two or more different speeds.

(c) A speed capable of being varied in fine steps.

Motors having a single speed are those in most common use and are almost invariably the type assigned to lineshaft and "group" drive systems. They include of course machines possessing any of the load characteristics already enumerated, the applications of which were mentioned in the preceding paragraphs.

Multi-speed motors having two, three and four separate speeds are finding an ever-increasing application for machine tool drives, where they provide an extremely simple and rapid method of multiplying the range of different speeds obtainable by mechanical means. Four-speed motors are now quite a common feature on individually driven turret lathes. There are a large number of installations in existence where two-speed motors are operating in conjunction with hydraulic couplings to obtain a variable speed over a certain limited range; many boiler house induced-draught fans utilise this arrangement. Yet another popular application of motors having one high and one low speed is for operating lifts. The low speed is used when starting and during the period just before the lift comes to rest, i.e., for "decking".

In the last category we have the so-called "variable speed" motor, where a speed is required which can be adjusted at will over a wide range or in response to some predetermined cycle. Such are the needs in paper manufacture and for cement kilns, printing presses, certain fans, stokers, many large machine tools, cranes and winches. Amongst motors with drooping, i.e., "series" characteristics, the demands of traction motors cover essentially variable speed machines.

As we saw when considering D.C. machines in detail, all of these speed requirements can be met quite easily in either a shunt, series or compound motor merely by arranging for the appropriate variation in the field current. Unfortunately, in the case of A.C. machines, the matter is not quite so simple and the following table has been compiled to convey a rough idea of how the same results can also be achieved in this field:—

METHODS OF VARYING SPEED WITH A.C. MACHINES

Speed Requirements	Load Characteristic		
	"Shunt"	"Compound"	"Series"
One nominal speed	Induction motor Synchronous motor. S.I.M.	Slipring induction motor with fixed external resistance. Squirrel cage motor with high resistance rotor.	A.C. series commutator motor.
Coarse variations in speed, i.e., two or more nominal speeds.	Induction motors arranged for change-pole switching. Induction motors with 2 or more stator windings.		ditto
Fine variations in speed, i.e. (1) short range.	2-speed induction motor with fluid coupling.	Slipring induction motor with variable external rotor resistance (inefficient).	ditto
(2) wide range.	A.C. variable speed comm. motor.	A.C. variable speed comm. motor.	ditto

To summarise, it will be seen that for variable speed duties direct-current machines are preferable to A.C. machines. They possess, in addition, the advantage that they can be built for any speed. Except in the case of commutator motors this is not so with A.C. motors, whose speeds depend on the supply frequency and must be a sub-multiple of 50 revs. per second, according to the number of poles.

TYPES OF SUPPLY

In most installations the choice of supply does not present itself, since three-phase alternating current is now the standard form in which electric power is supplied in this country. Having in mind that the majority of drives are at constant speed and remembering that induction motors are less expensive than D.C. machines, this is a desirable state of affairs.

In certain of the large installations, however, where many variable speed drives exist, as in boiler houses and paper mills or where most drives demand a "series" characteristic as in a rolling mill, it often pays to provide a separate D.C. supply from a D.C. generator driven by an A.C. motor. For marine work direct current motors are employed almost exclusively.

At one time relatively little attention was paid to the mechanical construction of a motor, that is, from the point of view of the user. This attitude has now disappeared, with the result that the mechanical features are now designed to afford the maximum help and least inconvenience to the owner. For example, brushgear covers employ easily released fastenings instead of a large number of bolts, inspection covers for the commutators of enclosed machines have armourplate glass windows to obviate the need for their removal and so on.

In some industries the need for suitable motors has been so great that machines have been developed specifically for those industries. Examples of this policy are to be seen in the design of machines for rolling mills, boiler house drives, oil refineries, and coal mining service (see Chapter 7). A steel, as distinct from cast iron, "mill-type" motor is shown in Fig. 28 from which the extremely rugged construction is apparent. The design permits a spare armature to be substituted in a matter of minutes, while a shaft breakage merely necessitates rotating the motor through 180 deg.

STEEL WORKS MOTOR

Fig. 28. A Metrovick D.C. "all-steel" mill-type motor showing double shaft extension. This motor is of particularly rugged construction.

Coal mining probably represents the field where the greatest degree of specialisation has taken place, particularly with regard to machines which operate in regions where inflammable gas is present. In such localities a motor is required to be "flameproof". This means that all joints, though not air-tight, must be sufficiently wide to prevent flames reaching the outside of the motor in the event of an explosion taking place inside.

ARMATURE WINDINGS

The term "Armature Windings" in its literal sense refers, as one would imagine to the windings present in the armature of a D.C. motor. It has, however, developed a broader meaning embracing all windings of the so-called "distributed" type, which consist of a number of individual coils distributed in slots situated in the outer periphery of D.C. armatures and A.C. rotor cores and in the bore of A.C. stators.

D.C. WINDINGS

An important feature to remember about all D.C. armature windings is that they form "closed" circuits. Fig. 3 illustrates this fact for one kind of winding. The joint between any two coils occurs where the "start" of one and the "finish" of the other are connected to the same commutator bar. The reason why no current circulates in the closed winding is simply that the voltage induced in the coils under a south pole exactly balances that induced in the coils under a north pole. The brushes make contact with the winding at the neutral zone between the different regions.

In the very early days armatures were actually built with windings of the kind shown in Fig. 3, that is "ring windings". In addition to the fact that in those days the conductors were wound on the surface of the ring-shaped core and not in slots, these windings possess the disadvantage that only one side, the outer side, of each coil is surrounded by the magnetic flux, and therefore active. They were accordingly soon displaced by the "drum-type" winding where both sides of a coil are utilised. For two sides of a coil to be active and produce similar torques, when the current in one half is flowing in the opposite direction to that in the other half, the two sides must move in fields of opposite polarity at any instant. In other words they must be under different poles as indicated in Fig. 29(a); that is why they are a certain distance apart which is known as the "coil span" and which is normally expressed in terms of slots. The coils in Fig. 29(a) have a span of 1 to 4 i.e., 3 slots. Where this span is identical with the distance between poles the coil is said to be a "full-pitch" coil.

Nearly all D.C. armature windings are so arranged that one side of each coil is in the top of a slot while the other side is in the lower part of another slot. Each slot therefore contains an upper and a lower coil side; and the winding is known as a "two-layer" winding.

Both the windings represented by Fig. 29 are known as "lap windings" and as far as the method of connecting the coils is concerned, they are the modern counterpart of a ring winding. The two diagrams, however, illustrate the difference between what is known as a "retrogressive" winding and that which is known as a "progressive" winding.

Another type of D.C. winding not perhaps quite so extensively used is the "wave winding", an example of which is drawn out in Fig. 30. Like the lap winding

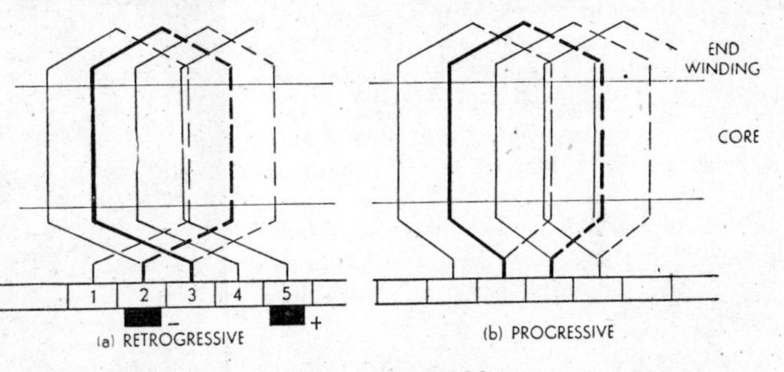

LAP WINDINGS

Fig. 29. Showing the two types of lap windings. They are in their connections the modern counterparts of the old-fashioned "ring" winding.

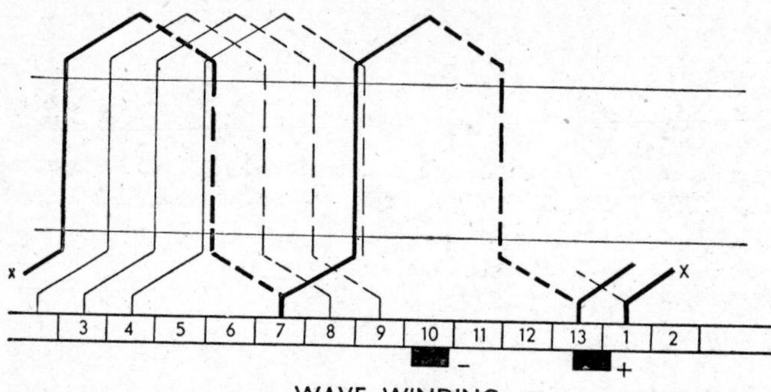

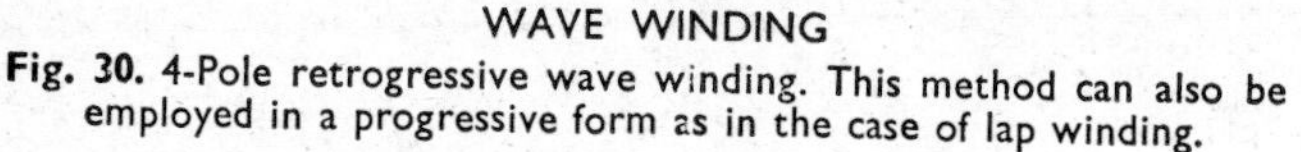
WAVE WINDING

Fig. 30. 4-Pole retrogressive wave winding. This method can also be employed in a progressive form as in the case of lap winding.

it can be employed in both the retrogressive and progressive forms, the former type being the one illustrated here. In a wave winding the circuit goes from one commutator bar, for example, No. 1 completely round the armature before reaching the adjacent bar No. 13 and in the other direction (not fully drawn in) to commutator bar No. 2. Irrespective, therefore, of the number of poles, there are only two circuits in parallel in a wave winding, accounting for the phrase "two circuit" winding. Electrically, it is in this respect that the lap and wave types differ, since in the lap winding all alternate pole groups of coils are connected in parallel by the brushes, which means that there are as many circuits as there are poles; hence "multiple" winding.

A.C. WINDINGS

In view of the almost universal use of the three-phase system for all but the smaller types of A.C. motor, we will confine our remarks to this field. Unlike D.C. armature windings the windings of an A.C. rotor and stator may be either of the single or two layer types. In an ordinary single layer winding the left-hand side of one coil fills one slot while the next slot is occupied by the right-hand side of another coil and so on alternately. Fig. 31 illustrates what is meant by a single layer stator winding. Again in contrast with the D.C. case, A.C. windings are not of the "closed" type. They consist, on the contrary, of three separate windings, one for each of the phases, each winding having its own start and finish. The phase winding is split up into a number of "groups" corresponding with the number of poles, so that over one pole pitch there is one group belonging to each of the three phases. (The poles are not of course present in the same physical sense as in a D.C. machine, that is, they are not of the salient type. They

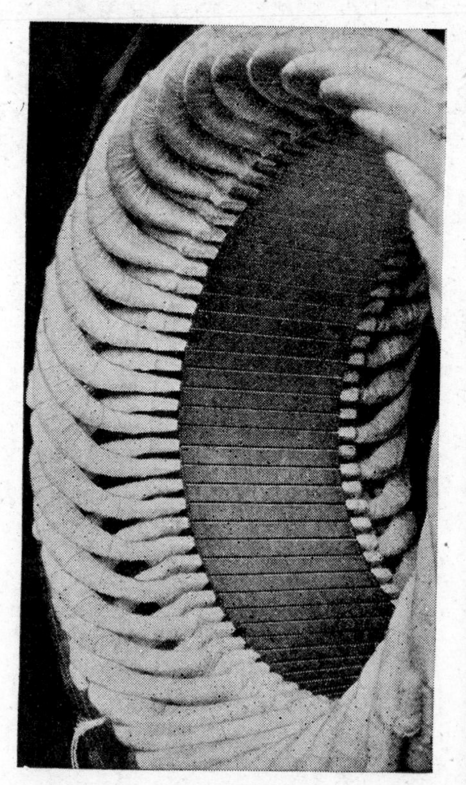

MUSH WINDING

Fig. 31. Single layer "mush" winding before impregnation. Each slot contains only one coil.

exist magnetically as a result of the distribution of the winding). Fig. 32(a) illustrates diagrammatically the arrangement of the phase groups in a 2-pole winding; there are two groups to each phase. The phase windings of a three-phase machine, whether of stator or rotor, can be connected in three ways. In two cases only three leads are taken to the terminal box, the windings being connected inside the machine in "star" or "delta", as outlined in Fig. 32(b). In the other method of connection all six ends of the three-phase windings are taken to terminals. This enables the windings to be connected in star or delta at will from outside the motor, as must occur where "star/delta" starting is employed.

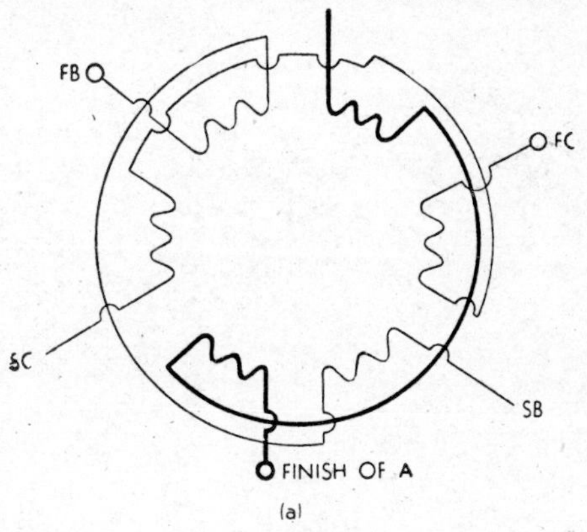

Fig. 32a. Arrangement of phase "groups" in two-pole, three-phase A.C. winding.

CONCENTRIC WINDINGS

A.C. windings from the physical standpoint fall into 3 classes, lap windings, wave windings, both of which we have already considered on D.C. machines, and a third type "concentric windings". The important feature of the latter is that the coils do not all have the same span. As the name suggests, a coil of a certain span is surrounded by another coil having a larger span and so on as depicted in Fig. 33. The inside coil has a pitch slightly less than the pole pitch and the pitch increases, the outside coil having pitch which is rather larger than the pole pitch. This winding is essentially a single layer winding having therefore only one coil side in each slot. In order to accommodate the end windings, the latter are dispersed in "tiers", that is, the ends of the coils have one of two distinct shapes in a 2-tier winding or three in the 3-tier version. The winding illustrated is of the 3-tier type with 9 coils per complete group.

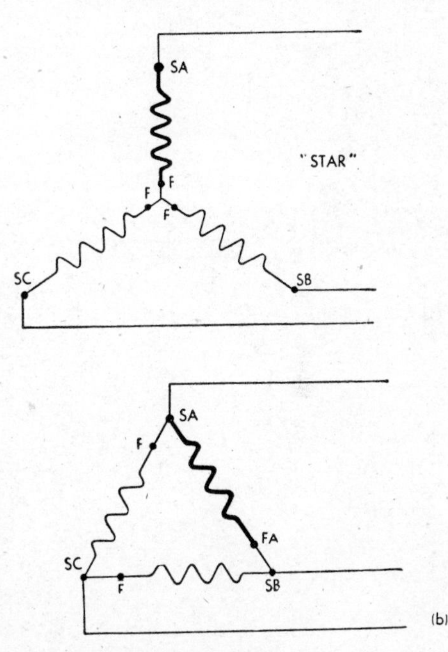

Fig. 32b. Methods of connecting the three-phase windings in star and delta.

COILS

When discussing armature windings, considerable confusion can occur if the meaning of certain terms is not clearly understood at the outset, particularly as these vary from one person to another. This is especially the case with the word "coil". Referring to D.C. armatures, many writers use the term to mean that part of the winding connected between two commutator bars, in which case there would be normally twice or three times as many coils (and commutator bars) as there are slots. On purely electrical grounds there may be some justification for this. It would be a theoretically correct use of the word in accordance with the standard definition of terms which states that a coil comprises one or more convolutions of bare or insulated wire. However, as this work is primarily of a practical nature, it is intended to employ the winding terms as actually met in industry and which in the Author's opinion will be of most value to the reader. By a coil is understood, that part of a winding which is ordered and handled as a separate element during manufacture and which fills half or the whole of a slot depending on whether we have in mind a 2-layer or single layer winding. Fig 35 will assist in clarifying this position. The portion of a winding connected between two commutator bars we know as a "section" of a coil. The description of the number of conductors in a complete coil, that is the "winding per coil", having a regular arrangement, is specified as "3 by 4" (for the case illustrated), i.e., "conductors in width" by "conductors in depth". Had there been two wires in parallel in depth, it would have been described as "3 by 2 double".

INSULATION OF WINDINGS

At the present time most coils, with the exception of those for the smaller type machines are of the "pre-formed" type. By this is meant that they attain their final shape before being inserted in their respective slots. Quite a number are actually bent to shape on a wooden former; particularly for very large machines, but the majority are of the "pulled" type. Fig. 34 illustrates three stages in the manufacture of a pulled coil, having two sections with five turns per section, the conductor being of rectangular section and cotton covered.

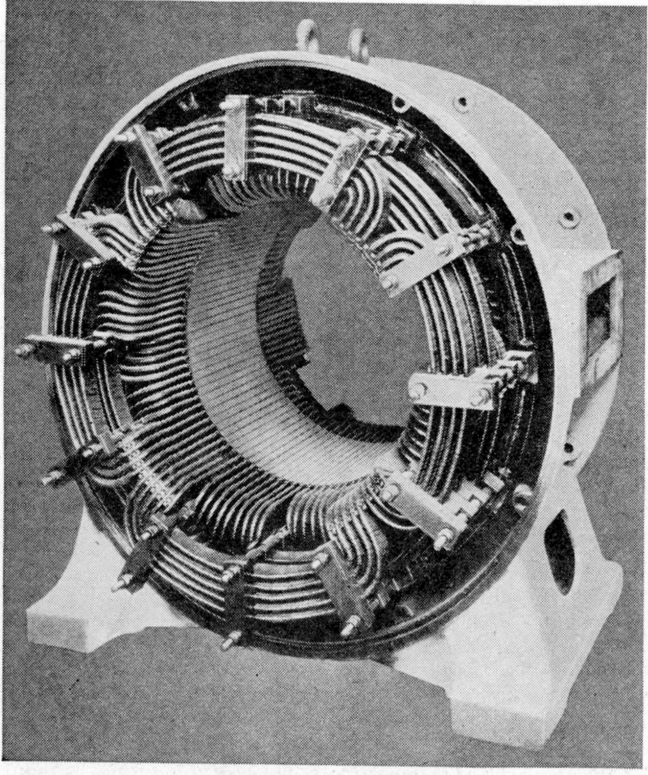

CONCENTRIC WINDING

Fig. 33. 3-Tier high voltage concentric winding for a Metrovick 4-pole induction motor. It is essentially of the single-layer type having one coil side in each slot. There are nine coils per complete group.

The purpose of the insulation on armature windings is first to prevent current flowing from the conductors to the steel core in whose slots the conductors are embedded and, secondly, to ensure that currents do not pass from one part of the winding to another, other than along the paths intended. These requirements lead us to what we know respectively as "insulation to ground" and "insulation between turns" or "between phases" as the case may be. The ability of insulation to withstand a large difference in voltage between its two sides, is referred to as its "dielectric strength".

Insulating materials, as supplied in modern practice to the windings of electric motors, can be viewed under two headings, namely, "Class A Insulation" and "Class B Insulation. Class A insulation is that employed in ordinary industrial machines where the temperature of the insulation is never likely to exceed about 90° C.

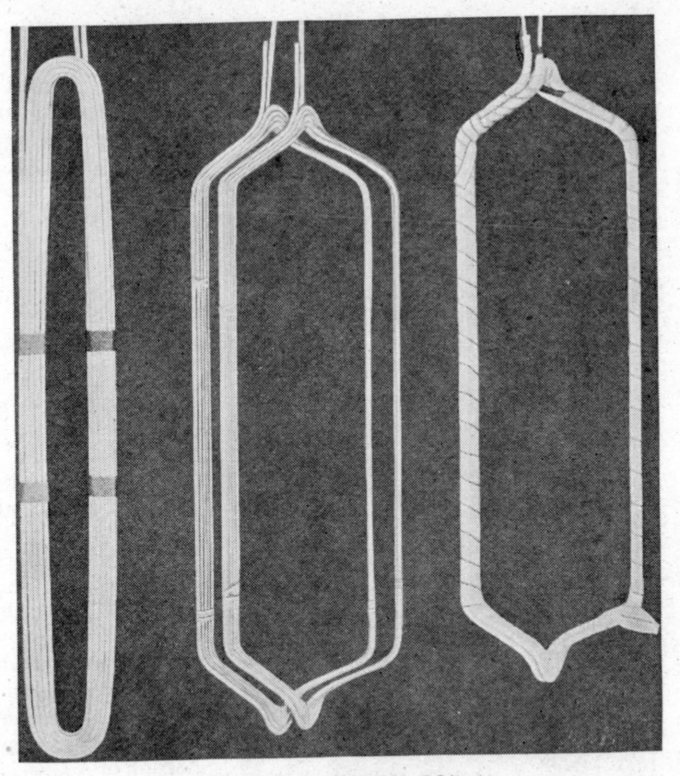

DIAMOND RIBBON COIL

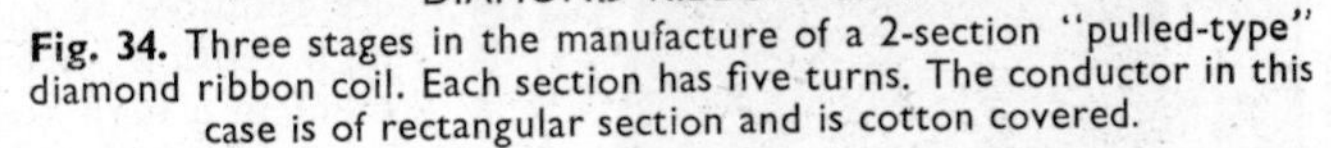

Fig. 34. Three stages in the manufacture of a 2-section "pulled-type" diamond ribbon coil. Each section has five turns. The conductor in this case is of rectangular section and is cotton covered.

It covers such materials as cotton, paper, silk, and similar organic materials, including certain cellulose materials recently developed. These are all normally impregnated with some insulating compound. Wire insulated with enamel is also included in this category. Paper usually appears as pressboard, presspaper or leatheroid in the form of slot liners and packing strips, see Fig. 39, and also as a base for the mica flakes in the manufacture of micafolium or micanite. Cotton and silk, as well as forming the coverings of wire, are extensively used in a variety of treated and untreated tapes and cloths. Silk being more expensive is used chiefly because it permits a smaller thickness of insulation to be employed than would be required in the case of cotton. It occasionally happens, however, that we require the insulation of a motor to withstand higher temperatures such as 115° C. due either to the fact that the ambient or surrounding air temperature may exceed the generally accepted maximum of 35° C. mentioned in B.S.S. 168 or because we wish to permit a temperature rise in the motor windings, for example of 75° C., as is customary in the case of many steelworks motors. It is then that we resort to Class B materials; they comprise such substances as mica and asbestos, in conjunction with some binding material to hold them in

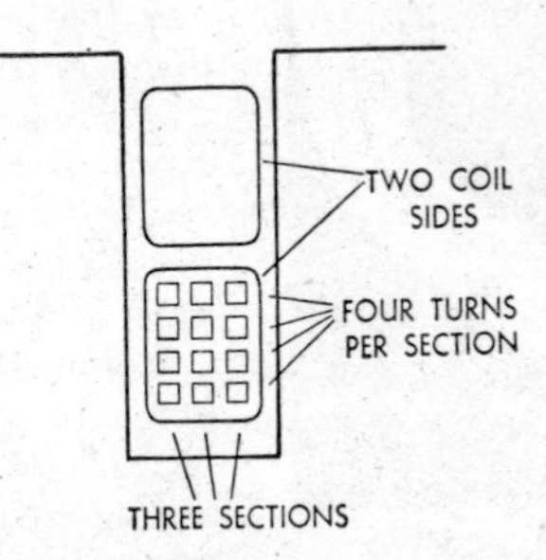

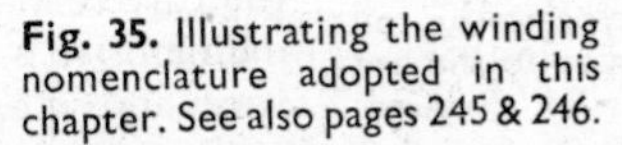

Fig. 35. Illustrating the winding nomenclature adopted in this chapter. See also pages 245 & 246.

place. In the last year or two glass has become more and more popular as a heat resisting insulation, both as a covering for wires and in the form of tape and cloth made from woven glass fibres. Even more modern developments in insulating materials having the necessary special qualities take the form of plastics, certain new compositions of this nature appearing to be of considerable promise.

METHOD OF INSULATING COILS

The insulation of a winding considered as a whole must possess both mechanical and dielectric strength. In the first place, for windings utilising covered wire, as is the case for all but fairly heavy current windings, the covering itself must be strong enough not to suffer damage while the coil is being wound. Further, the insulation of all windings must be sufficiently robust to withstand the fairly heavy handling to which it is subjected while the coils are being inserted into the slots; in addition, it must not be injured by the forces exerted on the conductors during operation.

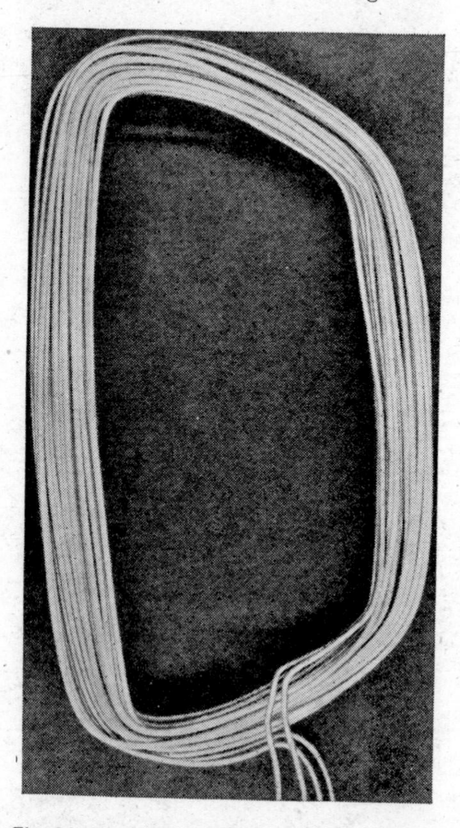

Fig. 36. "Mush" or "basket" type stator coil having two wires in parallel. Owing to the use of small gauge wire they are "wild" wound.

Ideally from the insulation standpoint, the most satisfactory procedure would be to insulate all coils completely before attempting to wind them into the core. Unfortunately, this is not always expedient. The way in which the coils of a particular winding, whether A.C. or D.C., are to be insulated is influenced by several factors:—

(a) Voltage to be applied to it.
(b) Size of conductor.
(c) Slot opening, i.e., the slot shape.
(d) Method of winding to be employed.

For normal industrial purposes the various supply voltages are classified as "low voltage" up to 650 volts and "high voltage" from thence up to 3,500 volts. In ordinary circumstances the windings of D.C. armatures and A.C. rotors are confined to the lower range, but a proportion of A.C. stators, on the other hand, are required to operate direct from the high tension supply. The only requirement in a high voltage winding is that a greater thickness of insulation is demanded between the conductors and the core.

SIZE OF CONDUCTORS

Generally speaking, the size of conductor used depends both on the voltage and the horse-power of the motor. For a given horse-power, the higher the voltage the greater is the number of turns required in the winding, and hence the smaller the copper section. With higher horse-power, however, the size of copper must be increased.

Commencing at the lower end of the range of sizes, for conductors of small section round wires are normally used having coverings ranging from enamel in the case of very fine wires, e.g., ·0084 in. diameter to s.c.c. (single cotton covered) wire and d.c.c. wire in the larger dia-

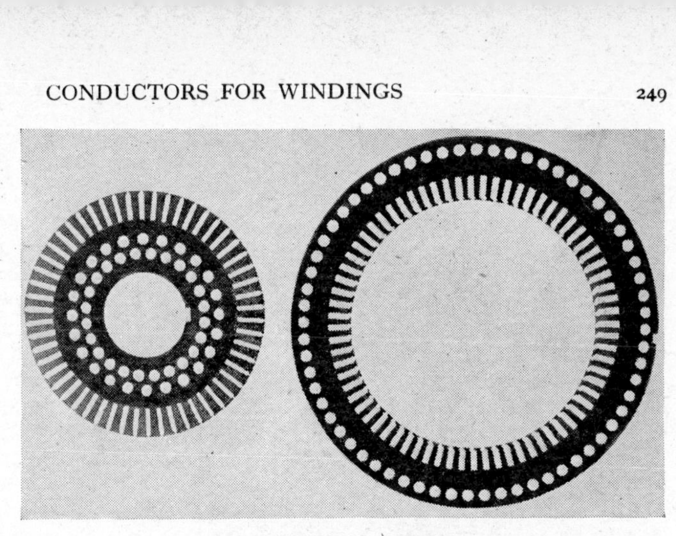

LAMINATION DESIGN

Fig. 38. Stator and rotor laminations for induction motor showing "half-open" stator slots and "semi-closed" rotor slots.

neters such as ·092 n. Windings utilis- ng these conductors re known as "mush" r "basket" windings nd resemble the ne illustrated in 'ig. 31, a coil of vhich can be seen in 'ig. 36. The wires re too small to per- nit of an orderly rrangement in the lot and are stated to e "wild wound".

Incidentally, these asket windings are uite different in orm from the so- alled basket coils which were at one ime frequently employed in the con- truction of radio receivers.

When it is required to employ a larger opper section, it is usual to turn to a quare or rectangular conductor known s "ribbon" which, like the round wires, as a double cotton covering. The ectangular section reduces considerably he amount of waste space in the slot and, n addition, enables the coil turns to hold ogether better during the "pulling" peration by which this type of coil gets ts shape. Three stages in the manufacture f a "diamond ribbon" coil are depicted n Fig. 35.

Beyond sizes such as ·25 in × ·18 in. otton covered ribbon gives way to bare opper strap. It is bare because it has not een found satisfactory to apply the ormal cotton covering to conductors vhere the width is several times greater than the thickness as, for instance, in 0·5 in. wide by ·125 in. thick copper. It is accordingly insulated by taping later when it has been cut to length and bent to the correct position.

SLOT SHAPE

Fig. 37, which indicates some of the types of slot shape incorporated in present-day designs, gives a very clear though by no means complete illustration of the diversity of available forms designed for modern motors. From the point of view of iron loss in the teeth the closed slot is the best and the open slots are the worst, due to the "flux swinging" which occurs when the machine is running. In spite of its mechanical desirability, however, the closed slot is now seldom used, since for A.C. machines it causes the winding to have an excessively high inductance and from the D.C. standpoint gives rise to commutation troubles. In addition, the coils have to be wound laboriously by hand, turn by turn.

The desirable feature of the open slot lies in the fact that it allows a com-

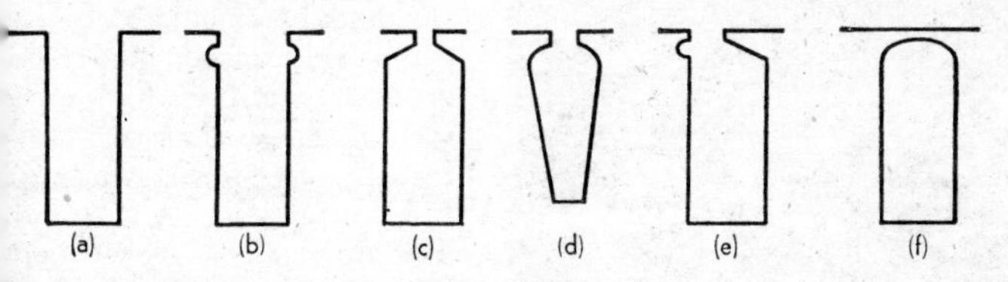

SHAPES OF SLOT

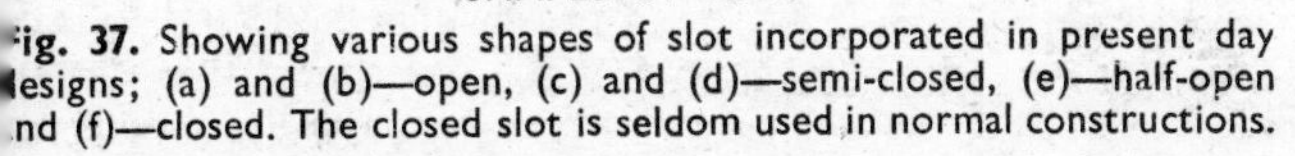

'ig. 37. Showing various shapes of slot incorporated in present day lesigns; (a) and (b)—open, (c) and (d)—semi-closed, (e)—half-open nd (f)—closed. The closed slot is seldom used in normal constructions.

pletely "pre-insulated" coil to be dropped in without difficulty. An actual armature punching having open slots is illustrated in Fig. 7, which appears on page 222, while two types of partially closed slots so called "half-open" and "semi-closed" are to be seen in the stator and rotor laminations in Fig. 38.

There are two ways of winding coils into slots which are not completely closed. They consist of:—

(a) Dropping the coil complete or part by part through the slot opening, and

(b) Pushing the coils through the slots from one end of the core, in which case the coils must be "open" or of the "hairpin" or push-through type.

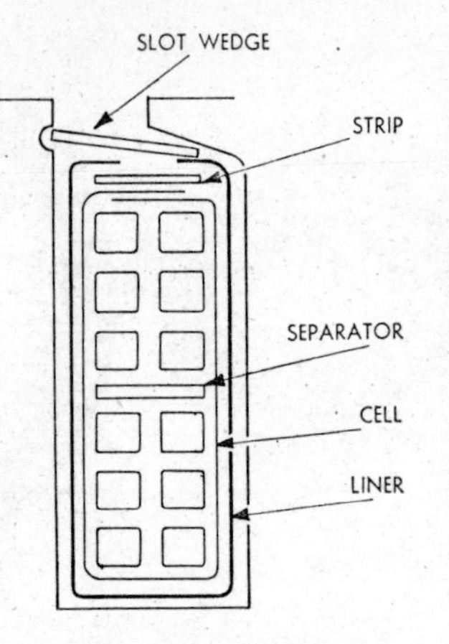

Fig. 40. Typical low-voltage ribbon winding as incorporated in medium-sized motors.

We have already mentioned the desirability of insulating a coil as far as possible before inserting it into the slot, and in the case of high tension machines, this course is usually adopted. For a diamond ribbon type coil to be employed, we would require open slots. The coil itself would resemble the one in Fig. 35 with several turns of micafolium wrapped round the slot portions and held in place by tape non-lapping. Where an open slot is not permissible from considerations of iron loss, a concentric type high tension winding like the one in Fig. 33 might be selected. The coils then would be of the type known as "hairpin" or "push-through", that is, open at one end. Again the slot portions would be wrapped with micafolium to furnish the necessary high dielectric strength.

Micafolium, as has been previously indicated, is a composite material in which mica is employed. It comprises a paper backing that is covered with mica flakes and varnish. It is widely used not only for such purposes as the above, but it also has several other electrical applications.

Turning now to the low tension windings, the open slot and pre-insulated coil is extensively used for D.C. armature windings for copper sections larger than that associated with mush windings. For low voltage A.C. windings it is not normally considered essential to employ a pre-insulated coil and accordingly one finds the various types of partially closed slot

LOW TENSION STATOR

Fig. 39. Partially wound low tension A.C. stator embodying "half-open" slots and 2-section coils. Note the slot liners.

TYPICAL MODERN ROTOR

Fig. 41. View of "bar" wound A.C. rotor in which can be seen the soldered clip joints. There are six bars in each slot.

ıdopted, into which the slot nsulation is inserted eparately before the coil itelf is dropped in. Fig. 39 is photograph of a low tension tator winding with only a portion of the windings yet n place. The pressboard slot iners can be clearly seen in he lower left-hand corner, ogether with the empire cloth ells which are projecting rom the lower slot openings. In this machine half-open lots are being used with a wo-section coil. To insert the oils one section is lowered nto the slot through the slot ppening after which it is moved to the side of the slot o allow the remaining section o drop in alongside it. In the llustration the second section of the extreme left-hand coil s just about to be pushed lown. The upper coil sides of the coils at the top of the photograph have been left out of the slot to permit the other coil sides occupying the lower half of those slots to be put in. Fig. 40 represents a typical slot design for a low voltage medium-sized motor.

The illustration clearly shows the disposition of the liner, cell and other items.

BAR WINDING

Where heavy strap conductors are involved, open slots and a pre-insulated coil frequently represent the practice adopted with respect to D.C. armature windings. Manufacture follows the same lines as for the open slot ribbon windings except that each strap has first to be taped all over with some kind of treated tape to replace the cotton covering possessed by ribbon conductors. A winding, however, which has been widely employed for both A.C. stators and rotors is the "bar" winding. In this the coils initially are only half-coils made in the form of straight bars. As far as the slot portion is concerned, the conductors are fully insulated before winding, one, two, or three being taped up together according to whether there are finally to be two, four, or six per slot. During winding, the insulated bars are pushed through the slots from one end, when the projecting lengths of the separate bars are then bent at an angle to form the conventional shape of coil end. The coils are finally completed by joining each top bar with an appropriate bottom bar by means of a soldered copper clip. The appearance of a rotor so wound with a total of 6 bars per slot is shown by Fig. 41. Bar windings combine the advantages of a pre-insulated slot portion with those of a semi-closed slot.

IMPREGNATION

It has been mentioned how cotton, paper and silk form the bases of insulation on low tension machines. These materials

MACHINES ON TEST

Fig. 42. View of main generator and motor testing shop at the Metropolitan Vickers works at Manchester. Several features of modern motor design as described in this chapter are clearly to be seen in this photograph. In the foreground a generator is being tested.

have unfortunately a common failing; they are "hygroscopic" which means that in their untreated state they tend to absorb moisture. In the moist condition they merely consist of a mass of fibres with the small interstices between the fibres filled with water. Quite obviously the insulation value is then much lower than in the dry condition. It is necessary, and is indeed universally accepted that some means must be employed to prevent moisture entering by completely filling the minute spaces where it can repose by an insulating compound, as well as by providing an impervious coating on the outside of the insulation. This can be achieved either by using materials which are already treated or alternatively by arranging for their impregnation during a subsequent stage of manufacture.

In the case of the smaller machines, the rotors, stators and armatures can be treated in the finished state, but for larger sizes it becomes necessary to treat individual coils. Insulating varnish or molten bitumen form the most common impregnating compounds. Where great penetration is desired, as with a mush wound stator or a completely pre-insulated coil, vacuum impregnation is very successful. In this process the unit is dried out in a vacuum to extract all air and moisture and then the liquid is allowed to flow in, the pressure being then raised. In this way a most effective penetration of the insulating substance into the interstices of the coil is secured. Bitumen does not require the final baking which is necessary with varnish and which in the vacuum process causes slight surface cracking due to the thinner layers from inside being driven off through the exterior layers which have already hardened. Unfortunately for rotors and armatures, centrifugal action would cause the bitumen to "flow" and, in consequence, it is customary to employ a "varnish dip" to provide the necessary impregnation.

CHAPTER 7

UTILISATION OF ELECTRICITY

lectrical Engineering Economics. Electric Lamps and Lighting. Lamp Circuits. ndustrial Lighting. Domestic Lighting. Street Lighting. Electricity in the Home. Electricity in the Factory. Electricity in Mining. Electricity in Agriculture.

AN engineer who is in charge of a proposed electrical installation system should, first of all, conider how such a system may be installed o the best advantage of the consumer. This calls for a great deal of forethought n deciding upon the most economical pparatus from the point of view of first ost, reliability, long service, and facilities or the expansion of the system, in due ourse, without unnecessary disturbance f the existing system. In domestic premises no real difficulties should be encountered, but in large factories engaged on important government work, alternative systems of supply should receive careful consideration so that in the event of a breakdown another system shall be immediately brought into use with the least possible delay. These items are dealt with as extensively as possible in this chapter and should enable the reader to comprehend modern methods of using electricity to the best advantage.

ENGINEERING ECONOMICS

SINCE engineering is the technique of satisfying human needs at the least ost in human labour, economics form an ssential element in every engineering peration. But in many cases the conomics involved are so obvious that hey escape attention, being merely a uestion of comparing a number of cost otals and choosing the smallest. The ngineer who designs a machine or an nstallation, or who plans a course of ction, is charged with the duty of nvestigating alternative ways of achievng the desired result. He must find out what size of frame or type of winding, tc., will necessitate least material and abour while complying with all the pecified requirements. When the things e compares are of the same kind and ccur at the same time, little need be aid on the matter. If machine "A" costs £1,000 whilst machine "B" costs only £900 and serves the purpose equally well, the comparison is merely arithmetical and the solution is obvious.

Difficulties arise when the costs compared occur at different times. Let it be supposed that machine B, whilst cheaper to purchase, costs £20 a year more to operate for the same output, or that its maintenance involves this extra compared with machine A. Let it further be supposed that both machines can be expected to be useful in their original capacity for a period of twenty years. Omitting all items which are common to both machines the relevant expenses are as follows. If the comparison is made only for the first year of operation, B will clearly be cheaper, since it costs £900 (purchase price) plus £20 (extra operating cost) whilst A costs £1,000. If on the other hand the comparison were made over the total life period, B will cost an aggregate of £900 plus 20 × £20 = £1,300, whilst A only costs £1,000.

On further investigation it becomes clear that neither method of comparison is correct. In the first case one neglects all expenses after the first year, whereas the cheaper machine carries with it a heritage of annual costs extending over its whole life period. In the second method of comparison one is crediting a particular moment (namely, the present purchasing time) with an accumulation of costs which are only going to occur in future years. Since £1 now is worth more than £1 five or ten years hence, it follows that this method falsifies the results in one direction just as the other method falsifies them in the opposite direction.

ANNUAL AND CAPITAL COSTS

A more difficult problem of the same kind is when one has to choose between, say, a wooden structure lasting 50 years and a more expensive steel structure lasting much longer; or between laying down a small cable capable of satisfying needs for the next five years or so, and laying down a larger size which will not become remunerative until a later date.

The primary problem in engineering economics is the weighing up of present and future costs and values. When we decide to use one size of cable or type of machine rather than another our decision may affect working results ten years ahead and it is, therefore, essential to be able to forecast these results and to say what is their cash value at some given time (e.g. the present). The mechanism whereby this comparison is made possible is the rate of interest on capital.

BASES OF COMPARISON

When we employ an elaborate and expensive machine we do so to save labour. In order to justify this expenditure we must assess the annual saving and compare it with alternative returns on the same capital. If the expenditure shows a satisfactory yield in view of the risks involved and alternatives available, the project is proceeded with. The same thing can be put the other way round by saying that if money can be hired for the enterprise at a certain rate, a knowledge of this rate will enable us to compare present and future values and so make a correct decision in any problem. There are two different bases of comparison to be used in solving such problems, namely annual costs and capitalised costs. In the former case all capital values and the lump sums are expressed as annual figures extending over each year of useful life of the plant. Thus in the case of the two machines A and B already instanced, it would be necessary only to annualise the difference in first cost, namely £100. Over a period of 20 years, assuming 5 per cent interest, this will represent a sum of £8 a year extra for A as will be seen from the tables given on page 255. It is then a simple matter to compare this with the extra cost of B, namely £20 a year.

The second basis, namely capitalised cost, is operated the other way round. All annual sums are capitalised and their present worth is found, which can then be directly compared with the first costs. In the above case an extra annual cost of £20 a year for 20 years is equivalent to a present worth of £249. This is 2½ times bigger than the extra first cost of A, and the latter is therefore the preferable choice.

It will be seen that both bases of comparison lead to the same result, namely the choice of A in preference to B. Moreover both methods are economically correct, and the results they yield are economically equivalent. This is easily shown from the same tables, for the annual saving of A over B is a net figure of £12 a year, and if this is capitalised it amounts to £149 which is the net capital difference. Thus it is purely a matter of convenience which basis is employed. When the items are small and no complications are involved, the capitalised cost method is simpler, but in large complex cases the annual cost method is preferable. The tables which are given on the opposite page will provide a basis for economic choice calculations.

The best way of illustrating the processes of engineering economics is by way of example. All branches of engineering involve applications of economic selection, but electrical engineering is particularly rich in examples. This is ecause electrical plant commonly has osses which can be reduced by a greater apital expenditure on the active naterials. There is therefore always a ossibility of improving the efficiency of uch plant, and the question then arises f how far such improvement will be vorth its cost. The two examples below vill sufficiently illustrate the method of rocedure, and the use of the tables.

TABLE I

Annual Value or Cost (Interest plus Depreciation) For present sum of £100			
Life in Years	Rate of Interest on Capital		
	3%	5%	7%
5	21·8	23·1	24·4
7	16·1	17·3	18·6
10	11·7	13·0	14·2
15	8·4	9·63	11·0
20	6·7	8·02	9·44
30	5·1	6·51	8·06

TRANSFORMER QUOTATIONS

To comply with a certain specification wo quotations are received for a static ransformer. Both are of the same size namely 1,000 kVA) and have the same opper loss, but they differ in first cost nd in the magnitude of their iron loss. One transformer is priced at £600 with n iron loss of 5·5 kW, whilst the second ransformer is priced at £640 with an ron loss of 5·1 kW. The plant is required for supply service, i.e., continuous connection, and the cost of the energy for a 24 hour load is estimated to be 0·5d. per kWh.

The basis of comparison proposed is annual costs, and the first step is to express the extra purchase price of £40 for the second transformer as an annual charge. Taking interest at 5 per cent. and a life of 20 years the overall figure for hire and replacement of capital is 8·02 per cent. (Table I). A first cost of £40 therefore represents a yearly figure of £3·21 per annum. The next step is to value the cost of the saving in iron losses Since this saving is 0·4 kW for 24 hours a day the number of units represented is $24 \times 365 \times 0{\cdot}4 = 3{,}504$ kWh per annum. At a price of ½d. per kWh this is worth $\frac{3{,}504 \times \frac{1}{2}}{240} = £7{\cdot}3$ per annum.

Thus the saving in iron losses is worth slightly more than twice as much as the extra price required to obtain it. In a fixed and stable situation the higher priced transformer would therefore be worth purchasing, and such might represent the appropriate course of action for

TABLE II.

Life in Years	Capitalised Cost or Present Value of £1 per annum			of £1		
	Rate of Interest			Rate of Interest		
	3%	5%	7%	3%	5%	7%
5	4·58	4·33	4·10	0·86	0·78	0·71
7	6·23	5·79	5·39	0·81	0·71	0·62
10	8·53	7·72	7·02	0·74	0·61	0·51
15	11·94	10·38	9·11	0·64	0·48	0·36
20	14·88	12·46	10·59	0·55	0·38	0·26
30	19·6	15·4	12·4	0·41	0·23	0·13

a public authority supply undertaking. If conditions were unsettled and a life of 20 years appeared problematic, or if the undertaking were a company expecting to earn a higher rate of interest, the annual charge corresponding to the extra first cost would be a larger figure. The advantage of the high grade transformer would be correspondingly reduced and the cheaper one might then be preferred.

MAINS PROBLEM

Installation Date. In a portion of a distribution system the immediate needs can be met by a certain cable, size A. After a number of years the load is expected to increase to the point where either a larger cable, B, or a supplementary cable C will be required. The costs per thousand yards, including the necessary laying cost, are as follows:—A, £520; B, £720; C, £418. The choice lies between putting down cable A now and C later, or putting down B now so that no further laying will be required.

If the larger cable is installed in the first place there will be an excess expenditure now of £200 per thousand yards beyond immediate requirements. Alternatively at some future date (say X years ahead) there will be an expenditure of £418 per thousand yards. The problem is to find over what period these two sums are economically equivalent to one another, i.e., in how many years would £200 amount to £418. Now the ratio between the two sums is 200/418 = 0·48, so that the question can be put, "How many years ahead will a sum of £1 have a present worth of £0·48?"

The answer to this question can be found from the second part of Table II (Present worth of £1.) Taking interest at 5 per cent. per annum as before, the figure of 0·48 corresponds to a period of 15 years. The answer to the question will therefore be that if the larger section is likely to be required any time during the next 15 years it will be more economical to put it down now. If, however, the anticipated load growth is slower than this and the larger size would not be needed for 15 years or more, the two-stage plan will be better.

Supply Costs and Tariffs. Another large field for the application of economics is in connection with the costing of electricity supply. The choice of a tariff by the undertaking, and its acceptance or rejection by the consumer must both be based on a careful study of the relevant costs. As regards the undertaking, the cost of electricity involves two major elements:—The fuel and other working costs dependent on the energy, and the plant and other fixed costs dependent on the power. The former are relatively easy both to assess and to allocate. The latter include interest and depreciation on the plant and overheads of various kinds. They are difficult to allocate with any accuracy and most tariffs are somewhat of a compromise between what the electricity costs and what it does.

As regards the consumer, particularly the industrial consumer, he must study the operation of the tariff on his particular load, and see if the cost can be reduced in any way, e.g., by levelling-out his load or improving his load factor. In some cases he must estimate the alternative costs of the private generation of power.

ELECTRIC LAMPS AND LIGHTING

The only purpose of lighting is to serve vision, and the development of lighting methods and of lighting equipment must be directed towards this end. The design and testing of lighting equipment is, of course, an accurate and well-established science, but it is only in recent years that the study of vision has influenced lighting practice to any extent. Depending upon the method of lighting used, fine details may be revealed or concealed; the eye may be protected from, or subjected to strain; the general impression of a work-place may be cheerful, depressing, or even distressing. While good workmanship is obviously

MODERN WORKSHOP LIGHTING

Fig. 1. Industrial efficiency and health are greatly influenced by the quality of lighting, and the five-feet fluorescent lamp has proved of great value in all classes of work. A marked improvement in health and in accuracy of workmanship was experienced in the B.T.H. model room shown above when fluorescent lamps were properly positioned for each type of machine and work bench.

dependent upon good visibility of detail, it is now generally appreciated that, for the maintenance of efficiency, it is also essential to aim at preserving eyesight and promoting a cheerful frame of mind. The acceptance of this outlook has been greatly accelerated by a study of factors affecting the health and efficiency of operatives in factories under war conditions. Investigations have shown that even where adequate quantities of light are provided, unsuitable methods of application produce poor visibility resulting in bad workmanship. Prolonged experience of such conditions was found to induce severe eyestrain, leading to nervous and psychological trouble. In such cases the introduction of lighting of suitable quality rapidly dispersed, not only eyestrain, but obvious physical and nervous fatigue which could therefore be attributed to the strain of unsuitable lighting (see Fig. 1).

Lighting engineering, therefore, differs from other branches of engineering in that designs must be based upon physiological and psychological considerations, and the ultimate aim and success of design cannot be stated in simple numerical terms. It is natural that some straightforward yard stick was sought in utilitarian applications, such as industrial and street lighting, if only to provide a convenient basis for lighting installation contracts. Installations were classified broadly in accordance with the illumination produced at a working plane, and arbitrary standards of illumination were adopted. These standards recommended "light quantities" at the working plane for various classes of work, and neglected other very important factors affecting vision. The natural result was to direct lighting development towards the most economical attainment of stated illumination values, rather than to a study of the basic requirements. In the design of equipment, important advances in efficiency were achieved both in the conversion of electrical energy to light, and in the redirection of light to the working plane. The characteristics of light sources, and the method of applying light were not dictated by consideration of th visual task other than in providing th quantities of light deemed adequate.

To understand the changing practic and status of lighting engineering, it i important to realise that increasin attention is being given to the effective ness of lighting as judged on the basis c the utilisation and conservation of huma resources, rather than of electrical an radiant energy. Such considerations hav already greatly influenced the trend c development and practice, and new ligh sources, equipment and lighting tech niques have been applied widely. Wher a completely standardised system is nc applicable—and the diversity of wor and of architecture in factories alone i very great—the design of suitable lightin installations calls for specialised know ledge and skill in place of the rule o thumb methods previously accepted a adequate in implementing purely quanti tative recommendations.

LUMINOUS INTENSITY, ILLUMINATION AND BRIGHTNES

Even a general discussion of lightin matters cannot be very helpful without correct use of the terms candle power illumination, and brightness. Elementar conceptions of the significance and inter relationship of these terms are no quickly derived from a study of the usua definitions, and Fig. 2 is introduced fo this purpose.

If the point source "S" is an "inter national candle" and is radiatin luminous flux uniformly in all directions then the *luminous intensity* of the sourc in any direction is said to be 1 candle "Candlepower" is not a measure o "quantity" of light, but is purely a state ment of the potentiality of the ligh source in producing illumination in given direction. Practical sources do no radiate light uniformly in all directions and their performance is recorded i polar or spherical co-ordinates relatin intensity with direction, as, for example in a polar curve of candle power.

When light strikes a surface, the sur face is said to be illuminated. The tern *illumination* is used in wider senses, but is defined in photometry as the density of luminous flux, or more concisely, flux density. It is the amount of light received per unit area of surface, and the unit of illumination is the "lumen per sq. ft." or the "foot-candle".

On the surface of the sphere in Fig. 2 is shown an area, ABCD, of 1 sq. ft., and luminous flux is received on this area at a rate of 1 lumen, the unit of quantity being the lumen-hour. (Incidentally, it follows that a uniform source of 1 candle radiates 4π lumens.) The illumination of ABCD is therefore said to be 1 lumen/sq. ft. It is also described as 1 foot-candle, and this brings in the inverse square law which states that the illumination of a surface is equal to the intensity (candle power) of the source illuminating it, divided by the square of the distance between source and surface. Thus the illumination of ABCD would be quartered if the radius of the sphere were doubled, thus doubling the distance between that surface and the light source.

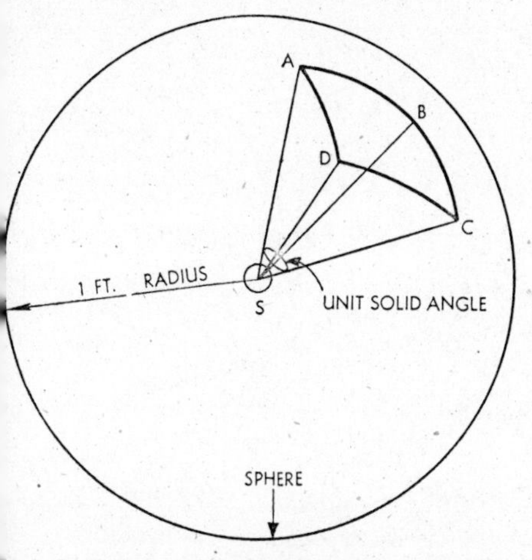

Fig. 2. Diagram relating luminous intensity, flux and flux density.

A body or a surface is described as "bright" when it emits or reflects light so that it becomes visible. *Brightness* is a statement of the amount of light per unit area radiated towards the point of view, and does not otherwise refer to the nature of the radiating surface. This point is stressed because it is an everyday practice to refer to a high polish as brightness. A polished surface may have a high reflection factor, but it will reflect the light it receives only in certain well-defined directions and can be described as bright only when viewed from those directions. Thus the brightness of any part of a mirror depends upon the brightness of the object seen imaged there, and upon the reflection factor or efficiency of the mirror. It follows that brightness is not confined to polished surfaces, which are described as "specular" reflectors. A "diffuse" reflector, such as a piece of blotting paper, will appear bright from every point of view because it reflects light in every direction even though illuminated from only one direction. The brightness of a diffusely reflecting surface does not depend upon the brightness of the object illuminating it, but only upon the amount of light received per unit area and the efficiency of the surface in reflecting light.

DEFINITION OF BRIGHTNESS

Thus the *definition of brightness* is as follows:—The brightness "in a given direction" of the surface emitting light is the quotient of the luminous "intensity" measured in that direction by the "area of this surface" projected on a plane perpendicular to the direction considered.

One unit of brightness is the candle per unit area of surface, and this method of specifying brightness applies particularly to the surfaces of high brightness such as light sources, or the opal panels of lanterns. Thus the brightness of the arc of a 400-watt mercury lamp is given as 160 candles/sq. cm. Illuminated surfaces, such as the walls of rooms, are at much lower brightnesses, and there is a more convenient unit known as the "equivalent foot-candle", the uniform brightness of a perfectly diffusing surface emitting 1 lumen/sq. ft. Such a surface, reflecting all the light received, would have a brightness of 1 E.F.C. when illuminated to a level of 1 foot-candle. Walls painted with a light coloured matt paint differ from the theoretically perfect diffuser mainly in respect of their reflection factors, which may lie between 30 and 80 per cent., the brightnesses produced by a given illumination being correspondingly lower.

EYE SENSITIVITY

The sensation of sight is produced when the retina of the eye receives a sufficient density of energy radiated between wavelengths of 4,000Å and 7,600Å. The "colour" quality of this sensation changes continuously from violet at 4,000Å, through indigo, blue, green, yellow and orange to red at 7,600Å. The sensitivity of the eye also varies with wavelength as shown in Fig. 3a. The "luminosity" or "visibility" curve of radiant energy gives the relative strength of the visual sensation produced by an equal quantity of energy at each wavelength. Thus the physical quantity "energy" multiplied by the eye sensitivity gives the psycho-physiological quantity "light", or luminous flux. This transformation is used in photometry, which deals essentially with luminous flux; that is, radiant energy evaluated by reference to the luminous sensation produced, or by the response of the eye. Portable "foot-candle meters" usually employ a photo-voltaic cell having a sensitivity differing from that of the eye, and separate calibrations are required for light sources having different energy distributions, i.e., different colours.

The lighting engineer, however, is primarily concerned with the "adaptation" of the eye, and the manner in which sensitivity is needlessly depressed by glare, thus depreciating the value of the

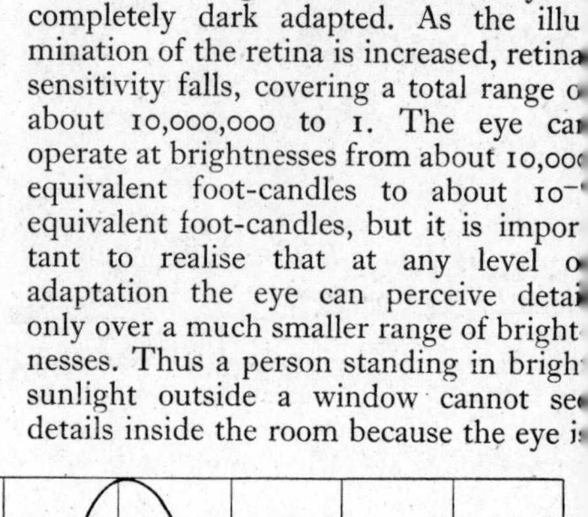

illumination provided. The sensitivity of the eye is automatically adjusted in inverse relation to the illumination of the retina, and is greatest when the eye is completely dark adapted. As the illumination of the retina is increased, retinal sensitivity falls, covering a total range of about 10,000,000 to 1. The eye can operate at brightnesses from about 10,000 equivalent foot-candles to about 10^{-} equivalent foot-candles, but it is important to realise that at any level of adaptation the eye can perceive detail only over a much smaller range of brightnesses. Thus a person standing in bright sunlight outside a window cannot see details inside the room because the eye is

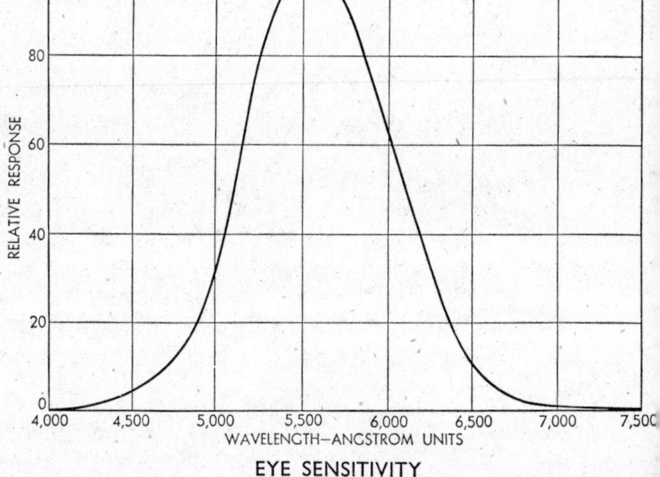

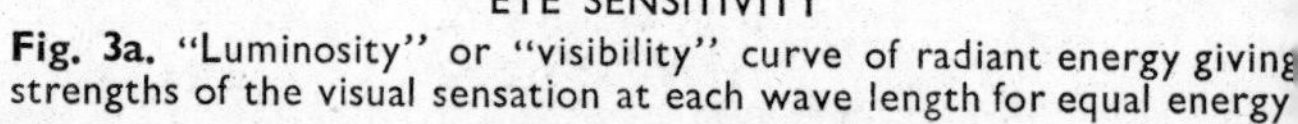
Fig. 3a. "Luminosity" or "visibility" curve of radiant energy giving strengths of the visual sensation at each wave length for equal energy

adapted to the much higher brightness level of objects outside. At the same time, a person in the room may see all details perfectly because his eyes are adapted to the lower brightness level of the room.

CONTRASTS OF BRIGHTNESS

Detail is to some extent perceived by colour contrast, but principally by contrasts of brightness and this fact is very well illustrated by the success of monochromatic photography. In perception of fine detail, the contrast sensitivity of the

ye is important, and is defined as the
:ast perceptible increase in brightness.
:ontrast sensitivity remains substantially
onstant over a wide range of bright-
esses, but decreases when the brightness
:vel is reduced below certain values.
Ience it is important to provide higher
:vels of illumination for finer work, and
or darker materials. Since, however, the
ye adapts its sensitivity to the general
:vel of brightness, only relatively big
ıcreases of illumination are appreciated
s giving a definite improvement in
isibility.

It will, therefore, be realised how im-
ortant it is to avoid any effect which
nnecessarily decreases the eye sensi-
vity, and it is for this reason that glare
ı any form should be avoided. If light
ources of high brightness are introduced
ıto the field of view, so that the surfaces
is desired to see appear to be reduced in
rightness, then the bright sources are
glaring". The apparent brightness of an
bject under such circumstances, as
istinct from the physically measured
rightness, is known as the "subjective"
rightness, and it is only this depressed
alue which is of use in conveying im-
ressions to the mind.

SUBJECTIVE BRIGHTNESS

In all lighting matters the engineer is
oncerned in providing satisfactory levels
f "subjective" brightness, and recent
:ends are towards an appreciation of the
ıct that a reasonable level of physical
rightness may be rendered valueless by
efects in the method of lighting, less
bvious than direct glare. It should be
oted that extraneous bright areas can
epress eye sensitivity seriously without,
owever, causing discomfort. Thus a
rilliant source causing disability glare
vill also cause intense discomfort, where-
s a larger area of lower brightness can
epress eye sensitivity to the same extent
ithout discomfort, except that due to
:raining to see details. This is very well
lustrated by the bad driving conditions
xperienced at dawn, when the increasing
rightness of the sky depresses eye
ensitivity without providing a sufficient
compensating increase in road illumination.

Incandescent filament lamps were used almost exclusively in the electric lighting of streets and factories until about 1933, when the introduction of new types of electric discharge lamps produced a notable advance in the efficiency of light production. Attempts to improve the colour of discharge lamps led to the development of tubular fluorescent lamps combining a high efficiency and a very flexible control of colour quality.

One aim in lamp design is to produce light as cheaply as possible, and this calls for consideration not only of efficiency in the conversion of electrical energy to light, but also of the life of the lamps and the cost of replacement. In filament lamp design, the basic consideration is a compromise between efficiency and life, and this is readily illustrated. The radiation from an incandescent source is determined by temperature as shown in Fig. 3b. These curves are for bodies of equal size, and the areas beneath the curves are proportional to the total energy radiated at various temperatures. It is seen that with increasing temperature more energy is radiated at all wavelengths, and there is also a shift in energy distribution which brings a higher percentage of the total radiation into the visible region. Hence, at higher filament temperatures a greater percentage of the electrical input is converted to visible radiation. The rate of evaporation of the filament is also increased ever more rapidly with temperature, and the life is correspondingly decreased. Practical experience has shown that a life of about 1,000 hours is economic for filament lamps in normal applications, and this limits filament temperatures to the neighbourhood of 3,000° K. The efficiency in light production of general service lamps ranges from 12 lumens per watt for a gas-filled 100-watt lamp to 20 lumens per watt for a 1,500-watt lamp of the type used in street lighting and factory lighting. In various special applications a higher efficiency and a shorter life are economic, as in the case of the photo-flood lamps

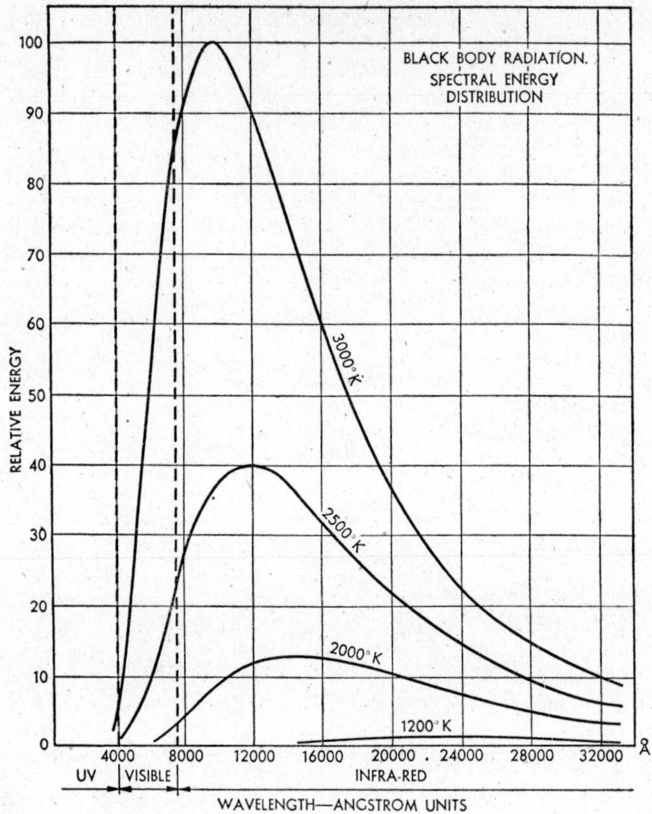

WAVELENGTH—ANGSTROM UNITS

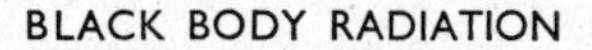
BLACK BODY RADIATION

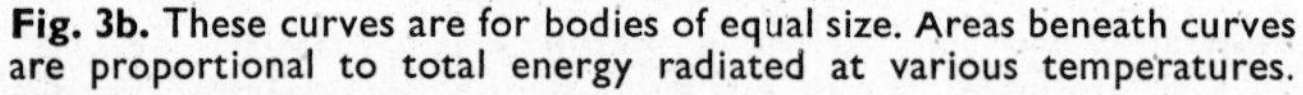
Fig. 3b. These curves are for bodies of equal size. Areas beneath curves are proportional to total energy radiated at various temperatures.

having an efficiency of 35 to 40 lumens per watt and a life of two hours.

Research work on the improvement of filament lamp efficiency has had two aims:—

(1) The discovery of materials which could withstand higher temperatures without serious evaporation.

(2) Methods of reducing evaporation at high temperatures such as gas fillings and coiled filament construction.

There has been a vast amount of engineering research into the processing and usage of each new material, but none more satisfactory than tungsten has been found. There is a strong indication that the present-day tungsten lamp is close to the final product o development alon the lines of incan descent sources, th most recent develop ment being th "coiled coil" desig of filament.

Referring again t Fig. 3b, it is see that the visibl energy radiated b an incandescen source varies from maximum at the re end of the spectrun to a minimum at th blue wavelengths The "daylight blue" lamp does not creat more blue light, bu improves the balanc by absorbing red an yellow rays in a blu filter glass, thu lowering the overal efficiency of ligh production.

If all the electrica energy input coul be radiated in a uni form distributio over the visibl wavelengths to giv a pure white light the efficiency of ligh production would be about 230 lumen per watt. At an optimum temperature c about 6,000° K. an incandescent sourc would have a theoretical limit of abou 90 lumens per watt, because the energ distribution would still be of the genera form shown in Fig. 3, and the radiatio could not be restricted to the visible ban of wavelengths. In seeking both a hig efficiency and control of colour, it i necessary to use a more flexible mechan ism for converting electrical energy t light.

In the electric discharge lamp, th radiation emanates from a conductin vapour and there is no limitation c source temperature as in the case c filament lamps. More important still, the spectrum is discontinuous, and radiation occurs in sharply defined bands of wave-lengths depending on the choice of vapour and other factors in lamp design. Already in practice this line of development has produced lamps of 3, 4 and 5 times the efficiency of filament lamps of the same wattage. High pressure mercury vapour lamps are made in 400 and 250 watt sizes, and extra high-pressure lamps are made in 125-watt and 80-watt sizes. The forms these lamps take are shown in Fig. 4, and the luminous efficiencies are given in Table 3. It will be noted that the 250-watt lamp is less efficient than the 400-watt, and the different design of the 125 and 80-watt lamps is adopted to overcome this tendency. Efficiency has been kept up at the lower wattages by the use of higher vapour pressures of the order of 10 to 20 atmospheres. Owing to the higher brightness of these more compact sources, the outer bulb is internally frosted. Lamp designs for special purposes use still higher vapour pressures giving the very compact and brilliant sources required, for example, in projection.

The visible radiations of the high pressure mercury vapour lamps described occur mainly in narrow bands of wave-lengths in the blue, green and yellow regions, and there is a marked deficiency of red light. Where the filament lamp produces about 25 per cent. red light, and sunlight about 15 per cent., the high-pressure mercury lamp gives only about 1 per cent. A measure of colour correction

TABLE 3.—ELECTRIC DISCHARGE LAMPS

LAMP		Lumens per Watt		Approx. Overall Dimensions (mm.)		
		Initial	Av. over Life	Diam.	Length	Arc. Length
H.P. Mercury Vapour	400 W.	45	37	51	325	160
	250 W.	36	31	51	290	120
E.H.P. Mercury Vapour	125 W.	40	32	90	178	30
	80 W.	38	30	80	160	20
Mercury Fluorescent	400 W.	38	32	165	330	—
	125 W.	40	32	130	233	—
	80 W.	38	30	110	178	—
Tubular Fluorescent (Daylight)	80 W.	35	26	38	1524	1455
Sodium Vapour	140 W.	71·5	57	65	540	395
	85 W.	71·5	57	50	425	295
	60 W.	65	49	50	310	180
	45 W.	55·5	42	50	250	120
Neon Floodlamp	400 W.	11	—	36	1180	960
Mercury ,,	250 W.	15	—	26	1180	960
Mercury Vapour Water-cooled	1000 W.	62·5	—	31	237	25

has been provided by using a larger outer glass bulb, and coating this internally with fluorescent powders which convert some of the ultra-violet radiation of the arc to visible red light. These mercury fluorescent lamps giving about 5 per cent. red are made in the 400-watt, 125-watt and 80-watt sizes, and are used in industrial lighting. Table 3 shows that the efficiency of the 400-watt fluorescent lamp is rather lower than that of the normal lamp, and this is due to some absorption of light in the fluorescent powder. The extra high pressure lamps are richer in ultra-violet radiation, so that the overall efficiency is maintained in the fluorescent type.

TABLE 4

SOURCE.	Intrinsic Brilliancy Candles/ Sq. cm.
Candle	0·4
Clear Sky	0·4
Moon	0·4
Tubular Fluorescent, 80 W.	0·51
Sodium Discharge ..	10·0
Tungsten Filament Pearl, 15 L/W. ..	20
Mercury Discharge, H.P., 400 W. ..	160
Tungsten Filament, Clear, 15 L/W. ..	800
Mercury Vapour, 250 W. (Box Type) ..	10,000
Electric Arc, 25 amp. ..	19,500
Mercury Vapour, 1,000 W. water cooled	30,100
Sun	160,000

Sodium vapour is also used in discharge lamps, and produces a "resonant" radiation giving a characteristic yellow-orange colour. The relatively high luminous efficiencies shown in Table 3 are due largely to this radiation being at wavelengths where the eye has maximum sensitivity. This type of lamp has been made in four sizes as indicated in Table 3, and is used principally in street lighting and floodlighting. It has been applied to industrial lighting, but the colour rendering, which cannot be improved, has restricted its use in this field.

The most significant development in lamp design is represented in the 80-watt tubular fluorescent lamp which is now being applied extensively to industrial lighting, especially in blacked out factories. In this lamp the visible radiation is produced almost entirely by fluorescence, the electric discharge being designed to produce ultra-violet radiation at wavelengths especially suitable for conversion to visible energy by fluorescent materials. Light of almost any colour quality can be produced in this manner, and a close approximation to daylight is obtainable by the blending of suitable fluorescent powders. In this lamp, the electric discharge takes place in mercury vapour at low pressure and the luminous efficiency depends upon the colour required and the consequent choice of fluorescent materials. The 80-watt lamp, intended primarily for industrial lighting, is usually characterised by a colour resembling the hard cool white of a north sky, and the efficiencies given in Table 3 are for this type. The development of tubular fluorescent lamps for domestic and commercial uses has already proceeded on a large scale in the United States of America and can be expected in Great Britain in the coming years.

Lamp design has so far been discussed principally in relation to luminous efficiency and colour rendering. The brightness of the source has a considerable effect upon lighting practice, and a comparison of brightnesses is given in Table 4. It will be realised that for a given luminous output, the brightness of a source must vary with the area of radiating surface.

The tubular fluorescent lamps described above are suitable for operation at mains voltages and are, therefore, readily applied in normal applications. They were, however, preceded by high

Fig. 4a. 400-watt mercury discharge lamp for factory and street lighting.

Fig. 4b. 140-watt sodium discharge lamp having a detachable outer envelope.

igs. 4c, d and e. Three types of mercury discharge lamps; 80-watt extra high-pressure, 400-att fluorescent and 125-watt fluorescent. Table 3, page 263, gives their luminous efficiencies.

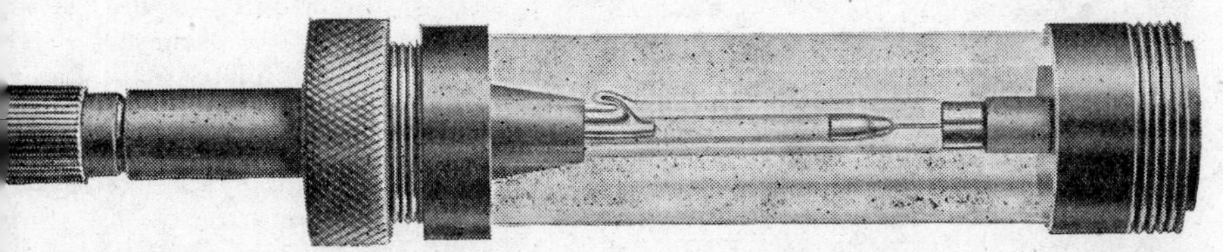

ig. 4f. 1,000-watt water-cooled mercury vapour lamp. The length of the arc is twenty-five mm.

ig. 4g. 80-watt tubular fluorescent lamp as employed in modern systems of factory lighting.

voltage tubular fluorescent lamps operating at circuit voltages up to 10,000 volts. Such lamps are used as architectural features in the lighting of public buildings, and have been used to a very limited extent in industrial lighting before the introduction of the mains voltage lamp. The electrical circuit in general resembles that of the tubular neon lamp used in electric signs. A 400-watt neon lamp, similar to the 80-watt tubular fluorescent lamp in size and electrical circuit characteristics, has also been developed as an efficient source of red light for floodlighting applications.

DISCHARGE LAMP CIRCUITS

The electric discharge has a negative current characteristic, and it is necessary to connect each lamp electrically in series with a current limiting device. If the lamp is connected directly to a mains supply, it is usually destroyed simultaneously with the circuit fuse links. Under normal running conditions, the lamp voltage drop should be not more tha 70 per cent. of the supply voltage fo stable operation, and the overall efficienc would be greatly reduced if a resistanc ballast were used. On alternating curren mains it is normal practice to use an iron cored reactor having a low watts loss On direct current mains, filament lamp have been used to stabilise discharg lamps and "dual" lamps have been mad incorporating both the discharge lam element and the filament in one bulb.

A normal circuit for high pressur mercury lamps is shown in Fig. 5. A switching on, the lamp current is abou twice normal and falls during th "running up" period of about fiv minutes required to vaporise the mer cury. The stabilising choke is especiall designed to provide suitable starting an running conditions, and is tapped elec trically for supply voltages from 190 t 260 volts. The power factor of a choke stabilised circuit is about ·5, and this i improved to about ·9 by the use of power factor correction condense which is connected directly acros the mains, usually at the lam point.

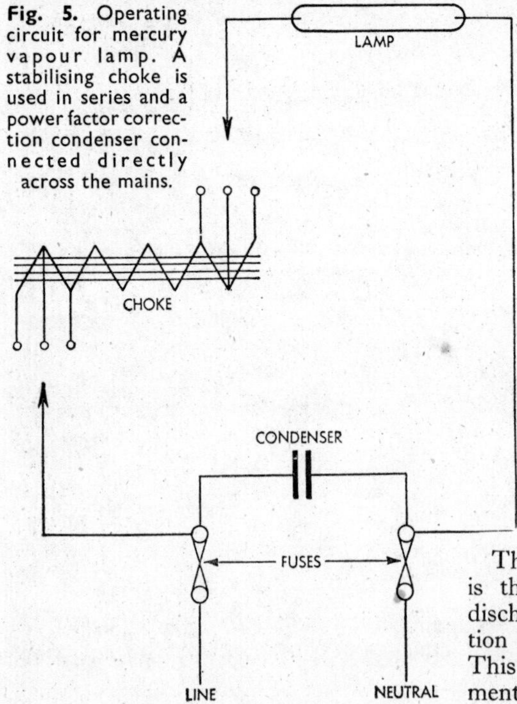

Fig. 5. Operating circuit for mercury vapour lamp. A stabilising choke is used in series and a power factor correction condenser connected directly across the mains.

Sodium lamps require a start ing voltage appreciably abov normal supply voltage and ar therefore, operated from trans formers giving a high open circu voltage. The use of an additiona current limiting choke is avoide by designing the transformer t have a high reactance which serve to stabilise the discharge. Fig. shows the complete circuit, havin an uncorrected power factor of · to ·35 for 45-watts to 140-wat lamps. The total run-up time i this case is twenty to thirt minutes during which the lam current rises to normal from low initial value.

The 80-watt tubular fluorescent lam is the quickest starting of the electri discharge range, being in normal opera tion 2 to 4 seconds after switching or This is made possible by a circuit arrange ment which pre-heats the lamp electrode and then applies a voltage surge between the electrodes. In the circuit of Fig. 7, the thermal switch is closed at starting, and the choke "short circuit" current passes through the lamp electrodes, and the switch heater coil. The switch is opened by the action of the heater coil on a bi-metallic strip after a delay of about two seconds, and a voltage surge from the choke is thus applied across the lamp. The passage of the lamp-operating current through the switch heater coil maintains the switch in an open position. This switch is known as a "thermal" switch, and another type used is the "glow" switch. The glow switch is open at switching on when a neon discharge occurs between the switch contacts at mains voltage. The contacts are mounted on bi-metallic strips, the heating of which by the neon discharge closes the switch, and passes the choke current through the lamp electrodes. Meanwhile the switch discharge has ceased and the cooling of the bi-metallic strips causes these to open, applying the choke surge to the lamp. With the lamp operating, only the lamp voltage drop is applied to the switch, and this is insufficient to initiate the neon discharge again.

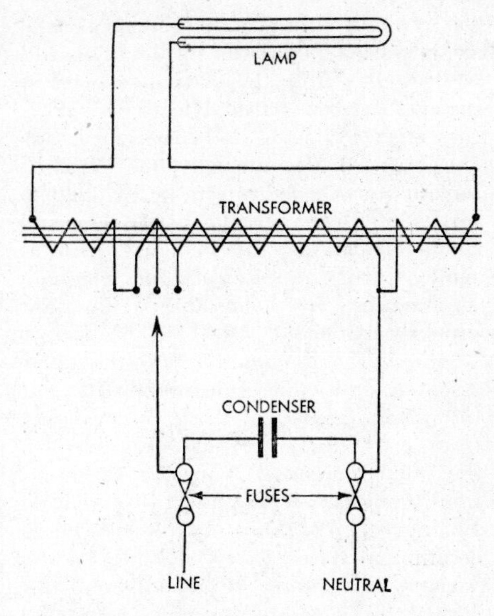

Fig. 6. Circuit for sodium vapour lamp. A transformer of high reactance is used so that an additional current limiting choke is unnecessary. The tappings permit an adjustment to different mains voltages to be made.

INDUSTRIAL LIGHTING

The industrial lighting problem is obviously most complex where the operative applies specialised knowledge and skill, and the visual task is continuous and exacting. If good workmanship is to be achieved in machining, fitting, inspection and similar precision operations, it is essential that vision should provide a perfect linkage between brain and hand. The lighting should also be conducive to economy and freedom of movement. If efficiency is to be maintained, it is equally vital that the lighting should not, in prolonged operation, produce eyestrain; nor should the general impression be depressing or unnatural.

Three main aspects have therefore to be considered:—physiological, operational, and psychological.

Physiological Aspect. This is concerned with the accomplishment of the visual

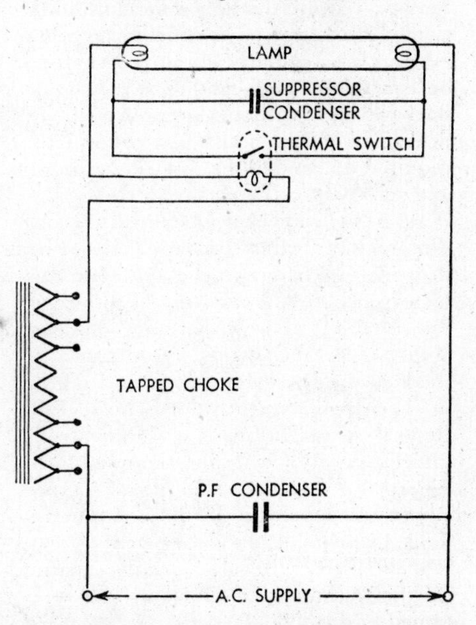

Fig. 7. Circuit for tubular fluorescent lamp using a thermal switch having a switch heater coil incorporated in it. By this means the opening of switch is delayed about two seconds.

task without strain, and for this purpose the necessary perception of detail should be brought within the normal capacity of the eye. Assuming that defective vision is corrected by glasses, and that optical aids are provided for unusually fine detail, it remains for the lighting to be planned to reveal detail by suitable brightness and colour contrasts. In general, this is achieved by the provision of adequate illumination from suitable equipment properly applied.

Adequate Illumination is the first essential, and values considered sufficient for various classes of work, and ranging from 2 ft.-candles to 500, are given in the "Recommended Values of Illumination" published by the Illuminating Engineering Society (London). These recommendations have been adopted by various Government Departments concerned to safeguard production in vital factories engaged on war work. In this respect, also, the Factories (Standards of Lighting) Regulations, 1941, issued by the Ministry of Labour and National Service, require that the general illumination over interior parts of factories where persons are regularly employed shall not be less than 6 foot-candles at 3 ft. above floor level, "without prejudice to the provision of any additional illumination required to render the lighting sufficient and suitable for the nature of the work".

It must, however, be realised that illumination which is adequate when properly applied may be quite unsatisfactory where the lighting is otherwise "unsuitable". The importance of "suitability" has been strongly emphasised by the Departmental Committee on Lighting in Factories, a study of whose Fifth Report (issued in 1940) will indicate the difficulties of specifying the qualitative aspects. It is recorded that "expert advice and supervision will be required in most factories if the best results are to be obtained". Several points bearing on this matter may, however, be mentioned briefly.

Positioning of the Light Source relative to the work and the operative is often very important in revealing detail; there can be little doubt that, in many classes of work, suitability has been sacrificed for the economy of a general overhead system of brilliant and powerful sources arranged in formal pattern.

Reflected Glare is another defect which arises from the reflection of sources of high brightness in material of a specular or polished nature. Excessive and meaningless brightness contrasts are thus superimposed upon surfaces where the operative is trying to perceive detail by contrast between much lower brightnesses. Where numerous overhead sources are involved, the operative cannot eliminate "glitter", although he often attempts to do so by continually changing his own position and that of his work. Thus there is waste of time and energy due to unnecessary operational movements, and spoilage due to faulty visibility. Reflected glare can be a very serious handicap, and in prolonged operation it is a most fruitful source of eyestrain. It can be eliminated only by the adoption of low brightness sources and by attention to the positioning of the light source.

The perception of detail sometimes depends to a large extent upon the discrimination of colour contrast as in colour coded wiring, and in such classes of work imperfect colour rendering will cause strain and inefficiency due to the difficulty of performing the visual task.

So far, suitability has been discussed only in respect of the local field of view and the effect on the immediate mechanism of perception. The distribution of brightnesses and intensities in the general field of view has a profound effect upon both eye sensitivity and eyestrain. This aspect of factory lighting also involves consideration of psychological requirements, the aim being to create a general impression of natural and favourable working conditions.

Direct Glare is a generally acknowledged defect, and the Factory Regulations require that "where a source is less than 16 ft. above floor level, no part of the source or of the lighting fitting having a brightness greater than 10 candles per

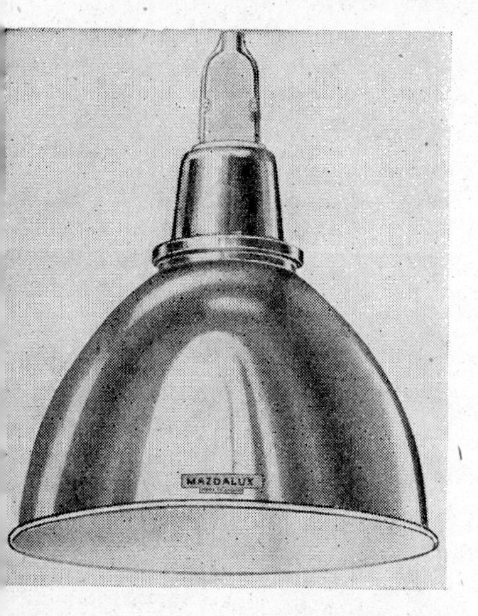

'ig. 8. Typical industrial reflectors for use with 00-watt and 250-watt mercury vapour lamps. 'he reflector on the right is complete with a uilt-in choke. In both cases the reflectors are rovided with finishes in white vitreous enamel.

quare inch shall be visible to persons ormally employed within 100 ft. of the ource, except where the angle of elevaion from the eye to the source exceeds o deg.". It may be noted that all such egulations merely place a limit on the oorness of lighting, and do not represent ecommended good practice. The cut-off t 70 deg. from the vertical does not liminate the glare of high intensity ources, and even at angles exceeding o deg. from the line of view, brilliant ources distract the eye and give an nnatural appearance when placed against relatively dark ceiling.

Another cause of fatigue is found where haded local lights are used without eneral lighting. Apart from the bad sychological effect of the gloomy factory aterior, eyestrain results from the conrast between light and shadow, and from he continuous and unnecessary adaptaion of the eye to the extremes of rightness.

Colour quality is also a factor to be orn in mind, especially in wartime when an operative spends most of his waking hours under artificial light of one sort or another. Many artificial sources have a spectral distribution differing materially from that of natural daylight, and little is yet known of the effect upon the eye of continued exposure to these distributions, unrelieved by lengthy recuperative periods in natural daylight. There can be little doubt that the average person finds a north skylight the most restful, whether for physiological or psychological reasons. Colour rendering has an important effect upon the general appearance of the factory and especially of the operatives, and must be regarded as a factor of prime psychological importance in blacked-out factories.

Thus, in planning industrial lighting to achieve and maintain full efficiency of the operatives, the physiological requirements involve not only the local field of view, but extend to the whole of the general field of view. The general brightness level should preserve the eye adaptation required for perception of detail, and brightness extremes should be kept well within the normal range of the adapted eye. Glare and reflected glare from sunlight and from natural windows, as well as from the artificial sources, must be avoided together with deep shadows on ceilings, walls, floors or any part of the working area. Colour renderings and contrasts should be natural and restful.

Purely *psychological* requirements introduce somewhat similar points. Here the aim is to achieve a general sense of well-being, and the first consideration is clearly to avoid any cause of eyestrain which may lead rapidly to nervous disorders and psychological upsets. An impression of space, cleanliness and freedom of movement is provided by the ample general illumination of light-coloured ceilings and walls. Lighting of daylight quality contributes greatly to the naturalness of the factory interior by giving normal colour rendering, especially of operatives' faces. The impression that natural daylight is entering the building gives a sense of good ventilation and comfortable working temperature which is most marked in places like foundries and is greatly welcomed in blacked-out factories.

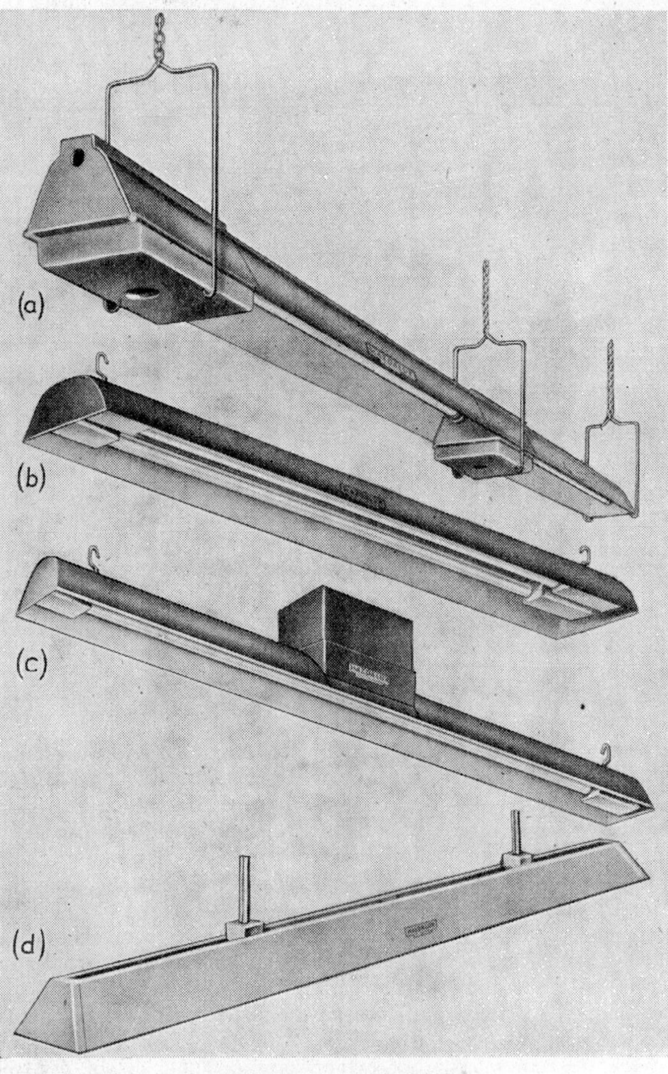

INDUSTRIAL REFLECTORS

Fig. 9 (a) Continuous type trough housing one or more lines of lamps. (b) Two lamp reflector. (c) Single lamp reflector with control unit. (d) Open top single lamp type. Similar fittings are made for bench mounting.

ECONOMICS OF INDUSTRIAL LIGHTING

From a study of basic considerations of all relevant factors concerned it is seen that industrial lighting cannot be re

EARLY EXPERIMENTAL FLUORESCENT LIGHTING

Fig. 10. This photograph of early experimental tubular fluorescent lighting very clearly illustrates the points raised in the text in reference to the illumination of machine shops. Note arrangement of overhead lighting supplemented by local, intensive machine lights. These have been displaced by the local fluorescent lighting giving the operators visibility equal to that of the inspection table.

garded as purely a plant problem, the only parameters of which are dimensions of building, foot-candles required at the working plane, and low initial and maintenance costs. It is a matter greatly influencing the efficiency and health of operatives, and expenditure should be assessed as for other production tools. The cost will be measured by the effect upon factory output, and if the total output is less than it might have been with really effective lighting, then the loss of output is the main cost of poor lighting. This is a most important matter in blacked-out factories where artificial lighting is a permanent factor. The cumulative effect of defective lighting is understood when it is realised that artificial lighting applies in wartime to 50 to 100 per cent. of working hours, as compared with 10 to 15 per cent. in a normal peace-time schedule. It has for some time been common practice in machine shop lighting to provide 15 to 30 foot-candles at the working plane from overhead installations, and to supplement this where necessary with local intensive fittings often attached to machines by adjustable arm supports. Various text books, and in particular the design publications of the Electric Lamp Manufacturers' Association, deal exhaustively with methods of design. The development of the overhead installation has been directed mainly towards the attainment of minimum initial and maintenance costs for a given level of illumination, and considerable advances in this direction have been achieved by the adoption of high pressure mercury vapour lamps. These are applied in white vitreous enamelled reflectors, typical forms of which are shown in Fig. 8. In industrial machine shop practice, this form of installation is being steadily supplanted by methods based on the scientific use of tubular fluorescent lamps giving lighting of daylight quality. Typical equipment is shown in Fig. 9, and the increased suitability of this form of lighting can be described briefly in reference to the early experimental installation shown in Fig. 10. This shows part of a typical machine shop where a total of 215,000 lumens is provided by an overhead system, and lighting essential to the visual task is supplied by low wattage local lights totalling 11,000 lumens. These local lights are commonly referred to as "supplementary", and yet, largely by virtue of suitable positioning, they contribute much more to the performance of the visual task than does the overhead installation. When tubular fluorescent lamps are applied locally as shown, many further advantages are found, apart from the use of daylight colour. The extended 5 ft. source provides good visibility over the whole machine, and eliminates shadows from head or hands during setting up and operating. Hence the need for constant adjustment of the position of the local lamp is avoided, and there is economy of effort and freedom of movement making for greater operational speed and accuracy. A high illumination of work and of machine verniers is provided while the use of the low brightness source prevents reflected glare. With the machine shop of Fig. 10 replanned on this basis, the distribution of light would be approximately 150,000 lumens for local lighting, leaving 65,000 lumens for supplementary general lighting.

Many modern installations use continuous trough reflectors arranged in lines above the machines, and the choice between these systems and single lamp reflectors is largely determined by the layout of shops. The most economic arrangement, especially where there are white or light-coloured ceilings to illuminate, is probably represented by the "open top" type of reflector. When placed between 2 ft. 6 in. and 3 ft. 6 in above the working plane these provide 50 to 75 foot-candles on the work, while the upward projection of light gives a diffuse and comfortable illumination of walls and ceiling.

The tubular fluorescent lamp is also used in artificial skylights as shown in

ARTIFICIAL SKYLIGHTS

Fig. 11. These artificial skylights use 80-watt tubular fluorescent lamps. A remarkably complete illusion of natural lighting is due to the daylight colour and to unobtrusively low lamp brightness

BENCH-MOUNTED LAMPS

Fig. 12. Bench-mounted tubular fluorescent lamps give excellent visibility of fine detail work. The open top reflectors illuminate the walls and ceilings and contribute an impression of space. With natural colour rendering, the general effect gives a sense of very favourable working conditions

Fig. 11, or in continuous troughs providing general overhead lighting. Fig. 11 shows artificial skylights in a blacked out foundry, and in such applications the illusion of natural daylight is complete, and has been found most advantageous in the preservation of health and efficiency. The success of this form of lighting is attributable to the fact that light of natural colour is projected from expected directions, and the low brightness of the source does not distract the eye, which turns naturally to the working plane. It is to be expected that factory lighting will ultimately move in this direction, and factories are being built already in the United States of America in which natural daylight is eliminated. It is pointed out that consistent results are thus obtained, as compared with the varying intensities of daylight, and the changes from the brilliance of sunlight to the much more favourable diffusion of an overcast sky of low brightness. In this country it is still necessary to consider the more economic forms of installation, and where light-coloured ceilings and walls are available or practicable, the open top type of fitting gives an excellent balance to the local and general fields of view. Fig. 12 shows a typical installation.

In the lighting of the high bays of shops engaged on heavy engineering work, as in shipbuilding and in turbine construction, the relatively great mounting heights involved render the high pressure mercury vapour lamp and high wattage incandescent lamp the only practical sources at present.

Future developments in industrial lighting must envisage a co-ordination of the work of the architect, the factory planner, machine designer and the lighting engineer. Thus the design of good workplaces must be largely dictated by considerations of both natural and artificial lighting, for many of the present-day problems in industrial lighting arise from the unsuitable nature of factory architecture, and the arrangement and design of machines.

DOMESTIC LIGHTING

In homes, and in public places devoted to relaxation and entertainment, low brightness sources are traditional and show an instinctive avoidance of directly distressing lighting effects. Low brightness sources are usually achieved, however, by a considerable sacrifice of efficiency in the lighting fittings owing to the highly absorbing materials used for the enclosure of brilliant light sources. Inadequate levels of illumination are therefore common, especially in domestic lighting.

Many of the visual tasks involved in domestic occupations and recreations are as severe as those in industry, and the protection of eyesight is at least as important as æsthetic considerations. For example, in reading print most people would choose an illumination of 75 foot-candles provided that this was not accompanied by reflected glare or other defects. In normal practice the majority of people read, and even sew on dark materials, at illuminations seldom exceeding 10 foot-candles, and often as low as 2. There is an obvious application for low brightness sources of high luminous efficiency, such as the tubular fluorescent lamp, and these considerations, together with the control of colour promised by this lamp, offer it great scope in the home lighting of the future.

Wartime Lighting introduces problems of a special nature which it is not proposed to discuss in further detail. Some references have been made to blacking-out in factories and it is probable that this will be more and more widely adopted as a permanent feature during both peace-time and wartime.

Other wartime lighting measures are largely concerned with the limiting of normal standards of illumination and regulations governing these are liable to be changed from time to time. Obviously, therefore, their detailed description is not warranted in a work covering the most efficient methods of normal practice.

STREET LIGHTING

Until about 1933, street lighting was treated technically as a special form of room lighting, and installations were classified according to the minimum illumination measured at specified points on the road surface. Thus BSS 307/1931 includes classes A to H for test point illuminations respectively of 2 foot candles and above, 1 foot-candle, 0·5, 0·2, 0·1, 0·05, 0·02 and 0·01. It was usually considered uneconomic to provide test point illuminations above about 0·2 foot-candles, and the basic difficulty was, of course, that detail could not be discerned at these low values of illumination. British Standards Specification 307 advocated sound trends such as higher illumination, higher mounting heights and shorter spacings of units; it gave no hint of the principle of silhouette vision

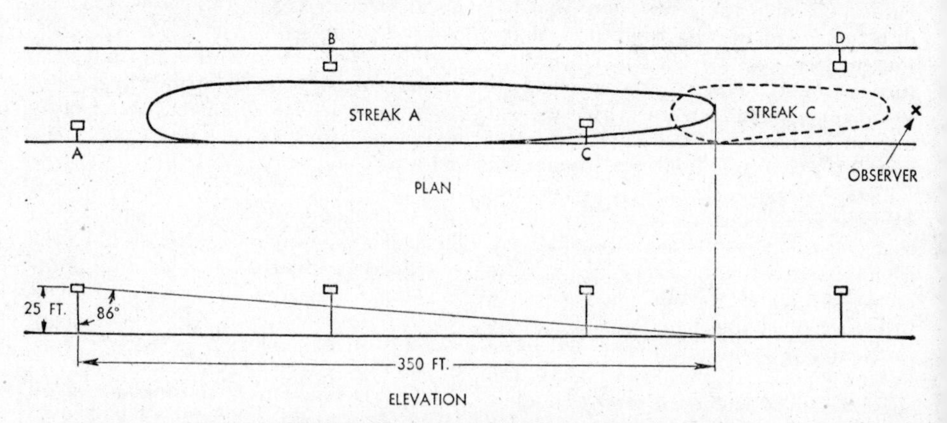

STREET LANTERN POSITIONS AND CUT-OFF

Fig. 13. Relationship between cut-off, spacing and mounting-height of street lanterns showing how streaks must overlap to provide continuous bright road surface to an observer situated at X.

PRODUCTION OF SILHOUETTES

Fig. 14. Objects on the road are seen clearly in silhouette when the street lighting installation is designed to produce a high road surface brightness. Such an effect is produced by projecting light on to the road at glancing angles and towards the observer, there always being a lantern beyond the area to be rendered bright. However, this practice results in the production of a great deal of glare.

ACTION OF INDIVIDUAL LANTERNS

Fig. 15. Each lantern produces a bright lane on the road surface, and as the observer moves, the bright lane moves so that the centre always lies on a straight line joining the observer to the lantern site. If the distant lanterns project relatively low intensities at the horizontal, additional narrow lanes of brightness are provided to fill in the road centre as depicted in this photograph

adopted and developed during the period 1933 to 1939. This was a period of intensive investigation of visibility in streets, initiated by the application of the new 400-watt high pressure mercury vapour lamp to street lighting.

The higher efficiency of light production made available generally higher levels of illumination, but it was found that improved visibility was not thereby consistently ensured. It was then noticed that safe perception of obstacles on the road was provided by "silhouette vision" resulting from the sharp contrast between a high road surface brightness and a low brightness of obstacle as shown in Fig. 14. Investigation showed that a high surface brightness could be produced by projecting light on to the road at glancing angles and towards the observer. Thus it was necessary to place street lanterns critically in relation to the road surface and the normal point of view, the ruling principle being that there must always be a lantern beyond the area to be rendered bright as illustrated in Fig. 14. The principle of siting street lanterns to produce high road surface brightness and silhouette vision underlies the technical recommendations contained in the Final Report (August 1937) of the Ministry of Transport Departmental Committee appointed in 1934.

The Report does not deal with the light distribution of street lanterns in detail, and this was a subject undergoing rapid development at the time the Report was issued. The significant point here is that the highest road brightnesses are produced by light striking the road surface at the most glancing angle. For some time, lanterns projecting very high intensities at and near the horizontal were advocated with a view to achieving the highest road surface brightnesses and the lowest brightness of obstacles. This practice resulted in a great deal of glare, and in fact the high angle light mostly missed the road surface, or when striking it produced very

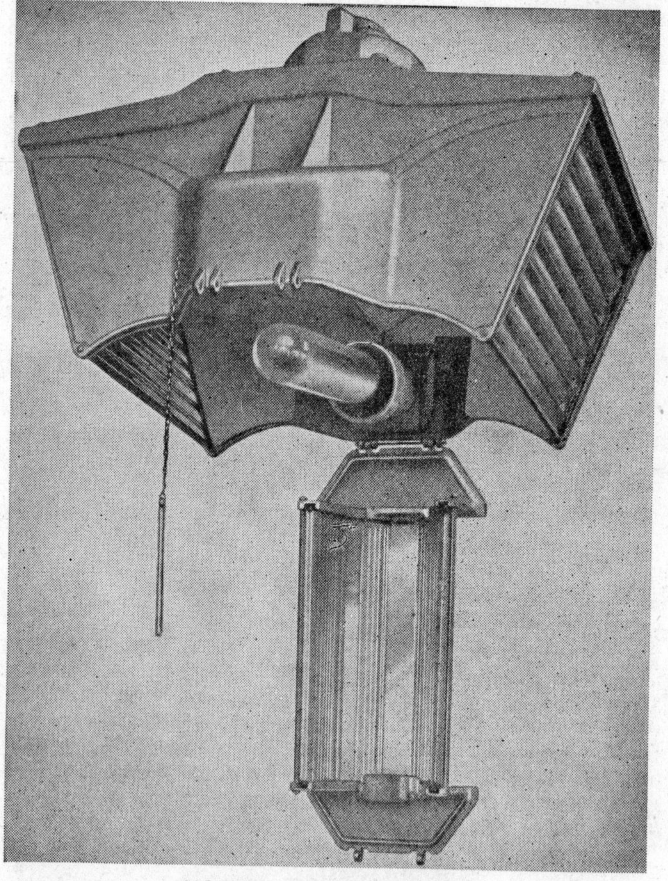

MODERN STREET LANTERN

Fig. 16. Street lantern incorporating a precision optical system and automatic focusing to give accurate control of cut-off. It has a mercury vapour lamp operated horizontally by means of a magnetic arc control.

narrow lanes of brightness. Consideration of these matters led to a lantern distribution based on a compromise between the production of glare and of road brightness. It was found that a "controlled" cut-off below the horizontal contributed very materially to visibility by reducing glare, and Fig. 13 shows how the angle of cut-off is determined so that road surface brightness does not suffer. In practice, lower intensities are provided between the "cut-off" angle and the horizontal, and these are of value under wet road conditions. Road surfaces become highly specular when wet, with the result that the broad lanes of light shown in Fig. 15 are narrowed down considerably. If the distant lanterns project relatively low intensities at the horizontal, additional narrow lanes of brightness are provided to fill in the road centre. A "controlled" cut-off requires accurate control of the lantern light distribution in the vertical plane, and this is not obtainable with high pressure mercury vapour lamps operating vertically. For this reason, the horizontal operation of these lamps become very prevalent in street lighting practice, and Fig. 16 shows the latest form of lantern designed on this basis. A magnetic device is incorporated, the field of which maintains the arc of the discharge horizontal and central in the lamp.

HORIZONTAL LANTERNS

Fig. 17. Glare reduced on well-lighted dual carriage-way by means of special horizontal lanterns. This most efficient installation provides a wide lateral spread of illumination over a very wide range of directions.

An adequate mounting height is essential in providing good visibility, and the Ministry of Transport's recommendations of a 25-feet minimum provides a round basis for the design of effective lantern optical systems.

A typical installation using horizontal lanterns is shown in Fig. 17. It will be noted that the wide lateral spread of this type of lantern is well adapted to dual carriageways where the lantern must be effective over a wide range of directions.

ELECTRICITY IN THE HOME

ELECTRICITY has been described as the best method of eliminating drudgery from housework, and many women have quickly appreciated its virtues in convenience and cleanliness. To gain the full benefit it can offer, however, the electrical installation for a home must be planned carefully and as a whole. Experience is necessary for this, as well as imagination and initiative, to provide all the facilities that will be needed by the occupants. Often the first cost of fitting a really adequate number of lighting points and suitably rated socket outlets is allowed to stand in the way, and the full convenience factor is not realised. If a proper equipment is provided and an appropriate tariff adopted, the annual cost is not usually considered excessive in an all-electric home, when regard is paid to the comfort and convenience secured. Indeed, certain artisans' dwellings have been successfully made all-electric to the great content of the tenants and without undue strain upon their pockets. There are direct and appreciable savings in cleaning materials and in the frequency with which redecorating is required. These partially offset any slight increase in the cost of operating an all-electric home, if any strict comparison must be made with the results of a less convenient and parsimonious scheme using competitive agents.

This convenience factor results from the fact that electrical light and heat do not involve the combustion of fuel in the home, with the accompanying consumption of oxygen and release of carbon dioxide, smoke and soot. The possibility of remote control by switches at a distance and if necessary from several points is another inherent advantage, while the portability of safe and light-weight electrical appliances commends them to the housewife.

LIGHTING ARRANGEMENTS

Instead of the single lighting point in the centre of the ceiling or near the window in each room, which was the conventional practice of earlier days, there is a fortunate tendency towards the use of several points, located in different parts of even a small room, in accordance with the normal use to be made of the space. The old-fashioned opal shade has nearly disappeared and improved artistic fittings, often made of plastic materials and with chromium or other permanent finishes, are available in great variety. In addition there are opalescent and coloured "architectural" lamps in straight lengths and various shapes and colours, which can be effectively employed to supplement or coalesce with the special features of important rooms. Flush ceiling fittings, concealed cornice lights, or tubular fluorescent lamps make interesting variations from conventional pendants. When such modern ideas are combined with convenient switching very pleasing effects are easily obtained. One switch per

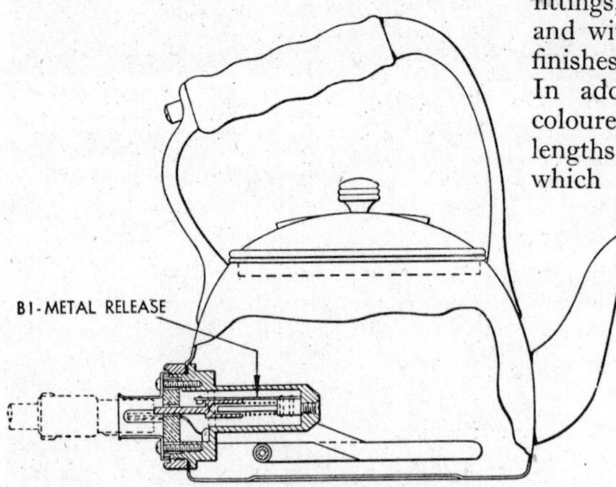

ELECTRIC KETTLE

Fig. 18. Section through Creda kettle with immersed element, showing connector ejection protective device which is operated by thermo action should the kettle be empty and the current on.

DETACHABLE HOTPLATE

Fig. 19a. Method of hotplate removal from Creda cooker, with hob raised showing earthing and circuit plugs and sockets. The elements are totally enclosed to render their use safe and clean.

point must soon be considered poor practice. In nearly every case double switching for general illumination is preferable for convenience and economy, and even in the small house control from at least three points is desirable for hall, passage and stairs lighting.

Another technical feature which adds security to convenience is good planning of circuits. According to standard practice (*Regulations for the Electrical Equipment of Buildings "I.E.E. Rules"*) no more than 10 points should be supplied by a final sub-circuit, i.e., be fed through a single pair of fuses. In order to minimise difficulties if a given fuse should blow, the points it supplies should preferably be distributed amongst several rooms and amongst main and subsidiary lighting points. No room ought to be left in complete darkness without a lighting circuit because one fuse has blown.

COOKING

Electrical apparatus of high efficiency is available for every form of cookery. Portable electrical equipment brings a new appreciation of freshness and palatability in many cases because the cooking can actually be done at table, and fixed kitchen cookers secure results otherwise unattainable because of the steadiness and strict control of temperature attainable and because no products of combustion are involved. But changes in cooking technique are admittedly essential if full advantage of and maximum economy from electrical equipment are to be attained, and these changes, though simple, are the main difficulty in popularising electric cooking. Because supply voltages are closely controlled it is possible, for instance, to reproduce conditions as to temperature in ovens and similar equipment with great accuracy, and cooking by the clock replaces the guesswork and continual anxiety inseparable from most other methods. Because, too, electrical cooking apparatus is fully lagged, in order to secure efficiency and pleasant ambient conditions, the heat is long retained and cooking can continue for substantial periods after the current is switched off.

The heating elements employed are usually wound with wire or strip made of some alloy which resists oxidation at the temperatures involved. This wire or strip is generally spiralled and mounted upon some refractory insulating material, but in one construction the wire is enclosed within a protective metallic sheath packed with magnesium oxide, which serves as an electrical insulator and heat conductor. An element of this kind can be immersed within a kettle, as in Fig. 18, but usually the heater is arranged as closely as possible to the exterior bottom of a kettle or saucepan, which has a lower false bottom, possibly with some heat insulating material interposed. In the false bottom there is often a thermostatic device which is utilised either to operate a switch or in one pattern to eject the supply plug from the kettle socket (Fig. 18), in both cases to safeguard the element if an attempt is made to use the kettle without water in it.

Exposed wire elements are sometimes used in ovens and hotplates on the top of cookers, but in such positions they obviously require careful protection and guarding. The tendency is towards complete enclosure of elements (see Fig. 19a); if this is done for hotplates the top surface should be stiff enough to be machined and stay flat, and the utensils employed on them should be of similar construction.

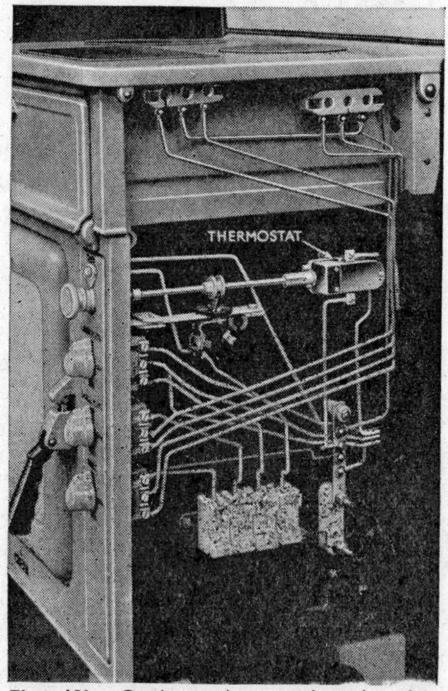

Fig. 19b. Creda cooker, with side plate removed, showing thermostat which controls oven temperature, and the circuit wiring.

For electric grillers an exposed type of element, or one with a metallic sheath running at a high temperature, is necessary because the cooking effect should be mainly by radiant heat. Most hotplates have, in fact, two elements which for maximum heat are run in parallel across the mains; for medium heat only one element is used, and for low heat (simmering) both elements are connected in series across the mains. This is what is done by the familiar rotary switch, and the same idea is applicable to the several elements for oven heating. Because there are no products of combustion involved, electric cooker ovens can be totally enclosed, with the result that meat, etc., cooked therein loses little weight and retains an excellent flavour. Thermometers are frequently provided to assist the cook and in some cases thermostatic control is fitted to maintain any set temperature automatically (see Fig. 19b).

WATER HEATING

Hot water for domestic purposes is usually wanted quickly and in fair quantities at a time and then there is no demand for a longer period. Some method of hot water storage is, therefore, desirable, and storage systems have the advantage that they can be adequately served by a comparatively small energy input continued steadily for a long time, which is a condition that is favourable for a cheap supply of electricity. Often an existing domestic hot-water system is converted to electrical operation by the addition of an immersion heater to the storage tank. An immersion heater consists essentially of a watertight cylindrical or flattened casing fitted by a flange or threaded joint into the tank; a heating element not unlike those used for cooking purposes is fitted within the casing, with terminals accessible from the outside; and sometimes there is a shrouding around the casing within the tank to improve water circulation. Thermostatic control is usually fitted and the tank should be carefully lagged (see Fig. 20).

Normal loadings for domestic storage tanks are about 100 watts per gallon capacity. To calculate the loading in watts required to raise a given quantity of water through so many degrees in a certain time, the first two factors in gallons and degrees Fahrenheit are multiplied together and then divided by the product of the number of hours times 0·34; this is based on the well-known equivalence of one kilowatt-hour with roughly 3,400 B.Th.U.

SPACE HEATING

For domestic purposes electrical space heating is generally undertaken by radiators, which may be of either the high or low temperature types. The former type (Fig. 21) comprises some form of wire-wound heating element arranged in a metal or tile surround, with a front guard. To secure directional effects the heater may be mounted in front of a parabolic or other polished reflector. The low-temperature heater also employs a wire-wound element, but the latter is run at a temperature below red heat. This kind of element can be employed in "convector" units for air heating (Fig. 22); in another form it is arranged in a metal tube the outside surface of which does not usually exceed 150° F. Such low-temperature heaters are particularly useful along the skirting below windows, but they have to be used in fair numbers to be adequate in the home without some supplementary heating means. Nevertheless, the maintenance of a relatively low temperature background is found a valuable step towards home comfort. Another factor that aids comfort is attention to ventilation, especially when electric heating displaces the conventional coal fire. Efficient but quite small and quiet electric fans are available for window mounting when there are no flues. Lighting points

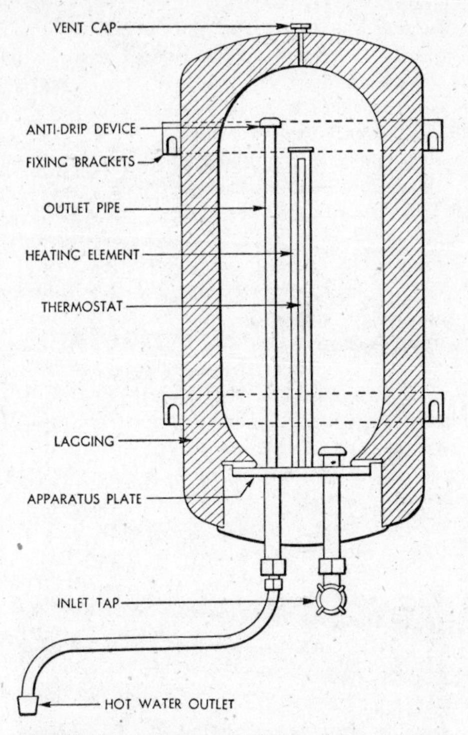

Fig. 20. Section through Creda domestic non-pressure type storage water heater with thermostat control. Note the generous lagging.

must not be used for such devices. In general, all heating socket outlets or points rated to carry 15 amps. or more must be supplied from a separate way in a distribution board. Cooking and water heating circuits are normally carried straight back to main switches and fuses.

ANCILLARY APPARATUS

Electric irons have wire-wound elements insulated from but closely packed against the sole plate. Irons for A.C. only may incorporate an adjustable choke to give control of temperature, but otherwise the principal variations are in weight, shape and connection.

Domestic refrigerators represent a great development in compactness and quietness compared with industrial prototypes. They usually incorporate a mechanical compressor and need no cooling water. Their consumption varies with cubical contents, but in the small family size hardly exceeds that of an average lamp.

Motors of the series type with laminated field cores, so as to be available to operate on either A.C. or D.C., are usual to drive the high-speed fans of vacuum cleaners, the suction of which draws dirt particles from among the pile of carpets, etc. The power required, even in the largest portable type, is only a fraction of a horsepower and the annual energy consumption, in view of its short-time use, is almost negligible. Some patterns have gear-driven beating devices, but in general the refinements of design leading to quiet operation and reliability are not very obvious to the uninitiated except as accounting for a higher price!

Ample socket-outlets in the home facilitate the convenient location of all-mains radio sets in various positions in every room, and, although modern radio receivers can usually operate with no external aerial and earth, better results are usually obtained if these are made available; accordingly an aerial in the roof space and an earth connection coupled to 2-pin plugs in appropriate locations are advantageous.

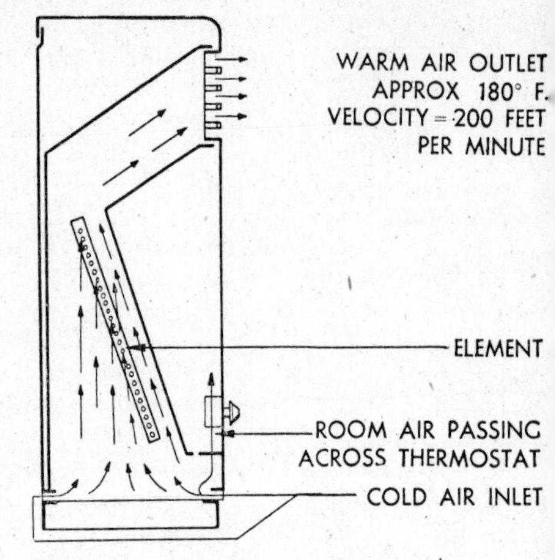

Fig. 22. Section through Creda convector for heating of low temperature type; the arrows show the paths which are travelled by hot and cold air.

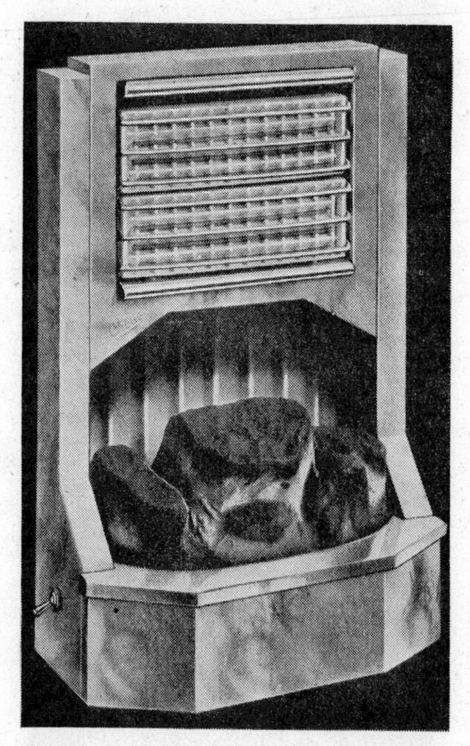

Fig. 21. Creda two-element reflector radiator with "flicker" fire. Each element is controlled by a separate switch. This type of radiator is usually referred to as a high-temperature type.

HOUSE-WIRING PRACTICE

Ordinary installations, representative of sound practice, employ vulcanised rubber insulated wires drawn into solid-drawn steel conduit, with steel-cased distribution boxes and metal boxes for all outlet switch points. The conduit is erected with screwed joints throughout and the Regulations for the Electrical Equipment of Buildings require that its resistance, measured between a point near the meter and any other point in the building, shall not exceed one ohm; only excellent workmanship can ensure that this requirement is met in such a fashion as to be reasonably certain that the test can be repeated satisfactorily a few years after installation.

All-insulated installations are allowed by the Regulations and have some advantages for house work. Plastic materials, resistant to damp, are likely to come into extended use for outlet boxes

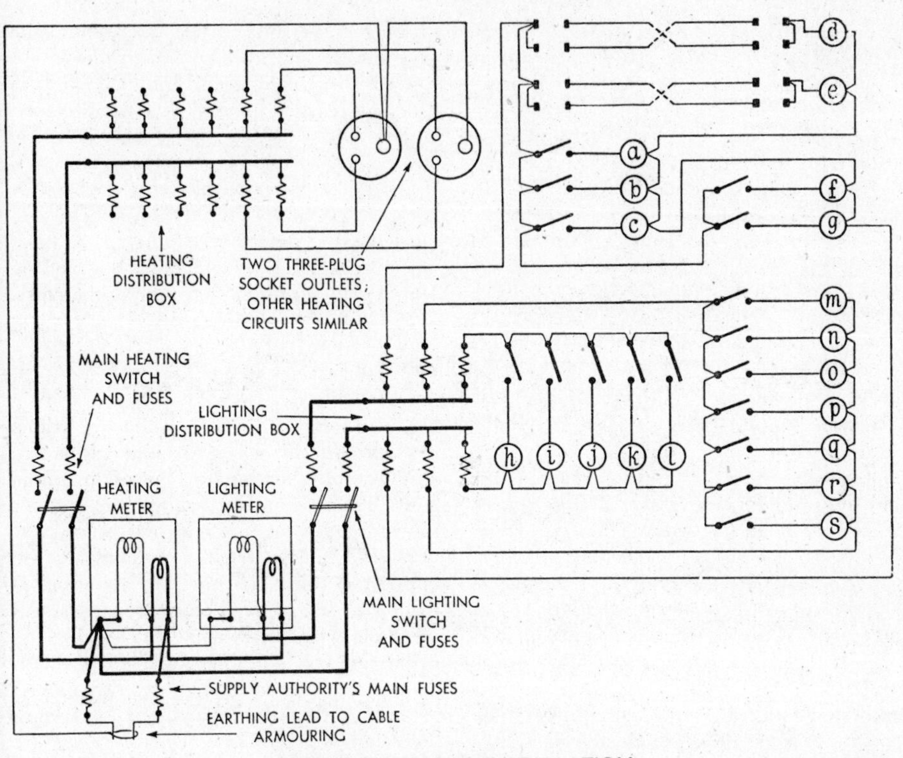

DOMESTIC WIRING INSTALLATION

Fig. 23. Schematic diagram of typical wiring installation for domestic heating and lighting services using the looping-in principle for the lighting points. Points (d) and (e) are each wired for two-way switching. Each of the heating circuits is provided with separate fuses at the distribution box.

and the like instead of wood and, combined with tough-rubber-sheathed cables, may displace conduit to a large extent in the future. Surface wiring systems, with special fittings and a semi-flexible metallic shrouding around each wire, are suitable for new installations in existing houses; in such cases they save a certain amount of mess and may save time in erection, but otherwise they are not cheap. Lead-covered wiring, unless very carefully installed, is not usually considered very suitable for domestic premises.

A schematic diagram of a typical domestic lighting and heating wiring scheme is shown in Fig. 23, but though this indicates the principle of "looping-in" for the lighting points and the use of only one socket-outlet per fuse-way for the heating system it will be understood that the various points are not grouped together locally, but intermingled to the best advantage throughout a house. The cable armouring is connected to earth via a cold water pipe.

SUPPLY CHARGES

Instead of a flat rate of so much per unit consumed, most supply authorities offer alternative two-part tariffs designed to encourage the liberal use of electricity for all domestic purposes. One part of the tariff is so much per unit consumed, as formerly, but the figure is kept as low as possible, usually being 1d. per kWh or less; the other part is a constant quarterly or monthly payment based on some factor intended to be proportional to the probable maximum demand of the household. This factor may be a percentage of the rateable value assessment, so much per principal room, so much per square foot of floor area, or one of several other variations. The greater the use of electricity, therefore, the less is the average total cost per unit, so that usage need not be stinted. In some cases a tariff of this kind is applicable only if either electric cooking or water heating or both are in use. Other tariffs depend on a measurement of the actual maximum demand, or charge different rates according to whether the units are consumed during or outside of peak-load hours. Another alternative is provided by the prepayment meter which, by a mechanical device actuated by an ordinary kilowatt-hour meter, cuts off the supply when the number of units prepaid has been consumed. Warning that this is to occur is sometimes given by a "flicker", a method frequently applied to coin-slot-meters.

ELECTRICITY IN THE FACTORY

POWER applications form the predominant use of electricity in factories, but it is employed also for lighting and for a multitude of purposes to supply heat and motion for industrial processes, as well as for electrolytic work. Since about 1910 the growth of the use of electricity in factories has risen at an increasing rate and there is now hardly an industrial works where it is not represented. Certain industries, such as iron and steel, mining and metallurgy, use enormous quantities of electrical energy but the ordinary factory has perhaps a more varied list of applications.

ELECTRIC MOTORS

Electric motors are commonly employed in factories in sizes ranging from fractional horsepowers to several hundred horsepower, the latter being, for instance, used to drive air-compressors, presses, calenders, and other large individual machines. Motors up to about 100 h.p. are also sometimes used to drive main shafting from which numerous pieces of equipment derive their power through belts or ropes. This method, known as the group drive, is, however, generally giving way to the use of a separate motor on each machine, known as individual driving. Though individual motors generally cost more in the first outlay, they cut out the losses in shaft bearings and belts, allow easier rearrangement of machines, secure safer working conditions, allow one or two machines to be efficiently operated for overtime work and avoid the throwing idle of perhaps a whole department through the breakdown of a single motor or shaft. Better machine control is also usual, through the smaller motors being in each case the most suitable kind for the drives to which they are applied. Group control of a series of machines serving a special process is still possible with individual drives by the utilisation of suitable switchgear, with central remote control if desirable. The grouping of motor starters is becoming increasingly common, control being by means of pushbuttons on the machines as well as by a group stop button at the central point.

With the progress of standardisation of industrial electricity supplies as three-phase alternating current, the use of direct current motors tends to decrease, but though all necessary speed characteristics can be readily secured from A.C. motors, D.C. is still often favoured where variable speeds are required. Variable voltage devices for machine tools are often obtained by the use of motor generators. Fig. 33 shows a case in point, with an enlarged view of the contactor control panel by which pushbuttons are sufficient for all the needs of the operator. In many factories a D.C. system (see Fig. 24) is perpetuated for the supply of magnetic chucks (Fig. 25), cranes, lifting magnets (Fig. 26) and lifts and for charging battery trucks (Fig. 27), etc. Modern practice favours the use of metal or other rectifiers for chucks, charging and plating and similar purposes, distributing all the main energy as A.C. Rectifying units can then be used as required to change this A.C. into the D.C. form necessary for these various purposes. Full details regarding the types of rectifiers in general use are given in appropriate sections. (See page 128 for description of theory and operation of mercury arc rectifiers.)

TYPES OF A.C. MOTORS

Large industrial A.C. motors, wherever possible, are preferably of the synchronous type because by over-exciting them some compensation can be obtained for the lagging power factor of other smaller motors, which are usually of the induction type. The latter is very robust, particularly if it has a squirrel-cage rotor, and in many ways is the best for ordinary factory work. It can be started, in sizes up to 10 or 20 h.p. if the supply authority permits, by being connected direct to the mains, which involves only a simple contactor switch and push-buttons. It will take all ordinary overloads without difficulty, requires little maintenance and, if not of too low a speed, has a reasonable power factor down to about half-load. If particularly small starting peaks are specified or if relatively slow acceleration is desired, slipring induction motors are very satisfactory, starting being done by gradually cutting out resistance across the sliprings in a manner quite like the starting of a D.C. shunt motor. Some speed regulation is also possible by the use of resistance in the rotor circuit, but only at the expense of proportional losses. Synchronous motors are inherently constant-speed machines, though they may be started as induction motors. Induction motors are also nearly constant-speed machines, the full load speed being

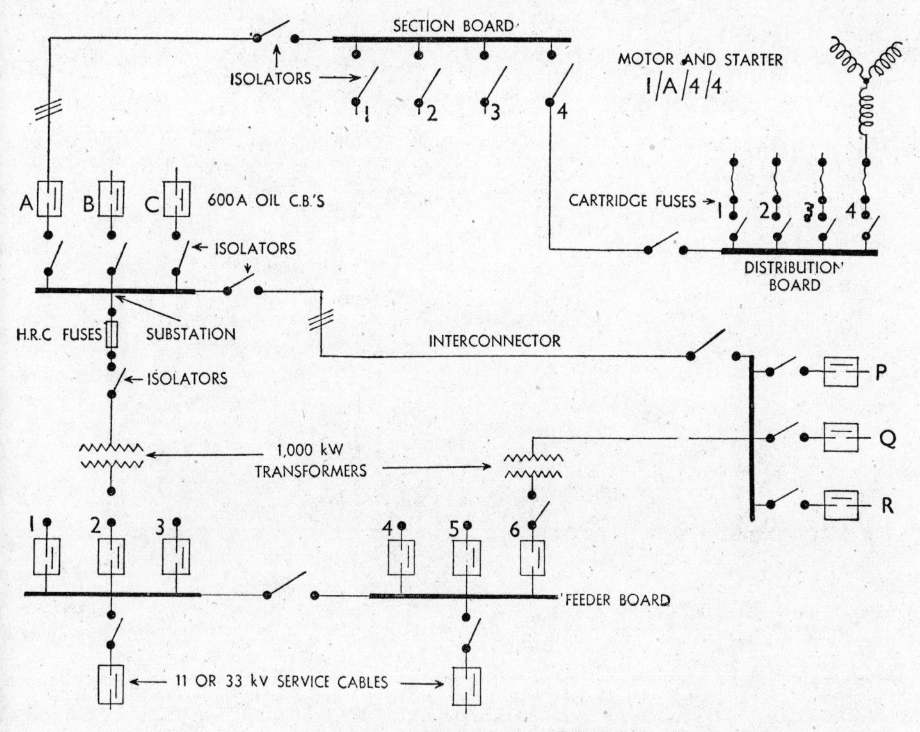

FACTORY DISTRIBUTION SYSTEM

Fig. 24. Single line diagram of typical three-phase distribution system for a large factory, showing only one final utilisation circuit completed for a motor which has been identified by code 1/A/4/4.

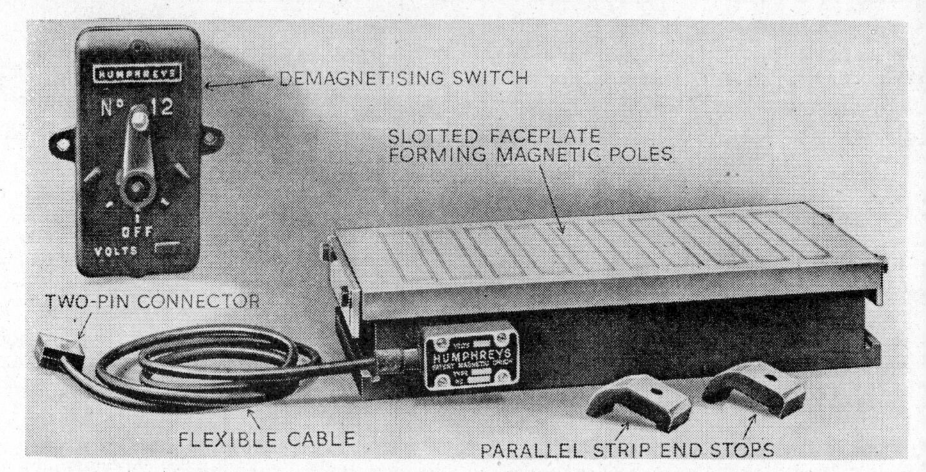

MAGNETIC CHUCK

Fig. 25. (Above) Humphreys magnetic chuck and switch. (Below) two of these chucks fitted to a Beyer, Peacock surface grinder. The chucks are particularly useful where rapid "setting-up" of a special job is essential. Grinding commences automatically when the current is switched on.

usually only two or three per cent. below that at no load. If a speed inherently variable inversely with the load (i.e., a "series charactistic") or a constant adjustable speed is required, combined with the elimination of rheostatic losses, recourse must be had to the A.C. commutator motor. Designs of this type are available to fulfil any specified speed-load relationship, but they are usually expensive machines, and some engineers would prefer to use a motor-generator and a more familiar series or compound D.C. motor.

D.C. MOTORS

Where D.C. is still used, most factory requirements are met by ordinary shunt-wound motors, which maintain nearly constant speed at all loads. For cranes, winches and some other cases, in which the load cannot be disconnected, series motors may give faster and safer service because their speed varies roughly inversely with the load; and there are a few cases in which compound windings are preferable. A predominantly series motor may be compounded cumulatively with a light shunt winding to avoid an excessively high speed at low loads, or a substantially shunt-wound machine may have a few differential series turns, to give either a more nearly constant speed instead of a slightly falling one with increasing load, or even a tendency for the speed to rise with the load, but this latter type is easily overloaded.

MOTOR ENCLOSURES

According to the factory conditions any of these A.C. or D.C. motors may have a variety of enclosures. Open-type motors (Fig. 28) can hardly be permitted in factories unless they are in a closely fenced space. "Protected" motors (Fig. 29) have expanded metal or similar panels to guard all ventilation openings. "Drip-proof" patterns (Fig. 30) use louvres to prevent the ingress of splashes, etc. Totally enclosed motors (Fig. 31) necessarily must be much larger and more expensive than normally ventilated types because the casing surface must be big enough to dissipate all the losses as heat without an excessive temperature rise. A compromise in the shape of a motor with air ducts communicating with the outside of the factory was the best alternative for dusty and damp locations before

Fig. 26. Igranic 24-in.-square lifting magnet, capable of handling 196 lb. of small iron castings and very useful in reclamation of scrap.

the introduction of motors with double air circulation and special radiating surfaces; it was known as the "pipe ventilated" type and the newer design is called by several trade names according to the makers. Factory engineers naturally use the cheapest enclosure that is suitable for the local conditions. See also Chapter 6.

INCOMING SUPPLIES

Most factories derive their electrical energy, in the form of A.C., from the local mains of public supply undertakings, and the latter organisations provide service cables to a convenient position for their meters and the factory main switchgear. If the supply is at "utilisation voltage" (which is usually 400/230 volts three-phase) this switchgear is all the equipment that is necessary at this point, but a higher supply voltage involves the provision of static transformers. Main switchgear is usually ironclad and its type depends very much on the maximum load required by the factory. Either air-break or oil-immersed circuit-breakers may be used for most factory main supplies; in either case they are preferably enclosed in vermin-proof steel panels and the panels accommodated in a locked compartment or room. Besides the circuit-breaker which the factory must contribute, the supply authority may provide its own, or a set of high-rupturing-capacity fuses, and will require facilities for the erection of its metering equipment. Modern industrial premises usually provide special accommodation for such purposes.

SUB-STATIONS

Step-down transformers are often accommodated out of doors (Fig. 32), but their switchgear on both primary and secondary sides is usually of the indoor type in factories. As a rule the supply undertaking provides and operates the high-voltage switchgear, though sometimes the factory electrician is permitted to switch transformers in and out as

ELECTRIC BATTERY TRUCK

Fig. 27. Greenwood and Batley electric battery truck for internal factory transport. In the majority of vehicles of this type a series-wound driving motor, driven from an accumulator battery, is used.

G.E.C. OPEN TYPE MOTOR

Fig. 28. Motors of this type which are open and not provided with protective enclosures cannot be used in factories unless they are closely fenced in. This form of construction was once a standard practice but is now confined to large machines installed where untrained personnel cannot approach them. Incidentally, this photograph clearly shows the constructional details of the motor.

required by the load, where there are several units. In many cases the automatic overload trips on primary and secondary switches of the same transformer are interlocked so that if either operates the transformer is immediately isolated. On the "utilisation voltage" side the several transformers usually feed through circuit-breakers into common busbars, from which feeders are taken through separate circuit-breakers to serve distribution points. The compartment housing this main switchgear is known as the factory sub-station even if outdoor transformers are employed.

DISTRIBUTION AND CABLES

In a large factory the main service cables and the cables from the intake chamber or sub-station to distribution points are usually of the four-core paper-insulated lead-covered and armoured type. At each distribution point the incoming cable feeds busbars whence other smaller feeders radiate, these ordinarily being vulcanised rubber insulated single-core cables, each three-phase set feeding a smaller distribution fuse box, whence the supplies for individual motors are taken. Thus a main feeder may supply a distribution point having five or six 200-amp. panels or "ways", each protected by a circuit-breaker or special high-rupturing-capacity fuse. From one of these 200-amp. panels a distribution box containing four 60-amp. "ways" or perhaps six 40-amp. "ways" may be fed, depending on the prevalent size of motors; and, further, if there are many small motors further distribution fuse boxes may be employed.

Some logical method of marking all circuits in a factory is much to be desired. One such system is indicated in the general layout diagram, Fig. 24, but there are many varieties. If the main feeders are

PROTECTED MOTOR

Fig. 29. Panels of meshing are provided to guard the ventilation openings in the case of this G.E.C. design.

G.E.C. DRIP PROOF MOTOR

Fig. 30. Special design of enclosure in which ventilation openings are covered by louvres to prevent ingress of splashes.

marked A, B and C, for instance, a certain motor may be fed by cables marked B/2/5, which would indicate that the supply comes from feeder B, through the second 200-amp. panel fed thereby and through the fifth "way" of the distribution box marked B/2.

All power cabling should be carefully installed in a permanent fashion. Some factories prefer paper-insulated cables throughout, but usually the smaller circuits are of vulcanised rubber insulated wire run in heavy-gauge conduit. For damp and difficult positions in factories the copper-clad, compressed mineral insulated cable known as Pyrotenax has favourable characteristics.

PRIVATE PLANTS

Where the location of a factory makes it difficult to secure a public supply of electricity and in certain other circumstances a private generating plant may be installed. Such circumstances may be a desire to use a non-standard frequency for special process work, the existence of a demand for low-pressure steam reasonably coincident in time and quantity with the power load, or the availability of an otherwise waste fuel. In such circumstances the expenditure of capital on a private plant may be well worth while.

Except in the case of a very large or straggling factory an industrial private plant usually generates at "utilisation voltage" and the distribution system should follow the general lines already discussed for a factory taking a public supply.

In a relatively few cases it is possible for the inter-connection of a privately generated system with a public supply to be arranged, either on a give-and-take basis or under some special scheme. For instance, one well-known firm has plant with automatic equipment to control the governors of its generating sets so that a constant load is taken from the public supply and all the peaks and valleys of the factory demand are dealt with by varying the amount of energy generated. It is a common stipulation by public electricity authorities that in such cases the private plant shall not be able to feed back into the public mains, and this is safeguarded by fitting the incoming circuit-breakers with reverse power trips. Special metering arrangements would otherwise be necessary to take into account the exchanged energy.

G.E.C. TOTALLY ENCLOSED MOTOR

Fig. 31. Casing surfaces of totally enclosed motors must be larger than those of normally ventilated types in order to dissipate losses as heat without excessive temperature rise.

The mechanical side of private power plants may be on very similar lines to that of a public generating station, using steam boilers and turbines or oil engines. In other cases, depending on the processes employed in the factory, much more complicated arrangements are employed and many of these plants are highly

FACTORY SUB-STATION

Fig. 32. Outdoor bank of three single-phase transformers, with spare unit, dealing with the high-voltage incoming supply to a factory. The switchgear in this case is installed inside the building.

efficient. Their economic aspect is a subject in itself. It has sometimes happened that an industrial undertaking has developed to an extent that rendered it more economical to run its own plant than to continue taking power from the nearest public supply.

FACTORY LIGHTING

It is good practice to keep lighting circuits in a factory entirely separate from those for power supplies, quite apart from the fact that lighting may be separately metered and charged for at a higher rate. The distribution box layout of wiring is always adopted, but on three-phase supplies the final sub-circuits are split up as evenly as possible between the phases and neutral to preserve balance and improve voltage regulation.

Illumination problems are much simplified when individual motor drives for machines are adopted, because of the absence of belting and shafting. In many cases the minimum suspension height of lighting units is fixed by the presence of an overhead crane, but sometimes good results can be obtained from directional reflector units fitted at a lower height on the crane stanchions. For operations demanding close accuracy lighting inten-

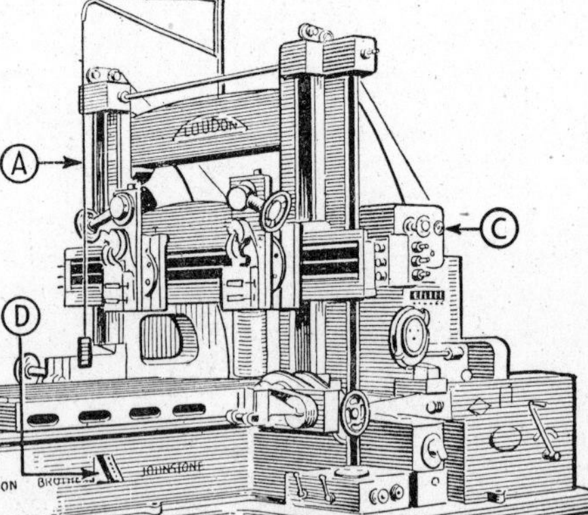

CONTACT CONTROL GEAR

Fig. 33. Brookhirst contactor control gear for the drive of a modern planer through a motor-generator, with pushbutton station. A—Resistance and contactor panel (see photograph). B—Standard drum starting panel for the motor-generator set. C—Operator's control panel with cutting, speed-up and return control hand-wheels. D—Auxiliary switches and pushbutton station. The incoming supply is A.C. and this is converted to D.C. by the motor-generator set.

sities as high as 25 foot-candles at the working plane are becoming common and in tool rooms and special departments much higher intensities are to be found. Mercury vapour lamps, because of their high efficiency, assist in providing these good conditions economically and their poor colour rendering is not a serious disadvantage in many factories. On the other hand fluorescent discharge lamps give a close approach to daylight, even for colour matching, and their use in factories is likely to become standard practice. The fittings in which any lamps are accommodated in factories are utilitarian rather than ornamental; they mostly employ vitreous enamelled finishes and are correctly shaped for maximum effectiveness. One firm specialises in the supply of prismatic glassware adapted to factory conditions. With large tungsten-filament lamps all fittings have to be specially ventilated in order to avoid the heat dissipated leading to such high temperatures as to injure the insulation of the connections.

LOCAL AND PORTABLE LAMPS

Local lighting is not always necessary in factories when adequate general illumination is provided, but for setting-up machine tools and some other work, especially where portable lights are essential as for internal boiler inspection, low-voltage lamps are very desirable. Small transformers to give, say, 25 volts from a secondary earthed at midpoint are recommended, so that dangerous shocks are eliminated; the primaries are often made for 400 volts, so as to be connected across phase-to-phase off a power circuit and avoid the necessity for separate single-phase lighting wiring. High-voltage lighting wandering leads are sometimes used with spring-loaded reels to avoid slack, but low-voltage supplies or battery lamps should be employed where-ever there is a damp floor or earthed metal in the vicinity.

(For detailed information on Factory Lighting, see Section on Electric Lamps and Lighting.)

For electric space heating in large factories there is, in general, a choice between two very dissimilar methods. Either a hot-water distribution system can be used, with a central electrically heated boiler, or a considerable number of unit heaters can be provided. The latter

Fig. 34. Two Bastian and Allen electrode boilers for steam raising, each rated at 200 kW. Similar electrode boilers are suitable for central heating by hot water circulation methods. Supply is taken direct from high-voltage mains.

method involves a heavy wiring system, preferably quite separate from those for power and lighting, with a proper layout of distribution boxes, etc., and the heating load has no appreciable storage capacity, so that it is, in general, superimposed on the power demand. Advantages of the central heating scheme are that an existing hot-water system can often be adapted to electrical heating and that considerable storage capacity can be readily added, so as to take most of the energy required at off-peak periods. Non-radiant low-temperature "radiators" are also sometimes used in factories,

ELECTRIC IMMERSION HEATERS

Fig. 35. Bastian and Allen hot-water supply by means of immersion heaters. Each of the four tanks of this installation contains heaters rated at 150 kW. The elements are of the resistance type and generally they are designed to operate directly at the normal utilisation supply voltage.

particularly for stores and similar departments, while ordinary domestic radiators are common in offices.

Central electric-heated boilers can be divided into two types. One, generally using energy direct from high-voltage mains, is known as an electrode boiler (see Fig. 34), the current passing through the water and the electrode being moveable (or an equivalent effect being obtained by the use of a weir to determine the amount of electrode immersion) so as to control the energy input as required. The other form approximates to the use of several heavily loaded immersion heaters (Fig. 35), the elements of which are of the resistance type, cut in or out of circuit as necessary to vary the input energy; this form of heating boiler generally operates at the normal utilisation voltage. With appropriate storage cylinders either form of boiler can take the majority of its demand during the night, or at least afford to be cut out of action during peak-load hours, so that advantage can be taken of a cheap tariff.

When hard water is in question the electrode boiler has the advantage that the high-temperature water circuit can be a closed one, so that scale deposition does not create difficulties.

PROCESS HEATING

Wire-wound resistance elements are employed for many special heating purposes in factory equipments. Muffle furnaces, bright annealing furnaces, salt baths, drying ovens, and many heat-treatment equipments are conveniently heated electrically, to name but a few items. Quite small electric heaters are also widely employed, for wax melting, sterilizing, soldering, glue-pot heating and so forth. Various devices of this nature are to be seen in great numbers in some plants, and greatly facilitate operations concerned with manufacturing processes involving skilled manual work and in assembly of a generally small scale. At the other end of the scale are metal-melting and refining furnaces of the arc, and of the low and high frequency induction types, the electrical demands of which are usually measured in hundreds of kilowatts. Arc furnaces generally have elaborate automatic equipment for the movement of their carbon electrodes, so as to keep the load as steady as possible. In low-frequency induction furnaces the melt forms the secondary circuit, and the power factor is generally rather low on account of magnetic leakage. Large high-frequency furnaces employ a motor-generator which feeds an oscillatory circuit composed of a bank of condensers in parallel with a water-cooled winding around the crucible. High-frequency eddy currents in the metal in the crucible are the ultimate heating agent. In certain other furnaces the heating current passes through the charge and, for instance, a resistance furnace of this type for the manufacture of calcium carbide may absorb more than 1,000 kW. Still more special are the arc furnaces used for the fixation of nitrogen from the air; few of the equipments just mentioned can, however, be considered normal factory applications of electricity.

RECTIFIERS FOR PLATING, ETC.

To a large extent the motor-generators previously used to provide low-voltage D.C. for electro-plating baths are being superseded by copper-oxide rectifiers fed through static transformers; selenium rectifiers are used for trickle chargers of telephone batteries, and similar static equipment cuts out rotating converters increasingly. For the conversion of A.C. to D.C. for general purposes mercury arc rectifiers of both glass-bulb and steel-cylinder types are represented in many factories. The factory electrical engineer thus has to be familiar with an astonishing range of equipment, including many items large and small of every description that cannot here be even enumerated.

ELECTRICITY IN MINING

THE ever-increasing use of electricity in mining may be considered the finest possible testimony to its reliability, safety and convenience, for the conditions of operation imposed by this industry are exceptionally arduous. Modern mining methods are largely conditioned by the availability of electrical energy either from public mains or from a self-contained generating plant, and the safety of the operating personnel no less than the maintenance of the planned output of mineral depend almost entirely upon its use. Very comprehensive Regulations (promulgated by the Safety in Mines Department of the Ministry of Fuel and Power, in the United Kingdom) govern electrical applications and must be scrupulously respected.

WINDERS

Except in certain gassy coal mines, where compressed air may be the only suitable power agent, many mines are all-electric, and they often employ machinery requiring thousands of horsepower in the aggregate. A colliery winder alone may readily involve peak loads exceeding 1,000 h.p., and such an equipment is one of the most impressive items in the industry. Usually there are two cages in the shaft, one ascending while the other descends, their supporting ropes being paid out from or coiling upon the same drum at the surface simultaneously. A cage may accommodate as many as 9 tubs of coal, each tub (a four-wheeled box, often of steel) holding perhaps 10 cwt. In order to raise the maximum output the winding cycle must occupy only a short time, and this involves high speeds and high rates of acceleration if the shaft is deep. Thus the reason for a big power demand can be easily appreciated.

The mechanical arrangements of the cages, ropes and drums do not concern us here, though they have important influences upon the power required. Motors to drive the drums can be of various types, the simplest perhaps being a wound-rotor induction motor with resistance rotor control, usually by means of a liquid rheostat. This arrangement, however, does nothing towards suppressing acceleration peaks and introduces appreciable energy losses in heating the water in the controller; it also involves stator reversing switches and contactor gear, which, if the motor is supplied at high voltage, as is usual if it is a large one, is expensive and may require a fair amount of maintenance. With the growth of modern interconnected power systems there is not the same necessity for load equalisation that formerly obtained when such winders were driven from comparatively small individual power plants, but nevertheless a straight induction-motor drive is seldom adopted for winders handling large outputs from deep shafts.

BRITISH PRACTICE

Modern British practice favours the provision of a Ward Leonard motor-generator and the driving of winder drums by a direct-coupled or geared D.C. motor supplied at variable voltage derived therefrom. With the motor separately excited its speed and direction are controlled very simply by the manipulation of the excitation rheostat of the generator; no main-circuit reversing switches are required. The motor driving the motor-generator may be a synchronous or an induction motor. If it is of the latter type, the addition of a flywheel to the motor-generator and of resistance across the sliprings will permit the speed to drop somewhat when peaks occur, thus allowing the flywheel to give up some of its stored energy to assist meeting the peaks. If it is a synchronous motor no load assistance is possible, but compounding for power factor improvement on peak loads can be arranged by rectifying the secondary output of current transformers in the main circuit. By the use of an A.C. commutator motor instead of either of these types a drop in speed for flywheel equalisation can be arranged, with the slip energy returned to the line instead of being dissipated in a rheostat as in the case of rotor resistance with an

MAIN WINDING MOTOR

Fig. 36. British Thomson-Houston main winding motor of a gold mine. Its output rating is 4,150 h.p. at a speed of 65 r.p.m. for winding from 5,000 ft. level. It is direct coupled to the rope drum.

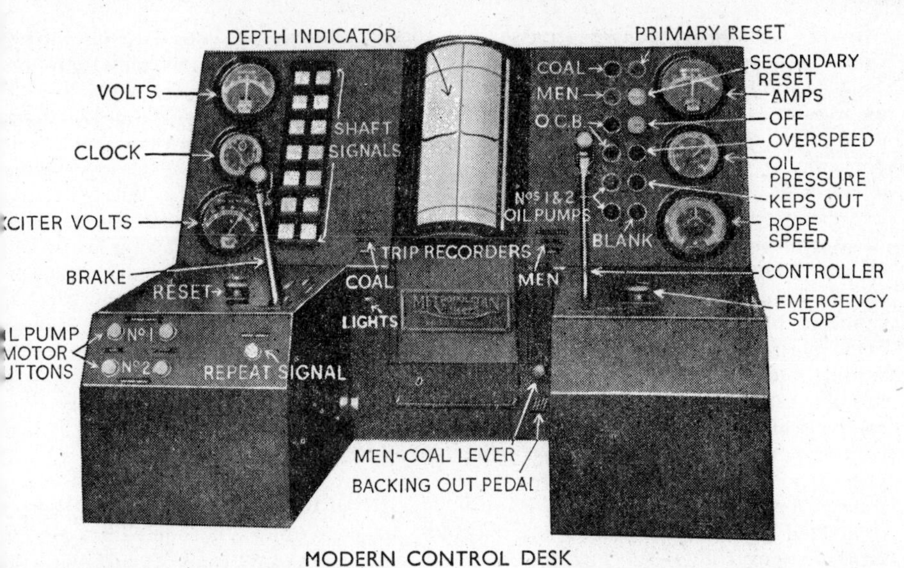

MODERN CONTROL DESK

ig. 37. Metropolitan-Vickers modern control position for electric winder at a British colliery, mbodying shaft signals, electrical instruments and other indicators. The two control levers perate servo-motor gear which permits the interposing of automatic accelerating and decelerating imiting equipment. The rope-speed indicator is a voltmeter energised by a tachometer generator.

nduction motor. In practice, whatever ype of motor is used, the control is entralised upon a single hand lever djacent to or combined with a power-ssisted brake control. Acceleration may e automatically limited and there are afeguards to prevent too rapid decelera-ion and overwinding. The operator has ll relevant electrical and distance indica-ions easily observable and works in esponse to signals usually electrically ransmitted from the pit bottom and anking out level.

SURFACE ELECTRICAL DRIVES

Fig. 36 shows a D.C. winder motor irect-coupled to the rope drum at a old mine installation. To supply the D.C. at variable-voltage in either irection a motor-generator, not shown, is mployed. The main motor has interpoles nd also a compensating winding em-edded in the pole-shoes, so that good ommutation is secured at all speeds rom standstill to maximum.

Fig. 37 shows the control desk for a British colliery winder, embodying the haft signals, electrical instruments and other indicators. Actual control is centred on the right-hand lever, braking being by the lever on the left, but in both cases these levers operate servo-motor gear which not only makes the physical effort required quite small but also permits automatic equipment to be interposed to limit the rates of acceleration and deceleration, and to provide interlocks. For winding men the automatic devices can be simply modified so as to decrease the allowable rates of acceleration and deceleration; moreover there is a rope-speed indicator, comprising a calibrated voltmeter energised from a tachometer generator driven by the winder, which enables the driver to be sure he is complying with a stipulated maximum banking speed of 5 ft. per sec. when riding men. This particular winder, which is a Ward Leonard variable-voltage installation, has two D.C. main motors geared to a single wheel which is coupled to the rope drum; the motor-generator is rated to handle a peak load of 3,920 kW and the normal maximum coal-winding cage speed is 40·6 ft. per sec., enabling a net load of 6 tons to be raised in 43·8 secs.

Mining Electrical practice appreciably differs from ordinary industrial methods because additional robustness is necessary on account of the rather rough and ready conditions usually associated with the handling of minerals, the frequent possibilities of overloads and the lack of care in operation taken by the personnel. Thus even the signal bell switches, which are operated in thousands for instance in the gold mines of South Africa, usually by rope pulls, are ironclad, with very heavy springs, and contacts of a type that would be capable of carrying tens if not hundreds of amperes. This kind of mechanical robustness is not to be confused with the heavy construction necessary to avoid damage from the internal pressure due to the explosion of infiltrated gas, as required for electrical gear in many collieries below ground.

Motors of the fan-cooled type, with internal and external air-cooling circuits, are particularly suitable to combat dusty conditions in mineral handling and treating plants. Electric operation has been chosen for large cranes, dra[g] scrapers, elevators, screens, telphers conveyors of all types, and for th[e] numerous drives of pumps and auxiliar[y] gear in mineral preparation plants, bu[t] the motors and switchgear are norma[l] except for the choice of robust patterns.

Ventilation of deep workings is gener[-] ally achieved by fans drawing air up on[e] shaft and discharging it to the atmos[-] phere: fresh air descends another shaft t[o] take the place of that abstracted. Severa[l] hundred horsepower may be absorbed i[n] such fans. Fig. 40 shows the electri[c] motor and V-belt drive for a very larg[e] axial-flow ventilating fan at a Britis[h] colliery.

UNDERGROUND CONDITIONS

In deep mines not only is total en[-] closure of motors (now usually with th[e] double air circuit cooling previousl[y] mentioned) essential because of dust an[d] humidity, but also the temperature of th[e] surrounding air is high, so that libera[l] ratings are necessary. Nevertheless

COLLIERY LAMP ROOM

Fig. 38. Typical lamp room at a British Colliery. It is from here colliers collect their lamps a[t] the beginning of shifts and to this room they are returned at the end of shifts. Clips are pro[-] vided into which the batteries fit for charging, this process being carried out between the shifts

UNDERGROUND HAULAGE SET

ig. 39. Two Metropolitan-Vickers 350 h.p. motors in tandem driving three rope haulages through ears and clutches below ground. This is one of the largest haulage sets in Gt. Britain. The motors e supplied at 3,300 volts. Starting is by means of contactor gear actuated by a drum controller.

ecause of restricted space for handling, ompactness is an appreciated virtue, so ıat high speeds tend to be favoured. For ansport through low headings, trans- ormers used below ground are frequently f special design, with cores and windings earranged so that the overall height is ower than normally would be considered est for industrial conditions, but this mitation does not, with careful design, eriously affect their efficiency.

A factor affecting electrical design very onsiderably is the presence of gas in iining, usually confined to collieries. ecause of the porosity of joints and the ievitable "breathing" that occurs owing temperature variations, it is impossible exclude gas from the interior of elec- ical apparatus or to ensure that an explo- ve mixture of gas and air shall not be ormed therein. It is possible to make the nclosure so strong that an internal xplosion will do no harm, but there is lways a risk of something going wrong. ccordingly, provision is made to relieve ıch pressure by permitting the escape of air through wide flanges. It is found that if the flange surfaces are left with their machine tooling marks and bolted up without jointing material the pressure will be relieved by passage of air or gas between the flanges, but if the latter are wide enough the gases will be so cooled in the process that there is no danger of an internal explosion igniting even the most inflammable mixture of gas and air in the outside atmosphere. To make quite sure, type tests of all apparatus designed on this principle are required before the Safety in Mines Department will award a "Flameproof Certificate" (also often called a "Buxton Certificate", from the name of the testing station where these tests were performed), permitting the equipment to be used below ground in coal mines. Nevertheless, it is a condition of the employment of electricity below ground in British pits that all current shall be cut off from any district where $2\frac{1}{2}$ per cent. of gas is detected. Periodical tests for gas are compulsory. Gas tests are usually carried out by the simple act of observing the "cap" of the flame of an ordinary miners' oil lamp, turned down low, and the personnel get very expert in correlating the appearance of the "cap" with the amount of gas present. Several electrical portable lamps have been devised to give this information, one of the best depending on the change of resistance of a heated element due to the presence of gas, the resistance being measured by a self-contained Wheatstone bridge. The additional apparatus increases the weight of an electric portable lamp, which is in any case greater than that of an oil lamp, so that even in pits where all the lamps are electric, only a proportion are fitted for gas testing.

FLAMEPROOF LAMPS

The great advantage of the electric lamp, which more than compensates for its relative heaviness, is the far better light it gives. It can also be switched off and on as required, even in gas, whereas an oil lamp must be sent to the surface or to a safe place for relighting if it goes out. The weight aspect is minimised if ca lamps are used, the lamp in its reflect on a man's cap being connected by flexible lead to the battery supporte from his belt.

Lamp batteries are available of bot lead-acid and nickel-alkaline types, th latter being somewhat lighter and re chargeable more quickly. A colliery lamp room contains tiers of racks into whic the lamp batteries clip very convenient for charging, and the necessary D.C. now very generally derived from met rectifiers, a number of cells being usuall charged in series across about 100 volt The lamp cases, containing the batterie switch, fuse and bulb, are flameproof an so arranged that if a well-glass is broke the circuit is interrupted. They are neces sarily very robust. Fig. 38 shows a typic colliery lamp room, from which eac collier collects his lamp at the beginnin of a shift and to which he returns it; he also the lamps are charged and main tained. The equipment comprises mainl racks with appropriate clips into whic

MODERN MINE-FAN DRIVE

Fig. 40. Comprising a Crompton auto-synchronous motor driving a propellor type fan throug V-ropes, the motor is rated at 100 h.p. The large, axial-flow fan is rated to withdraw from the min up to 120,000 cubic feet per minute. This equipment is used for the ventilation of deep mines

HAULAGE EQUIPMENT

g. 41. Metropolitan Vickers 250 h.p. motor-driven colliery underground main and tail haulage uipment. The motor operates a main and tail ropeway through friction clutches. These clutches able the motor to be run continuously and thus frequent starting and stopping are eliminated.

e lamp batteries fit for their charging nnections. Necessary current supplies e furnished by motor-generators and atic rectifiers.

Face lighting by mains-fed lamps has t yet been adopted in collieries, but here a good stationary light is required is possible to use a self-contained mpressed-air-driven alternator and mp, fully protected by safety devices.

HAULAGES AND CONVEYORS

Instead of using ponies to pull trucks coal or ore from the face to the pit ttom, various arrangements of wire-pe haulages are widely employed, nerally driven by electric motors. hese may require to be rated at a ndred or more horse-power and are sually of the slipring induction type ith liquid starters. Where frequent arting is required or the speed has be held below full speed for appreciable eriods, the liquid may have to be pumped rough radiators to dissipate the heat nerated. Often, however, the motor ns continuously, the rope drums being riven through friction or hydraulic utches; and friction brakes are provided. ig. 39 shows one of the largest under-round haulage sets in Great Britain. This has three drums, each serving an endless rope haulage system for a separate district and each of 6 ft. diameter. They are coupled as required to the driving shaft by Fisher-Walker rim clutches operated by water pressure. All-steel double-reduction gearing is employed, totally enclosed; the first train has double-helical teeth and the second straight spur teeth. Two induction motors in tandem are used, as can be seen in the background of Fig. 39. They are each rated at 350 h.p. at 485 r.p.m. and are supplied at 3,300 volts; starting is by contactor gear actuated by a drum controller. Fig. 41 shows a smaller haulage equipment, this having a 250 h.p. motor operating a main and tail ropeway through friction clutches. In other conditions long belt conveyors are often used, again electrically driven, but in this case usually by squirrel-cage induction motors; there is one type in which the motor is built into the driving pulley itself. Frequently, such conveyors run along the face and deliver the mineral into trucks, which are then handled by rope haulages to the pit bottom, but the tendency is for the conveyors to be extended the whole of the distance. Similarly, instead of cutting the coal by

ELECTRICITY AT COAL FACE

Fig. 42. View of a coal face, with Mayor and Coulson electrically-driven coal cutter and fa conveyor. The coal face is on the right. A slot at floor level is being cut to a depth of about 4 6 in. by a gib which is at right angles to the axis of the cutter machine and carries a chain arme with picks. Such a machine is able to cut as much as 100—200 yards length of face in a shi

hand picks, electrically driven machines (Fig. 42) are increasingly utilised, so that almost the whole sequence from the face to the surface is mechanised. A coal cutter comprises a motor geared to a chain or disc on which are mounted cutter picks. This is worked into the face horizontally to cut out a slot perhaps 6 ft. deep and only a few inches in width, after which explosives are used to bring the coal down. Electricity is brought to the machine in armoured flexible cables and the motor controller is isolated at a point further away from the face. The trailing cables are multicore and the controller is operated through low-voltage pilot wires, which are interlocked with the protective devices, so that any damage to the cable or fault on the coal cutter disconnects the supply. Several ingenious safety systems of operation have been evolved. The cutt motor also operates a winch, by means wire ropes on which the cutter picks a fed into the slot; and the winch can b used to pull the machine from place t place. Both D.C. and squirrel-cag induction motors can be used in coa cutters, but the latter predominate.

SAFE SIGNALLING

In many mines signals are give mechanically by rope pulling; sometim the ropes are arranged to operate switch for electric bells. In Great Britain, how ever, it is customary to operate electri signals—particularly along haulage way by pinching together two bare wire supported on insulators along the sid The break-flash, when this was done, ha been proved able to ignite explosiv mixtures of gas and air, and sever lisasters have been attributed to this ractice. The system is now only allowed, nd all electric signalling is similarly for- idden, unless the circuits are made 'intrinsically safe". This can be done in everal ways, fundamentally in order to ive the inductive bell coil a means of discharging when the circuit is broken. The most popular method is the provision of a non-inductive resistance in parallel with the coil, but condensers, chokes and rectifiers can be employed. If properly arranged the break flash is so diminished that ignition cannot possibly take place.

ELECTRICITY IN AGRICULTURE

AGRICULTURE is one of the world's largest and most important industries pon which depends the bread of man. lectricity comes to the farmer's aid in nany and varied ways; it helps to meet nortage of labour and to produce food nder the most hygienic conditions.

When electricity is brought to the farm is often first employed in the house, nd for lighting the yard and buildings. : has been estimated that the electric light alone will save the average farmer about 100 man-hours of labour per winter; but once a supply of current has been connected, the progressive farmer soon puts it to numerous labour-saving uses. In agriculture there are many applications for power, and the electric motor serves as an ideal prime mover; it is clean in operation, free from objectional fumes, can be started instantly by the touch of a switch and its operating

FOOD-PREPARING PLANT

g. 43. Eight-horse power, three-phase electric motor driving line shafting and food-preparing ant installed in a barn attached to a modernised farm. The boiler in the foreground has a capacity 10 gallons and is used for heating water for pig food and other requirements of a similar nature.

costs are less than those of most modern paraffin or oil engines. Electricity is also much used for heating, especially in the dairy, and the heating of incubators and foster-mothers.

WIRING AND EQUIPMENT

Owing to conditions of dampness and the presence of fumes in buildings, the farm wiring and equipment must be of a suitable type and properly installed. Motors required to work in dusty situations should be protected, and those used for portable work in the open should be designed so that the wet cannot get in.

PUMPING

The health of the stock depends largely upon an abundant supply of pure water, an average of from 10 to 15 gallons being required per cow per day for drinking purposes alone. Farms are often situated far from public water mains and have to fall back on their own resources, which often take the form of a well. Han pumping involves much labour, but th can be done away with entirely by small motor coupled to drive a pum and arranged with a float switch aut matically to switch on when the tan is nearly empty and cut off when ful On the average, a unit of current wi pump about 500 gallons of water.

FOOD PREPARING

The preparation of food for the stoc involves the use of machinery such chaff cutters for chopping hay and stra root slicers and pulpers for preparin turnips and swedes, cake breakers fo cattle feeding cakes and mills for grindin corn. Fig. 43 shows the barn machiner being driven by an eight horse-powe motor coupled to a line shafting. On th left of the picture is seen a ten-gallo wash boiler used for heating water fo pig food and other similar requirement For occasional drives such as the elevato

ELECTRIC MILKING MACHINE

Fig. 44. G.E.C. motor driving a milking machine. Pails, tubing and rubber teats are seen in t foreground. The small motor drives a vacuum pump thus causing the necessary pulsations of t rubber cups. Electric milking apparatus is relatively inexpensive to operate and easy to maintai

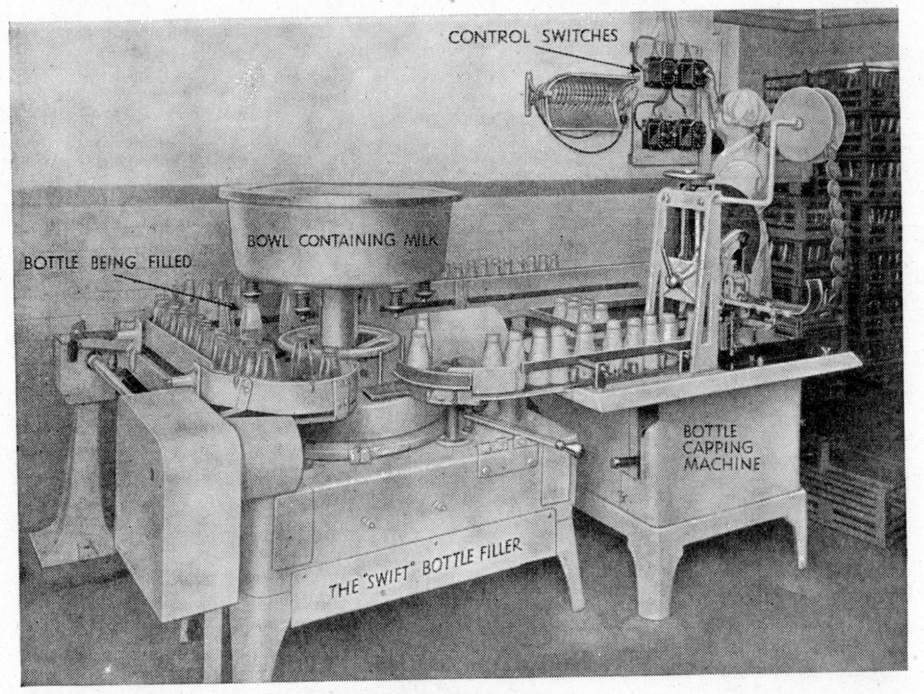

MILK BOTTLING

Fig. 45. Electrically driven milk bottling and capping machine. The bottles, having been filled, are then automatically carried along by the conveyor to be capped by the machine on the right.

for stack building, threshing, circular saws and isolated machinery, the portable motor is convenient. Small units can be mounted on skids, a two-wheeled truck, or they may be of the drum type in which the whole unit is in the form of a steel drum which enables it to be easily transported. When a portable motor is required to drive several machines, not all designed to run at the same number of revolutions, speed variation can be obtained by means of different-sized pulleys, slow speed countershafts or gearing. The trailing cable supplying the motor with current should be made of material such as tough rubber to resist the arduous conditions under which it has to work.

Owing to the heavy weight of the batteries required to drive the motor, the electric tractor has not come into general use. The main difficulty to be met with in electric ploughing is the provision of a convenient means of supplying current to the equipment. The fields require to be provided with a system of overhead lines which can easily be tapped to supply a portable transformer which is connected by a trailing cable to the motors driving the plough. One system, similar to that used by steam ploughs, employs two electric haulage sets placed at opposite sides of the field and connected by a moving wire rope that pulls the plough backwards and forwards across the land. As the ground becomes ploughed the haulage sets are moved forward so that fresh ground can be covered.

MILKING

Electricity on the dairy farm is used throughout, from the washing of the cows before milking to the bottling of the finished product. Electric milking is widely employed because it is such a great labour saver, cheap to operate and simple to look after. A vacuum pump driven by a small motor, as shown in Fig. 44, causes the necessary pulsations of the rubber cups which are placed over the cow's teats. The milk collects in containers placed beside the cows, and the vacuum comes from a pump through hoses and a pipe running above the mangers. For small herds self-contained portable milking plant is convenient, because no fixed piping is necessary, the motor and pump being mounted on a trolley and connected by rubber hosing to the milking units.

DAIRY

In order to produce milk of Grade A standards, scrupulous cleanliness is necessary in cow houses and the attendants should wash their hands before stripping the cows. A towel may spread germs, but this can be obviated if a hot-air electric hand-drying machine is used.

In the dairy the warm milk direct from the cow is cooled in order to preserve its quality and keeping power. One form of cooler employs cold water which passes through tubes over the outside surface of which flows the milk. If, however, an electrically driven refrigerator type cooler is used, better results can be obtained, the milk being reduced to 40–45 deg. instead of 60–65 deg., which is often the lowest temperature which can be reached with the water cooler in hot weather. In order to store milk and thus be able to meet the fluctuation in the demand of supply, a cold storage chamber is necessary, and one worked by electricity under the control of a thermostat is ideal.

Electricity can also serve in many other ways in the dairy, such as cream separating, churning, butter working, bottle washing and bottling milk, an example of a machine for the latter purpose being shown in Fig. 45. The supply of hot water and steam for sterilising is another important use and electric boilers, with

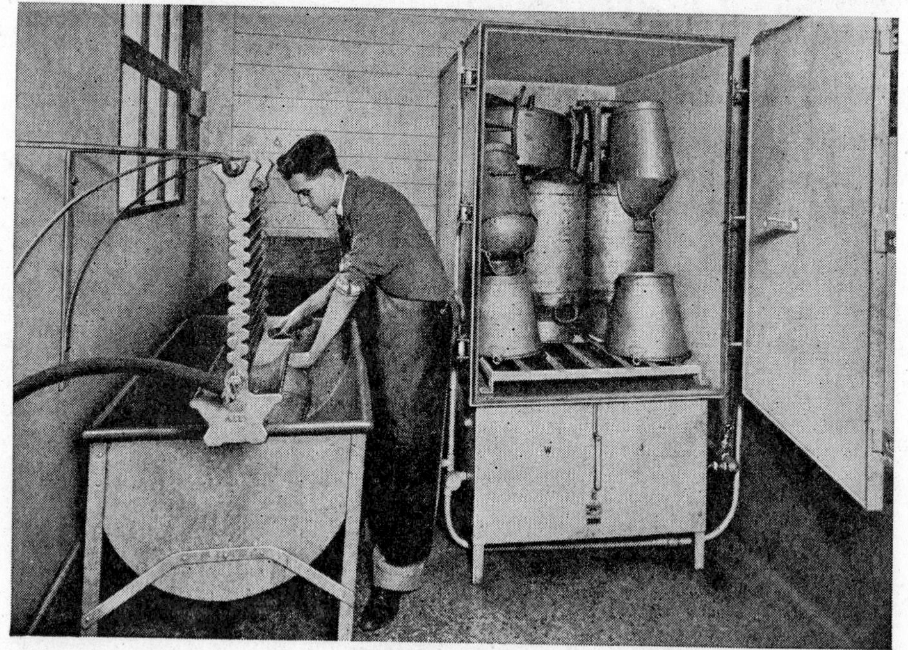

STERILISING CHEST

Fig. 46. G.E.C. electric sterilising chest for milk pails, milking-machine parts, etc. The chest is quite self-contained and has built-in heating elements. When larger supplies of boiling water are needed for the more extensive dairy farms, storage type water heaters with thermostat control can be used.

ELECTRIC INCUBATOR

Fig. 47. Cabinet incubator with G.E.C. motor accessories. The electric heating can easily be controlled to temperature variations within a fraction of a degree. Fire risk is practically negligible

automatic control by means of a pressure switch to turn the current on or off according to the demand for steam, occupy little space and will raise steam in a few minutes. The steam is supplied to a steel cabinet in which are placed the utensils such as milking pails, milking machine parts, etc., for sterilising. For small dairies self-contained sterilising chests with built-in heating elements and requiring no separate boiler or steam pipes are convenient and efficient; such a unit is shown in Fig. 46. A tap on the left near the bottom of the chest (hidden by operator) permits the withdrawal of several gallons of boiling water, but should larger supplies be required an electric water heater of the storage type with thermostat control similar to that used for domestic purposes can be employed.

POULTRY

In all sections of the poultry farm electricity saves labour and increases production. The success of an incubator depends largely on the maintenance of a uniform temperature throughout the hatching period. These conditions can well be fulfilled by electricity used in a number of heaters distributed throughout the egg tray, thereby diffusing a gentle heat evenly over the whole area. The heaters are connected to an automatic regulator which adjusts the number in circuit so as to keep the temperature in the incubator constant. Another type of incubator employs a water jacket which stores sufficient heat to prevent harm to the hatch should the supply of current fail for several hours. Large incubators are often provided with an electric fan which circulates the warm air uniformly throughout the interior, thus preventing the formation of any cold or hot pockets. Electric incubators having capacities as great as 70,000 eggs are obtainable.

ELECTRIC BROODERS

Electricity is used with much success for rearing chicks in foster-mothers. In the ordinary oil-heated foster-mother the heat is concentrated round the lamp where the chicks naturally crowd together and are liable to get overheated; also there is a considerable fire risk. With the electric brooder the heat is supplied either by resistance elements or lamps distributed throughout the interior which results in uniform heating and the prevention of crowding. Temperature control is usually simple, and there is a three-heat adjustment. Medium is sufficient for normal conditions, full heat being provided chiefly for emergency use during extremely cold weather. Low heat may be used for cooling off or during mild weather.

A cabinet electric incubator is illustrated in Fig. 47, where the heat is directed round the trays containing the eggs by means of easily controlled electric heating elements.

Electricity is much used to illuminate poultry houses for a few hours in the mornings and evenings, thereby making the length of the days more even throughout the year. The birds will therefore take more exercise and food and as a result give an increased egg production. The hours of artificial light naturally vary according to the season of the year, and the lamps are controlled by means of a time switch. In addition, some farmers employ a dimming device gradually to decrease the light before switching off at night and cause it slowly to increase in brightness in the morning, thereby imitating natural conditions. It is important that the lamps be placed in the right positions so as to illuminate the perches as well as the floor, or the birds may not be affected by the artificial lighting.

VARIOUS USES

Radiant heaters have been used with success in pig sties, the heaters being fixed to the roof or walls and made adjustable by a swivel so that the warmth can be directed downwards on to the piglets as well as the sow. It is claimed that the application of artificial heat during the first few weeks has saved many piglets.

Electricity is very convenient for soil heating in order to accelerate the growth of seeds in greenhouses and frames. A special resistance cable buried in the soil gives the necessary warmth.

Among the numerous other uses of electricity in agriculture may be mentioned grass drying which enables the crop to be dried artificially instead of in the open. Many small, but labour-saving appliances, such as poultry plucking machines, sheep shearers and groomers are very suitable for electric driving. The last appliance can also be used for other purposes, such as general suction cleaning, and it can be converted into a blower to remove dust and dirt from awkward positions. To save labour on fruit farms there are electric fruit graders for apples, plums and even soft fruit.

ELECTRIC FENCES

The electric fence is an interesting novelty and it is worked from a harmless battery of only a few volts. A single strand of wire run from post to post is sufficient, and the unusual sensation experienced by a cow, sheep, horse or pig once it has touched the wire is sufficient to prevent it from coming near the fence again.

In conclusion, it has been shown that electricity can help the farmer in all his activities. As yet only a relatively small proportion of the agricultural industry has been electrified so it is obvious the future offers great scope for development.

CHAPTER 8

APPLICATIONS OF ELECTRICITY

Electrical Equipment of Automobiles and Principles of Operation. Electrical Equipment of Aircraft. Circuits. Miscellaneous Electrical Fittings. Electricity Aboard Ship. Special Auxiliary Arrangements. Electric Traction. Electricity Versus Steam. D.C. and A.C. Systems. Current Conductors. Control Methods. Electric Service Speeds. Electricity and its Applications in Modern Medicine and Surgery.

IT may be said that the subjects dealt with in chapters 3 to 7 are in one way and another applications of electricity. But in this chapter and the two succeeding, some further aspects of this subject are dealt with. Those included have been discussed in order further to introduce the subjects of electrical engineering to the apprentice or those contemplating entering the industry, and it is to be hoped that the reader who makes a close study of them will be able to select a suitable branch which will provide him with a very interesting and remunerative career.

ELECTRICITY IN AUTOMOBILES

THE most important application of electricity to the internal combustion engine is that of ignition. Probably the principle of the internal combustion engine is familiar to most people, but to make this article complete, a very brief description will be given here. Most modern automobiles operate on the Otto cycle or four-stroke principle. Consider the instant when the inlet valve is open, the exhaust valve closed, and the piston descending in the cylinder. The petrol-air mixture will be drawn into the cylinder. This is called the "induction stroke". When at the bottom of its stroke, it begins to rise again. Both inlet and exhaust valves are now closed, and the rising piston compresses the mixture drawn into the cylinder during the induction stroke. This is known as the "compression stroke".

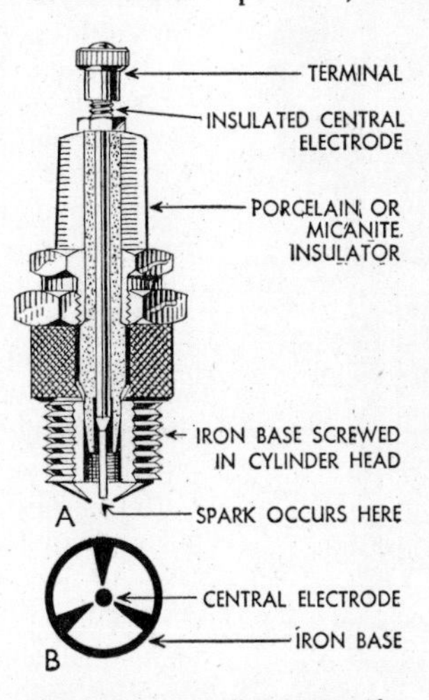

Fig. 1. Diagram illustrating the essentials of a commonly used type of sparking plug. A—shows section through side. B—section through the base.

When the mixture is fully compressed, it is exploded by means of an electric spark, and the expansion of the burning gases drives the piston down the cylinder again. This is the "power stroke". Finally, after again reaching the bottom of its travel, the piston once more rises, the exhaust valve now being open. The effect is to drive the burned gases out of the exhaust valve and this stroke is called the "exhaust stroke". A complete journey of the piston from the top of the cylinder, down to the bottom, and back again, occurs every revolution, and thus one explosion, and one power stroke, occurs every two revolutions. Such, briefly is the Otto cycle (or four-stroke principle There is another principle of operation known as the two-stroke cycle, but this is largely confined to engines for motor bicycles and motor boats of low horse-power rating. In either case it will be seen that the electric spark which causes the ignition of the gases is one of the essentials of the engine, so it is true to say that ignition is the most important application of electricity to the automobile.

In the top of each cylinder of the engine a sparking plug is screwed which consists of a central insulated electrode, and a point (or points) attached to the casing (see Fig. 1). The actual gap between the electrode and point(s) is usually of the order of twenty thousands of one inch (or about half a millimetre). To create a spark between two electrodes considerable voltage is necessary. Between needle points in air about 3,000 volts are required to cause a 1 mm. spark and if the electrodes are larger, the necessary potential difference is increased. If the spark has to take place under high pressure, as in the cylinder head of an internal combustion engine at the end of the compression stroke, the voltage necessary is much greater. It is obvious that a potential difference of the order of thousands of volts will be necessary for ignition purposes. The methods of producing this high voltage will now be discussed.

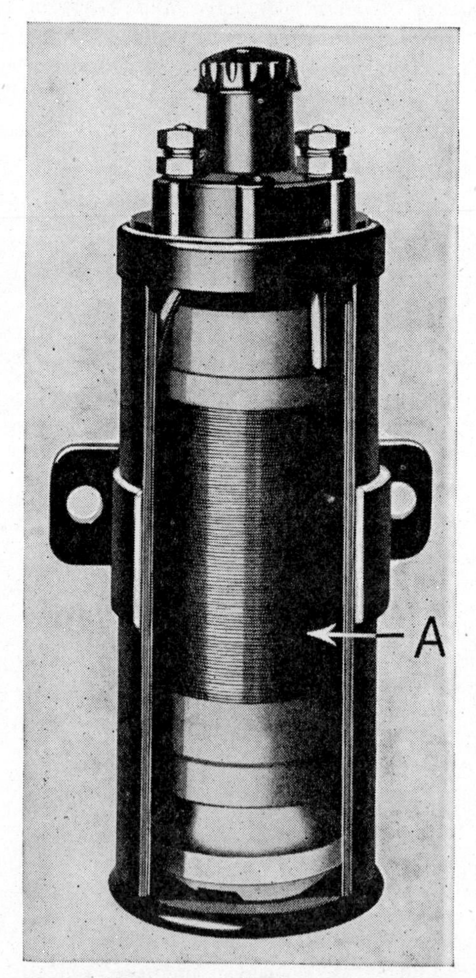

Fig. 2. Typical ignition coil. The primary winding, A, comprises only a few hundred turns. Note the heavily insulated High Tension terminal.

COIL IGNITION

The simplest method of producing the necessary high-voltage for ignition is by means of a modified induction coil. A few hundred turns of wire are wound over a stranded iron core. This winding is known as the "primary winding". Over it, and heavily insulated from it, is wound a "secondary winding" of many thousands of turns of fine wire (see Fig. 2). If a battery is connected to the primary coil, a current will flow and a magnetic field will be set up. By the ordinary laws of electro-magnetic induction, when this field either grows or collapses, and interlinks with the secondary turns, it will induce an electro-motive force in the latter. The changing field will also induce an e.m.f. in the primary and, neglecting the resistance, the primary e.m.f. will be equal to the voltage applied from the battery. The secondary has many more turns than the primary, and as, by the laws of electro-magnetic induction, the induced e.m.f. is the product of the number of turns and the rate of change of the magnetic field, it is clear that the secondary e.m.f. will be far higher than the voltage of the battery applied to the primary circuit. Since, neglecting losses, the secondary energy must be equal to that of the primary, if the voltage is greatly increased the current must correspondingly be reduced. Thus the secondary voltage is many times higher than the battery voltage, but the secondary current is much less than the primary current.

It is very important to notice that the secondary e.m.f. is only produced when the magnetic field and, therefore, the primary current, are changing. In practice, therefore, some form of interruptor is necessary so that the primary circuit is made and broken, thus inducing a secondary e.m.f. each time the current rises and, again, each time it falls. This is arranged by means of a contact breaker, which is operated by means of a cam driven by the engine (see Figs. 3 and 4).

Since a spark is required each alternate revolution, the contact breaker must be driven at half engine speed. But the system, as described, is still not quite

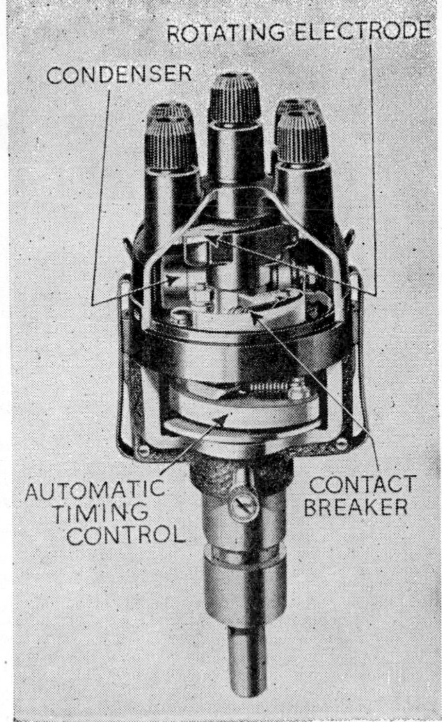

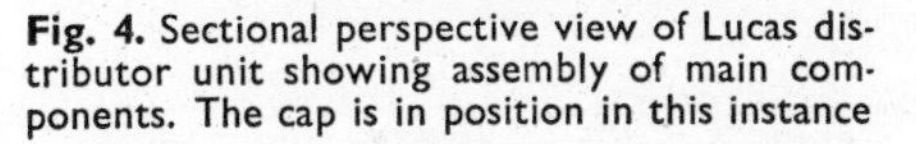

Fig. 4. Sectional perspective view of Lucas distributor unit showing assembly of main components. The cap is in position in this instance

complete. The primary circuit has a considerable inductance and a very small resistance. The rise or fall of current through such a circuit is determined by the ratio $\frac{\text{inductance}}{\text{resistance}}$, so it will be realised that, if the resistance is small, and the inductance large, the primary current will rise and fall comparatively slowly. The secondary voltage is proportional to the rate of change of primary current and, if that current changes slowly, the secondary e.m.f. will be comparatively small. If the current can be made to rise or fall more quickly, the secondary voltage will be increased. If a comparatively large condenser, say $\frac{1}{2}$–1 microfarad, is connected across the make and break contacts, the energy of the collapsing magnetic field will be expended in charging the condenser. The effect will

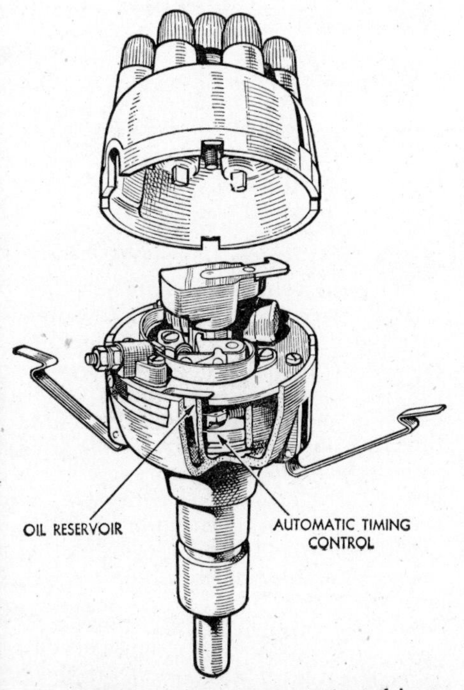

Fig. 3. Diagrammatic representation of Lucas distributor unit, with cap removed, in which the contact breaker and timing control can be seen.

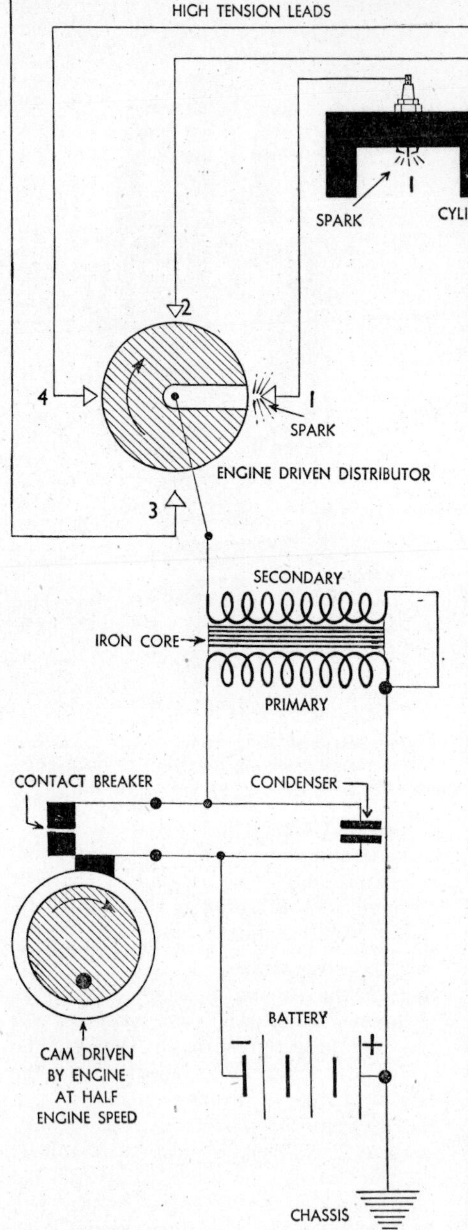

Fig. 5. Electrical circuit of coil ignition system for 4-cylinder engine. It will be noted that the positive terminal of the battery is earthed instead of the negative pole as used to be the case. This has several advantages (see page 314).

be to cause the current to fall far more rapidly than without the condenser, and thus, at the break of primary current, there will be a very high secondary e.m.f. In fact, this voltage will be so high that the induced voltage at "make" can be neglected in comparison with it. For all practical purposes, there will be an induced voltage in the secondary each time the primary circuit is broken.

The contact breaker is so arranged that this break occurs near the end of the compression stroke. If the engine has two or more cylinders, as is usual in automobile practice, a distributor is added so that the explosion may occur in each cylinder in the correct sequence. This distributor simply consists of an engine-driven rotor which makes the high-tension circuit to each sparking plug in turn, so that the correct firing sequence may be maintained (see Fig. 5).

MAGNETO IGNITION

The earliest automobile ignition system was a battery and coil, but it was soon superseded by a magneto generator. In a modified and much improved form the coil has staged a "come-back", and is now the most popular system. But a sufficient number of cars are still fitted with magnetos to justify some description here. A magneto is really a form of alternating current generator. An "H" armature is wound on the usual laminated stampings and arranged to rotate, driven from the engine, between the poles of a powerful permanent magnet. This armature, at normal engine speed, will generate a comparatively low voltage, say 6–12 volts. Wound over this low-tension armature is a secondary of many thoussands of turns of wire, so that, if current flows in the low tension armature, there will be a high secondary e.m.f. A machine of this type generates alternating voltages, and it would seem that no interruptor would be necessary, since the alternating currents flowing in the primary are continually changing in their amplitudes. But the secondary e.m.f. can be enormously increased by fitting the primary with a contact breaker and condenser as with coil ignition systems, and, again, there will be a very high secondary e.m.f. at each break of the primary circuit. The magneto is, in fact, very like a rotating induction coil. A typical modern magneto is shown in Fig. 6.

COIL AND MAGNETO IGNITION COMPARED

Both systems have advantages and disadvantages. Consider, first, the case of coil ignition. The strength of the spark is quite independent of the speed of rotation; if the engine is turned over quite slowly by means of the starting handle a full strength spark will be obtained at the plugs. This is an obvious advantage for easy starting, but it has the disadvantage that the effectiveness of the spark is dependent on the condition of the battery. If the battery is fully discharged, it is impossible to cause a spark and, therefore, the engine cannot be started. With a magneto, on the other hand, the generated voltage, and thus the strength of the spark, is dependent on the speed of rotation. Consequently, it is not so easy to start an engine fitted with a magneto ignition, though, in practice, if the magneto, contact breaker and sparking plugs are maintained in good condition, it is not really difficult and starting is, of course, quite independent of the battery. For high-speed engines, the magneto is definitely more satisfactory, for the higher the speed, the greater the generated voltage and the stronger the spark; but with coil ignition, at very high engine speeds, the current in the primary of the coil does not have time to rise to its full value before the contact breaker operates. Obviously, this will give a weak spark, so it is seen that magneto ignition is more satisfactory for high speed engines. One or two high grade cars have both systems fitted as alternatives.

CAR BATTERIES

The battery or accumulator is one of the most vital parts of a modern car. As shown in the preceding paragraph, it is an essential in engines fitted with coil ignition, but, even where magneto ignition is employed, it is a very great convenience, since it allows the use of a self-starter and of electric lighting which can be fully effective even when the car is stationary. No attempt will be made here to describe the principles of storage batteries, since the subject is fully covered elsewhere in this book. All that will be done here is to mention briefly the features of design peculiar to automobiles.

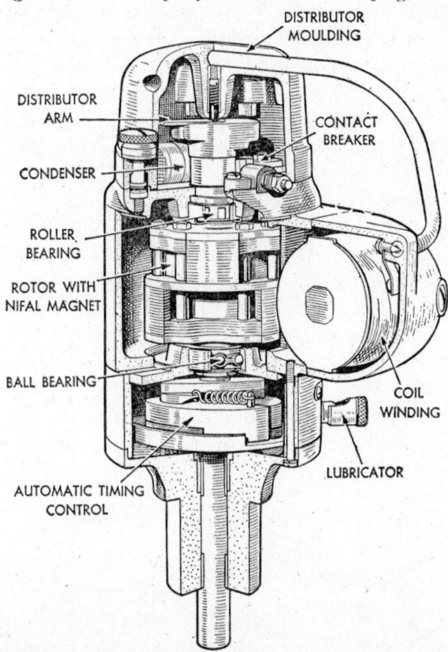

Fig. 6. Sectional arrangement of Lucas car magneto. A magneto acts like a rotating induction coil. It not only generates the electrical energy required but also transforms it to the high pressure necessary for ignition purposes

In the first place, the car battery must

be of very rugged construction, because it is subject to vibration and other rough usage. British and American cars almost invariably employ lead-acid batteries, but Continental cars, and some British motor-cycles are frequently fitted with nickel-iron cells. These, of course, are far more robust and will stand up to overcharging and excessive discharging better, but the voltage per cell is lower and they are more expensive in first cost. Almost all American cars and the smaller powered British cars are fitted with six-volt batteries, while the larger British cars have twelve volts or, in the case of a few expensive models, twenty-four volts.

Car batteries are usually built into composition cases and have thick plates and separators of either perforated ebonite or cedarwood (see Fig. 2, p. 5). The specific gravity of the electrolyte is higher than is normal for accumulators employed in other services. Such batteries usually have electrolytes whose specific gravities vary, when the battery is fully charged, from about 1,210 to 1,250, but the corresponding figure for car batteries is about 1,280 to 1,300. The object of this increased specific gravity is to reduce the internal resistance of the battery, thus allowing very heavy currents to be taken from it for short periods, which is necessary when starting from cold.

One side of the battery is invariably connected to the frame or chassis of the car, and is then said to be "earthed". Until recently the negative side of the battery was so connected, but modern practice tends to earth the positive side of the battery. This modification confers two advantages. The negative side of a spark is the hotter and, if this is the side connected to the chassis, the great capacity for heat of the latter prevents the negative points of the plug reaching their maximum temperature. But if the central electrode, which is comparatively small and well insulated both electrically and thermally from the chassis, is made negative it can attain a high temperature, thus giving a hotter and more effective spark. In addition, it is claimed that the positive "earth" reduces electrolysis, and therefore minimises corrosion of connections, terminals, etc.

STARTER MOTORS

Early cars were started by means of a starting handle and, for a large engine, this often meant considerable physical effort. Present-day cars can be started by the operation of a switch or by pushing a button. A series-motor is arranged with a small pinion capable of travelling up and down a screwed shaft. Operating the starting switch causes the motor to rotate, and the pinion travels to the end of the threaded shaft where it meshes with teeth cut on the flywheel of the engine. Since the flywheel is very much larger than the pinion, the flywheel will rotate

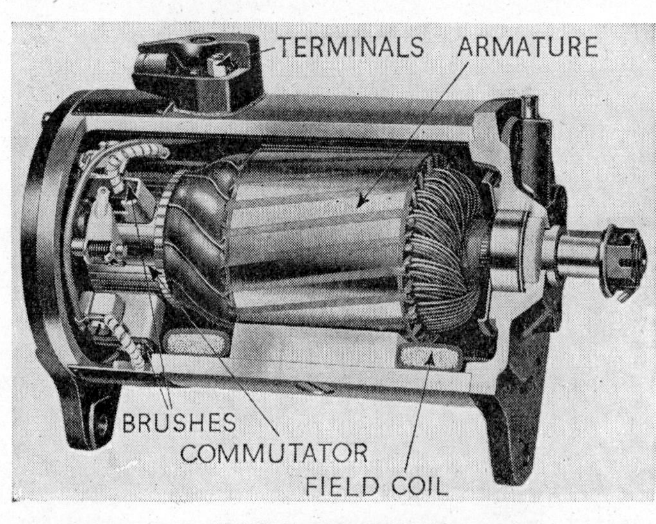

12-VOLT CAR DYNAMO

Fig. 7. Sectional perspective view of Lucas 12-volt car dynamo. Normally a car dynamo is shunt wound and arranged for constant output voltage.

ıore slowly than the pinion, but with onsiderably more torque.

Normally, after one or two revolutions, he engine "fires", and the rotating fly-vheel then disengages the pinion by orcing it back along the thread. The tarter motor is a series motor because his type exerts its maximum torque at its owest speed, so that, when the engine is old and difficult to turn over, the motor ıas ample energy available, assuming hat the battery is in good condition. But when the engine is at rest, the only actor limiting the current is the resist-ınce of the starter motor, which is xtremely small. It is easily seen that the nitial value of the current from the battery is very high—it may be of the order of several hundreds of amperes. The importance of using a strong electro-yte and very low internal resistance in the battery is manifestly important.

CAR-TYPE DYNAMO

Obviously, if a car includes an accu-mulator, it should also incorporate a means of recharging that battery. So a practical car is invariably fitted with a dynamo. The car-type dynamo is a modified shunt-wound machine some-times employing a special third brush for output voltage control. The field winding is connected between the third brush, whose position is adjustable and a terminal mounted on the terminal block of the generator alongside the main ter-minal (see Fig. 7). To complete the field circuit the two terminals must be con-nected together and very often a resistance is wired across them; thus the resistance is in series with the field winding. If the third brush is wound against the direction of rotation of the dynamo, the voltage applied to the field winding will be less—resulting in a weaker field and lower output voltage. On the other hand, if the third brush is moved to its utmost limit in the direction of rotation, almost the full generated voltage is applied to the field which thus becomes strong and produces high terminal volts.

In winter, when the battery is used more, owing to lighting and the engine

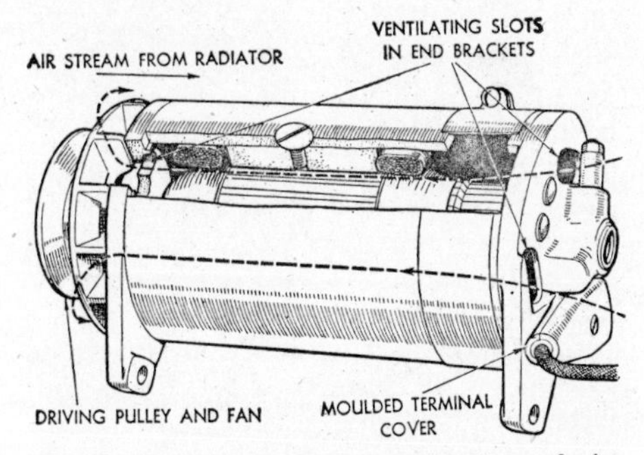

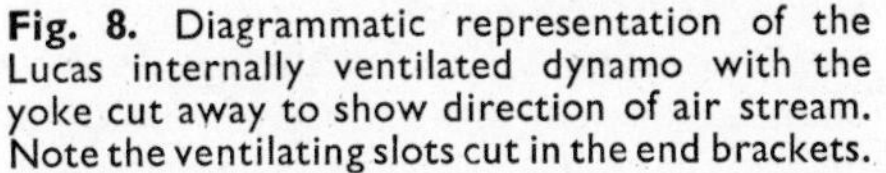
Fig. 8. Diagrammatic representation of the Lucas internally ventilated dynamo with the yoke cut away to show direction of air stream. Note the ventilating slots cut in the end brackets.

being colder thus needing more energy to start it, this resistance is short-circuited, allowing a high charging rate, but in summer the resistance is in circuit, thus reducing the charging rate and safe-guarding the battery against overcharging. The objection to the third brush type of dynamo is that charging current is higher when the battery is well charged than when it is discharged since a rise in battery voltage is accompanied by an increase in dynamo field current and con-sequently a higher charging current. This effect is contrary to the requirements of a charging circuit but has to be accepted as one of the disadvantages entailed by this method of control.

A more modern system is the so-called constant voltage control system where the field excitation of the dynamo is con-trolled by a magnetically operated con-tact breaker which normally short circuits a resistance in series with the field wind-ing. When the dynamo voltage rises above a predetermined value the short across the resistance is removed by the opening of the contacts and the field current is reduced. In this way a charging current consistent with the state of charge of the battery is maintained.

DYNAMO CUT-OUT

If the dynamo were directly connected to the battery the latter would tend to drive the dynamo as a motor when the engine was stationary or turning over at low speeds. This would quickly discharge the battery. To avoid this trouble a cut-out is used. One arrangement is shown in Fig. 9. The unit comprises two coils, one having many turns of fine wire and the other comparatively few turns of heavy gauge wire wound over an iron core. The fine coil is shunted across the dynamo and when the voltage is sufficiently high the magnetic effects of the current pull a spring loaded armature downwards to close a set of contacts. The closed contacts permit a charging current to flow through the second coil which is in series with the ammeter and battery. While a charging current flows the magnetic fields of the two coils are supplementary, but when dynamo volts fall below battery volts a reverse current flows in the series coil and the two fields cancel out, the armature is released and the circuit between the dynamo and battery is broken. A warning lamp is usually connected between the ignition switch and the dynamo side of the contacts. If ignition is switched on and the dynamo is not charging the lamp will glow, but when it is charging the lamp is short circuited by the closed contacts.

LIGHTING

The main lighting system of a car consists of two side lights, which indicate the width of the car, two headlights and a red tail light. But there may be many other additions. During peace-time a specially designed driving lamp, which diffuses light more or less evenly ove a wide area instead of in a beam like th normal headlight, is a common fittin on cars whose owners travel much a night. Fog-lights are also common, whil many owners have a reversing lamp In addition, the "trafficators" are elec trically operated and illuminated.

Head lamps are usually 24-watt o 36-watt and 6 volts for American and th smaller British cars, and 12 volts fo larger British cars. Side lights are usuall 6-watt bulbs, and the red tail light i either 3- or 6-watts. If a braking light i fitted in the tail light casing, it may be o rather higher power than the tail ligh itself—probably 12–18 watts. Specia road-lamps, fog-lamps and reversin lamps are usually of about the same powe as head-lamps (see Fig. 10).

The above paragraphs cover the mai automobile applications of electricity but there are several other fairly commo cases of its use. One very interesting on is the "de-froster", which consists o a coil of resistance wire mounted in frame fitted to the windscreen and con nected to the battery. When curren passes through the resistance coil, th heat produced vaporises the condensatio that occurs on the windscreen during ver cold weather, and also prevents the forma tion of ice on the outside of the wind screen. In some cars the windscree wiper is also operated electrically b means of a small motor. Frequently in terior lighting is fitted, and mis cellaneous applications of electri city, such as cigarette lighters an electric fans, are fairly commo

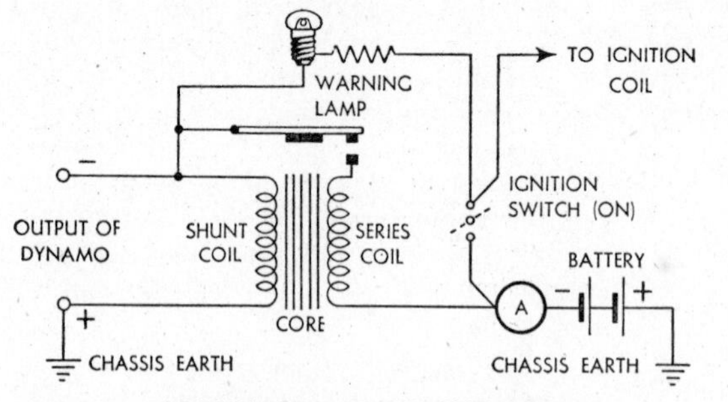

ARRANGEMENT OF CUT-OUT

Fig. 9. Coil A is normally connected via the upper contacts across the dynamo armature. When the generator voltage becomes sufficiently high, the soft iron armature is pulled down. This has the effect of completing the battery charging circuit via the series coil B, providing the switch is closed.

ELECTRIC CARS

In its widest sense, the term electric cars might include trolle buses. These are mains driven although they all carry batterie sufficient to drive them for som distance in case of emergency Furthermore, they are chiefl restricted to certain main road and cannot be considere as electric cars in the usua sense. But electric cars, batter

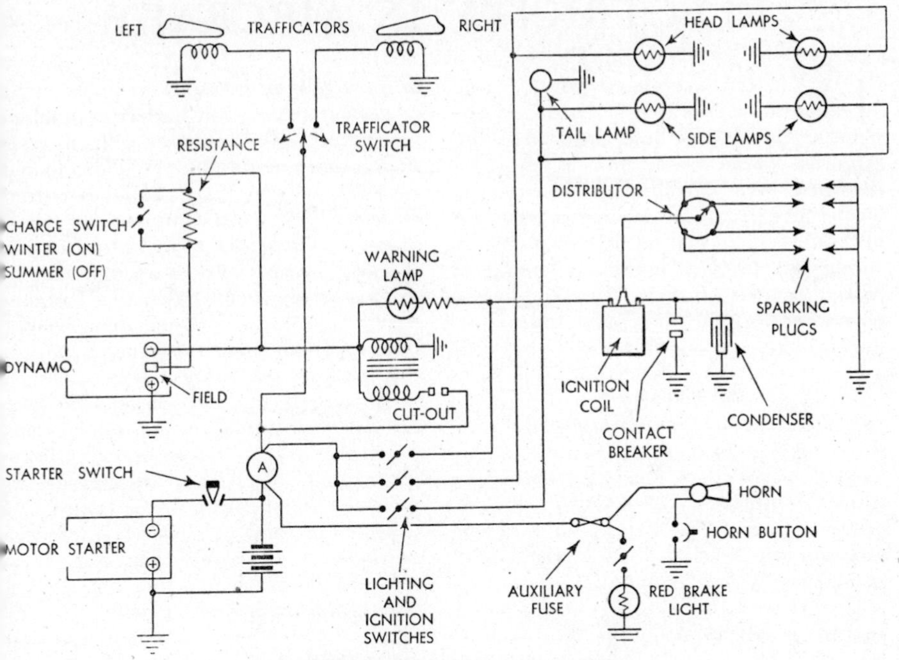

WIRING CIRCUIT OF SMALL CAR

Fig. 10. Typical electrical wiring layout suitable for a small four-cylinder car using coil ignition. The red brake light operates in conjunction with a switch incorporated in the foot brake mechanism.

driven and independent of any mains supply, are employed for restricted service. Their difficulty is that they cannot run for long distances without the battery being recharged. Of course, this would not matter if either batteries could be recharged in a few minutes or if the number of electric cars on the road justified service stations maintaining a battery exchange service.

Another disadvantage is that the battery is heavy and, therefore, reduces the power to weight ratio of the car, so that performance comparable with an internal combustion engine is impossible.

USE OF ACCUMULATORS

Some years ago there was considerable publicity given to a battery originating in Ireland which could be recharged in a few minutes. It was stated to have been successfully employed on some Irish railways, but there are no recent records of any development along these lines. Employing ordinary accumulator batteries an electric car can travel only thirty-five to forty miles per charge. For the smaller kinds of electric vehicles the maximum speed is about fifteen miles an hour.

There does not appear to be any standard form of design for such vehicles as there is to a large extent in the case of petrol-driven cars. However, the electric motors used are normally of the series-wound type, though the transmission in some instances is with two motors, and in others only the one is employed.

Electric traction is often applied to factory and railway platform trucks, and one of these is illustrated on page 288. There are also battery driven municipal vehicles and town delivery vans.

"Petrol-electric" vehicles, in which internal combustion engines operated generators for supplying current to driving motors, were fairly widely used, but can now be considered obsolescent.

ELECTRICITY IN AIRCRAFT

THE modern aircraft contains a large amount of electrically operated apparatus. Many of these appliances are required when the aircraft engines are throttled back or stopped, so that the electrical aspect of an aircraft is basically very similar to that of a motor-car. A supply of electrical energy independent of the engines is necessary, but engine power can be used to recharge the supply during flight.

BATTERIES

A secondary battery (accumulator), as shown in Fig. 11, is therefore used as the main reservoir of electrical energy, whilst a suitable dynamo driven by one of the engines serves the double purpose of supplying load currents in flight and also charging the accumulators.

Two types of accumulator are used in aircraft, the lead-acid and the alkaline cell, which are described in the section on Accumulators and Accumulator Charging (Chapter 2).

A battery means a combination of two or more cells to give some required e.m.f. or capacity. A 12-volt battery is obtained by connecting six lead-acid cells in series, the capacity of the battery being that of a single cell. A nickel-cadmium battery of nominally 12 volts comprises ten cells in series. It is not usual to make up batteries of more than 12 volts in a single case on account of the inconvenience in handling which would result from their weight. Where 24-volt systems are used, two 12-volt batteries are connected in series. In such cases, the load circuits are sometimes divided into 12-volt and 24-volt systems, the higher voltage being used for heavy load circuits in order to compensate for increased voltage drop in the cables.

Figs. 12 and 13 show alternative methods of arranging this. Fig. 13 is, perhaps, the better scheme, but in both cases the battery as a whole is unbalanced. This matters much less with alkaline cells because overcharging has no effect on them, and the charging rate can be set to cater for that part of the battery experiencing the greater load without damaging the other cells.

The aircraft battery is charged from an engine-driven generator, such as the type shown in Fig. 14, which is, of course, a D.C. dynamo. Wind-driven generators have been used for the purpose, but these are now obsolete.

The dynamo is a shunt-wound or compound-wound machine, the usual sizes for aircraft being 12 volts (250 watts); 12 volts (500 watts) and 24 volts (1,000 watts); the last being suitable

TYPICAL ACCUMULATOR

Fig. 11. Dagenite accumulator type 6-DA11-B, made by Peto and Radford. A secondary battery such as this constitutes the "main reservoir" of electrical energy in the electrical installation of an aircraft.

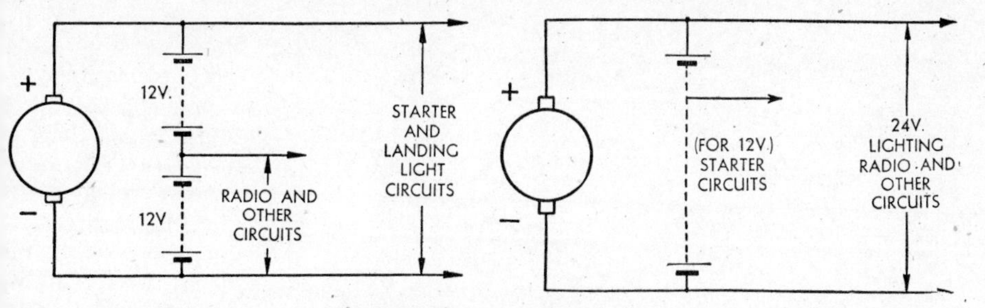

DISTRIBUTION OF VOLTAGE

Fig. 12. (left) Circuit in which various voltages are used for different parts of the electrical equipment. Fig. 13 (right) An alternative arrangement to Fig. 12 giving better balance of the battery.

for the largest types of aircraft. It is essential that the dynamo should be connected to the battery through a reverse-current relay or "cut-out", and the circuit arrangements are exactly the same as in motor car practice.

GENERATOR VOLTAGE CONTROL

In Fig. 15a H is the high resistance or shunt winding, which is permanently connected across the generator, and L is the low-resistance or series winding which carries the output current. C represents the cut-out contacts, and A is the adjusting screw for spring tension. With 12-volt systems, A is adjusted so that the cut-out closes at about 14 volts, and it opens again when the reverse current reaches a value of 4 to 6 amperes. The centre-zero ammeter is in the positive battery lead and indicates charging and discharging currents. The electrical load on the generator will vary between fairly wide limits, and generator speed will also vary, not with the same frequency as in the case of a motor-car, but to a comparable extent. It is, therefore, necessary to stabilise the generator e.m.f. in some way. The use of a floating battery assists this (see Fig. 15a).

It is clear that the e.m.f. across the output circuit cannot rise much above the maximum charging e.m.f. of the battery, nor fall below the discharging e.m.f. This, however, is not a sufficient control, and all modern aircraft electrical systems

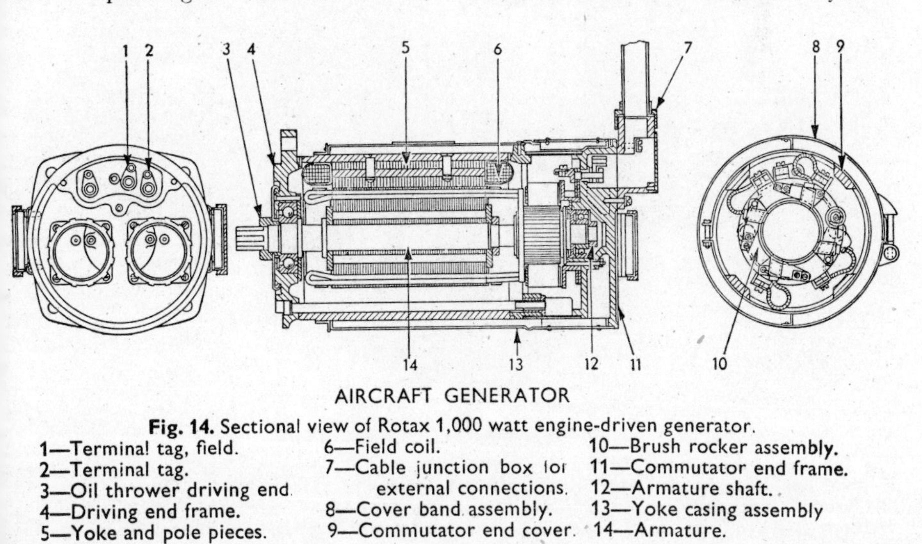

AIRCRAFT GENERATOR

Fig. 14. Sectional view of Rotax 1,000 watt engine-driven generator.

1—Terminal tag, field.
2—Terminal tag.
3—Oil thrower driving end.
4—Driving end frame.
5—Yoke and pole pieces.
6—Field coil.
7—Cable junction box for external connections.
8—Cover band assembly.
9—Commutator end cover.
10—Brush rocker assembly.
11—Commutator end frame.
12—Armature shaft.
13—Yoke casing assembly.
14—Armature.

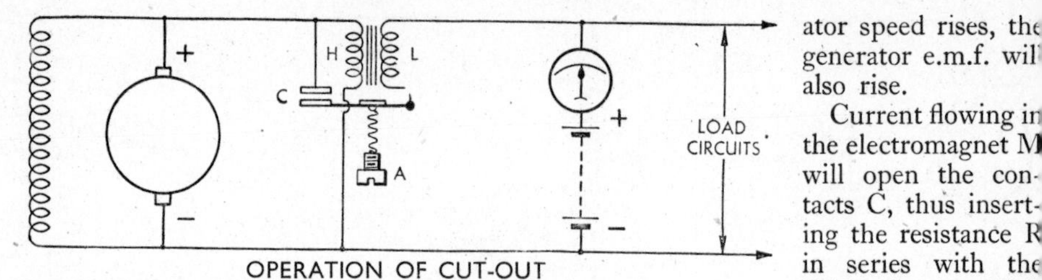

OPERATION OF CUT-OUT

Fig. 15a. Arrangement of the charging and load circuits, showing the operation of the cut-out in a constant voltage system.

make use of a method known as compensated voltage control (c.v.c.), or alternatively, constant voltage system, Fig. 15b shows the Rotax cut-out and regulator unit which is used for this purpose. The principle of the system is shown in Fig. 16a. The shunt field is completed through contacts C, and in parallel with these is the resistance R. When the engine is opened up and generator speed rises, the generator e.m.f. will also rise.

Current flowing in the electromagnet M will open the contacts C, thus inserting the resistance R in series with the field circuit. This reduces the e.m.f. and hence the current in M. The contacts C then close again and the process is repeated at a frequency depending upon the mechanical details of the contact system.

This frequency is usually about 200 per second, so that the generator e.m.f. actually rises and falls to a very small extent about some steady mean value, and it is this that is the constant voltage.

The exact value of this e.m.f. is

CUT-OUT AND REGULATOR UNIT

Fig. 15b. Rotax cut-out and regulator unit with dust cover removed. A—Armature Fixing Screws, J—Main Regulator Frame, K—Regulator Coil, L—Regulator Armature, M—Output Armature, N—Bobbin Core, O—Cut-out Armature Regulating Stop, P—Condenser, R—Resistance (field limiting), S—High Frequency Chokes. The principle of this apparatus is illustrated in Fig. 16a.

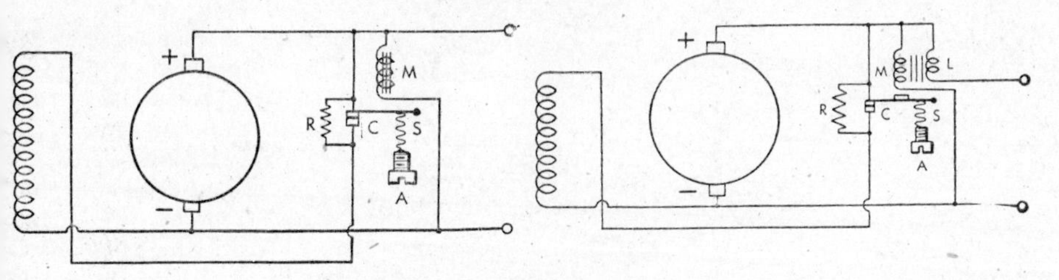

CONSTANT GENERATOR VOLTAGE

Fig. 16a (left) Showing the principle of the Tirrill regulator, which gives a constant generator voltage over a wide speed range. **Fig. 16b** (right) The addition of the coil L is necessary to prevent overloading of the generator should the battery be in a low state of charge.

determined by the setting of the adjusting screw A, which controls the contact spring tension. The usual setting gives 14·5 volts for a 12-volt system, or 29 volts for a 24-volt system. One of the most important advantages of the constant voltage system is that the charging current delivered to the battery is suited to its state of charge. A discharged battery having low e.m.f. will receive a large boosting current, while a fully charged battery having high e.m.f. will receive only a small trickle charge.

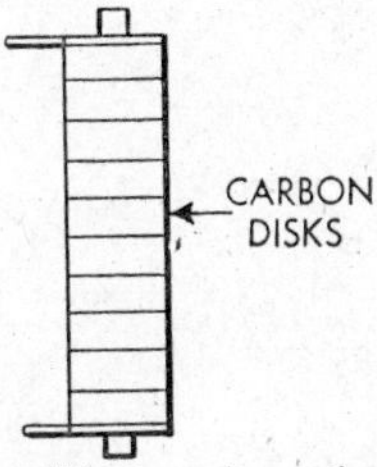

CARBON DISKS

Fig. 17. A carbon-pile resistance, the value of which varies with the pressure applied to it. It is used as a shunt field resistance to control generator voltage.

Should one or more load circuits be in use during flight at a time when the battery is in a low state of charge, a generator with a constant voltage system might be seriously overloaded. The simple circuit of Fig. 16a has, therefore, to be modified in practice as shown in Fig. 16b.

The compensating coil L carries load current and acts in the same direction magnetically as the shunt coil M. With large output currents, the generator e.m.f. is, therefore, decreased and overloading is avoided.

Another method of generator voltage control makes use of a carbon-pile regulator. The basic principle is the same as that of the vibratory type of regulator, but the use of vibrating contacts is avoided. The shunt field resistance takes the form of a "carbon pile", which consists of a number of carbon disks threaded over a rod as shown in Fig. 17. When two such pieces of carbon are in contact, the resistance across them is, within certain limits, inversely proportional to the contact pressure so that the arrangement shown in Fig. 17 gives a resistance which varies with the pressure applied to the pile.

Fig. 18 shows the principle of the torque motor used with the carbon pile regulator. The full line gives the position of the permanent magnet armature at rest, and the dotted line shows the position which

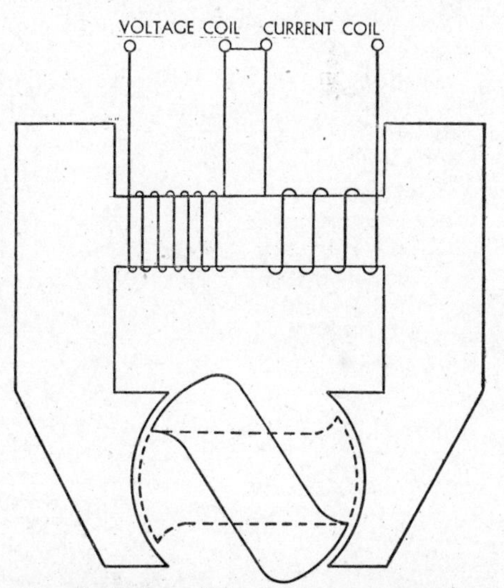

Fig. 18. Action of the torque motor used in conjunction with a carbon-pile voltage regulator.

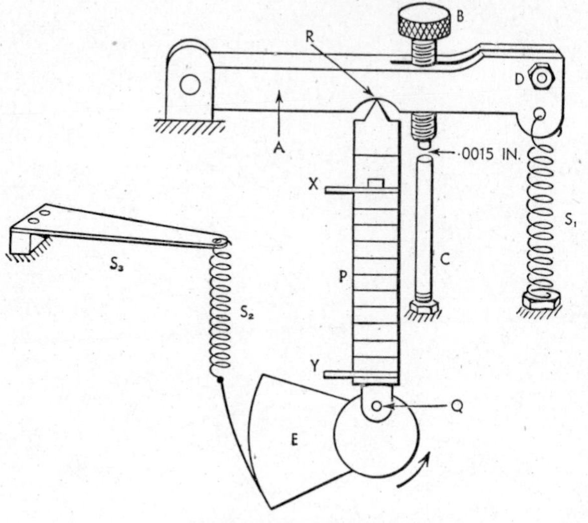

VOLTAGE REGULATOR

Fig. 19. Mechanism of a carbon-pile voltage regulator. The circuit connections of the device are shown in Fig. 20 which includes the adjustable series resistance for initial settings.

this armature tends to take up when current passes through the voltage or current coil. (Compare the action of a moving-coil indicating instrument.)

Movement of the armature controls the pressure on the carbon pile by means of the mechanism shown in Fig. 19 (not to scale).

The carbon pile P is held between the knife-edge R and the crank-pin Q which is mounted on the torque motor armature spindle. Connections to the pile are made at X and Y by flexible leads. When the generator is not running, the pressure on the carbon pile is determined by the spring S_1 attached to the pivoted arm A. This pressure is comparatively strong, and reduces the resistance of the pile to a low value. As the generator speeds up, current in the shunt coil causes the armature to move in the direction shown by the arrow. Crank-pin Q is, therefore, carried downwards, allowing the arm A to descend. On the screw B coming into contact with the fixed rod C, the arm A cannot move further.

The pull of S_1 is, therefore, removed from the pile, and the point R becomes a pivot only. Further movement of the armature will clearly reduce the pressure on the pile, because the crank-pin is moving downwards. Pile resistance thus increases and generator e.m.f. will fall. A steady voltage is reached, which is determined by the tension of the springs S_2 and S_3. These are not adjustable, but an adjustable series resistance is provided in the shunt coil circuit in order to carry out voltage setting. This is shown in Fig. 20.

In Fig. 20 at F is the generator shunt field, S the charging switch, P the carbon pile, L_1 the voltage coil, L_2 the current (compensating) coil, and R the adjustable resistance.

The torque motor armature is fitted with an air dash-pot damping to prevent

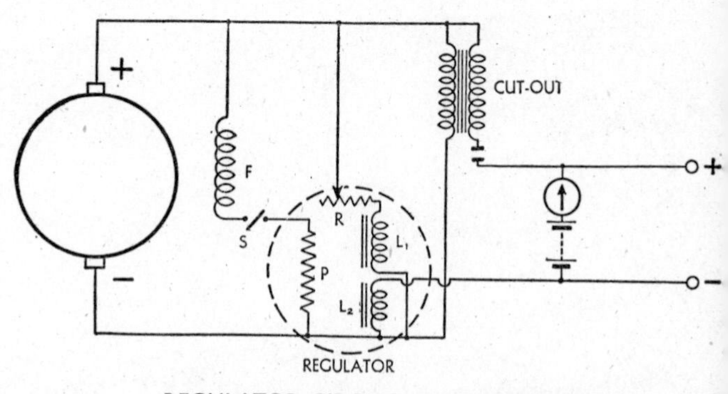

REGULATOR CIRCUIT CONNECTIONS

Fig. 20. Circuit diagram of the carbon pile regulator. The adjustable resistance, R, is provided so that a close setting of voltage can be obtained. The cut-out prevents the flow of excessive reverse currents.

instability. The systems for the supply and storage of electrical energy on aircraft having been outlined above, the various load circuits will now be described in detail so far as space permits.

ENGINE STARTERS

As in the case of motor cars, the engine starter constitutes the heaviest electrical load on the accumulator, but the case is more severe in aircraft because the engines to be started are so much larger. A medium-sized aircraft of say 600 h.p. requires an electric motor of at least $1\frac{1}{2}$ h.p. to turn it, and even then the cranking speed is not above 30 to 40 r.p.m.

Therefore, starting has to be aided by artificial carburation (doping) and a temporary ignition device such as a hand starting magneto or booster coil. Allowing for voltage drops and various losses, the starting motor current may easily peak to over 200 amperes, so that the battery can supply starting currents for only very short periods.

The normal design of a starting motor is a straightforward series-wound type such as is shown in Fig. 21, giving maximum torque at zero r.p.m. For aircraft work it is usually a 4-pole machine with a single-turn wave-wound armature, the conductors being flat copper strip.

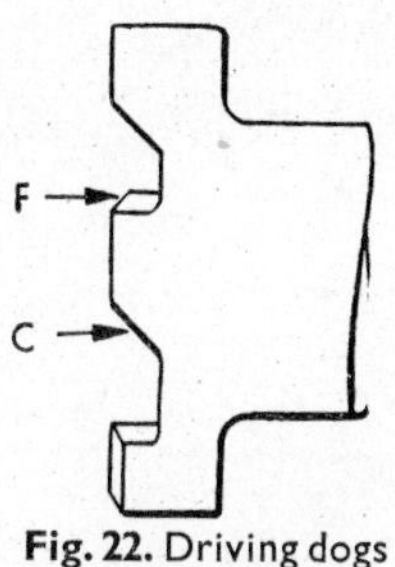

Fig. 22. Driving dogs for engine starter. The drive is taken on the square face (F) the starter subsequently being disengaged by the cams, C.

A reduction gear of the order 100 to 1 is incorporated, and the following items are required in addition.

1. Automatic engaging mechanism, which also throws out when the engine fires.
2. A friction clutch to transmit the torque. This also serves the purpose of protecting the gearing should the engine backfire.

A sliding pinion Bendix drive as used on cars is not suitable for this class of work, and the starter jaws usually take a form similar to that shown in Fig. 22.

The drive is taken on the square faces F, which engage with similar jaws fitted on the engine. When the engine fires, the starter is thrown out by the engine fitting, which rides over the cams C and pushes the starter jaw away.

The initial advance of the starter jaw is obtained by means of a special friction device which holds the starter jaw temporarily when the motor first starts. A quick thread then causes the jaw to advance and engage with the engine fitting.

Direct switching of the starting motor is not convenient, and a solenoid switch is employed.

Fig. 23 shows the circuit arrangement. The push-button P is in the pilot's cockpit, and completes the circuit through the magnet winding W. The armature A is drawn

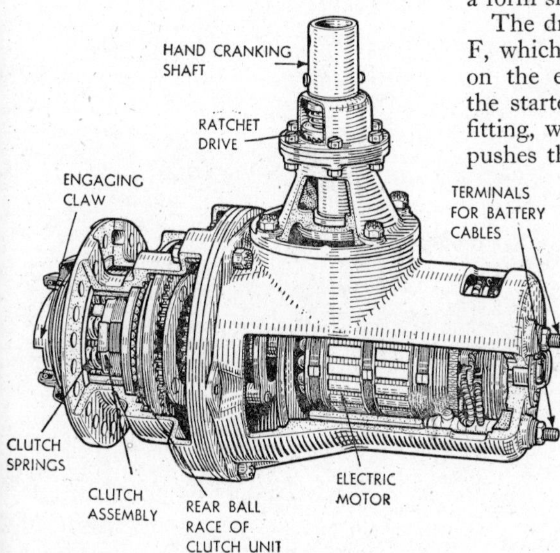

Fig. 21. Perspective view in section of the Rotax type E 160c direct cranking electric starter with hand turning gear. The motor is a series-wound type fitted with a friction clutch.

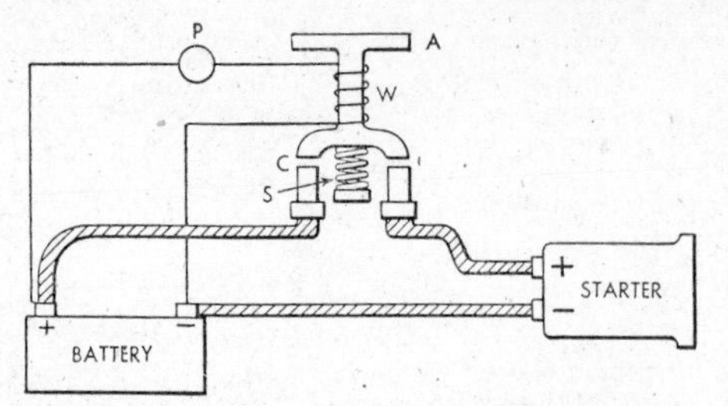

Fig. 23. Circuit connections for the solenoid switch of an engine starter. P is a remote control push-button which is in the pilot's cockpit.

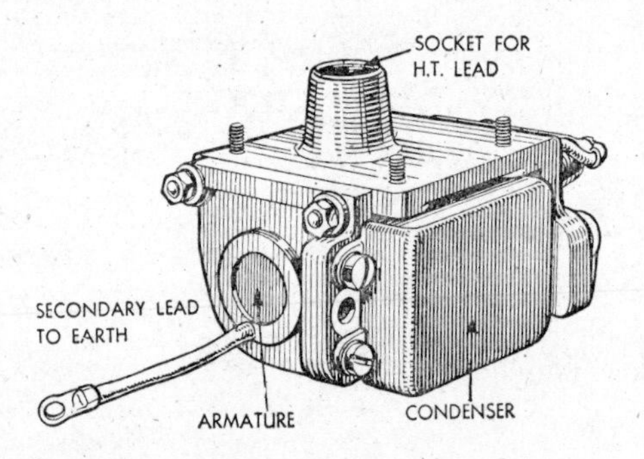

Fig. 24. Cranking speed at starting is too low to enable the magneto to function so a booster coil, such as the Rotax Nika, is used as an alternative method of providing the necessary ignition.

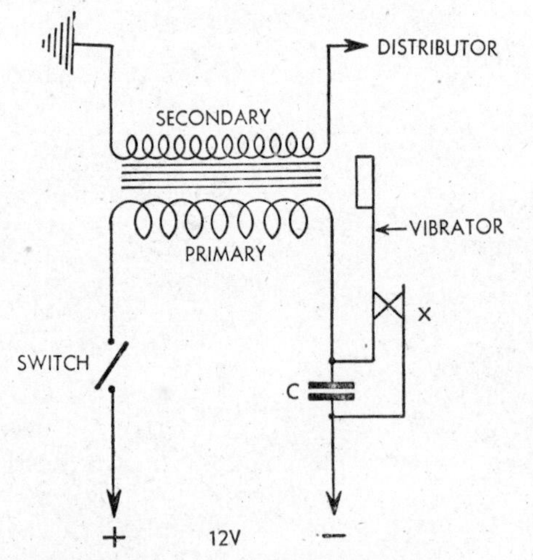

Fig. 25a. Circuit for the booster coil, which is a small induction coil working on the electric bell principle. In multi-engined aircraft there are independent circuits including separate starters, boosters and push-buttons for each engine

down and closes the contacts CC which complete the motor circuit. When P is released, the return spring S pushes the armature back and opens the motor circuit.

BOOSTER COIL

As the cranking speed at starting is too low for the engine magnetos to function, ignition is provided by an alternative means. A booster coil is merely a small induction coil (see Fig. 24) having a vibrating contact working on the electric bell principle.

Fig. 25a shows the circuit of the booster coil. The vibrating contacts are at X, and the condenser C across them is to intensify the secondary voltage pulse on "break" and to prevent the burning of the contacts. Fig. 25b shows the connections of the booster coil. The booster switching is done by the starting button so that the operation of the device coincides with operation of the starter. In multi-engined aircraft, there would, of course, be a separate starter, booster coil and push-button for each engine.

AIRCRAFT LIGHTING

A land aircraft has to carry certain compulsory lights if it is used at night.

Fig. 26 shows the position of these lights and the cut-off angles, which are obtained by masks built into the lamps.

Seaplanes and flying boats have additional compulsory lights, and all information on lighting regulations can be obtained from the publications of the I.C.A.N. (International Council for Air Navigation).

The wattages of navigation lights are not fixed, but 24 watts is a reasonable size and is in general use.

The wireless operator and the navigator need lights, and a few small-power shrouded lamps for the pilot's cockpit are required. Many of the cockpit instruments have faintly luminous dials and needles, so that very little lighting is needed in the cockpit. It will be appreciated that even a very small light in the cockpit soon appears to be a blinding glare to a pilot looking forward into blackness. The tendency is, therefore, to have the cockpit in total darkness when flying at night.

The other important light on an aircraft is the landing light for use at aerodromes which are not floodlit or in emergency landings. A 150-watt lamp is the smallest useful size, and provided it is very carefully placed in the correct position will give sufficient light for a safe landing. 250-watt or 500-watt lamps can be used with advantage on the larger aircraft.

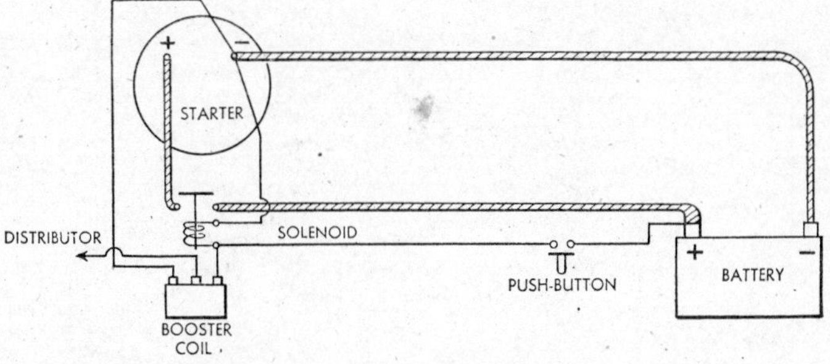

BOOSTER COIL CONNECTIONS

Fig. 25b. Showing in practical form the connections of a booster coil and the solenoid switch for remote control from the pilot's cockpit.

If the lamp is not set in the nose or faired into the leading edge of the wing, it may be of the retractable type. The lamp face is then flush with the underside of the wing when not in use, and is lowered to a suitable angle when required. The lamp movement may be achieved mechanically, but electrical retraction is often used. The driving motor must clearly be reversible, and this is arranged by the use of a series-wound machine with a split field.

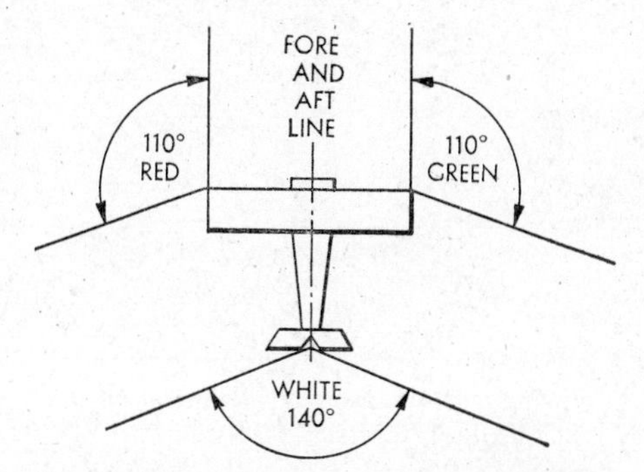

Fig. 26. Navigation lights on land aircraft. The cut-off angles are fixed by masks of appropriate design which are built into the lamps.

Fig. 27 shows the circuit arrangement. The motor is a 4-pole machine, and the field windings give all poles the same polarity. When the supply is connected across − and + 1, poles AA are excited and poles BB become consequent poles. With the supply across − and + 2, poles BB are excited and AA become consequent poles.

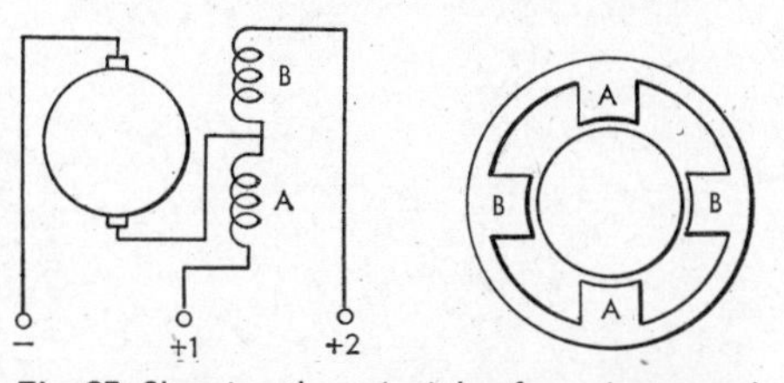

Fig. 27. Showing the principle of a series wound driving motor for retractable lamp mechanisms. Note the split field and also the arrangement of the poles to render the motor reversible.

It is obviously necessary that the motor should be switched off automatically at the correct limits of lamp movement, and this is done by means of limit switches.

Fig. 28 shows the action of a limit switch. Two terminals are provided, and these are clearly to be seen at A and B. The two metal spring blades CC make contact with the metal ring M. When the plunger P is pushed in against the spring S, the metal ring moves away from the blades, which then rest on

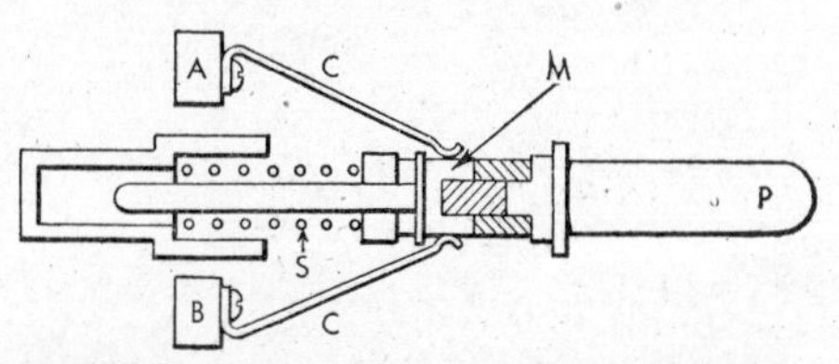

Fig. 28. Four-pole limit switch for automatically switching off the motor at correct limits of lamp movement. The circuit is shown in Fig. 29.

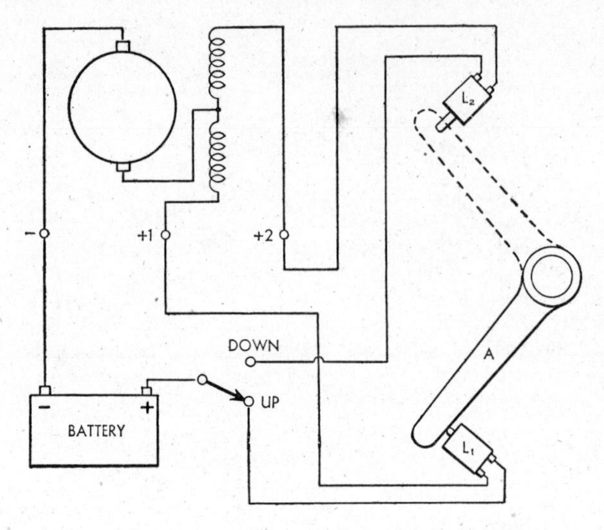

RETRACTING LAMP CIRCUIT

Fig. 29. Circuit for retracting lamp. By means of a reversible electric motor a landing light can be lowered or retracted as desired. Two single-pole limit switches, L_1 and L_2, are used.

that the lamp is fully home without being strained owing to a slightly late motor cut-off.

RETRACTING UNDERCARTS

On modern land aircraft, the undercart is usually retractable in flight, the object being to reduce the wind resistance it offers. The undercart is a heavy component, and power operation is needed. The principles of electrical retraction are identical with those just described for a retracting lamp, but the following additional items are necessary.

1. A system of indicating lights to show the position of the undercart, such as the one which makes use of flag type signals. These are clearly visible by day and night.
2. A warning device to prevent an inadvertent "belly landing".

Fig. 30 shows a typical circuit arrangement. Limit switches L_1 and L_2 control the undercart motor, a series-wound

insulation thus breaking the circuit. On release of the plunger the spring S drives it forward, again completing the circuit across A and B. In other words, the device functions as a simple on and off switch, and the circuit in which it is included is broken each time the plunger is pressed in by an appropriate part of the mechanism.

Fig. 29 shows the circuit for a retracting lamp. The arm A represents some suitable moving part which can be used to operate the limit switches L_1 and L_2. An adjustment is provided either on the arm A or on the limit switch mounting bracket so that the moment of cut-off can be accurately set. This is specially important in the "up" position, so

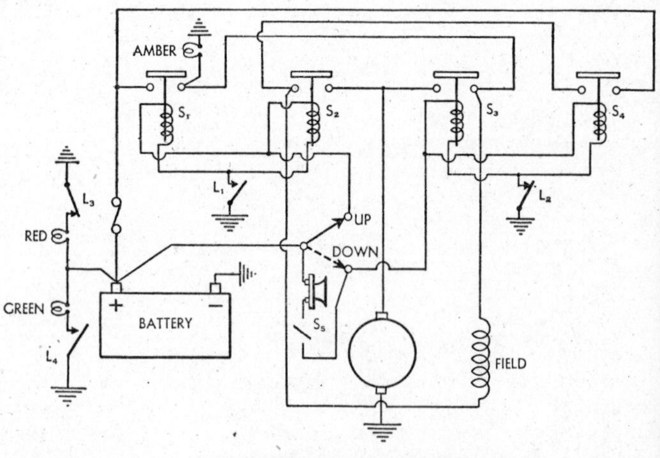

RETRACTING UNDERCART

Fig. 30. Circuit for a retracting undercart with indicating lights and electric horn. The purpose of the horn is to provide audible warning for the pilot should his undercart not be lowered at moment of landing.

motor of about 1 h.p. for a medium-sized aircraft. The motor circuit is completed through the solenoid switches S_1, S_2, S_3 and S_4, and reversal is obtained by reversing the field current.

Limit switches L_3 and L_4 control the indicating red and green lights, and the amber light is on whilst the motor is running. The warning horn circuit is via switch S_5 and limit switch L_2, so that the horn is out of action when the undercart is down. S_5 is associated with the engine throttles, and if the engines are throttled back with the undercart raised, the horn sounds continuously until the throttles are opened or the undercart lowered.

The undercart motor drives the retracting mechanism through a friction clutch. The object of this is to limit the load on the motor and also to prevent the aircraft "kneeling down" in the event of accidental operation of the retracting motor on the ground.

WING FLAPS

Most modern aircraft are fitted with wing flaps. When lowered, these have the effect of steepening the gliding angle and reducing the landing speed.

On any but the smallest types of aircraft, power operation of the flaps is called for, the motor being of approximately ½ h.p.

The electrical aspect of a flap system is essentially the same as that for a retracting lamp or undercart.

In the circuit of Fig. 31, the flaps are assumed to be in the "Up" (closed) position, limit switch L_1 being open. On moving the control to the "Down" position, solenoids S_3 and S_4 are energised via limit switch L_2. This completes the motor circuit and the flaps are lowered until limit switch L_2 is opened by the flap mechanism. The position of the flaps is indicated to the pilot by means of a dashboard instrument, which is merely a 0—12 or 0—24 voltmeter connected to a potentiometer resistance R, the slider of which is operated by some suitable part of the flap gear. The flaps can be left in an intermediate position by placing the control switch centrally, and they can then be closed or opened according to which way the control switch is next moved. Blowing of the flap motor fuse may take place if the flaps are lowered at excessive air speeds, because the flap motor is then overloaded.

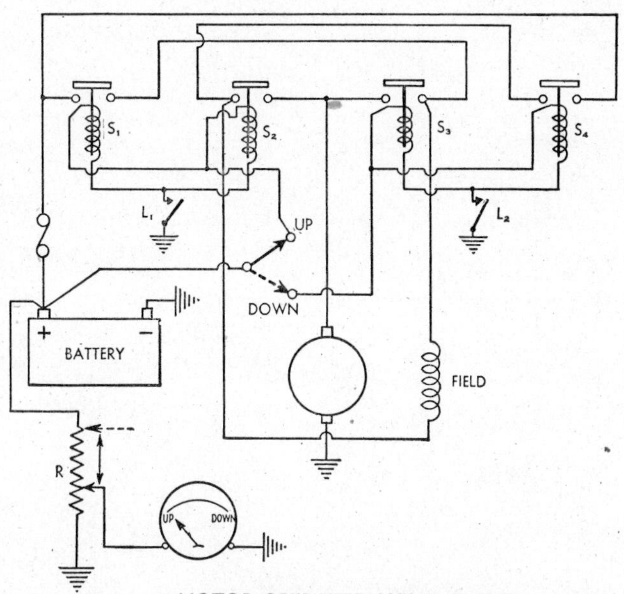

MOTOR-OPERATED WING FLAPS

Fig. 31. Circuit for motor-driven flaps with instrument showing flap position. The flap gear operates the variable resistance R, and this in turn affects the reading on the indicator. Switches, L_1 and L_2, limit the action of the motor at the extreme points of flap movement.

OTHER LOAD CIRCUITS

The most important electrical load other than those described is the radio equipment. The load when receiving is comparatively light, but is fairly heavy when the transmitting key is pressed. On large aircraft, the transmitting load may peak to the neighbourhood of 40 amperes and is, therefore, comparable to the load of motor-driven flaps. In the event of a forced landing, the radio may be required, and an unaided accumulator, even if fully charged, can supply the current needed for transmission for only a short period. On really large aircraft, particularly flying boats, a small petrol engine and dynamo for battery charging is sometimes fitted, thus making the battery to some extent independent of the main generator. Some additional radio equipment of aircraft is dealt with in Chapter 10.

Minor loads which may be found on aircraft are windscreen wipers, de-icing motors, and heating circuits. Two examples of the latter are electrically heated Pitot heads (used in connection with the air-speed indicator) and electrically heated clothing for very high flying.

ELECTRICITY ABOARD SHIP

Commencing with lighting alone, electricity has won for itself an acknowledged place in every sort of ship for the most diverse purposes, but, contrary to the expectation of some years ago, the progress of electric propulsion has been disappointing. This is primarily due to the perfection of mechanical gearing, which, since the two features of meticulous accuracy of tooth shape and a stiff casing were recognised as essential, has proved itself silent, efficient and reliable in operation.

There is only a limited size of ship in which direct connection between the prime-mover and the propeller gives the best all-round efficiency, for it is difficult to design really efficient screw propellers for a speed of rotation at full power much above 110 r.p.m. For powers up to, say, 2,000 h.p. per propeller many ship owners still prefer the vertical reciprocating steam engine, which can be economically designed for about this speed, as can Diesel engines, and these units have the advantage that they are familiar, simple, reliable and reasonably economical. Moreover, they are directly reversible and can be easily manœuvred. For larger powers the steam turbine is ideal, and very economical at full speed and with high steam pressures and temperatures; at sea too, there is no difficulty in getting a good vacuum because of the availability of plenty of circulating water. But the turbine is inherently irreversible and in a direct or geared drive special astern turbine blading must be provided, which means additional weight and complication, and it is usually designed to give only a proportion of the power available ahead.

The use of a generator and motor as a link between the turbine and screw secures reversibility with ease and can give full power astern if necessary. It allows the speeds of the turbine and propeller to be arranged for optimum efficiency at full power and has other advantages in the layout of the machinery, in particular by the elimination of the long shaft tunnel from the engine-room amidships to the stern. This convenience of layout and the relative difficulty of using gearing with a variable torque such as that given by even a multicylinder Diesel engine is a strong recommendation for electric drive when that type of prime-mover is employed.

Another advantage of the electric link is that in a two, three or four propeller ship it is possible to drive all propellers from one or all of the prime-movers, which, is, of course, impracticable with a geared drive. Moreover, in a given ship the power required for propulsion varies as the cube of the propeller speed, so that half normal power will drive it at about 80 per cent. full speed. One turbo-alternator out of duplicate sets will thus suffice to bring a ship to port with little loss of time in the event of an accident to one unit, without the constant helm that a twin-screw geared turbo ship would need in similar circumstances. And for cruising purposes, one prime-

MODERN PROPULSION MOTORS

Fig. 32. One of the two main propulsion motors in the *Strathnaver*, each rated at 14,000 h.p., 125 r.p.m., 3,000 volt. Maximum lightness and efficiency are achieved by the employment of the salient pole synchronous principle in these motors. They are supplied by two 10,700 kW turbo-alternators.

mover at full power is obviously more economical in operation than working two at half power each. Thus it will be seen that with electricity a very flexible as well as economical system of propulsion is possible.

D.C. or A.C. DRIVES?

Pioneer electrically propelled ships were mostly D.C., because variable motor speed can thus be easily secured with the prime-movers running at constant speed. This is advantageous for tugs and in general for smaller ships, but the larger ships run most of their time at full speed once they are clear of narrow waters so that this factor is not so important as it might at first appear. Moreover, D.C. machinery is relatively heavy and expensive. Liners and other large ships have usually, therefore, employed A.C. for propulsion, in which case the turbo-alternators are almost exactly similar to those designed for stationary power-station practice and thus benefit from the development work done in that direction and are highly efficient. Economical operation at reduced ship speeds can be secured by the use of pole-changing motors if necessary, but speed variations are usually achieved by throttle or nozzle governing of the turbines. Reversal merely means the changing of the electrical connections, which is generally arranged to be done with the main circuit dead, by control of the excitation; this has been worked out so as to be easily accomplished by hand levers operating switches and isolators. For Diesel-electric ships where several prime-movers may be provided, the British Thomson-Houston Co., Ltd. has a special system using double-unit alternators which, by suitable excitation, ensure that the various generators will remain in synchronism, although the main motor supply voltage can be reduced to zero for changing over their connections to give astern driving. The same firm employs salient-pole synchronous propeller motors instead of the induction motors frequently utilised, in order to secure maximum efficiency and lightness. Fig. 32 shows one of two 14,000 h.p. motors of this type in a P. and O. passenger liner, running at a full speed of 125 r.p.m. on 3,000 volts

MAIN TURBO-ALTERNATOR

Fig. 33. One of the two 10,700 kW main propulsion turbo-alternators in the *Strathnaver*. It i. interesting to note the clean lines and freedom from visible moving parts as compared with the old fashioned reciprocating steam propulsion units formerly used in all ships which made thei presence felt by considerable vibration. The *Strathnaver's* control panels are shown on Page 331

DIESEL-ELECTRIC SETS

Fig. 34. Three of the four Diesel-engine-driven main propulsion D.C. 600 kW generators in the *Brunswick*. Each set is fitted with a 75 kW auxiliary D.C. generator to provide electricity fo various ship services. In some cases the reciprocating type of steam engine is still used for the driving of generators supplying current for these many purposes other than propulsion in a ship.

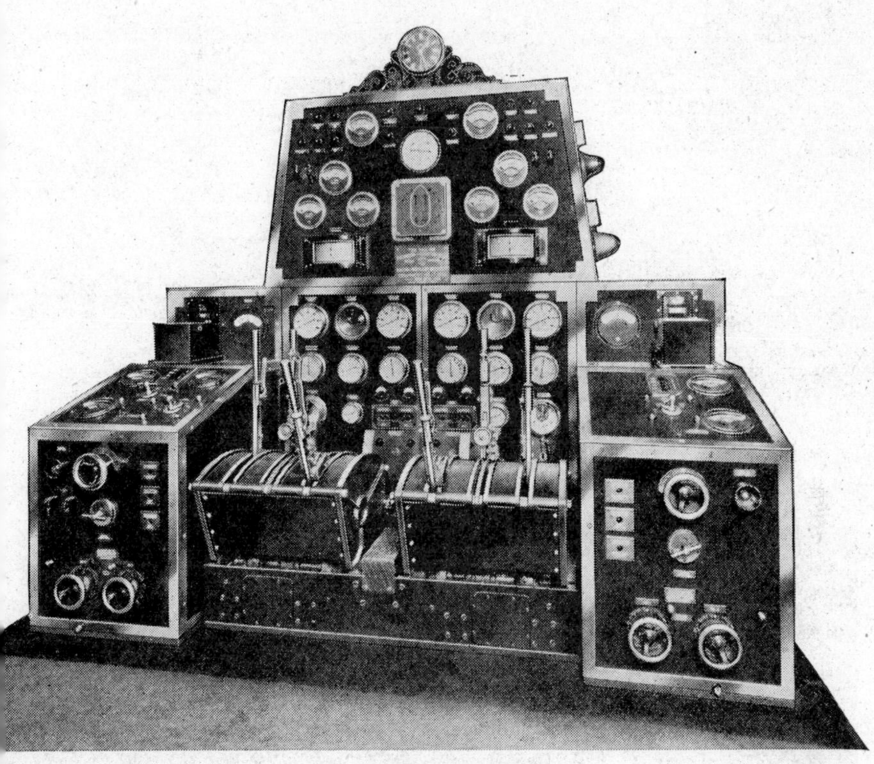

MAIN CONTROL PANELS

;. 35. Control position of the electrically propelled twin-screw liner *Strathnaver*. The levers on :h side control the speed and direction of the ship and are fully interlocked. This interlocking only possible by the use of electric propulsion systems. The dials indicate circuit conditions.

C., and Fig. 33 shows one of the main rbo-alternators, each of 10,700 kW ting, in the same ship. The instrument nels and control levers for this equipent are illustrated in Fig. 35; the levers each side control respectively the citation circuits, the direction (ahead astern) and the speed, and are fully terlocked. Fig. 34 gives a partial view of e engine room of the tanker *Brunswick*, owing three of the four D.C. Dieseliven B.T.H. propulsion generators.

AUXILIARY GENERATORS

Though it would be an exaggeration to aim that electricity has ousted all her agents for power purposes aboard ip other than propulsion, there is a markable recognition of its advantages all sides. Many ships are almost wholly all-electric in their auxiliary drives and very few are without electric motors somewhere. The system is nearly always D.C., generally two-wire at about 100 volts in small ships or 220 volts in large ones. A big liner may absorb a normal load of 1,000 kW or more for its "hotel" services and as much again for navigation aids, engine room auxiliaries, cargo handling, ventilation, etc. A tramp ship may have but a couple of electric winches, lighting, and a few fan motors, with generating plant of 50—100 kW. The conditions are thus very diverse.

Perhaps the majority of ship generators are driven by high-speed vertical reciprocating steam engines, but there are plenty of examples of Diesel-driven units and of steam turbo-generators, the latter generally geared. Fig. 36 shows three of seven

B.T.H. 1,300 kW auxiliary turbo-generators aboard the R.M.S. *Queen Mary*. These are of the geared turbine type, the steam turbines running at 5,000 r.p.m. and exhausting to self-contained condensers, while the generators run at 600 r.p.m. and operate at 225 volts. In construction the generators used for marine auxiliary purposes differ little from stationary practice; they often have fabricated frames and run at fairly high speeds in order to secure lightness, and are usually of the open type for ease of access and ventilation.

The derived energy is used for purposes ranging from desk fans to boat hoists or capstans, and in many cases is employed for such vitally important work as driving the steering gear. In order to save weig and space, motors for marine use a specially compact, although they are oft totally enclosed because of their locatio most of the controllers are also e closed in watertight cases. Vertic shaft motors (Fig. 37) are frequen employed. Main cables are often of t paper-insulated lead-covered type, som times armoured, and these as well smaller distribution wiring are cleat every few inches to the bulkheads or perforated metal racks where necessa Some ships have a ring main, to whi generators in different parts of the sh are paralleled by remote control from central point and from which lo feeders, also remote controlled, are tak

TURBO-GENERATORS FOR AUXILIARY POWER

Fig. 36. Three of seven geared turbo-generators, each of 1,300 kW, 5,000–6,000 r.p.m., 225 v supplying auxiliary power in the *Queen Mary*. These power sets are used for lighting and drivin kinds of auxiliary electrical gear from desk fans to compressors, boat hoists, capstans and winc

VERTICAL SHAFT MOTORS

. 37. Some of the eight 285 h.p. vertical motors driving circulating pumps in a celebrated liner. ese motors of special design directed to a particular purpose serve to illustrate the great adapt-lity of electrical apparatus, and it is this factor which makes it so useful in marine application.

supply section boxes and distribution ıeboxes. More usually the generator oles are brought to a central switch-ard and feeders radiate therefrom on ite orthodox lines. Section and dis-bution boxes are invariably of water-ht construction and this feature extends the final lighting points and switches in posed positions. Vulcanised rubber ulated, lead-covered wire is used for distribution runs, and, indeed, also en for main cables. Special sealing nds are employed wherever cables pass ough watertight bulkheads, and metal ıders are fitted to protect the cables ıd glands) near the decks. Both sides of e circuit are insulated, i.e., the ship's me is not used for the return, except in ry unimportant installations.

The arrangement of auxiliary genera-rs direct-driven by the main propulsion ime-movers, as in the case of the *Brunswick* previously mentioned, makes for economy and appears to be satisfactory when D.C. is employed and when several prime-movers are available. It is not suitable when the propulsion system is A.C. and the ship speed is varied by the speed of the prime-mover in the conventional way. Proposals have, however, been made to use an auxiliary generator on the shaft of the main prime-mover during periods of steady steaming and to change over the auxiliary load to a separate set when manœuvring is in prospect and in harbour. There are also difficulties in the employment of A.C. for ship's auxiliary loads, mainly because of the necessity of synchronising; and the advantages of A.C. are not great because of the compact nature of a ship's electrical system, which does not offer scope for saving by the introduction of high voltage and transformers. Moreover, D.C. permits convenient speed control by familiar methods; similar characteristics could be achieved by A.C. commutator machines, but they would be new to nearly all the personnel affected.

A few ships have been equipped with constant-current D.C. systems for special purposes, notably for winch operation. The Austin system employs a motor-generator, the generator of which has a series excitation circuit compensated to maintain a constant current in the main external circuit, the volts rising with the load. Motors have small exciters and are short-circuited when not running. They can give a torque to hold a load at standstill and will regenerate if driven against the torque setting, all without rheostatic losses except for those in the exciter field controller. The unfamiliarity and non-standard nature of the equipment appears to be the main disadvantage of constant current systems on board ship although it has positive operational advantages.

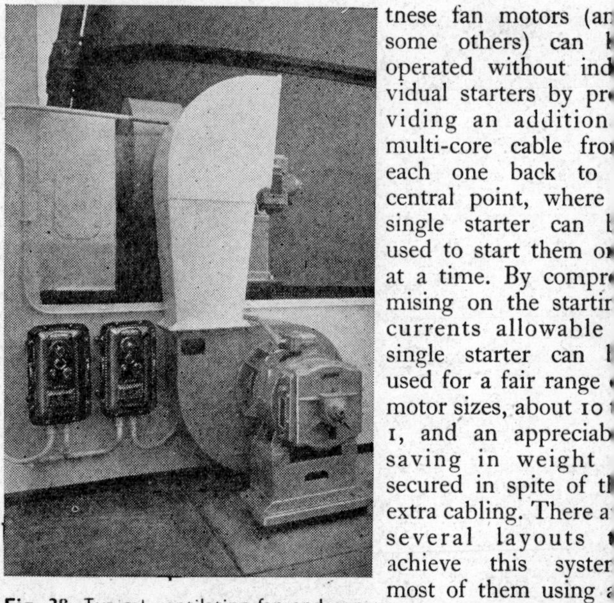

Fig. 38. Typical ventilating fan and control gear on the upper deck of a liner. Its operation is described in the text.

VENTILATION

Ventilation provides a big proportion of the load in many ships. The units (see Fig. 38) generally blow fresh air from the top deck through ducting so arranged as to interfere as little as possible with the watertight divisions of the ship, the ducting dividing up below decks so as to supply several compartments within the same watertight section from each fan. It is often arranged that if, with one or two auxiliary generators running, the load becomes just more than they can handle, some ventilating circuits are automatically tripped until another generator is started up and paralleled. Moreover, many of tnese fan motors (ar some others) can b operated without indi vidual starters by pro viding an addition multi-core cable fro each one back to central point, where single starter can b used to start them o at a time. By compro mising on the startir currents allowable single starter can b used for a fair range motor sizes, about 10 1, and an appreciab saving in weight secured in spite of th extra cabling. There a several layouts achieve this syster most of them using automatic starter wi central and local pus buttons for starting ar stopping, and provision is made to avo complications from the simultaneous u of two or more local pushes. Althou apparently complicated the syste operates quite simply and satisfactoril

CAPSTANS, STEERING GEAR, ET

Electric capstans for raising ancho such as the one that is illustrated in Fi 39, and warping winches are importa auxiliaries which may require quite lar motors in spite of their relatively slo speed of operation. They are frequent contactor operated and require libera rated controllers. Big liners that u warping cables to aid their movemen alongside landing jetties sometimes ha variable-voltage control through moto generators for this service, in order avoid the considerable rheostatic loss that might otherwise be incurred by the operation for relatively long periods low speeds.

The same system is also employed some ships for the supply of electrici to steering-gear motors (Fig. 40), b quite often normal shunt or compoun

ELECTRICAL STEERING GEAR

Fig. 40. Two 120 h.p. motors driving steering gear of modern liner. Quite often normal shunt and compound motors are used. An electric tell-tale on the bridge indicates the exact rudder position.

ound motors are used or this purpose, the udder head being hen actually moved y hydraulic pressure upplied by variable-troke pumps driven y them; in the latter ayout the motor runs onstantly, with the umps giving no de-very except when the udder position is equired to be altered. n electrical tell-tale n the bridge is usually rovided to show the xact position of the udder head; this ometimes takes the orm of a voltmeter egistering by virtue of ne position of a con-act mechanically oved on a potentio-neter resistance close the head, or a Wheatstone-bridge circuit ay be employed. Sometimes such electric eering equipments are held in reserve, e old-fashioned steam steering engine eing normally used and the electric or ectro-hydraulic plant being coupled up through dog clutches only if required. The amount of power demanded depends largely of the speed with which the rudder is required to be operated with the ship under way; where only 5 or 10 h.p. may be necessary in normal steering changes, an emergency "hard over" operation at speed may call for ten times that amount in a large ship.

WARPING GEAR

ig. 39. The anchor and warping gear motors of the *Queen Mary* e supplied by motor-generators to give variable-voltage control.

Electric cargo winches (Fig. 41) are still in fierce competition with steam winches, for the latter are very familiar to crews and can give excellent and fast service. The development of specialised motors and controllers by certain enterprising electrical manufacturers has, however, made the electric winch almost equally flexible, and it is accepted as more convenient in many steam-driven vessels, since it

MOTOR-DRIVEN WINCHES

Fig. 41. Winch deck of the *Strathallon*, showing several motor-driven winches, each of which has own self-contained controller. Electric winches are practically standard in Diesel-driven shi

does not require long steam and exhaust mains. In Diesel-driven ships electric cargo winches are almost standard practice, for not only have they the advantages already mentioned but also their use may avoid the necessity of providing and operating a donkey boiler solely for cargo handling.

NAVIGATION AND SAFETY AIDS

Navigating lights at masthead, port and starboard are generally electric, wired in series with tell-tales on the bridge and preferably duplicated. A separate feeder from the main switchboard supplies the wireless room. The "Fathometer" is an ingenious electrical instrument for the bridge which enables the depth of water below the ship to be observed. Usually, watertight doors through watertight bulkheads can be electrically operated fro the bridge, where pilot lamps sho whether they are open or closed. In ord to avoid the use of long main wiring f each such equipment to and from t bridge, relays are usually employed, a the actual closing and opening motor automatic in operation once its contr circuit is energised. Limit switches a used to stop the motor in the extren positions of the door, and sometim friction clutches are interposed. T starting torque of a heavy door may very high and in at least one system t motor runs up to speed before it clutched to the driving mechanism, whi is arranged to deliver almost a hamm blow to start the motion.

Passenger vessels carry emergen generating sets—usually petrol or Diesel

ELECTRIC COMPRESSOR PLANT

Fig. 42. Motor-driven compressors in the *Tegelberg*, each rated at 90 h.p. Besides being used for central ventilating systems air-compression is employed for many purposes in a ship, including the blowing out of tanks in oil tankers. Paint spraying with compressed air has enabled two men to paint the hull of a ship in 40 hours as against six men working for 136 hours with ordinary tools.

located above the water line and usually operated automatically in conjunction with a battery, if the main supply fails, to feed a system of "panic" lights with wiring completely separate from the normal supplies. There are always separate circuits for police lighting, with key switches to prevent unauthorised operation.

Low-voltage systems for telephone operation, bells, signals and so forth, follow normal stationary practice except for the watertight enclosure of all apparatus as far as possible. Loud-speaking telephones are used freely in noisy situations and large liners have either a considerable manual exchange or one of the well-known automatic systems.

Electric lifts are frequently provided in big ships and a few even have escalators. The electrical and mechanical details hardly differ from land practice apart from the use of lead-covered wiring and enclosed motors, with perhaps some extra guides to facilitate operation when the ship may be listing or otherwise moving in bad weather.

Fire pumps and sanitary pumps throughout big ships are frequently electrically driven and usually of the centrifugal type with direct-coupled high-speed motors.

"HOTEL" SERVICES

Mention has already been made of several amenities beyond electric lighting common in passenger liners. The lighting is often elaborate in character, with fittings and layouts to accord with the architectural features of the public rooms. In cabins, also, advanced examples of lighting equipments are frequently employed, and electric fires and fans are usual, apart from any central ventilation (Fig. 42) and heating equipment. For the service of the passengers, electric galleys of considerable size and loading are commonplace, with all the ordinary electric appliances found in modern restaurant practice. Local pantry refrigerators—quite apart from any cargo hold refrigerating plants—are provided and most of this equipment is precisely similar to normal land types.

Searchlights are supplied through motor-generators, sometimes with vertical shafts in order to conserve space; their generators are so compounded as to give a stable characteristic suitable for the arc, and the carbons of the latter are often controlled and fed automatically.

Where flexible leads are required on board ship, phosphor-bronze wire-woven armouring is frequently provided in order to give mechanical protection without reducing flexibility too much, and the plug and socket connectors are invariably of watertight design for deck use, with a screw seal-cover over the socket when no plug is in place. Distribution boxes on and near top decks of liners and warships are usually provided with numerous spare ways and socket outlets to accommodate temporary supplies for illumination displays and gala lighting, as well as for more utilitarian purposes such as moveable lamp clusters for cargo handling.

Other miscellaneous applications of electricity found in the larger ships include ozonisers and medical equipment, cinema and stage apparatus of all kinds, public address systems, synchronised clock circuits, workshop machine-tool drives and, in fact, examples of most familiar stationary uses; in every case the principal modifications of standard apparatus to make it suitable for marine use are precautions against water, excessive heat and humidity, and a measure of additional robustness to enable it to withstand the special conditions of marine use.

ELECTRIC TRACTION

RAILWAY electrification is an extremely costly business, and certain well-defined conditions are essential if the turning over of any given route from steam to electrical operation is to be a paying proposition. These conditions, in brief, are:—(1) very dense traffic, (2) heavy gradients, and (3) readily available and cheap sources of electric power, or (4) a combination of any two or all of these factors. In the case of dense passenger traffic, with frequent stops, electric motors, which may be distributed through the length of a train, offer more rapid acceleration from rest than steam locomotives; this makes it possible to crowd more trains on to any given line, with shorter intervals between them than steam trains, and so to offer a service that is both faster and more frequent. This is why busy suburban routes round large cities are generally among the first to be selected for electrification; and seldom, if ever, has such electrification failed to attract additional traffic. One could hardly have a better illustration of this than is given by the Southern Railway, which has the biggest suburban electrified system in the world, and has almost suffered embarrassment in handling the enormous numbers of Londoners who have migrated to districts well into the outer suburbs, largely owing to the attraction of the electric services. Busy main routes benefit equally by electrification, which may so increase the capacity of existing tracks as to render doubling and quadrupling of tracks unnecessary when increasing traffic has to be carried, and so in the end prove the less costly of two alternatives. The most remarkable example in this category is probably the 225-mile main line of the Pennsylvania Railroad in the United States, between New York, Philadelphia, Baltimore, and Washington, which is the busiest route of its kind in the world.

In operating over steep gradients electricity offers many advantages, especially where heavy freight traffic is

USE OF WATER POWER

Fig. 43. The Great Barberine Dam, Swiss Federal Railways. The dam is 935 feet long and 256 feet high at the centre, and cost £800,000. The wall is 196 feet thick at the base and the dam contains 269,000 cubic yards of masonry. The cost of the pipelines and one power station was £1,200,000.

being handled. Electric locomotives have been developed for such work with power ratings of from 7,000 to 12,000 h.p., under the control of a single crew which, as compared with the use of two or three steam locomotives, makes it possible to effect considerable economies in working. It is this consideration that has influenced the London & North Eastern Railway in its decision to electrify the 41-mile route through the Pennines from Sheffield to Manchester, which goes over an altitude of 966 ft., and over which a very heavy traffic, particularly in coal, is worked daily. A particularly important factor here is the 3-mile Woodhead Tunnel, at the summit of the line; this is on a rising gradient, and eastbound steam-worked freight trains need 10 minutes to clear it, so that a service of five or six trains an hour is the utmost that can be worked in this direction with steam. Electrification will roughly halve the tunnel transit time and nearly double the line capacity. It will also cheapen and expedite the working up the long and steep approach gradients from both Sheffield and Manchester to the tunnel. Also in mountainous regions, where severe gradients are inevitable, Nature generally compensates the railways by offering abundant resources of cheap power, in the water that rushes down the valleys from the higher altitudes, especially when the neighbouring mountains have permanent coverings of snow and ice. The many railways now electrified on the mainland of Europe are in almost all cases thus operated by hydro-electric power derived from mountain torrents in the Alps and elsewhere. The principal expense in hydro-electric generation is usually the damming up of the mountain torrent used as a water supply, in order to ensure an ample and continuous flow of water to the power-station, winter and summer alike; some of these dams have been extremely costly, such as the Barberine Dam in the south of Switzerland (see Fig. 43), 256 ft. high and 935 ft. long, which alone cost the Swiss Federal Railways £800,000, or with the pipelines and the Chatelard power-station a total of £2,000,000; the Vernayaz railway power-station, a short distance away in the Rhone Valley, cost another £1,400,000.

In countries with ample water power but no indigenous coal supply railway electrification has flourished to the maximum degree. In Switzerland, out of the 1,807 route miles of the Swiss Federal system, 1,361 miles have now been electrified, and 94 per cent. of the traffic is now electrically worked; in addition, the great majority of the privately-owned railways in the country are electrified.

In Italy, though the percentage of lines operated by electricity is not, as yet, as high as in Switzerland, the total electrified route mileage is now 3,370, a greater figure than in any other country in the world, even the United States. It is possible to travel from Modane on the French frontier, Domodossola and Chiasso on the Swiss frontier, or the Brenner Pass on the German frontier, southwards through Italy to Reggio on the Straits of Messina, with electric locomotives throughout. The connecting lines in France, Switzerland, and Germany are all also electrified; indeed, electric traction now obtains throughout from Saalfeld in Germany, through Nuremberg and Munich to the Brenner, and from there onwards to Reggio, a total distance of 1,268 miles. Sweden, however, holds the world's record for continuous railway electrification, which now extends over the 1,376 miles from Narvik, in Norway, to Trälleborg in the extreme south of Scandinavia; 1,349 miles of this distance is on Swedish soil. The value in war-time of the change from steam to electricity needs no stress; it was the complete cutting-off of coal supplies to Switzerland in the latter part of the 1914–1918 war that hastened the electrification of that country's lines, and similar conditions have undoubtedly spurred on the electrifying of Italian main lines, which previously were dependent on imported coal for their steam locomotives.

ELECTRICITY VERSUS STEAM

The electric locomotive has one material advantage over the steam locomotive in that it can, if necessary, give almost 100 per cent. service throughout the day, whereas the steam locomotive requires intervals between its runs for attention to the firebox and various other details. Further, by centralising at a power-station all the power necessary to move the trains, a much higher efficiency is possible with electric than with steam working, and this is true whether the electricity is produced by steam or water power. The steam locomotive is a self-contained power-station on wheels, drastically limited in its size by the tunnels and bridges through which it has to pass, and in its weight by the strength of the underline bridges and of the track. The fixed power plant, on the other hand, is hampered by no such restrictions; it may consist of very large water-tube boilers, mechanically fired, high-speed turbines, and condensers which reduce the back pressure to well below atmospheric pressure, thus greatly increasing the proportion of energy in the steam that can be turned into useful work.

Attempts have been made to mount the power plants on wheels, complete with steam boilers, turbines, condensers, and dynamos producing the current that has been used for propulsion; but space and weight limitations have been too severe, and none of these experiments has proved successful. On the other hand, electric power plants driven by Diesel engines are coming more and more into use, especially in high speed streamline trains.

The idea was first popularised by the German State Railways with the two-car "Flying Hamburger" in 1933, and was later developed by them extensively for inter-city high-speed transport, but not

SOUTHERN RAILWAY ELECTRIC LOCOMOTIVE AT WORK

Fig. 44. Multiple-unit operation over the electrified lines of a railway is entirely with passenger trains, and over such routes freight trains have been operated by steam locomotives. The modern electric locomotive illustrated was designed for the Southern Railway for both passenger and freight service which is the normal practice on all lines using independent electric locomotives.

in greater than three-car units, certain of which were operated in pairs with multiple-unit control. The same principle has since been developed on a far greater scale in the United States. Here every variation in Diesel-electric haulage can be found from single self-contained cars to trains of 14 to 18 streamline cars, hauled by 420-ton triple-car Diesel-electric units, each carried on 36 wheels, 210 ft. in length, and fitted with Diesel engines which develop a total of 6,000 h.p. for traction and 1,800 h.p. for auxiliaries, or 7,800 h.p. in all. The Diesel engines are directly coupled to dynamo sets, and the power thus generated is used through electric motors for propulsion. Of all the journeys made by these trains, the most spectacular are between Chicago and the Pacific Coast, with continuous runs of 2,260 to 2,299 miles completed in 39¾ hours without change of engine, and the 1,000-mile stretch across the prairies taken at an average of 70 to 75 m.p.h. throughout, including stops. On a test run one of these trains—the "Denver Zephyr" of the Chicago, Burlington & Quincy Railroad—ran the 1,017 miles between Chicago and Denver non-stop in 12 hours, 12½ minutes, at an average of 83·3 m.p.h. throughout, a feat that would probably have been impossible with a steam locomotive.

D.C. ELECTRIFICATION

In railway electrification in different parts of the world, there has been considerable difference of opinion as to whether direct or alternating current should be used, and also as to the ideal current and voltage characteristics. For dense train services, maximum reliability and minimum costs of maintenance, direct current is the more advantageous, and it is for this reason that most British electrification, including in particular that of the Southern Railway and the London Passenger Transport Board, has been direct current at 600 to 650 volts. In direct current systems the equipment of the sub-stations at which the high-pressure alternating current is transformed into low-pressure direct current for feeding the line conductors is more complicated and costly than at stations in which the alternating current has merely to be reduced to the correct pressure for line use. In the latter case voltage transformers only are needed, though, of course, they may be large and require oil cooling; but for change from alternating to direct current rotary convertors or mercury arc rectifiers are essential. In other parts of the world direct current is used at voltages up to as much as 3,000, but with every increase in the pressure of the current the weight and cost of the motors, and the complexity of the control equipment, tend also to increase, so that such higher voltages are usually confined to lines with less frequent services and longer distances than with 600–650-volt installations. The limited size of the motors required in the latter case makes it practicable to instal motors at various points along the length of a suburban train, all under the control of the one motorman's cabin, and this in its turn makes possible the economical method of working which is known as multiple-unit, which actually proportions the motive power to the load to be moved. Most of the suburban electric working round London is conducted with three-car units, each unit having two motor-cars and a central trailer; at rush hours two units are coupled, making six coaches with four sets of motors, and on exceptionally busy routes, a couple of additional trailer cars may be marshalled between the two three-car trains, making eight cars in all.

ALTERNATING CURRENT SYSTEMS

The major part of the world's electrified railway mileage, especially on the long-distance routes, is equipped for the use of alternating current. In the United States the pressure most favoured, as, for example, in the great Pennsylvania electrification, is 11,000 volts, but in Europe 15,000 volts is the common figure, as in Switzerland and Germany, though Sweden has a preference for 16,000 volts. These are the line voltages, the main transmissions from the power-stations being usually at 66,000 or 132,000 volts. The main line systems mostly use single-phase current at $16\frac{2}{3}$ cycles, the chief exception being Italy, which electrified 990 miles of its line on a 3-phase alternating current system, at 3,700 volts, and

ELECTRICALLY HAULED EXPRESS TRAIN

Fig. 45. Pennsylvania Railroad train using overhead electrification at 11,000 volts A.C. The "GG-1" streamlined locomotive shown is the 2-C-C-2 type, weighs 213 tons, has a normal continuous rating of 4,620 h.p. and is geared for a maximum speed of 100 m.p.h. Its route is the busiest one in the world.

FOURTH RAIL EQUIPMENT

Fig. 46. Junctions at Acton Town (London Passenger Transport Board) well illustrate the complications caused by fourth-rail equipment in the arrangement of switches and crossings in the track.

then in later conversions adopted direct current at 3,000 volts. This means, of course, a change of locomotive at all points where the two different systems join one another, and another disadvantage of the 3-phase method is that all the overhead line conductor equipment must be duplicated, which entails very complicated wiring at junctions. With such high line voltages as 10,000 to 16,000, comparatively little copper is needed in the distributing circuits, and this tends to cheapen initial costs, but in all alternating current systems the locomotives must be equipped with transformers, and they become considerably heavier and more bulky vehicles in consequence. Where high pressure alternating current is used, independent electric locomotives are the general practice also.

CURRENT CONDUCTORS

There are two methods of picking up current—from conductor rails at the side (Fig. 44) or in the centre of the track, or from overhead wire conductors (Fig. 45). Third-rail electrification is used only in connection with direct current, and the main cost of the lineside equipment is concentrated in the weight of steel in the conductor rails themselves. These are rolled from what is known as "conductivity steel", which is practically pure iron, and opposes less resistance to the flow of current than an ordinary mild steel; also the greater the cross-section of the conductor rail, so much lower the resistance; this leads to the use of conductor rails of 100 to 150 lb. weight per yard, which is greater than the weight of the track rails themselves. In third-rail systems the current is returned to the power-station through the track running rails, as on the Southern Railway, but resistance is reduced still further when a fourth rail is used for current return; as on lines of the London Passenger Transport Board (see Fig. 46). The positive or conductor rail is laid outside the track, and the negative or return rail in the centre. Again the advantage of third-rail and fourth-rail systems is maximum reliability and minimum maintenance costs, but both methods entail complicated bonding and insulation through switches and crossings in station yards and at junctions, as well as the necessity for locomotives and trains to carry more than one set of conductor shoes, spaced well apart, in order to bridge the maximum gap caused by breaks in the continuity of the conductors. There is also, in winter, especially in countries with heavy annual snowfall, the disadvantage that the conductor rails easily become covered with snow, causing short-circuits, and even in this country the icing of conductors in consequence of rain which freezes as it falls has, at various times, caused severe interruption of traffic on electrified lines in the open. In single-phase alternating current systems, return of current is always by the running rails, which require, of course, to be earthed.

DIRECT CURRENT MOTORS

The sub-stations feed the current to the conductors in sections. In each section the conductors are always at line voltage when the power-station and the particular sub-station concerned are in operation, but current is not actually flowing until a train enters the section, completing the circuit through its controllers and motors. At any given time a number of trains may be in motion in the section at one time, taking power from the conductors in parallel, like the electric lamps off the mains supply in a house. Only a certain proportion of the many different types of electric motor are suitable for railway use; the type employed must be capable of exerting a maximum turning moment on starting, but one in which speed of rotation automatically decreases as the flow of current increases, as otherwise the motors would overload themselves at times of maximum demand, by trying, say, to take their trains at excessively high speeds uphill. Direct current motors probably meet these conditions in the simplest and most effective way. They are always arranged in pairs, in order to give two main running speeds—half speed when they are connected in series by the controller, and full speed when they are in parallel. They have the advantage, also, of being more compact than alternating current equipment of the same power output; in all the latest London Passenger Transport Board electric stock, for example, the entire electrical equipment is arranged underneath the floors of the cars, so that the whole of the body of a motor-coach,

LONDON TRANSPORT ELECTRIC MOTOR-COACH

Fig. 47. At the leading end is seen the automatic coupler, destination indicator, roster number of the train for the day and four headlamps for route-indicating. Current is collected by brushes attached to the bogie frames. Note the small space occupied by the driver's compartment.

MODERN TUBE CAR

Fig. 48. Interior of a London Transport modern tube car. Entry is through three pairs of double doors, pneumatically operated on either side; the wide gangways are to facilitate the movement of passengers. On the roof on the extreme right is seen the route diagram for passengers' information.

apart from a small driving compartment, is available for seating (see Figs. 47 and 48). Direct current motors also have the advantage of being comparatively cheap and of maximum efficiency.

SOUTHERN RAILWAY CONTROL METHODS

On the Southern Railway control of all the motors in a multiple-unit train is effected very ingeniously. When the driver moves the handle of his master-controller to the first running position, the motors automatically accelerate at a fixed rate. On starting, each pair of motors is in series, so that each motor receives only half the line voltage. In order that there may be no excessive rush of current, resistances are inserted in series with each motor, and are cut out step by step as the speed increases to the maximum possible with series working; then the resistances are reinserted, and each pair of motors is changed over from series to parallel working, the resistances again being cut out step by step until full speed is attained. Through the master-controller only a small auxiliary current is passed, operating a series of contactors underneath the motor-coach, which make and break the main current as each stage of acceleration is passed through. The contactors are operated by electric or pneumatic power. With automatic control, the acceleration is governed by a limit switch, which automatically operates the next contactor as soon as the motor current has dropped to a certain predetermined value. It is this automatic control that makes for such precision in acceleration, and so makes possible the exact timing and systematic working which are characteristic of an electrified suburban passenger train service. In cer-

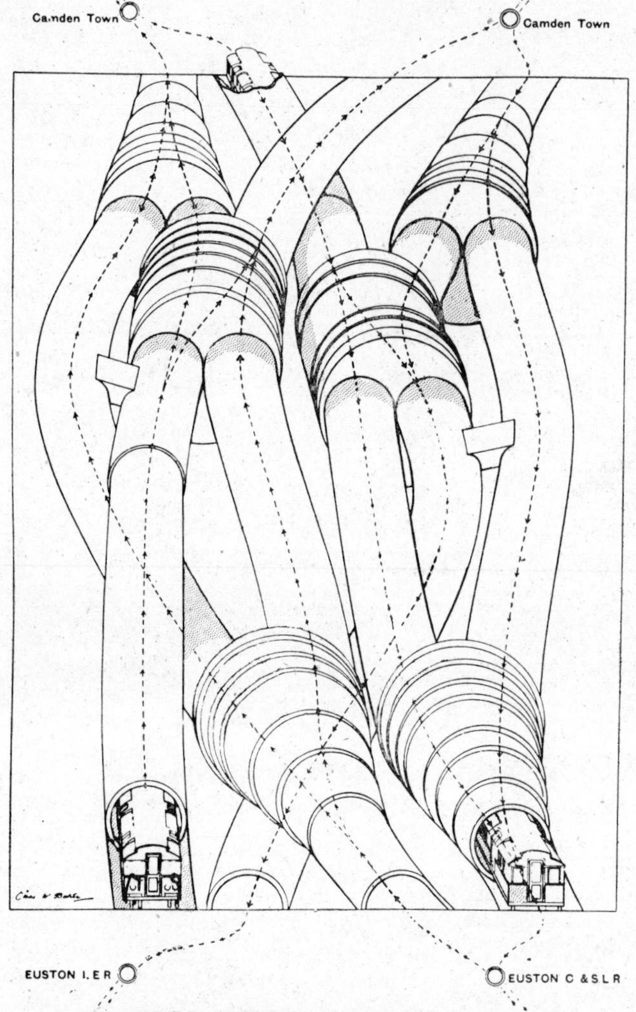

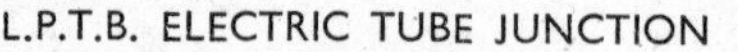
L.P.T.B. ELECTRIC TUBE JUNCTION

Fig. 49. Arrows show that with this system no train in any direction needs to cross the paths of trains travelling in other directions.

tain cases, these have been even further facilitated by the adoption of the "fly-over" system at tube junctions. London's most notable example of this plan is seen in Fig. 49.

METADYNE CONTROL

In recent years the London Passenger Transport Board has brought into operation a new method of control with direct current which is known as the metadyne. The metadyne unit gives any desired speed-torque characteristic from starting up to full speed, relatively to the characteristics of the traction motors, and takes the place of the starting resistances, accelerating relays, switches, groups of cams, and other equipment normally used. Not only so, but it provides for regenerative braking; that is to say, the resistance necessary to bring the train to a stop is provided by a reversal of the action of the motors, whereby they both reduce the train speed and at the same time produce current and feed it back to the conductors. The metadyne unit consists of three machines of commutator type all mounted on one shaft. The first is the regulator, which starts the machine and keeps it running at a fixed speed; in its simplest form this is a shunt machine. The second is the metadyne proper, which consists of an ordinary armature with its commutator, operating in a field system; without going into abstruse technicalities, it is sufficient to say that the metadyne acts as a convertor, automatically giving a positive or negative boost to the back electro-motive force of the traction motors in order to balance the line voltage. The third machine is the exciter, which provides excitation for the metadyne "variator winding", and for the fields of the traction motors. The metadyne regenerative braking is not sufficient alone to give the high retardation force necessary, and so is supplemented by electro-pneumatic braking of the Westinghouse type, which also provides a stand-by in the event of any failure of the electrical apparatus.

Another emergency provision is made in the design of the handle of the master-controller in the driver's cabin. In the centre of this there is a button, pressing against a weak spring, which is normally kept depressed by the palm of the driver's hand; but in the event of the driver being overtaken by sudden illness or fatal seizure, so that his hand leaves the controller, the button rises, all current supply to the motors is cut off, and the brakes on the train are automatically applied. This precaution is general in all motor-coaches and electric locomotives on railways, owing to the danger of an electric train being in uncontrolled motion; it is generally known by the sinister name of "dead man's handle". Yet another possible failure of the human element is guarded against on all busy suburban routes by trip gear connected with the signals; should a signal be passed at danger, an upstanding trip lever strikes an interceptor on the track, also automatically cutting off the current and applying the brakes. Such precautions are essential on the busiest suburban routes, where trains may be running at intervals of 1½ minutes or even less. In addition, such frequency of service would be impossible without elaborate systems of electrical signalling and point operation. The interlocking of these, which is essential for the safe operation of busy lines, is facilitated by the use of electricity. Signal lamps of special design, distant-controlled fog signals, audio and visual cab signals are other modern developments in electric train working.

ELECTRIC SERVICE SPEEDS

A few notes on the speed of electric services may fittingly conclude this section. On the London tubes, with very short distances between stations, speeds seldom exceed 35 to 40 m.p.h., but on the longer sections in the open 50 m.p.h. is common. The Southern Railway suburban electric trains frequently reach 60 m.p.h., and the main line trains on the coastal services commonly attain maxima up to 75 m.p.h. The Pennsylvania Railroad of America has the fastest electric service in the world, of which in 1942 the trains every day were making a total of 301 runs timed at 60 m.p.h. or over from start to stop, with a total mileage of 13, 058, and 83 runs totalling 4,676 miles, timed at 66 m.p.h. and over from start to stop; such schedules entail normal running speeds of 70 to 85 m.p.h. The fastest run ever yet made on rails was achieved by a three-car high-speed streamlined unit of the Italian State Railways, which on July 20th, 1939, covered the 195·8 miles from Florence to Milan, on an experimental run, in 115·2 minutes; this works out at an average for the entire distance of 102·0 m.p.h. The highest speed reached on the journey was 126 m.p.h. This was on one of the Italian main lines operating on a 3,000 volts D.C. supply, and using a system of overhead conductors to pick up the current similar to that shown in Fig. 45.

ELECTRICITY IN MEDICINE

Electricity can be of service to the doctor or surgeon in two ways: by its direct application to the body to cure disease or alleviate pain, and by its indirect help in diagnosing disease through the many electronic devices which have been invented for the purpose.

The effects of electric shock are well known to anyone who has worked with electricity, but, provided that the strength of the shock is carefully controlled, its effects can be turned to good use in stimulating wasted or paralysed muscles into action. Various forms of shocking coil are used for this form of medical application, and the later forms of shock apparatus are able to administer a wide range of strengths and frequencies. The use of direct current for stimulating the

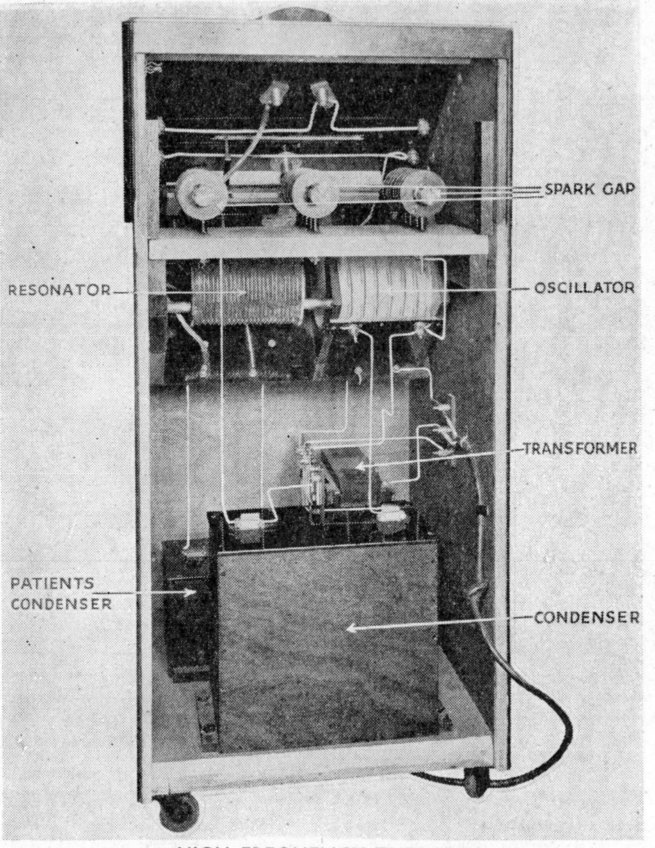

HIGH FREQUENCY THERAPY

Fig. 50. Interior view of a spark oscillator which is used for high frequency therapy. The various components are clearly marked and the complete apparatus in this case was manufactured by Stanley Cox, Ltd.

tissues is limited as it tends to damage them by polarization if it is too strong. Alternating current of mains frequency also has an irritating effect on the nervous tissue, but if its frequency is raised to a value comparable with that used in radio engineering practice it is possible to apply currents of considerable strength to the body without risk of damage to the tissues.

It was found that a high frequency current could produce local heating of the tissues to relieve pain and inflammation if it were applied by suitable electrodes placed on either side of the affected part. The body tissue acts as a capacity and part of the energy applied is converted into heat in th tissue. The word "diathermy" ha been applied to thi form of electrica treatment, meanin "heating through" and diathermy ap paratus now form part of the equip ment of all hospitals

DIATHERMY

Diathermy appar atus is designed and built on similar line to that of a radi transmitter, th main difference be ing that the energy has to be applied to a small area instead o being radiated fron an aerial. One of th difficulties, in fact in the design of dia thermy circuits is t prevent unwante radiation whicl reduces the efficiency and causes interfer ence with local radi receivers.

Early forms of os cillator were of the spark type, similar t the first radio trans- mitters, and operated on a wavelength o about 200 metres. These, such as the type shown in Fig. 50, are still used successfully for certain forms of treat- ment, but it was later found that a different effect could be produced by increasing the frequency of the applied current, and valve oscillators giving a frequency of 50 megacycles/sec. are now used in many cases. The energy from such an oscillator can be applied to the patient either by electrodes placed near the body, but insulated from it, or by winding a coil round the limb. The electrode is shown in Fig. 52 and consists of a metal plate enclosed in an insulating

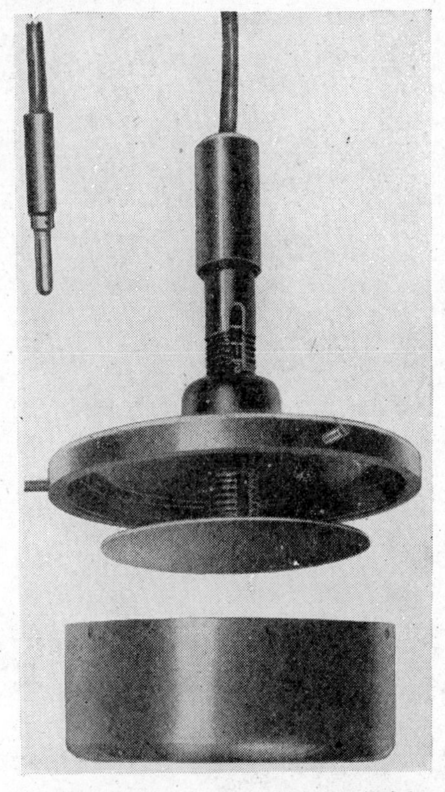

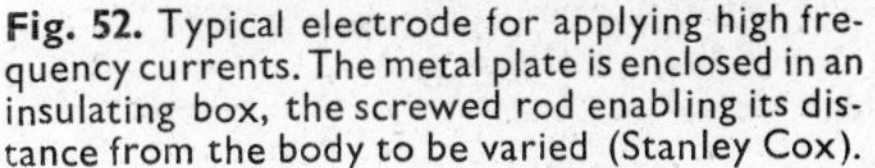

Fig. 52. Typical electrode for applying high frequency currents. The metal plate is enclosed in an insulating box, the screwed rod enabling its distance from the body to be varied (Stanley Cox).

box which can be adjusted to bring it nearer or further away from the patient.

Fig. 53 shows how the energy can be applied by winding a few turns of flexible cable round the limb, the coil forming part of the oscillatory circuit and inducing a current in the tissues.

The circuit of a typical diathermy oscillator is shown in Fig. 51. This gives an output of 300 watts at 50 megacycles/sec.

The valve is fed directly from the A.C. mains through a high voltage transformer, which saves the use of a rectifier and does not affect the efficiency of the circuit appreciably. The patient electrodes are coupled to the anode circuit of the valve by the coils L_1L_2, the coil L_2 being tuned by the condenser C_2 which is in parallel with the capacity of the patient and electrodes. Meters for controlling the output are inserted at various points in the circuit.

The output is varied by altering the tapping on the H.T. transformer or by lowering the temperature of the valve filament. The latter method is not always to be recommended owing to the risk of shortening the life of the valve if the filament is under-run.

The oscillator may also be used for cautery or bloodless cutting by using a thin platinum electrode as a knife. The cutting is actually accomplished by the aid of a small intensely hot spark which passes between the "knife" and the tissues, and this spark sears the tissue at the same time, preventing loss of blood from the capillary vessels.

It has recently been found that currents of mains frequency (50 cycles /sec.) have a remarkable stimulating effect on the human brain in the case of mental disorders, and many cases of improvement have been noted after treatment by this so-called Shock Therapy. The current is applied to the sides of the skull by means of

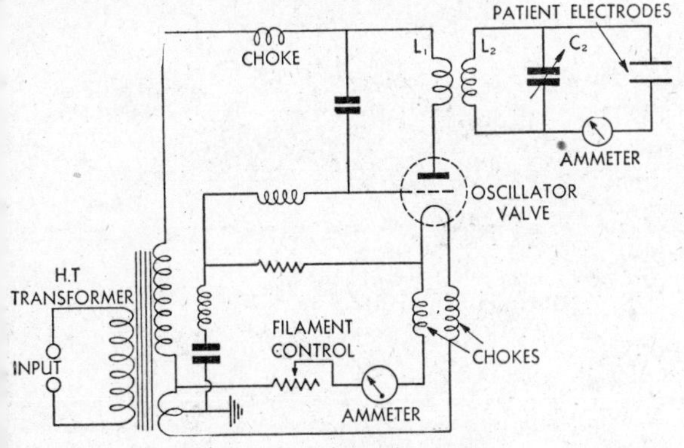

Fig. 51. Simplified circuit of single-valve high-frequency oscillator for diathermy, showing how the patient is coupled to the anode circuit of the valve by the H.F. transformer L_1 L_2.

moist pads and allowed to flow for only a fraction of a second, which corresponds to a few cycles. Owing to the attenuating effect of the bone and tissue overlying the brain the actual current passing through it is small, although the current in the external circuit may be as high as 0·5 ampere.

The principal successes of this form of treatment have been in the treatment of melancholia and schizophrenia ("split mind") and it may undergo more developments in the future. Needless to say, the application of electric current under such conditions must be made by skilled medical men owing to the risk of damage to the tissues.

X-RAYS

The most important application of electricity in the diagnosis of disease was in the discovery of X-rays, which enable the interior of the body to be examined in detail and even photographed on ciné film to show the various movements taking place. X-ray examination of patients is now almost a routine in many hospitals and the surgeon frequently operates with a shadow picture in front of him to guide his search for foreign bodies or tumours.

X-rays, or Röntgen rays, as they are sometimes called after the name of their discoverer, are electromagnetic radiation of very short wavelength—less than one tenth that of the shortest wavelength of light. The radiation is produced by allowing a stream of electrons at very high velocity to bombard a metal surface, known as the target, which is contained in an evacuated bulb. The electrons are produced from a heated cathode in a manner similar to that of the thermionic valve, and their high velocity is produced by applying a potential of several thousand volts between the cathode and the

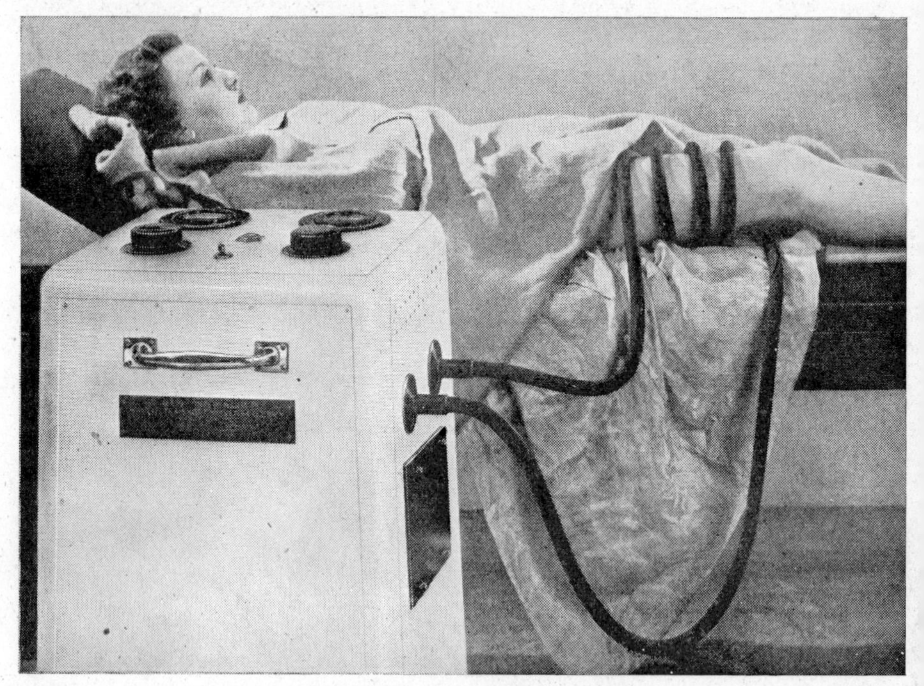

DIATHERMY APPARATUS IN USE

Fig. 53. Treatment by diathermy apparatus manufactured by Stanley Cox & Co., showing how energy is applied by means of a coil wrapped round the patient's limb. The coil of wire forms part of the anode circuit of a powerful high frequency oscillator similar to the one illustrated in Fig. 51.

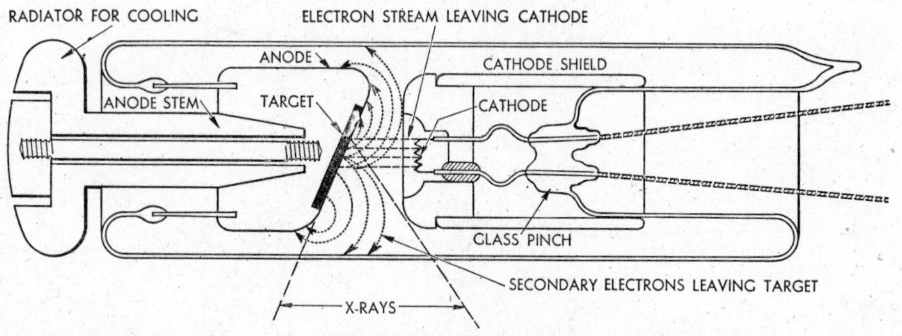

X-RAY TUBE IN SECTION

Fig. 54. Sectional diagram of an X-ray tube showing the electrodes and the path of the X-rays produced by impact of the electrons on the target. Radiation is, therefore, a result of the bombardment at high velocity of this metal target by the electrons which are emitted from the cathode.

anode, in the centre of which is the target. An outline drawing of an X-ray tube is shown in Fig. 54 the various parts being marked on the drawing.

According to their wavelength, X-rays will penetrate opaque substances to a varying degree, and if a beam of X-rays is passed through the body it will produce a shadow picture of the substance in its path. This shadow picture can either be viewed directly on a screen coated with a substance which fluoresces under X-rays (for example, barium platino-cyanide), or a photograph may be taken by exposing a plate to the action of the rays.

Fig. 55 shows a complete X-ray equipment employing an electrically operated camera for mass radiography of the chest. The patient stands on the platform facing the fluorescent screen which reproduces the X-rays in the form of a shadow image.

In addition to their penetrative power, X-rays have a powerful destructive action on certain tissues and can be used for curing certain growths. On the other hand they can be dangerous if the operator is not protected from their action when exposed to them for long periods. Lead is one of the metals which offers most resistance to the passage of the rays, and it is usual to wear lead-lined gloves and a lead apron when working with X-ray plant for any length of time.

Modern X-ray tubes are completely enclosed in metal, with a small window through which the radiation can pass, and the high voltage supply from the transformer is protected by metal-covered insulated cable. With these precautions the equipment is perfectly safe in the hands of a skilled operator.

ELECTRO-PHYSIOLOGY

Another valuable aid to the diagnosis of disease is by the use of electronic apparatus for measuring the electrical effects produced by muscular and nervous action in the body.

It has been known for many years that the movement of muscle is accompanied by the generation of electrical potentials and that electrical impulses are carried along the nerves to convey messages to the brain in a manner similar to that of a telegraph system.

The potentials produced by nerves and muscles are very small, of the order of 50-100 microvolts, and it is, therefore, necessary to amplify them in a similar manner to that used in radio circuits before they can be recorded. The investigation of the electrical efforts produced in living tissue is termed "electro-physiology" and this subject offers a wide and interesting field for research in devising more efficient methods of studying the behaviour of the body under all conditions.

An outstanding example of the use of electronic apparatus in diagnosis is in the cardiograph, the apparatus for recording the electrical impulses produced by the heart beat. The normal heart develops an

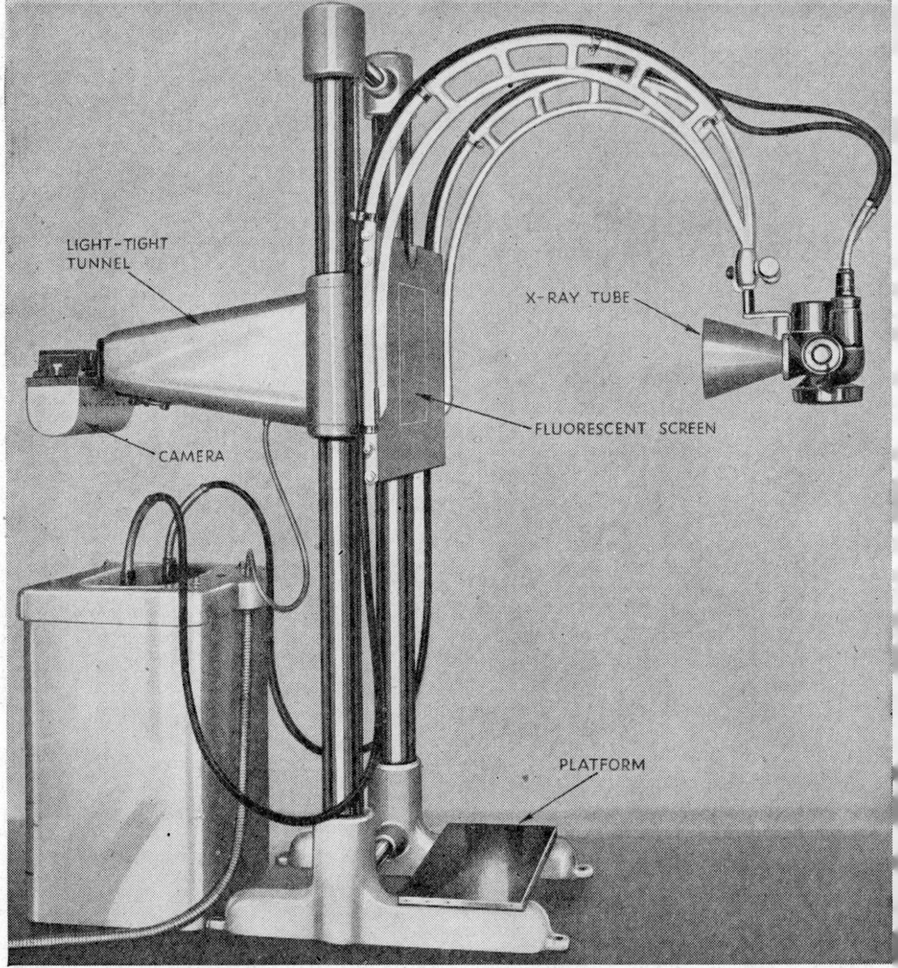

MODERN X-RAY EQUIPMENT

Fig. 55. The Pulmograph, a modern X-ray equipment designed for mass radiography of the chest. X-rays are projected through the patient onto the fluorescent screen in the form of a shadow image. The latter can be photographed by an electrically operated camera at the rate of approximately 200 images per hour. Thus it is possible to expeditiously to examine large numbers of patients.

electrical potential at each beat in the form of a complex wave. This wave is obtained by connecting a lead to each arm or leg of the patient and amplifying the small potential produced.

In a similar manner it is possible to pick up and record from the human brain potentials, the existence of which was first discovered by the German physiologist, Berger. Although the presence of these "brain waves" was known for some years, it is only recently that improved electronic amplifiers have enabled accurate records to be obtained.

The normal brain gives rise to electrical impulses which are lower in magnitude than those of the heart and which require a correspondingly higher degree of amplification. These impulses can be detected by means of pad electrodes placed on the scalp and, in a healthy adult, are approximately ten per second.

CHAPTER 9

TELEGRAPHY AND TELEPHONY

Electrical Communications. Telegraphy. Morse Telegraphy. Relays. Double Current Working. Machine Telegraphs. Teleprinters. Duplex Telegraphy. Telephony. Sound. Telephone. Microphone. Receiver. Circuits. Signalling or Ringing. Magneto Switchboard. Common Battery Systems. The Multiple. Automatic Telephony.

OF the five senses with which we are endowed, only three, i.e., touch, sight and hearing are of any use for communication and, of these three, only one, touch, is a direct method and is used to such a very limited extent that it may be disregarded. Both of the two remaining "communication senses" depend upon transmission of waves, light waves in one case and sound waves in the other. To extend the range at which communication could be carried out in former ages, such devices as signal lights, fires, drums and cannon were used. In the present age, electrical methods of transmitting signals are employed, either directly over wire circuits, as in the case of line telegraphy and telephony, or by means of electromagnetic waves through space, as in radio and television. In all these methods, however, it is clear that something is reproduced which is perceptible to the human ear or eye, and that electricity merely acts as a carrier for what is called "intelligence"; by that is meant not mental ability, but the essential ideas which are to be communicated by one means or another.

TELEGRAPHY

WHILE the semaphore is strictly a telegraph, this term is now generally restricted to electrical methods of transmitting messages letter by letter, or "still" pictures element by element. The huge modern industry which serves the needs of telecommunications may be said to have evolved from the electric telegraph. In its simplest form, this makes use of the Morse code, which is a system of signals whereby different combinations of "marks" separated by "spaces" are interpretable as letters and signs, with longer spaces between letters and still longer ones between words. The shortest signals in this code were chosen for the most frequently occurring letters, thus one dot for "E", in order to minimise the time required for transmission of messages. This question of the maximum speed of working must very necessarily be taken into account in all systems of telegraphy, in addition to that using the Morse code, since it is extremely important in considering their economic aspects.

SIMPLE MORSE TELEGRAPH

The basic apparatus for this would include a battery and key (which is simply a switch adapted for rapid manipulation), a wire or line and a sounder connected with a ground return. Closing and opening of the key, in accordance with the Morse code, transmits pulses of current which energise the sounder. This consists of two iron-cored electromagnets which, on the passage of current, pull down an armature against a stop, producing a characteristic sound. Since the armature is under the control of a restraining spring, it flies back when current ceases, strikes another stop, and gives a different sound for the end of the "dot" or "dash" of the Morse code. In this way, the different letters are read by ear.

In order to check the right value of current going out to the line at the sending end and being received at the distant end, galvanometers are placed at each end of the line. These give deflections about a central zero position, corresponding to the direction of current passing. The above circuit is fully described as a single-current direct sounder-worked system.

The term single-current implies that current flows during marks, and ceases during spaces. Fig. 1 shows the "X" station transmitting to the "Y" station. Note the positions of the keys.

An intermediate station may be operated on such a circuit, the line from the "X" station being connected to the common terminal of the sounder and battery, while the remaining connection goes from the centre of the key to the galvanometer and line.

TELEGRAPH RELAYS

Where a line is long, the conductor resistance is relatively high, so that the current is low in value. In wet weather, too, owing to leakage over the surface of insulators, the amount of current received over the line is further reduced, and may be insufficient to operate the sounders. As it is expensive and uneconomical to compensate for these effects by using more batteries to obtain an increased voltage, relays are used (Fig. 2). A relay is essentially a sensitive electromagnet, the armature of which is moved by the passage of current through its windings and makes or breaks an electrical connection in another circuit. Small received currents may, therefore, be used to operate

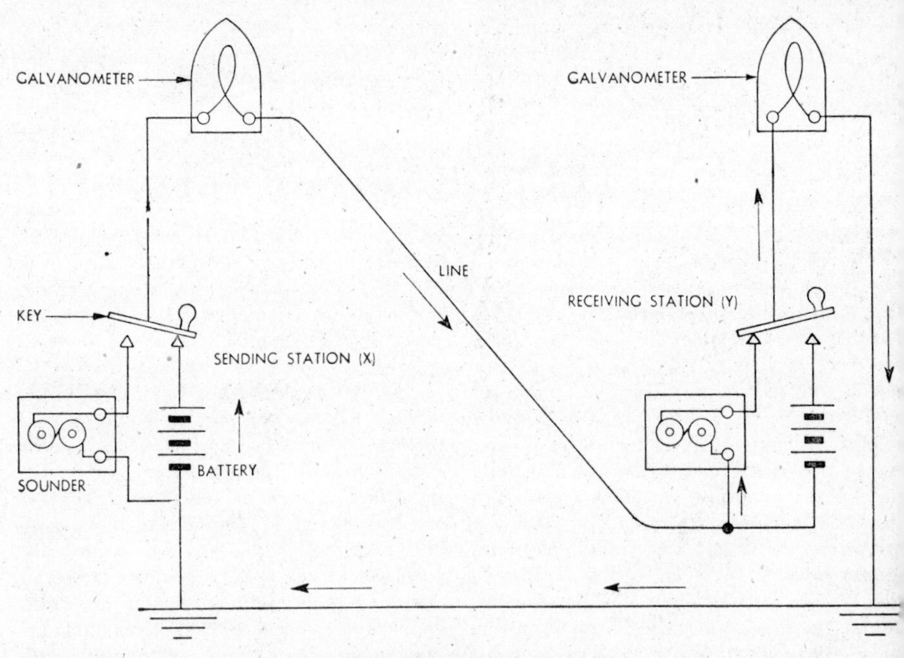

SIMPLEX TELEGRAPH CIRCUIT

Fig. 1. Current flows from battery at "X" over front contact of key through galvanometer and line to "Y". At "Y" current passes through sounder, back contact of key, galvanometer to ground and back to battery at "X". Since signals can be sent only in one direction at a time, the system is termed simplex as distinct from the term duplex which implies simultaneous two-way working.

ndirectly, sounders or ther mechanisms requiring much larger urrents.

To use a relay in the imple circuit shown n Fig. 1, the operating vinding would be conected in place of the ounder winding. The ounder would be conected in series with a ocal battery and the ontacts on the armaure of the relay, as hown in Fig. 2.

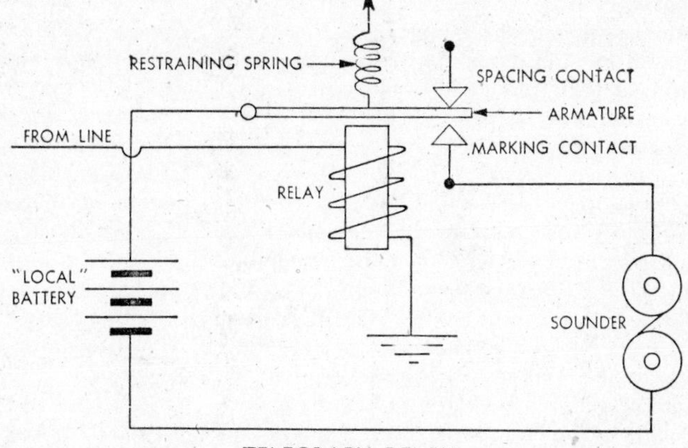

Fig. 2. Current from line passes to ground through relay winding, so pulling down armature and closing marking contact. Current then flows from local battery through sounder, operating it. End of marking impulse allows armature to be pulled to spacing position under the action of the spring thus breaking the local battery circuit.

The place of the relay nay be taken by a simiar device called a direct nker, where the armaure pulls down a ivoted arm, which noves a small inked wheel into contact vith a paper tape moved by mechanical neans. Lines are thus inked on the paper, he length corresponding to the time of ontact, which depends upon the duration f the signal, either a dot or a dash. The nker enables received messages to be tored and deciphered when convenient, nstead of being read at the time they are eceived. Inkers are employed also on ircuits where the Morse signals are ransmitted by high-speed mechanical neans, instead of by hand operation, and hus are too rapid to read by ear. The ngths of the inked signals can be djusted by the speed of the moving aper tape. In this manner very fast vorking is possible over a line or through wireless link.

DOUBLE CURRENT WORKING

This is a method of transmitting signals y reversing, instead of interrupting, the urrent during spacing periods. Since nes have capacitance to ground, the ondenser so formed must be charged efore an applied signal can have any ffect at the end of a line. At the end f a signal, this condenser must be disharged, and the discharge current is in direction which prolongs the signal impulse. Reversal of the current, however, accelerates this discharge, and so tends to keep the signals clear and free from distortion, thus permitting a higher speed of transmission.

MACHINE TELEGRAPHS

It is clearly of advantage to be able to send as many messages as possible over a telegraph circuit. The messages handled are termed "traffic". The greater the traffic, the greater the revenue or return on the capital outlay represented by the lines and equipment of the circuit. The speed of transmission, and hence amount of traffic in a given time, which it is possible to send by hand using the Morse code, is clearly limited. By using paper tapes punched with holes, so arranged that when fed into an automatic transmitter the code is sent mechanically, the speed of transmission can be increased considerably.

The signals at the receiving end of the circuit are recorded by means of an inker. A noteworthy advantage of this arrangement apart from the speed, is the fact that messages punched on tape can be stored and transmitted as soon as the line is available. At the receiving end of the circuit, the inked tapes for various messages may be deciphered in turn by one operator, or if urgent, by several operators simultaneously. The important thing is that traffic can be kept streaming over the line, which is thus used at its greatest efficiency.

TELEPRINTERS

These may briefly be described as telegraphic typewriters which enable signals to be transmitted by what is termed a five-unit code, instead of the Morse code. In general appearance, they resemble typewriters, principally by reason of the same type of keyboard and roller-carrier for paper (see Fig. 3). By means of an extremely ingenious mechanism, striking the key for any letter or symbol causes a particular combination of five possible consecutive impulses of current to be sent to line by means of a rotating distributor driven by a small motor. At the beginning of each letter is a starting impulse, and at the end, a stopping impulse. At the far end of the line, the received impulses, in order, actuate electromagnets, the particular combination controlling a stop on a type wheel, so that the correct letter is placed in position and struck against the paper. The message is thus printed letter by letter and line by line on a roll of paper, just as if it were being typed directly. There is a teleprinter at each end of the circuit, combining sending and receiving mechanisms, so that messages can be sent in either direction, and also a "home record" printed on the sending machine.

DUPLEX TELEGRAPHY

So far, telegraph circuits where messages could be sent in either direction, but only one way at a time, have been considered. These are termed "simplex" telegraph circuits. Transmission can be made in both directions simultaneously by using the duplex principle, which is basically that of the Wheatstone bridge. Referring to Fig. 4, each end of the circuit comprises what resembles half a Wheat-

AUTOMATIC TELEGRAPH APPARATUS

Fig. 3. Creed teleprinter, with front cover removed, showing essential features of construction.

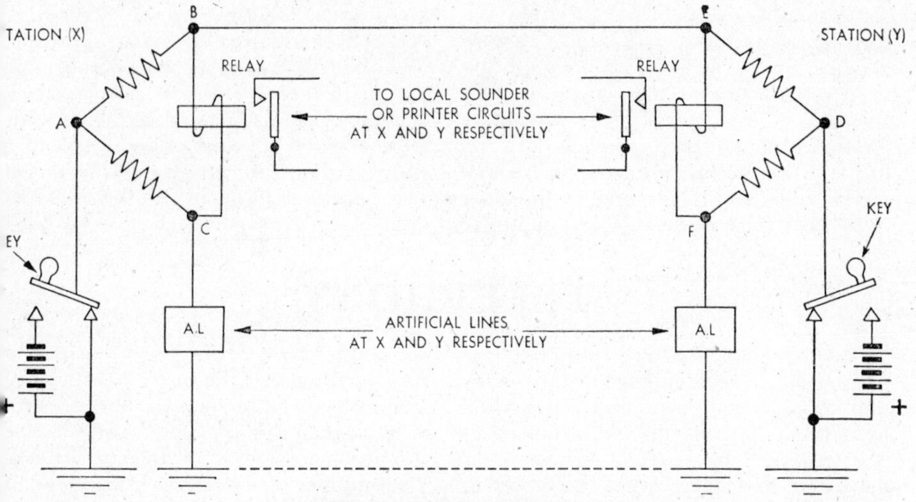

BRIDGE DUPLEX CIRCUIT

Fig. 4. Key at "X" is depressed, operating the relay at "Y" but not affecting that at "X" since this occupies the position of a galvanometer in balanced Wheatstone bridge circuit. Each relay is operated only by a key at distant end of the circuit and signals can be transmitted simultaneously in both directions. For this reason the arrangement is referred to as a duplex telegraphic system.

stone bridge, the galvanometer being replaced by a telegraph relay which operates the "local" circuit. The telegraph battery is connected, when the key is depressed, to one common point A of the bridge. When the key is on the "back stop", point A is connected to earth. If point C of the bridge is connected to an "artificial line" which has electrical properties exactly similar to those of the actual line connected to point B, then the identity with a bridge circuit becomes clear.

DIVISION OF CURRENT

If "X" now presses his key, current flows from A to C and thence to earth, while some flows from A to B and thence to point E at station "Y". Here it divides, some passing through the winding of the relay, causing it to operate, and thence through the artificial line to earth. Current will also flow from E to D to earth, and some through D F. It should be noted that the relay at the sending end "X" is unaffected by signals from that end, if the arms A B and A C are equal and if the impedance of the artificial line from C to earth is the same as that of the circuit from B through the line leading to earth.

In a similar manner, if "Y" presses his key, it affects the relay at "X", but not his own. Suppose now both "X" and "Y" press their keys. Then both batteries are connected to line at the points B and E, which are, therefore, at the same potential and no current flows to line. At "X", current from A will divide through A B and A C. That through A B will pass through the relay to C. The currents unite here and return through the artificial line and earth to the negative pole of the battery. Thus at each station, "X" and "Y", the relay is operated by current from the "home" battery, but only so long as the key at the distant end is depressed. The effect is the same, however, as if current were coming over the line from the other station. The important principle can now be understood, that it is possible to send messages over the circuit in both directions at the same time. This is not the only method of effecting this. Where many telegraph circuits are operated from a single station they are supplied from a common battery of accumulator cells as with telephone circuits. Earth-return circuits are often liable to interference resulting from the earth-currents of power and traction systems, and from induced voltages due to overhead lines. It is, therefore, an advantage if a pair of wires in an underground cable is used to provide both the line and the return conductor, but where several such circuits are used in the same cable, they must be arranged to minimise the mutual interference or "crossfire" between themselves to avoid confusion in working. This is, as can be imagined, a considerable problem where trunk telegraph cables operated at high speeds are concerned. The use of highly selective systems has been developed in recent years in order to overcome this inherent difficulty in multi-channel cable working.

TELEPHONY

THE telephone differs from the telegraph in that intelligence is communicated directly over electrical circuits by means of speech, instead of having to be translated into a code of signals, letter by letter, and then, after transmission, back again into letters which are read by the ear or eye.

We are accustomed now to the ease with which this is performed, but previous to the invention of the electric telephone by Alexander Graham Bell in 1875, all kinds of fantastic schemes were put forward for extending the range over which the spoken word could be directly heard. If we were not familiar with the telephone, then the solution of such a problem would appear extremely difficult and involved, but the astounding feature about Bell's invention, using electrical means, is its simplicity. To understand the telephone, it is first of all necessary to understand the nature of sound and speech.

NATURE OF SOUND

Sound is a form of wave motion transmitted by the vibration of air particles in a similar way to that of waves being transmitted over the surface of a pond by the up and down vibration of the water particles. A cork on the surface of water shows that, while the waves move away from the source of disturbance, the surface of the water vibrates up and down. Sound waves are similar, except that the particles of air move to and fro along the direction of the wave motion, thus forming layers of air which are alternately compressed and rarefied. The amplitude of movement from the mean position is very small and of the order of only ·004 inch even for loud sounds. The strength or intensity of a sound corresponds to the amplitude of vibration of the air particles. The number of vibrations per second is termed the frequency, and thus sounds of a small number of vibrations per second are low-pitched, while a large rate of vibration corresponds to high-pitched sounds. It is known that alternating electric currents of different frequencies in a particular combination give a wave of an irregular but distinctive shape and, similarly, air vibrations of different frequencies combine to give sounds of distinctive characters. Thus, the note of middle C,

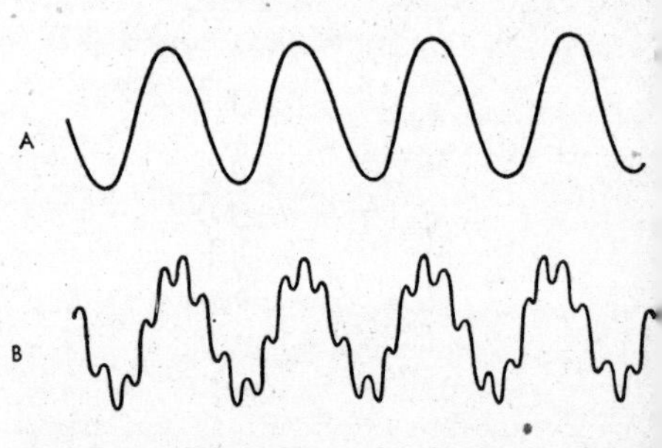

Fig. 5. (a) Wave form of a fundamental frequency. (b) Complex pattern of speech sound showing harmonic frequencies combined with the fundamental.

when sung or played on a piano, a violin or a flute, has the same fundamental frequency of 256 vibrations per second, but a different number of over-tones or harmonics combined with it in each case. It can thus be understood that an analysis of speech sounds, as well as those

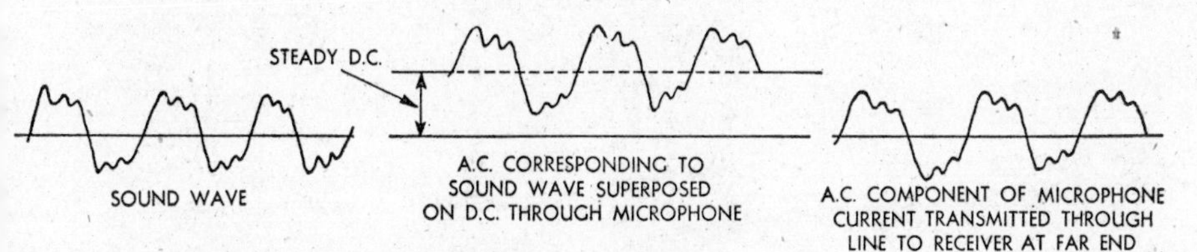

Fig. 6b. Showing the steps in transforming sound waves into alternating currents of electricity by means of a microphone so that speech can be transmitted over a telephone line.

of music, would reveal a complex pattern of different frequencies (see Fig. 5).

Air vibrations produced by the voice, instruments or other sources, act upon the mechanism of the ear and produce the distinguishing sensations we know as sound.

TELEPHONE CIRCUIT

The basic apparatus of the telephone consists, firstly, of a microphone, the purpose of which is to transform the vibrations of sound into electrical vibrations or alternating currents, secondly, a circuit over which these can be transmitted, and thirdly, a receiver which is capable of changing the electrical vibrations back into air vibrations, detectable by the ear, which will correspond as nearly as possible with those which acted upon the microphone. (See Fig. 6b.)

MICROPHONE TRANSMITTER

As used in ordinary telephone circuits, this is commonly termed the "transmitter", and depends for its action upon the variations in electrical resistance of the contact surfaces of carbon granules when changes in pressure are made between them. The granules, which are smooth and fairly uniform in size, fill part of the space between two circular polished carbon electrodes, which are placed in a circular cup lined on the inner surface with a paper strip to prevent its short-circuiting the granules. The front electrode is free to act as a piston and is attached through a metal plunger to the diaphragm, which is placed just behind the mouth-piece (see Fig. 6a).

When sound waves strike the diaphragm, it will move to and fro in accordance with the air vibrations and will thus produce corresponding variations in the pressure upon the granules. If these, through connections to the front and back electrodes, are in series with an electric circuit (see Fig. 6a), then clearly the resulting variations in resistance will cause variations in the value of the current flowing, above or below some steady value. These fluctuations are equivalent to the production of alternating currents at frequencies corresponding to the frequencies of the air-vibrations contained in the sound wave. The purpose of the receiver is to cause alternating currents to produce air vibrations of corresponding frequencies. This is achieved by passing the currents through the windings of two electro-magnets on the pole-pieces of a horseshoe-type permanent magnet (see

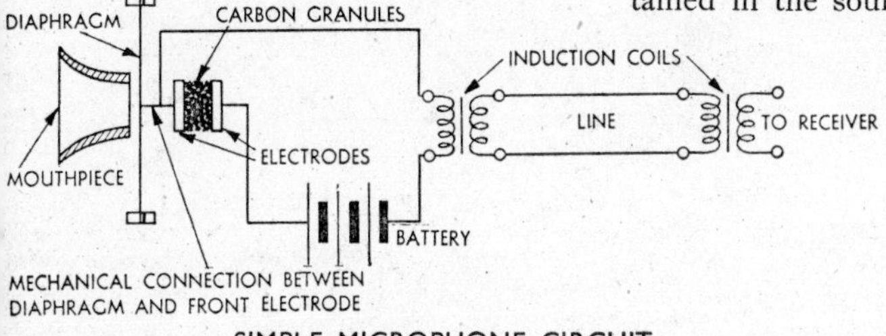

Fig. 6a. Sound waves cause the diaphragm to vibrate. These movements compress or release the carbon granules contained between two electrodes of microphone connected to a battery, and consequent resistance variations produce A.C. superimposed on a steady D.C.

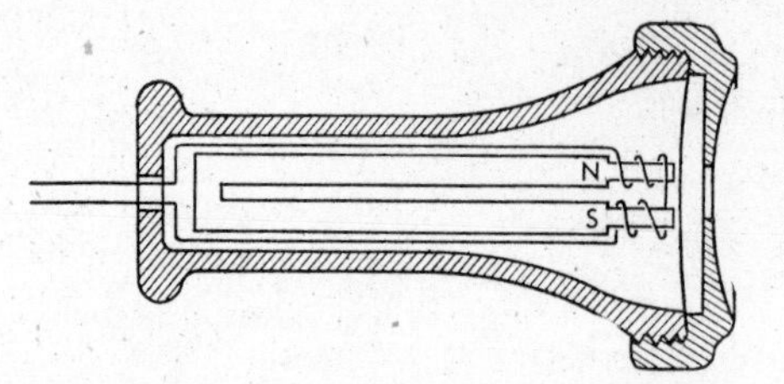

Fig. 7. Telephone receiver consists of an electromagnet and a permanent magnet so arranged that the magnetic fields of both act on a thin ferrotype-iron diaphragm, producing a sound corresponding to the fluctuations in current.

Fig. 7). The latter normally exerts an attractive force upon an iron diaphragm clamped in a position near the pole-faces and, therefore, has the same effect as a direct current through the windings. If through the windings is passed a simple alternating current, of which a positive half-cycle, say, assists the steady attraction on the diaphragm, then the latter will be moved nearer the magnet, producing a rarefaction of the air on the outer surface of the diaphragm. A negative half-cycle of current will correspondingly oppose the effect of the permanent magnet and will tend to release the diaphragm, causing a compression of the air in contact with it. Thus the alternating current causes the diaphragm to act as a source of sound vibration of the same frequency, or, for complex currents, of the several component frequencies (Fig. 8).

If it were not for the permanent magnet, then the diaphragm would be moved inwards, irrespective of the direction of the current through the windings, that is, for both positive and negative half-cycles. One complete alternating cycle would thus produce two successive attractions and give rise to air waves of double the frequency of the alternating current instead of the same frequency which is required. The permanent magnet, in proportion to its strength, also increases the sensitivity of the receiver.

SIMPLE TELEPHONE CIRCUIT

If a microphone, battery and receiver are connected in series, then speaking into the microphone produces air vibrations, which cause corresponding variations in the value of the steady D.C. passing round the circuit. The receiver should be so connected that this D.C., through the windings, assists the effect of the permanent magnet, in order to obtain the maximum sensitivity from the receiver and to avoid impairing the permanent magnetism. The fluctuations in current are equivalent to alternating currents and reproduce air vibrations and, therefore, sensations of sound in the ear of a listener, similar to those of the voice acting upon the microphone. Depending upon the length of the connecting wires, the microphone and receiver can be placed in suitably distant locations, but such a circuit permits only conversation

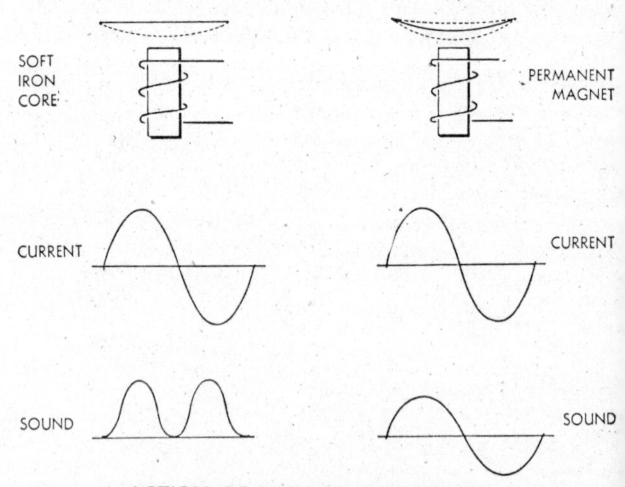

Fig. 8. If soft iron is used (a) the sound wave has a frequency double that of the current which produces it. When a permanent magnet is employed (b) the sound wave which is produced will have the same frequency as that of the alternating current energising the receiver.

in one direction. A two-way circuit is shown, and can be readily understood from Fig. 9. Such an arrangement, however, produces an inefficient circuit, particularly on account of its relatively large losses due to the D.C. flowing in the interconnecting wires.

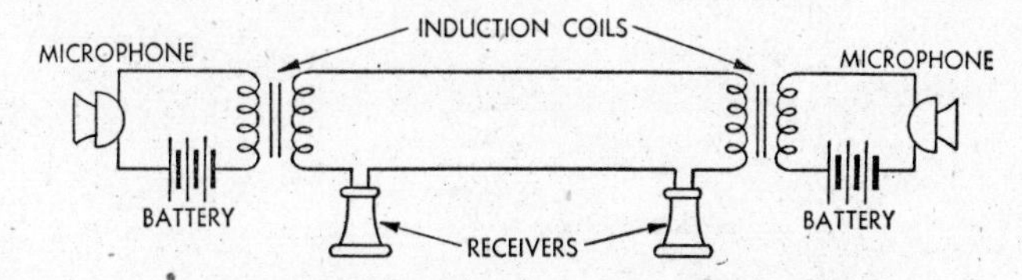

TWO-WAY TELEPHONE CIRCUIT

Fig. 10. Simple two-way telephone circuit with "induction coils" and a separate battery for each microphone. D.C. of each microphone is prevented from flowing through line, but alternating components of the current are transmitted by the transformer action of the coils.

By means of the arrangement shown in Fig. 10, it will be seen that the D.C. necessary for the microphone circuit does not pass through the wires or "line" connecting the two stations. The alternating components of the microphone current will, however, induce corresponding currents in the secondary winding of the transformer, or "induction coil" as it is called, which is part of the line circuit. The receiver at each end of the circuit is placed in series with the line so that there is no D.C. through the windings but only the required alternating speech currents. From either speaker, these pass through both receivers. Conversation may thus be carried on in either direction. The induction coil is designed also to step up the voltage of the microphone circuit, a feature which may be looked at from the point of view of keeping the current in the line low, in order to minimise the I^2R loss, or it may be regarded as a means of matching the impedance of the line. The use of the induction coil also permits a greater percentage change in resistance in the microphone circuit than if the latter were included in the line, thus effectively increasing the alternating current components. It will be noted that this arrangement requires a separate or "local" battery for the circuit of each speaker or "subscriber".

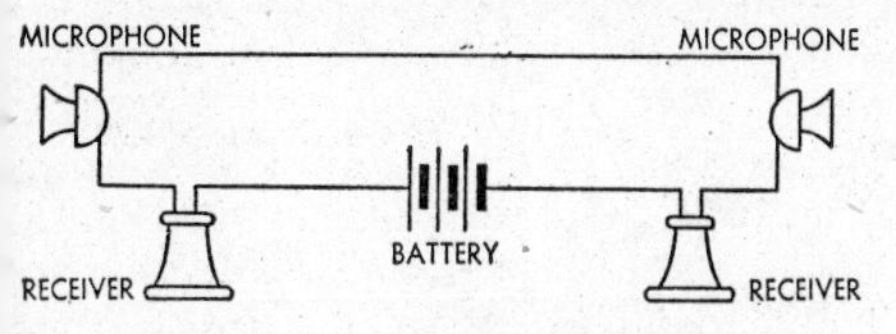

Fig. 9. Simple two-way telephone circuit, direct connection. D.C. flows through the interconnecting line. This is, however, an inefficient circuit because of the relatively considerable losses owing to D.C. flowing through the wires.

SIGNALLING OR RINGING

In order that one subscriber who wishes to speak to the other may attract the attention of the latter, an arrangement for ringing a bell must be provided. The

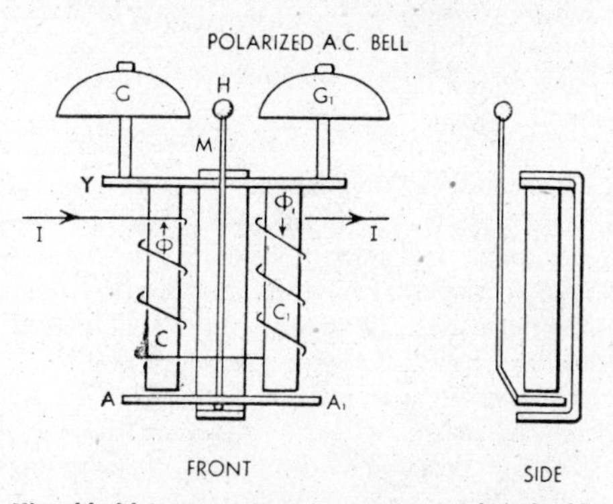

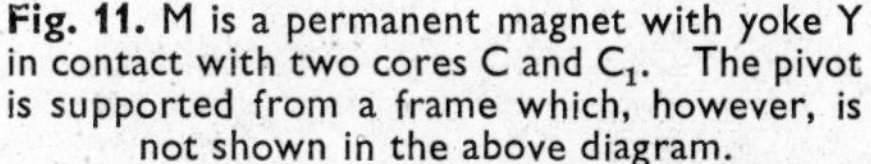
Fig. 11. M is a permanent magnet with yoke Y in contact with two cores C and C_1. The pivot is supported from a frame which, however, is not shown in the above diagram.

bell is of a type operated by alternating current which is provided by a small hand-driven generator or "magneto". The bell is polarised, that is, it has a permanent magnet in its construction, indicated by M in Fig. 11. At one end of this is an iron yoke Y in contact with two iron cores C and C_1. At the other end of M is a pivoted iron armature AA_1 to which is affixed a hammer placed midway between two gongs G and G_1. The magnetic flux of M thus divides in the

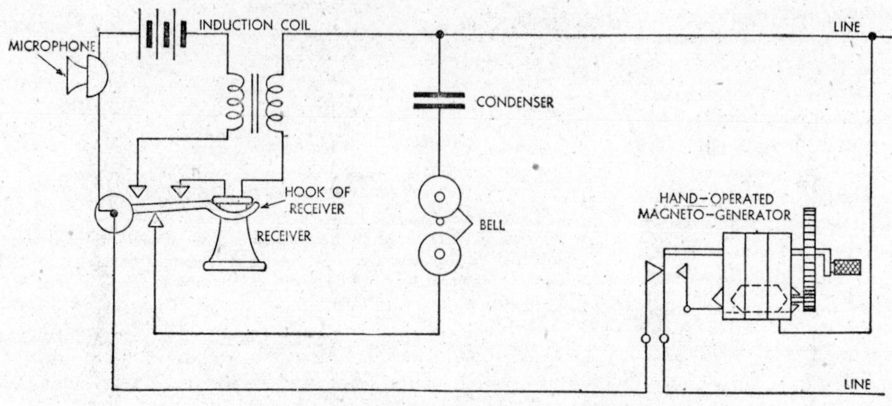

LOCAL-BATTERY MAGNETO SET

Fig. 12. Turning the magneto moves the spring contact to the right and sends a current of 17 to 20 cycles per second to the line at about 75 volts. This operates the bell of the wanted subscriber.

middle of the yoke and armature, passing in two parallel paths through the cores. On these are placed two windings in series, through which the operating A.C. flows. Suppose the polarity of M is such as to give the ends of the armature a south polarity, then this will not be biassed to one core or the other, and will occupy a balanced position. When an A.C. flows through the windings, say, at one particular instant, having the direction of the arrows, then it will produce magnetic flux as shown. This will make the lower end of core C_1 stronger and that of C weaker, each as a North pole. Thus the armature will be attracted to C_1, causing the gong G to be struck. Reversal of the current similarly causes gong G_1 to be struck, i.e., the pair of gongs will be struck at the rate of double the frequency of the A.C.

The magneto is a two-pole permanent-magnet type, having an H-section armature driven through gearing by a hand wheel so that at the normal speed it generates an e.m.f. of about 75 volts at 17 to 20 c.p.s. Arranged on the shaft is a switch which is engaged as soon as the handle is turned, the purpose of this being to cut the magneto out of circuit when not in use. The connections of a subscriber's local-battery magneto set, as used even nowadays in private communication systems, would be as shown in Fig. 12. Normally the receiver is on the hook, but when it is removed the contacts at the hook are closed, permitting D.C. from the battery to flow through the microphone. This arrangement only brings the battery into use when required and so conserves its life. The microphone and induction coil act as already described for transmitted speech, and the receiver for currents coming from the far end of the line. When one subscriber wishes to call the other he operates the hand generator, which sends 17 c.p.s. current down the line, operating the bell at the far end where the second subscriber will lift the receiver off the hook, so establishing communication between the two. The magneto at each end is only bridged across the line while being operated, so that it does not offer a shunt path which will weaken the effect of the received currents of either ringing or speech.

MAGNETO SWITCHBOARD

Where telephones are to be used for public service, means must be provided for any one subscriber to talk to any other. The simple arrangement described would therefore be impossible, for it would require a pair of lines to be run from every one subscriber to every one of the others. The desired object is obtained by taking a pair of lines from every subscriber to one central position, called the exchange, where the lines from any one subscriber to another can be interconnected at a switchboard by an operator. The sequence of operations is that a subscriber, wishing to call another, cranks his magneto in the usual way and then lifts his receiver. The A.C. from the magneto passes to a relay or electromagnet on the switchboard, causing it to attract an armature which trips another hinged armature. The latter, in falling, raises a shutter which exposes the printed number of the calling subscriber. The operator is able to make rapid connection between circuits by means of flexible twin conductors termed cords, the ends of which have contacts in a plug. The plug at each end fits into contact sockets called "jacks". There is a jack on the switchboard connected to the line of every subscriber, as well as the calling relay of that subscriber. The operator has a telephone set and a magneto of her own which she can connect to the circuit of an inter-connecting cord by means of a switch or "key". When the shutter of a calling subscriber is raised, she answers the incoming call by plugging the end of one of the several cords at her disposal into the jack of the calling line. This operates spring-contacts in the jack, which break the relay circuit so that it no longer shunts the line now required to be used for talking. It also connects the battery to an additional winding on the relay, which then attracts the hinged armature and restores the shutter.

The operator then puts the key of the cord circuit to the listening position, and takes the number of the wanted subscriber from the one who is calling. The other end of the cord circuit is then plugged into the jack of the wanted subscriber and her key is put into the ringing position. This disconnects from the cord circuit both the operator's telephone set and the line of the calling subscriber. The operator has then completed the required connection and she now cranks her magneto which rings the wanted subscriber who will answer in the usual way.

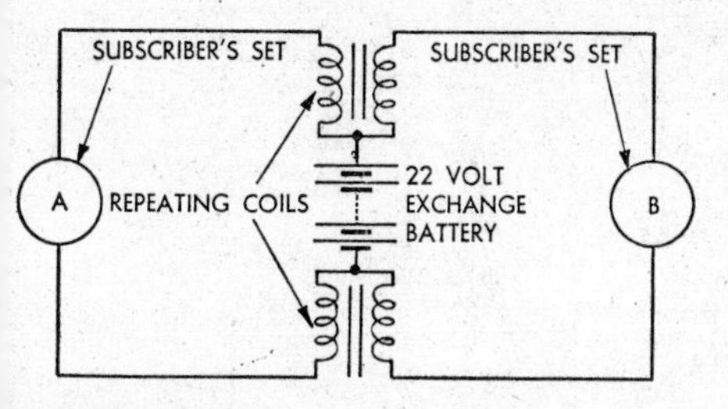

Fig. 13. Connections from a common battery through repeating coils, which prevent interference from "cross-talk" effects between lines.

COMMON-BATTERY SYSTEMS

It would clearly be an advantage if the current for the microphone of all subscribers could be supplied over the lines from the exchange, thus avoiding the costs of maintenance and renewal of separate batteries, and this is achieved in the central battery system. This also has the advantage that the magnetos can be dispensed with, signalling from a calling subscriber to the exchange being effected by means of the current from the central battery at the exchange, and ringing from the exchange to the wanted subscriber by means of a small continuously-running alternator at the exchange.

BATTERY CONNECTIONS

The battery itself is a 22-volt accumulator of capacity suitable for the number of lines to be served. If several microphones are supplied in parallel from the same battery, it is clear that the speech currents from any one will produce fluctuations in potential across this battery, owing to its internal resistance. These potential fluctuations will, therefore, appear in all the other circuits supplied from the same battery, thus causing "cross-talk". Of several methods to avoid this, only one will be described. In this system, each of the "cord-circuits" connecting two subscribers is supplied with current through one-to-one ratio transformers or "repeating-coils" as shown in Fig. 13. The alternating components of the speech currents, say from A to B, cause voltage variations across the A side of the repeating coil windings which are reproduced by transformer action across the B side windings, so operating the receiver of B. Now if the A and B windings are connected to the battery in the correct way, the alternating current on the A side, say, will flow through the battery in one direction, and the induced current of equal value on the B side will flow through the battery in the opposite direction; that is, there is effectively no alternating current through the battery and, therefore, no alternating potential across it to cause cross-talk into other cord circuits supplied from the same battery. Since all the lines coming into an exchange are not likely to be in use at once, the operator has only a small number of cord circuits at her disposal, but each is supplied through repeating coils.

OPERATING DETAILS

Suppose subscriber A wishes to call subscriber B (Fig. 14). A lifts his receiver, which allows the contacts to "make". Current from the 22-volt exchange battery then flows through the line-relay L over the line wires, and through the microphone to A. This current operates the line-relay, attracting the armature which lights a small signalling lamp CL, located on the switchboard, against which is A's number. The operator plugs an "answering cord" into the adjoining jack. The T, R and S (Tip, Ring and Sleeve) contacts of the plug then connect with the corresponding T, R and S contacts of the jack. The relay CO is then energised over the S connection. This breaks the contact CO2 in the circuit of the L relay, thus releasing contact L1 and extinguishing lamp CL. Direct current now flows from the central battery CB to the microphone of A, passing through relay LA, which, holding up its armature, short-circuits the supervisory lamp LS and prevents it from lighting. The operator "throws" her speaking key to the left, connecting her telephone set to subscriber A, and ascertains the number required. If the required line is not busy, she inserts the

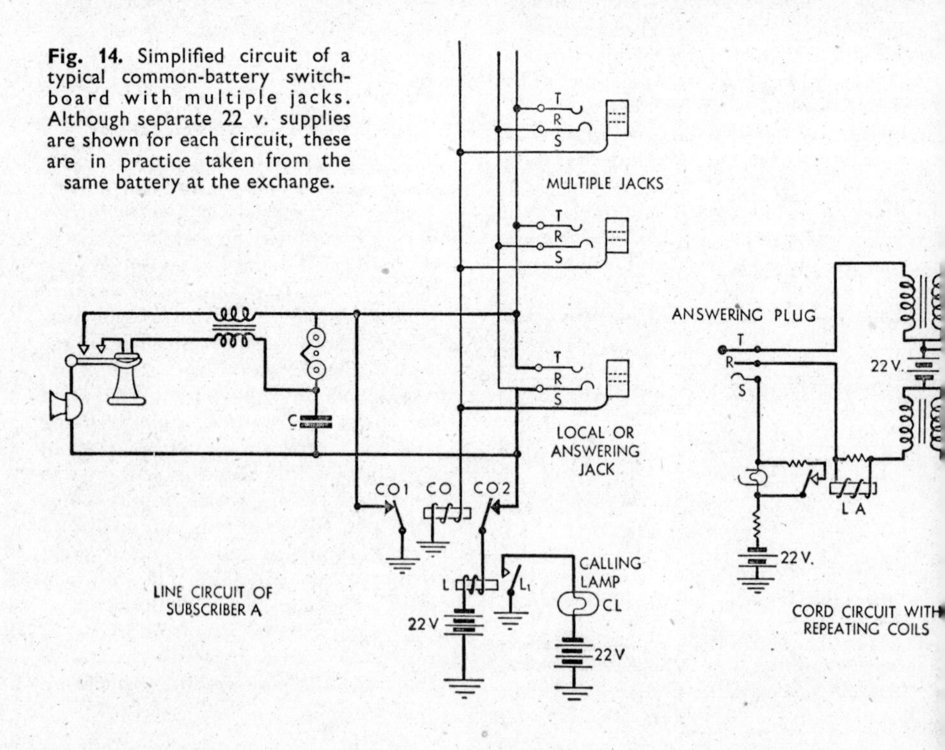

Fig. 14. Simplified circuit of a typical common-battery switchboard with multiple jacks. Although separate 22 v. supplies are shown for each circuit, these are in practice taken from the same battery at the exchange.

other plug of the cord circuit in the jack of B, the wanted subscriber. The T, R, S contacts are made but, since B's receiver is on the hook, no current can flow through his microphone, so that the supervisory relay LC cannot operate. Current will, however, flow through the supervisory lamp LS1, lighting it, and through the windings of relay CO at B, causing the armatures to be attracted, thus breaking contacts in the circuit of the line relay L at B.

The operator throws her key to the right, which disconnects the calling subscriber A from the line and sends 17 c.p.s. current from the ringing alternator to the bell at B through the condenser C which blocks the D.C. for the microphone. Upon B lifting his receiver, the speech circuit from A to B is complete.

When the conversation has been completed, and either A or B replaces his receiver on the hook, the path of the D.C. through the subvisory relays LA and LC is broken, releasing their armatures and removing the short-circuits from the lamps, LS and LS1, which light and inform the operator that she can now remove the connecting cord.

THE MULTIPLE

A single operator can only effectively serve a limited number of jacks, say 200, on the switchboard in front of her, and when the number of lines in an exchange exceeds this figure they are assigned to different operators. The problem will then arise of a subscriber, whose line goes to one operator's "position", requiring to be connected to another, whose line is served by another operator. This is solved by means of the "multiple", which means that every line from the exchange has a number of jacks connected to it in parallel A complete set of jacks, one for each line in the exchange, is then arranged in front of each operator. These are in addition to those lines, a fraction of the total, which she serves by answering and taking the numbers of the wanted subscriber. Connection to the latter is made by selecting the required jack on the multiple, when she has made sure that it is not "busy".

AUTOMATIC TELEPHONY

In comparison with the manually operated system, the required connection between different subscribers may be made automatically by what is known as machine-switching. In this

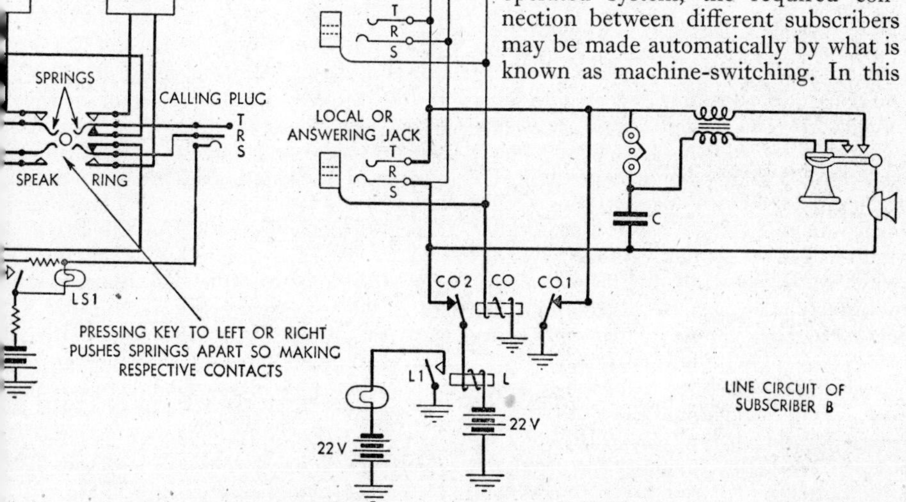

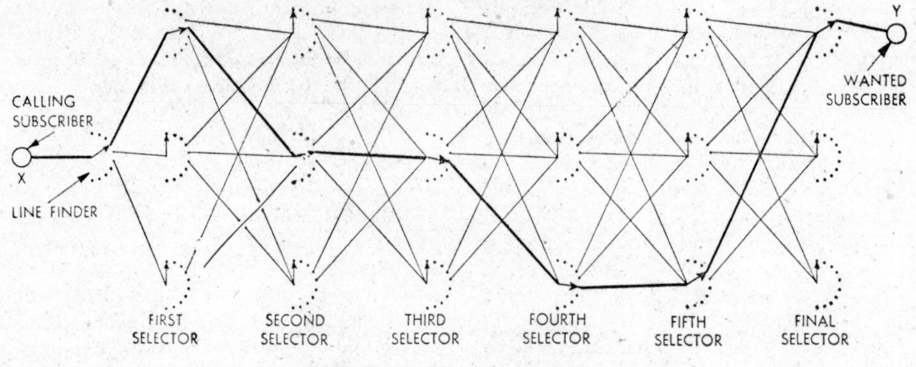

PRINCIPLE OF LINE FINDER

Fig. 15. Instead of automatically hunting for a free selector when the receiver is lifted off the hook, the line finder actually searches for the calling line in order to connect it to a free selector.

case, the calling subscriber, by the now familiar method, "dials" the required exchange and number. Turning the dial causes the dial contacts of the device to break the circuit of the receiver and to short-circuit the microphone. Releasing the dial makes a series of regular interruptions in the current flowing from the exchange battery, over the lines and through the primary winding of the induction coil. The resulting current-impulses operate the switching mechanism at the exchange. In what is known as the "Step-by-Step" system, there are three kinds of switch, distinguished by the functions they perform, known as the line-finder, selector- and final-switches respectively. These switches consist in essential principle of an electro-magnet and armature, with a pawl which engages a ratchet. Movement of the latter steps the switch-blades on to any particular contact, in a bank of several, depending on the number of impulses through the electro-magnet. The row or line of the required pair of contacts is found by the switch being moved by one magnet along the direction of a shaft, which then, by another magnet, can be rotated so that the blades find the required position.

Suppose a subscriber wishes to ring up ABErcorn 4321. He lifts the receiver and listens for the dialling tone. Lifting the receiver causes the line-switch to find an idle first-selector, and to connect the calling subscriber to this selector. The line-switches avoid the necessity for every line in the exchange having a separate first-selector switch which would be unnecessarily expensive, since it is only used when that particular line is calling. In the same way, in the manual exchange, only a limited number of interconnecting cord circuits is provided for all the incoming lines. When the subscriber calls ABErcorn 4321, the first release of the dial for A sends out one impulse, the second B, two, and third E, two. The single impulse for A passes over the line-switch to the first selector, and the shaft will be stepped along two rows, then being rotated until a contact to an idle second-selector is found. The two impulses of B pass over the line-switch, through the first selector to the second selector, causing this to step up two rows, and find a line to an idle third selector. The two impulses for E similarly connect to a fourth selector. The number 4 then connects to a fifth, and 3 to a sixth switch. We have thus reached the stage ABErcorn 4300 and the last connections are made by a final selector. Number 2 steps the switch up to the second row, and number 1 rotates the shaft one place to the right, thus making connection with the required subscriber. Ringing is automatic. Instead of the line-switches here mentioned, a line-finder may be installed. This is shown diagrammatically in Fig. 15.

CHAPTER 10

RADIO COMMUNICATIONS AND TELEVISION

Principles of Radio. Aerials. Radio Reception. Receiver Circuits. Thermionic Valves. Broadcasting. B.B.C. Apparatus. Short-Wave Radio. Heaviside and Appleton Layers. S.W. Aerial Systems. Reproduction. Transmitters. Ultra-Short Waves. Radio Direction Finding. Radio Receivers. Car Radio. Future Developments. Radio Servicing. Tools. Spare Parts. Television. Modulation and Scanning

BOTH from the point of view of technical interest, and from that of practical utility, radio-communication is one of the most important branches of electrical engineering. Its technical interest lies in the specialised apparatus employed, and also in the extremely high frequencies of the alternating voltages and currents used. Whereas ordinary power is supplied at a frequency of 50 cycles per second, the alternating currents of radio may have a frequency as high as one hundred million cycles per second. Naturally, the employment of these ultra-high frequencies raises many special problems, which make the principles of radio a fascinating study. But radio is not just a scientific hobby; it is one of the most useful applications of electricity. Without it, communication with ships and aircraft would be impossible over any but the shortest ranges. Fog, the great enemy of navigation, has lost much of its terror since the introduction of radio-direction finding. Even between fixed points, where there are alternative methods of communication, radio-telegraphy is an invaluable stand-by. Broadcasting makes it possible for the ordinary man in his own home to hear the finest artists in the world, or the leaders in every field of thought and action; whilst in peacetime, television provides still further realism and enables the public to obtain much pleasure by being able to view the actual performance that is being broadcast.

PRINCIPLES OF RADIO

WHAT was the real distinction between Hertz and Marconi and earlier research workers? The difference is of fundamental importance. Whereas the earlier experimenters used inductive fields, similar, for example, to the magnetic field around a coil carrying alternating currents, Hertz and Marconi employed electro-magnetic waves, which are a combination of both electric and magnetic fields. The range of electro-magnetic waves is far greater than that of any inductive field, for while the induction is inversely proportional to the square of the distance from the source, radiation is inversely proportional to the first power of the distance. For example, if the radiated and inductive fields are equal at some given point, then, at some other point ten times the distance from the transmitter, the inductive field will be one-hundredth of its former value. Theoretically the radiated field will only be reduced to one-tenth of its original value though in practice, of course, this condition will not be realised owing to inevitable attenuation effects. Now wave-motion has several fundamental laws. In any one medium, waves of any length have the same velocity, i.e., the disturbance covers a certain distance in a constant time. Clearly, then, the greater the frequency of the waves, the shorter must each be; or conversely, the longer the wavelength, the less the frequency (see Fig. 1). Thus the following statements are true:—

Velocity
= frequency × wavelength.

Wavelength
= velocity ÷ frequency.

Frequency
= velocity ÷ wavelength.

To clarify this point, consider sound waves in air. The velocity of air waves is 1,100 feet per second. Let a note of 256 cycles per second (middle C) be played on a musical instrument. By the laws stated above, the wavelength is $\frac{1,100}{256} = 4$ feet 3 inches, approximately. Upper C, that is one octave higher (512 cycles per second) would have a wavelength of 2 feet $1\frac{1}{2}$ inches, and so on. But electro-magnetic waves are not air waves. The proof of this statement is obvious. Many electric light bulbs are exhausted, yet they radiate both light and heat, and Clerk Maxwell proved that both these effects are fundamentally electro-magnetic. Again, there is no evidence of any

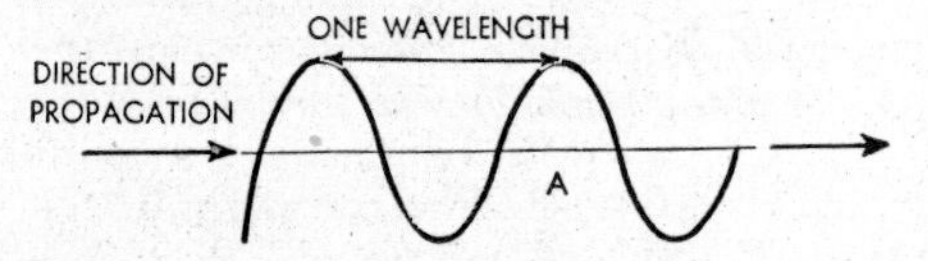

Fig. 1a. Diagram illustrating principle of wave motion. Suppose there is an observer at point A. Then the number of complete waves that pass him per second is the wave frequency.

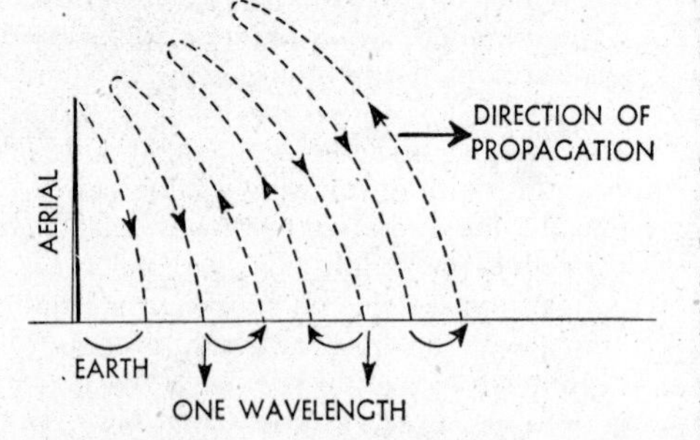

Fig. 1b. Arrows on dotted lines show, instantaneously, directions of electric fields. These are associated with a magnetic field at right angles, that is, in the direction of propagation. For clearness this magnetic field is not included.

material substance existing in space outside the earth's atmosphere, yet the sun radiates both light and heat.

These waves are believed to be produced in a medium called ether, which is so tenuous that it permeates all material substances even the spaces between molecules. The velocity of wave-motion in a medium is inversely proportional to the density of the medium, and it is, therefore, not difficult to see that in a medium so rarefied as ether, the velocity is extremely high. Actually, it is 300 million metres per second, or in British units, about 186,000 miles a second. That is to say, such radiation would travel round the earth in less than one-seventh of a second. Since light and heat are also electro-magnetic waves, though of much shorter wavelengths, it will be understood that their velocity is also 186,000 miles per second. Since wavelength is velocity divided by frequency, it will be readily appreciated that even for long waves, the frequency of the alternating currents required is very high. For example, if the wavelength is 300 metres, the frequency required is $\frac{300,000,000}{300} = 1,000,000$ cycles per second.

ELECTRO-MAGNETIC WAVES

As shown above, the first requirement of a radio transmitter is a generator of alternating voltages of extremely high frequency. Except for very long waves, any kind of rotating machine is impossible, and other methods have to be adopted. Consider a weight suspended from a solid, horizontal support by a coiled spring. Now pull the weight sharply and release it. It will not just return to its original position, but will execute a number of vibrations of gradually decreasing amplitude about that point. It may be said to produce "damped" oscillations. If the weight is reduced, or the spring made stronger, the vibrations will increase in frequency. Now it can be shown (see section on Alternating Currents) that inductance in electricity has an analogy with mechanical mass, and that an electrical condenser

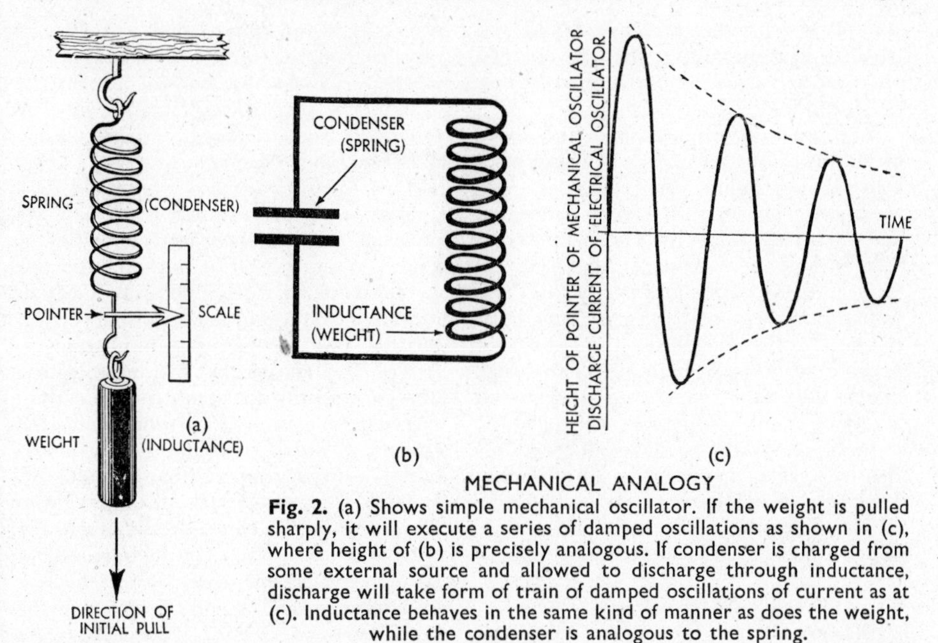

MECHANICAL ANALOGY

Fig. 2. (a) Shows simple mechanical oscillator. If the weight is pulled sharply, it will execute a series of damped oscillations as shown in (c), where height of (b) is precisely analogous. If condenser is charged from some external source and allowed to discharge through inductance, discharge will take form of train of damped oscillations of current as at (c). Inductance behaves in the same kind of manner as does the weight, while the condenser is analogous to the spring.

obeys laws very similar to those of a spring. A large condenser will correspond to a weak spring, and *vice versa.* Thus, if a condenser is charged and allowed to discharge through an inductance, there will be electrical oscillations, that is alternating current (see Fig. 2).

DAMPED OSCILLATIONS

Returning for a moment to the analogy of the weight and spring, it will be seen that it was not necessary to apply an alternating force to the weight in order that it should produce oscillations, and, in fact, so long as the frequency of pulling the weight is lower than the natural frequency of the weight-spring oscillator, there is no general relation between the two frequencies. Each time the weight is pulled and released, it executes a series of damped oscillations, and this will occur no matter how many times a second the operation is performed. Thus, by suitable choice of weight and spring, very high frequencies may be obtained from a low frequency driving source. Now consider an alternating current circuit. Let a condenser be connected in series with an inductance. Next charge the condenser from some external source, and allow it to discharge through the inductance. It will produce a number of cycles of alternating current of gradually decreasing amplitude. The decrease of amplitude or damping is due to the fact that the circuit must possess some resistance, and the energy of the oscillations is thus gradually dissipated. By suitable choice of inductance and condenser, these damped oscillations can be made of very high frequency and, as may be argued from the analogy of the weight and spring, the frequency does not depend, in any way, on the frequency of the supply which charges the condenser.

EARLY SPARK SYSTEM

Each discharge of the condenser will produce a number of such oscillations, called a "train", and the number of trains of oscillations per second depends on the charging frequency. For example, if the inductance is 100 microhenries, and the capacitance ·001 microfarads, the frequency at which the circuit will oscillate freely is approximately 500,000 cycles per second. Now, if the condenser is charged from 50 cycle mains, it may be charged once per half-cycle, or one hundred times per second.

The practical application of the above ideas was in the early "spark" system of transmission. Here, the condenser and the inductance in series were connected across the secondary of a step-up transformer with an output of the order of thousands of volts. Also, across this transformer was a spark-gap. When the potential difference across the condenser became sufficiently high, the gap broke down, and the condenser discharged across it with oscillations through the inductance. With various modifications, this was, for many years, the normal generator of radio-frequency oscillations. (Radio-frequencies are defined as those above 10,000 cycles per second.)

AERIALS

In order that the above generator should produce electro-magnetic waves, it is necessary that it should be connected, in some way, to an "open" circuit, that is, one whose capacitance and inductance are distributed, as, for example, a long line. In radio-engineering, such circuits are known as "aerial" circuits, and more details of them will be found in the section on Short-Wave Radio. Briefly, an aerial tunes to a wavelength twice its physical length—it is, in fact analogous to an open organ pipe.

Speaking rather loosely, it may be said that an open or distributed circuit "gets a better grip on the ether", much as a large source of sound such as a loud-speaker diaphragm or organ pipe radiates sound better than a small source, say a tuning fork.

One of Marconi's contributions to the early development of radio-engineering was the introduction of the "earthed" aerial. Instead of having both ends of the aerial free, as did Hertz, he connected one end to earth. Now the earth is a conductor of large physical dimensions, and it can be shown that it acts like an electrical mirror. Thus, a vertical wire with one end earthed will radiate a wavelength roughly four times its physical length, for it will behave like a Hertz aerial of twice its real length, the "missing" half being made up by reflection from the earth. This is clearly illustrated at (a) in Fig. 3.

This Marconi aerial is thus basically a quarter-wave aerial, that is to say, its physical length is one quarter of its wavelength of radiation, just as the Hertz type is fundamentally a half-wave aerial. Marconi soon found that a simple vertical earthed rod had several disadvantages It was soon shown that maximum radiation comes from that point in the system carrying maximum current, but the current in an aerial is not evenly distributed, as it is in an ordinary conductor. In the Marconi aerial, the maximum current is at the earthed end, while the current at the top of the aerial is zero. Now height is very desirable for effective transmission, and it will be seen that the high portions of a vertical wire are practically non-radiating, since they carry only very small currents.

An early improvement was to fold the aerial over at right angles, thus giving a "flat-top" (or "roof"). The effect of this was to increase the capacitance at the top, and, therefore, increase the current. The vertical portion then has almost a constant current and, therefore, radiates efficiently from all points. When long distance work was first attempted, it was proved that if the horizontal portion is much longer than the vertical portion, the aerial is directional, radiating mostly in a direction away from the bend. During the first twenty years or so of radio development, the tendency was to use ever longer waves, because the advantages of transmission by reflected ray were not appreciated. Since an earthed aerial tunes to a wavelength twice as long as would the same length of wire with both ends free, it is easily understood that the Marconi aerial was almost the only type seriously employed. To-day, however, the majority of long distance point-to-point communication is carried out on short waves, and, therefore, the Hertz (or half-wave) aerial, which is a more efficient radiator, is in

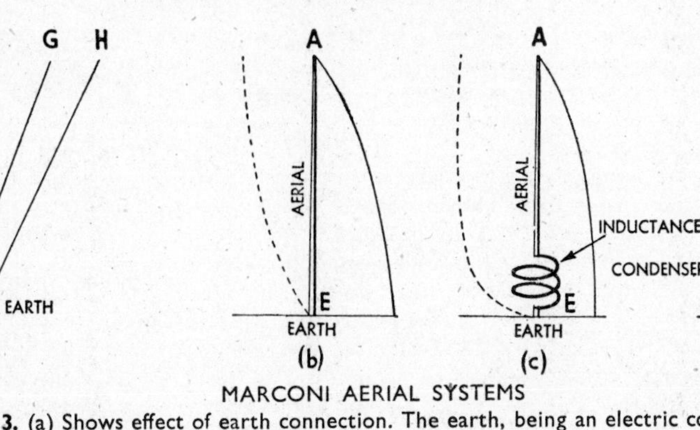

MARCONI AERIAL SYSTEMS

Fig. 3. (a) Shows effect of earth connection. The earth, being an electric conductor, acts like a mirror. Assume that three rays from top of aerial strike earth at points B, C and D. By ordinary laws of reflection, reflected ray will make same angle with line perpendicular to earth as does the incident ray. Thus BF is reflected ray of incident ray AB. Observer at F could receive a direct ray along AF, and a reflected ray BF. Similar arguments will apply to points F, G and H. It will be seen that the system is acting as if there were an imaginary aerial EJ, in the earth, exactly equal to real aerial AE. (b) shows current and voltage distribution in simple earthed vertical aerial. Note that current is very small towards top of aerial. (c) Shows a similar aerial, but it has to be tuned to a wavelength longer than natural wavelength of aerial. An inductance is used for this purpose. (d) Shows the condition where the aerial is tuned by a series condenser to a wavelength that is shorter than the natural wavelength of the aerial.

common use. Incidentally, it has rendered mobile radio practicable for police, military and other purposes. (*Hertz aerials are dealt with in the section on Short-Wave Radio*).

CONTINUOUS WAVES

The spark transmitter radiates a series of trains of damped oscillations. The disadvantages of this type of radiation were soon realised. In the first place, the power radiated is small compared with the maximum values of current and voltage that have to be employed. A spark train may last for, say, one twenty-thousandth of a second, and then there will be a quiescent period till the condenser is charged again, possibly one-thousandth of a second later. It is obvious that the transmitter is not radiating during the majority of the time that the operating key is depressed. Power, of course, is defined as energy per second, so, if a reasonable power is to be maintained, the energy per charge in the condenser must be very high, necessitating bulky and cumbersome apparatus.

As a matter of interest, it has been calculated that in a certain marine type spark transmitter, with one and a half kilowatts input from the mains, the initial current in the closed oscillating circuit was 1,500 amperes. If the same power could be produced by alternating currents of normal sinusoidal wave-form, it is obvious that much smaller components could be employed. There is another disadvantage with the spark system. Damped waves are not confined to one frequency, but radiate on a wide band of frequencies, which means that a spark transmitter causes a great deal of interference in receivers tuned to neighbouring frequencies. For these reasons, early inventors tried to develop a generator of "undamped" oscillations.

Theoretically, any device with a negative temperature coefficient will maintain oscillations in a tuned circuit, and a considerable amount of success was obtained by the use of carbon arcs. About the period of 1914–1918, undamped oscillations (or continuous waves) were normally produced by this method. The necessary condition for the maintenance of continuous oscillations is as follows:—

The normal oscillating circuit comprising inductance and capacitance has some unavoidable resistance. As a matter of fact, radiation can be shown to have some of the properties of resistance. It is the loss of energy in resistance that causes the oscillations to be damped. Now if, in some manner, energy could be fed to the circuit at the correct time, so that it made up these resistance losses, the circuit could be made to behave as if it had no resistance, and the oscillations would be quite undamped. Or, if the energy fed back were greater than that lost in resistance, the amplitude of the oscillations would build up, and the circuit would be said to have "negative resistance".

Evidently, what is required is a kind of automatic valve to contribute energy to the oscillating circuit at the right moment. Stated very simply, that was the function of the carbon arc. But the American scientist, Lee de Forest, subsequently improved the original thermionic valve of Fleming, by adding a third electrode (or grid) between its cathode and anode. This improved valve would not only rectify, as did the Fleming valve, but it would also amplify, and, if suitably connected to an oscillatory circuit, would generate continuous oscillations. (See Section on Thermionic Valves.)

At first these valves could be made only in small sizes suitable for receivers, but it soon became possible to construct larger types, and to-day valves can be made to produce undamped oscillations of any desired power. (See section on Broadcasting.) It is not too much to say that the thermionic valve has revolutionised radio-engineering. It has made possible the design of compact, low power transmitters, as well as receivers of sensitivity many hundreds of times greater than was possible before its use. The usual overall efficiency of a spark transmitter was of the order of 10 per cent. or less, but a modern valve transmitter may average more than 50 per cent. For further details of valve transmitters, the reader is referred to the sections on Broadcasting and Short-Wave Radio.

RADIO RECEPTION

As described above, radio transmission is based on electro-magnetic waves produced by alternating currents of very high frequency. If these waves strike a conductor, they will induce e.m.f.'s in it and, of course, these e.m.f.'s correspond in frequency to those at the transmitter which produces the electro-magnetic waves, and it has been shown that these

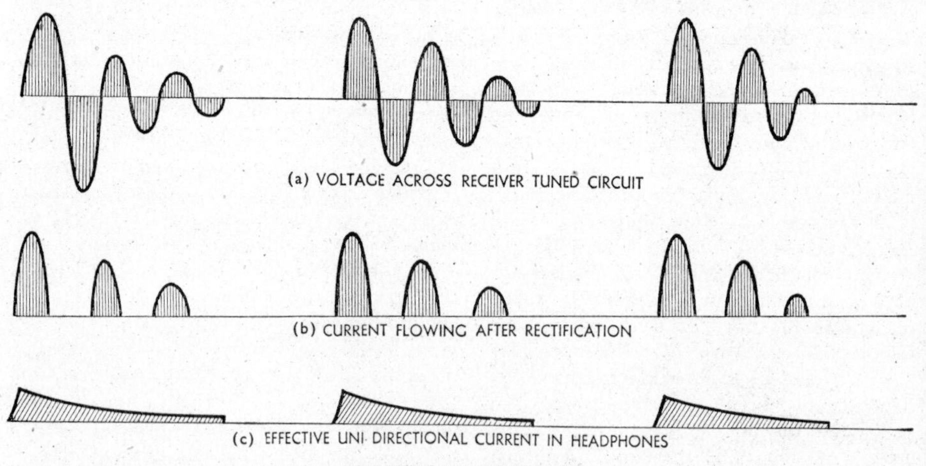

RECEPTION PRINCIPLES

Fig. 4. (a) Shows effects of rectifier. Trains of damped oscillations in (a) are rectified in (b). Effect of inductance of headphones is to smooth out current as shown in (c). Suppose there are 1,000 trains of oscillation per second, each train shown in (a) results in a spurt of current, as in (c), and thus there will be 1,000 such impulses per second to be heard as a sound of that frequency.

RADIO IN A SHIP

Fig. 5. Marconi wireless installation aboard a large passenger liner. The main transmitter is on the right behind the operator. In front of him is the receiver, while on the extreme left is the direction finder. Reception is with headphones as shown; the messages are being recorded on a typewriter.

frequencies must be of the order of many hundreds of thousands of cycles per second, at least. It is obvious that a practical system of radio-communication must involve a device which will appeal to one of the human senses. For example, the aerial currents might operate a galvanometer, whose deflections would correspond to the Morse symbols sent out by the transmitter. But such a method would not be very sensitive, and it would also be unsatisfactory for many other reasons. For most forms of radio-communication, except, of course, television and picture transmission, the final detector is the human ear, and so the problem of reception resolves itself into making the electro-magnetic waves audible. The extremely high frequency currents produced by these waves are, of course, completely inaudible, since the upper limit of the human ear is in the neighbourhood of 20,000 cycles per second.

If the high frequency voltages which can be obtained by allowing the high frequency currents to flow through a suitable impedance are applied to a rectifier, a uni-directional current will result. Suppose a pair of head-telephones were connnected so that this rectified current flowed through them; there would be a "click" every time the transmitter operator pressed his key, and another as he raised it. Every Morse symbol would be represented by a double click, the interval between them deciding whether the symbol was a "dot" or a "dash". This is a possible but not a very satisfactory method of signalling, since the clicks would be very difficult to read through atmospheric noises, etc. If the waves could be made to produce an audible note, conditions would be much improved.

A spark transmitter will produce an audible note in a receiver. Suppose that the transmitting condenser is charged five hundred times per second. Each charge will produce a corresponding discharge, and resultant train of damped oscillations. Now, if these trains produce similar trains in the receiver, and are then rectified, each train will be represented by a short spurt of uni-directional current. Since there are five hundred such trains per second, it is clear that the output of the rectifier will produce an audible note, of a frequency of 500 cycles per second, in the receiving head-telephones (see Fig. 4). Thus, the essential condition of good, reliable communication is that the radio-frequency oscillations should be varied in amplitude at audio-frequency. A valve oscillator, which, as has been shown produces continuous undamped oscillations, can be employed in two ways. Its grid or anode voltage may be varied at audio-frequency. This method is known as "modulation", and the type of radiation is called "modulated continuous waves". Alternatively, plain continuous waves may be employed, the necessary audio-frequency variation being supplied at the receiver end.

Originally this was done by an interruptor in the receiver circuit which operated at audible frequency, but modern practice uses a "beat" method. Briefly, the principle is as follows:—

Suppose two notes of slightly different frequency are played simultaneously on a piano. There will be a rise and fall of amplitude corresponding to the frequency difference between the notes. For example, if the notes are, say, 256 cycles per second, middle C, and 320 cycles per second, G, there will be an audible rise and fall of amplitude at $320-256 = 64$ cycles per second. This effect is called a "beat" (or heterodyne). Suppose a transmitter radiates continuous waves. At the receiver end let there be a local oscillator of radio-frequency, but differing in frequency from that of the signals by some audible frequency, say 1,000 cycles per second. Now, if the signal frequency voltage and that due to the local oscillator be applied to a rectifier, with a pair of headphones in series, the result will be a variation of telephone current at the beat frequency. Thus, if the transmitter output is controlled by a Morse key, the symbols will be repeated, at an audible frequency, at the receiver. Fig. 5 illustrates a typical radio installation aboard a large liner.

RECEIVER CIRCUITS

For full details of the design of radio receiver circuits, the reader is referred to the section dealing with that subject, but this section would not be complete without at least some reference to the general principles involved. The electro-magnetic waves are originally received on an aerial system similar to that employed in the transmitter—in fact, the same aerial is generally employed for both purposes in many commercial radio stations. But aerial circuits tune very flatly and, also, they generally have low impedances. Most rectifying devices have high impedances, so the aerial is coupled, very often by mutual inductance, to a tuned circuit, which has the effect of sharpening the tuning and supplying a convenient high impedance to operate the rectifier efficiently. The rectifier, in modern receivers, is invariably a thermionic valve of some type. As will be shown in the section on Receivers, very frequently a radio-frequency amplifier is connected between the aerial and the rectifier, and this addition has the effect of increasing both the sensitivity and the selectivity.

THE THERMIONIC VALVE

THE thermionic valve is the heart of modern radio-communication. In fact, it is not too much to say that it is one of the key inventions of this century, for its applications are by no means confined to radio or even within the limits of electrical engineering. Its operation depends upon electronic activity (The Electron Theory is discussed in Chapter I). The essential factor now is that when a conductor is heated, the forces holding the free electrons to the central nucleus are much reduced and the free electrons may acquire considerable velocity. Provided that the temperature is raised sufficiently, they may actually leave the conductor in a manner similar to evaporation from a liquid and the conductor is said to emit electrons (Fig. 6). The space around such a heated conductor will acquire a negative charge generally known as the "space charge". This fact can easily be demonstrated by placing a red-hot poker near a charged gold leaf electroscope and observing the change in divergence of the leaves (Fig. 7). But in air the effects are not very pronounced and have very little practical application. For it will be realised that the electrons are far smaller in mass than the gas molecules contained in the air. Collision between electrons and molecules will occur and the electrons will be able to travel only very short distances from the conductor. An obvious improvement would be to seal the conductor in a vacuum chamber; glass is very convenient. Of course, the only practical method of heating a conductor in a vacuum is by an electric current. The conductor is, therefore, made in filamentary form to make this possible. The filament itself may be employed as the emitting surface; this is the method employed in battery valves which are known as directly heated. Or it may be employed to heat by conduction a specially designed emitting surface to which the filament is not directly connected. This is a practice in mains valves which are said to be indirectly heated. It has been shown that the space around the heated conductor becomes negatively charged. Before any further discussion on the thermionic valve, this space charge must be briefly dealt with as it constitutes a fundamental factor in the operation of the device.

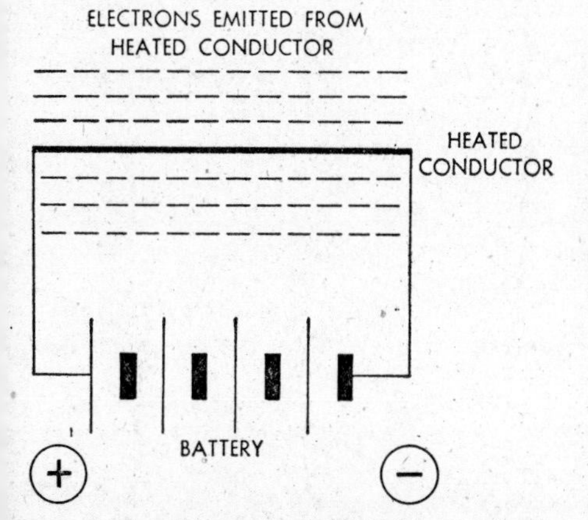

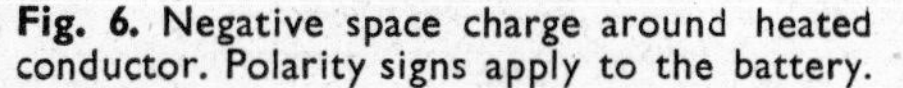

Fig. 6. Negative space charge around heated conductor. Polarity signs apply to the battery.

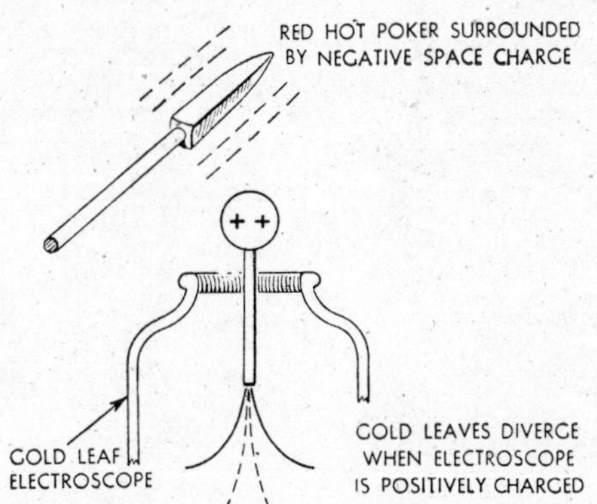

Fig. 7. Red hot poker and gold leaf electroscope experiment to illustrate the presence of a space charge round the poker as a result of the emission of electrons. The dotted lines (at the foot) show the new position of the gold leaves after the loss of charge caused by the hot poker.

THE ANODE

If electrons leave the conductor, it must acquire a positive charge, and unless the electrons have attained sufficient velocity to pass out of the field of the conductor they will be drawn back to it. It will be seen that the conductor will be surrounded by a pulsating cloud of electrons. If another electrode, positively charged, is now fitted in the container, it may, if its positive charge is sufficiently high, exert such force on the electrons that they do not return to the conductor, but stream across the vacant space between the heated conductor and the cold positive electrode, which is generally called the "anode". Since this device can only conduct in one direction, i.e., electrons may pass from heated electrode or "cathode" to the anode, but not *vice versa*, it was originally called a valve. As will be shown later, valves may have more than two electrodes, so the simple two-electrode type is frequently called a "diode", i.e., two electrodes. See Fig. 8.

The obvious use of a device which will conduct in only one direction is to convert

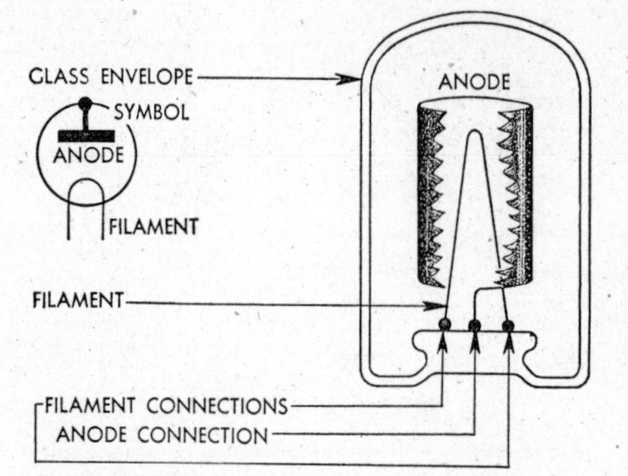

Fig. 8a. Construction of diode thermionic valve with part of anode cut away to show filament.

alternating current to uni-directional current. In the section on Radio Principles it is shown that the energy radiated from a transmitting aerial and arriving at a receiver is in the form of alternating current of very high frequency. It is also shown that these radio-frequency currents can be made to appeal to human senses if they are passed through a rectifier. Clearly, a diode performs this function excellently. It was, in fact, first introduced by Sir Ambrose Fleming for that purpose on the early Marconi Transatlantic stations in the opening years of this century. The relation between current and voltage in the diode, or the anode current-anode volts characteristic, as it is called, is interesting. Until the space charge is neutralised no current can flow across the inter-electrode space so that if, as in Fig. 8b, the anode current is plotted against anode volts, there will be voltage applied before appreciable current flows. As the anode voltage is increased, the space charge becomes partially neutralised and a small current passes across the space, increasing as the anode voltage is raised till there is a direct relation between current and voltage. Finally, a point comes when all the electrons emitted from the cathode are flowing across the space, no further increase of anode voltage can have any effect and the valve is said to be saturated. In Fig. 8b the point A is where the space charge begins to be materially neutralised, the distance AB is the straight or linear portion and the point B represents saturation. There is a rapid change of curvature at the point A; if the diode has its anode voltage adjusted to this point by the potentiometer shown, it is more sensitive. A typical circuit is shown in Fig. 9. Large diodes may be employed

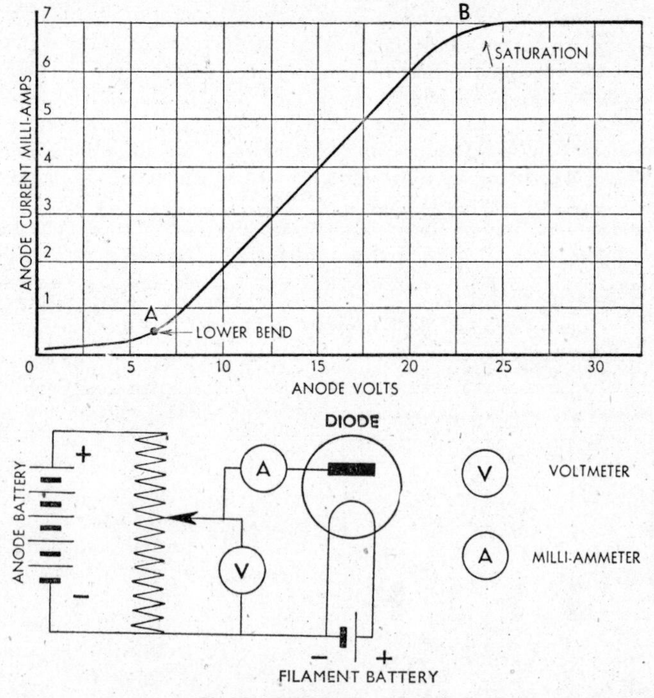

Fig. 8b. Diode characteristic and circuit for its investigation. Note the symbols used for the two types of measuring instruments employed.

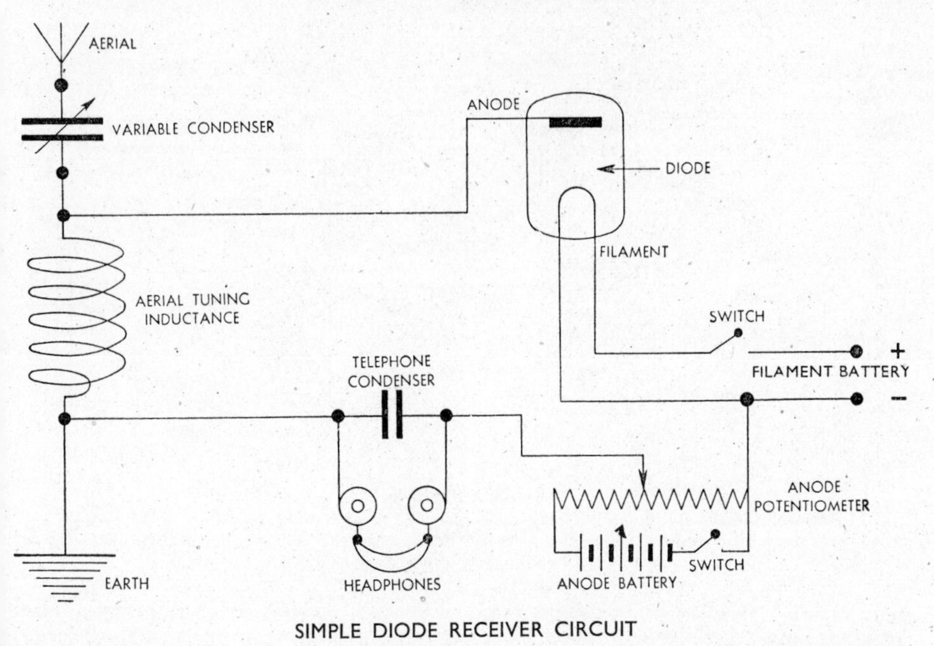

SIMPLE DIODE RECEIVER CIRCUIT

Fig. 9. Aerial circuit is tuned by inductance and capacitance in the usual way, and the radio-frequency voltage is rectified by the diode detector valve, thus operating the headphones.

as power rectifiers, that is to say, instead of being used to rectify the small radio frequency voltages reaching the aerial they may, in conjunction with suitable smoothing apparatus, be applied to the rectification of alternating current mains supplies. A more recent development still in this connection is the use of valves filled with mercury vapour. The effect of this modification is considerably to reduce the internal resistance of the valves, and thus materially add to their rectification efficiency. Many modern radio installations use rectifying valves of this type.

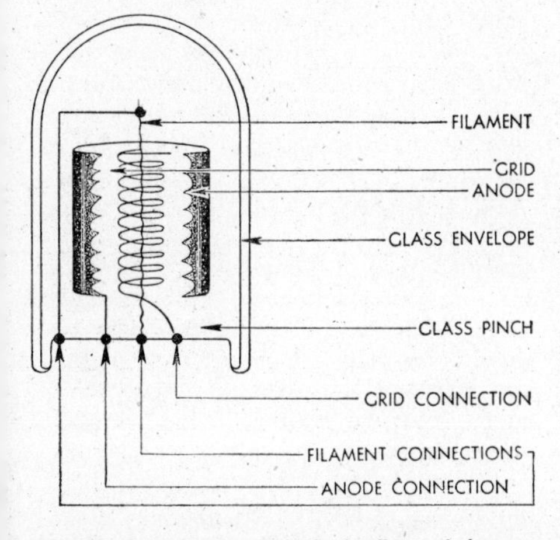

Fig. 10. Construction of triode. Part of the anode has been cut away to show grid and filament.

THE TRIODE

The diode will only rectify, but by the addition of further electrodes thermionic valves may be made to perform many different functions. As already described the electrons leave the cathode at almost zero velocity, but in their journey to the anode they are greatly accelerated. Now it is quite obvious that far less force is necessary to stop or change the motion of a slowly moving body than one moving at high velocity. A man can easily push a light car along a smooth road, but he could not stop it at full speed by pushing against it. Using a similar line of argument, it would seem that a small electric force introduced near

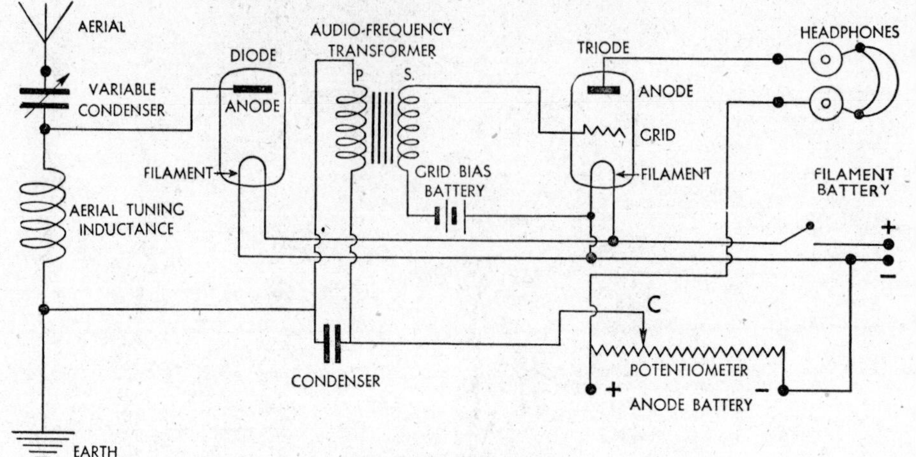

Fig. 11. Headphones of Fig. 9 are replaced by primary of intervalve transformer, P. The secondary of this transformer is connected to the grid and filament of the triode, and an amplified output appears across the headphones in the anode circuit of the triode.

the cathode, where the electrons are travelling slowly, will have as much effect as a considerable force placed at the anode, where the velocity is very high. This suggests that the valve would amplify, since a small voltage on a third electrode could be made to control a much larger voltage on the anode. This third electrode is made in either mesh or spiral construction (see Fig. 10) and is called a *grid* and the three-electrode valve is called a *triode*. A triode with an elementary amplifying circuit is shown in Fig. 11. One of the most remarkable properties of the triode is the fact that it can be made to amplify alternating currents of frequencies up to many millions of cycles per second. Again, due to the amplifying properties the energy in the anode circuit is much greater than that in the grid circuit. If some of this anode energy can be handed back to the grid circuit, an alternating current, once started in the latter, will continue indefinitely. The valve is thus acting as a generator or oscillator and will generate at almost all frequencies.

Space does not permit of more detailed descriptions here, but thermionic valves have been developed for many purposes and may have many more than three electrodes. More detailed description of some of these types will be found in the sections on Broadcasting and Receivers.

BROADCASTING

No branch of radio-engineering has changed the life of the ordinary man more than broadcasting. Until the early 1920's, "wireless" had been a romantic mystery to all but professional radio-engineers and operators, and a few amateurs. The advent of broadcasting gave the ordinary man access to the best of modern culture, and opportunity to hear the leaders of current thought at first hand under ideal conditions by his own fireside. Also, in many cases, it gave him his first introduction to applied science, since the early broadcast receivers lent themselves readily to home construction, and frequently the interest thus stimulated led to further study of the principles of electricity.

The function of any form of microphone is to convert the energy of sound waves into electrical energy. The earliest form of microphone was based on the

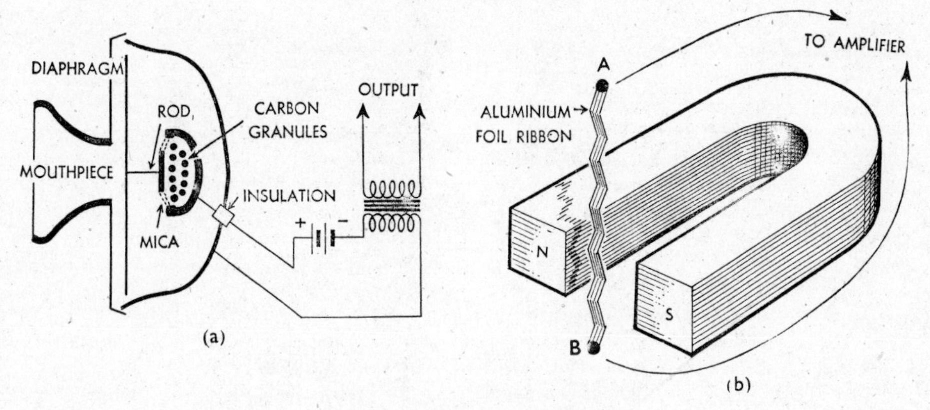

THEORY OF MICROPHONE

Fig. 12. (a) Shows principle of the carbon-microphone. (b) Illustrates principle of the ribbon microphone which can be made to give excellent quality of reproduction, but its output is very low

principle of imperfect contact between pieces of carbon. If two pieces of carbon are in light contact, slight variations of pressure cause considerable changes in their apparent resistance. If one piece of carbon is attached to a diaphragm which is acted on by sound waves, the differences of pressure on the diaphragm will cause the resistance of the carbon contacts to change in accordance with the sound waves. Thus, if a constant e.m.f. from a battery is applied to the circuit, the current will change in direct proportion to the strength of the sound reaching the diaphragm (Fig. 12). The first practical form of this simple microphone used carbon granules whose contact pressure was controlled by a diaphragm acted on by sound reaching it through a collecting mouthpiece. With slight modifications, this type of microphone is still employed in ordinary line telephony, and was used in the early days of broadcasting (Fig. 12a). It was soon found that it did not give good enough reproduction for high quality broadcasting, and improved types of microphone, adapted specially for broadcasting, superseded it.

Modern practice is moving away from the carbon contact principle, and employs the alternating e.m.f. generated by either a very light moving coil, or a corrugated aluminium ribbon, suspended between the poles of a powerful permanent magnet. The sound waves cause the coil or ribbon to move, and so, by the principle of electro-magnetic induction, an electro-motive force is generated. Unfortunately, these modern microphones are very insensitive—their output voltage may be only one hundredth of a volt—and considerable amplification is necessary before they can be used to control a broadcasting transmitter. Fig. 12b shows the ribbon type.

STUDIOS AND EQUIPMENT

In practice, the microphone is fitted in a broadcasting studio. This is a room specially designed for the purpose, kept free from extraneous sounds by walls of sound-insulating material and frequently fitted with special curtains, drapings or other devices so that its acoustics may be controlled. The headquarters of a modern broadcasting station may include many studios, owing to the varied types of programme radiated. For example, a news studio or a talks studio need only be a small, comfortably furnished room in which the broadcaster may sit at ease before a microphone and thus broadcast in a natural, intimate manner. But, obviously, such a studio would not be satisfactory for a dance band or a large orchestra. In practice, not only can the acoustics of the studio be controlled, but artificial echo, produced electrically, can be introduced to a varying degree. It is, in fact, quite possible to "fake" the acoustics of a small studio so that it sounds like a large cathedral or even the open air. This extreme use of artificial echo is not, of course, normal practice, but it is useful as an "effect" in broadcast plays.

RECORDING SYSTEMS

Another important item in studio and associated equipment is the recording system. The obvious case is the broadcasting of ordinary gramophone records, which is done by means of a pick-up, similar to that used in an ordinary radio-gramophone, but rather more elaborate in design. But recording is used for many other purposes. For instance, an important item of news, such as a speech by a prominent statesman, may occur at a time when broadcasting is inconvenient. In that case, a recording van can attend at the point where the speech is made, and the record may be broadcast when desired and repeated at will. Other methods are sometimes used for broadcasting such as steel tape magnetic recording. Sound on film has also been widely adopted though records are generally employed in present practice as "effects" in plays.

From the studios, the small speech voltages pass, generally after preliminary amplification, to the nerve centre of a broadcasting system, i.e., the control room. (Fig. 13). The outputs from the microphones are brought to a modified telephone switchboard, whence they can be connected to any one of a number of amplifiers mounted on racks. These amplifiers have two functions, first, the obvious one of increasing the amplitude of the microphone voltages and, secondly, to provide a means of controlling the amplitude of these voltages. These amplifiers are known as "B" amplifiers, and each is provided with a very accurate means of gain control. Each "B", with its control potentiometer network, is known as a control point, and is operated in practice by a specially trained control engineer. The output of the "B" amplifier is measured by a special type of valve voltmeter known as a "programme meter", and this instrument is calibrated against the modulation meter of the transmitter. The control engineer keeps his programme meter reading between two defined limits, so that the transmitter is neither over-modulated nor under-

CONTROL ROOM AT BROADCASTING HOUSE.

Fig. 13. Engineers are controlling either actual transmissions or rehearsals of transmissions. Behind the control positions is the amplifier rack—an engineer is seen making adjustments.

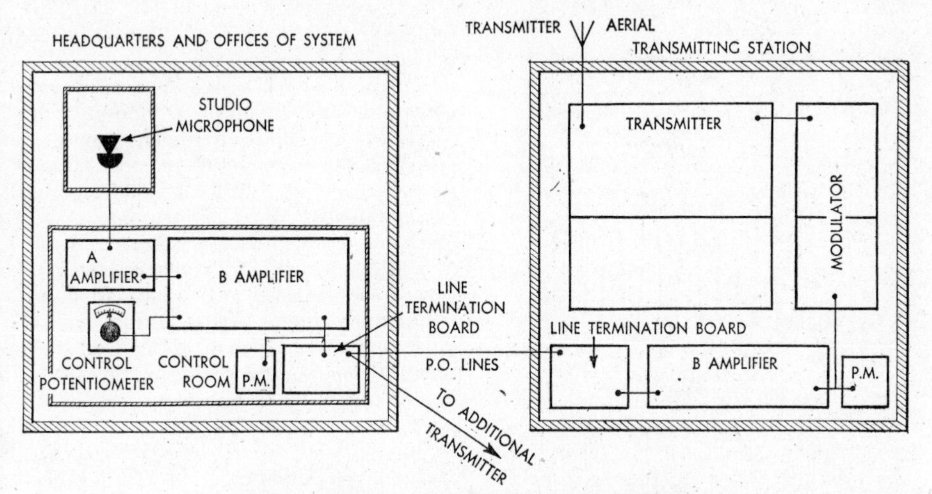

ARRANGEMENT OF BROADCASTING SYSTEM

Fig. 14. Programme is amplified by the first or "A" amplifier, then passed to the "B" amplifier where it is controlled by the control potentiometer. Programme meter (PM) is checked by P.M. at transmitting station. The connection to the transmitter is usually provided by ordinary Post Office telephone lines but these are specially balanced in order to reduce distortion to a minimum.

modulated as either must be avoided.

The studios and control room are usually in one building, whereas the transmitter may be many miles away. Or, frequently, one programme is simultaneously broadcast to several transmitters. The link between the control room and the transmitter is by means of ordinary Post Office telephone lines, so the outputs of the "B" amplifiers are fed to line termination boards, which, of course, connect to the P.O. lines. But, although ordinary lines are used, they are not suitable for broadcasting without modification. Good commercial telephony can be made with a frequency range of from 150 cycles to 2,000 cycles, but high quality broadcasting needs a frequency range of from 50 to 10,000 cycles per second. Owing to their distributed inductance and capacity, ordinary lines are unsuitable for this wide range, so special correction is necessary (Fig. 14).

MODULATION

The lines reaching the transmitter terminate on a switchboard of similar design to the line termination board at the control room. At this point, they will need further amplification to make up for the losses in the line, and another "B" amplifier is interposed. The output of this "B" is monitored by another programme meter, and fed to the modulator system of the transmitter.

Before following the broadcasting chain further, it is necessary briefly to examine the principles of modulation. A radio transmitter is primarily a device for the production of alternating current power at very high frequencies. Instead of 50 cycles per second, the normal mains frequency, a transmitter works at frequencies of hundreds of thousands or even millions of cycles per second. The frequency of a broadcasting station is usually quoted as so many kilocycles per second, a kilocycle being one thousand cycles.

In the case of a telegraphic system the output from the transmitter is perfectly normal alternating current, except for its high frequency. Signalling is accomplished merely by making and breaking one of the transmitter circuits in accordance with the dots and dashes of the Morse code, but, in radio-telephony, a much more complicated system of control is necessary. The transmitter output must vary in proportion to the

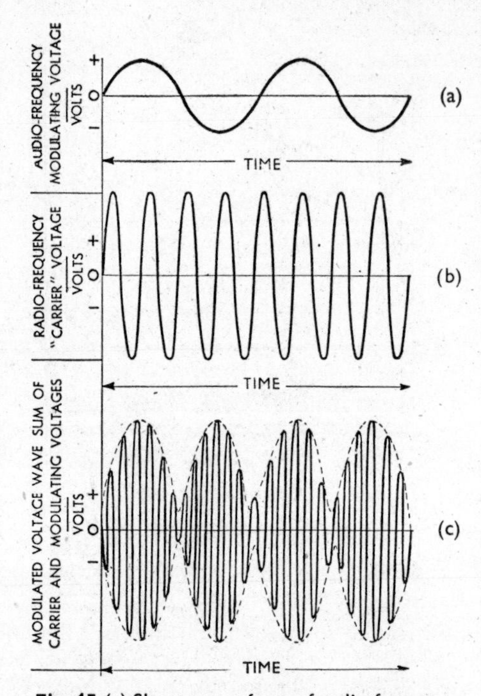

Fig. 15 (a) Shows wave-form of audio-frequency voltages originally produced by microphone. (b) Un-modulated carrier voltage of transmitter stage to be modulated. (c) Effect of combining two voltages correctly in a modulated amplifier. Since maximum value of (a) is half the maximum value of (b), it will be seen that (c) represents 50 per cent. modulation of the carrier wave.

strength of sound waves striking the microphone, not just be made and broken. Since the amplitude and frequency of the alternating voltages produced by the sound waves are continually varying, it will be realised that such control of the transmitter output is a comparatively complicated matter compared with the "keying" of a telegraph transmitter. This variation of transmitter output by means of sound wave voltages is known as "modulation" (Fig. 15).

In practice it is accomplished either by varying the effective grid bias, or the instantaneous anode voltage of one stage of the transmitter by means of the alternating voltages produced originally by the microphone. If the sound wave voltages are used to vary the grid bias of a transmitter stage, the process is known as "grid modulation". If the anode potential is controlled, it is "anode modulation". Each system has its advantages and disadvantages. Grid modulation needs but little audio-frequency power—perhaps ten per cent of the radio-frequency power handled by the stage to be modulated, but, unfortunately, its efficiency is low, and it is rather difficult to adjust for high quality broadcasting. For those reasons grid modulation is not employed for broadcasting transmitters in Great Britain, though, at one time, it was very popular on the Continent, especially in Germany.

ANODE MODULATION

Anode modulation, on the other hand, needs considerable audio-frequency power. For 100 per cent. modulation—that is to say when the audio- and radio-frequency peak voltages are equal—it can be shown that the audio-frequency power must be half the radio frequency power. So, if a modulated stage supplies a carrier power of one kilowatt, five hundred watts of audio-frequency power are necessary fully to modulate it, and the total power, during 100 per cent. modulation, will be 1½ kilowatts. It is very difficult to design iron-cored apparatus, such as chokes and transformers, to handle high power, say up to 100 kilowatts or more, and still maintain the wide frequency response necessary for modern high quality broadcasting. Thus it is easily seen that the modulator stage for high power transmitters presents very difficult problems.

These difficulties would clearly be minimised if the modulator stage could be made to operate on less power, and there have been two main approaches to this problem from that point of view. The first is the system known as "low-power modulation." A radio-frequency amplifier, quite early in the system, is anode modulated in the usual way. If an aerial were connected to this stage, it would be a complete broadcast transmitter, but of comparatively low power. The output, however, is not connected to an aerial, but to one or more further radio-frequency amplifiers, so that the final output is at the desired power level. If the aerial power is of the order of 100 kilowatts, the modulated amplifier, that is, the radio-frequency stage to which modulation is applied, may have an output of say, 1 kilowatt. For 100 per cent. modulation, the audio-frequency power supplied by the modulator should be half this value, or 500 watts, which is not much greater than is required for a large public address system.

However, low-power modulation has several disadvantages. A modulated signal is not radiated on one frequency, but over a band of frequencies, equal in width to twice the modulation frequency. For example, let a transmitter have a carrier frequency of 1,000,000 cycles per second (a wavelength of 300 metres). If middle C (256 cycles per second) is played on an instrument in front of the microphone, the transmitter will be modulated at this frequency, and radiation will take place over a band from 999,744 (1,000,000—256) to 1,000,256 cycles per second. For higher notes, of course, the band is wider.

These new frequencies are called "sidebands". A tuned circuit tends to select one frequency, and each radio-frequency stage following the modulated amplifier will tend to cut sidebands, thus impairing the quality of transmission. If the circuits are designed so that they tune very flatly, and accept all sidebands, they are very inefficient. Also, for technical reasons beyond the scope of this section, radio-frequency amplifiers designed to deal with inputs already modulated cannot be run at the same valve efficiency, as distinct from circuit efficiency, as those handling unmodulated inputs. Summarising, therefore, it is seen that the low-power modulation system economises in audio power, but can only be operated at low efficiency.

CLASS B MODULATION

An alternative method is the employment of two valves in class B push-pull as a modulator. Valves are said to be in push-pull when their grids are connected to points of opposite phase with respect to earth, so that when one grid is positive the other is negative. Their anodes are similarly connected to opposite sides of the anode load, which has a centre connection at low A.C. potential. Valves are operated in class B when their

B.B.C. HIGH-POWER TRANSMITTER

Fig. 16. Each stage of this transmitter is enclosed in a metal case, with access by means of interlocking doors which, as a safety precaution, break the high-tension supply when they are opened. The main controls of the apparatus are centralised, for convenience in operation, at the control desk.

Fig. 17a. Marconi transmitting valve capable of operating as radio-frequency amplifying valve in short-wave circuits.

grid bias is sufficiently negative to cut off their anode current, so that they only conduct during positive half-cycles of input voltage. One valve so connected would introduce intolerable distortion, but, when two are connected in push-pull, the distortions are in opposite phase and, therefore, cancel. The steady current in such a stage is extremely low, and, therefore, the efficiency may be very high. As the steady current is so small, iron-cored chokes and transformers may be worked under better magnetic conditions. A class B modulator is applied to the anode circuit of the final radio-frequency amplifier of the transmitter.

TRANSMITTERS

Modern broadcast transmitters (Fig. 16) are usually of considerable power, often of the order of 100 kilowatts. For smaller powers, the valves may be air-cooled and may be regarded as enlarged receiver valves, though they may be of very different external appearance. But, for high power work, air-cooled valves cannot be used, and water cooling is necessary. The valves are made of glass in the ordinary way, but the anode is in the form of a large copper thimble, sealed to the glass, so that the external appearance of the valve is partly copper, partly glass. This anode fits into a water jacket, through which water is pumped

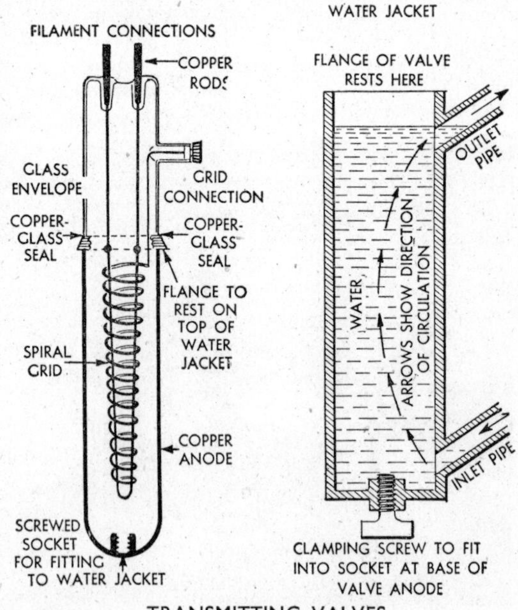

Fig. 17b. Diagram shows the detailed arrangement of a water-cooled transmitting valve as used at high-power broadcasting stations. In high-power transmitters, these valves may be from four to five feet in length.

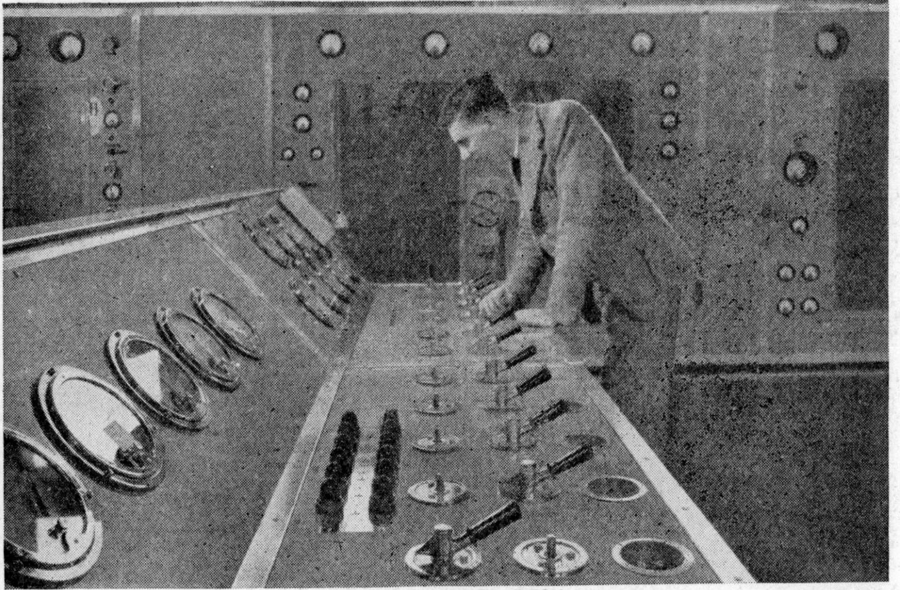

B.B.C. CONTROL DESK

Fig. 18. All the main transmitter supplies can be controlled from this point, and meters are provided for each. An engineer is seen adjusting the anode potentials of one of the stages of the apparatus.

at a rate of several gallons per minute (Fig. 17). The water circulating system is very elaborate, sometimes costing several thousand pounds. Water is stored in a large tank, pumped through long coiled hoses to the water jackets of the valves, thence out to a large water grid, something like the radiator of a car but on a very much larger scale. This radiator is mounted over a cooling pond, from which water is sprayed on to the grid by specially designed spray pumps. An interesting point is that the cooling pond is usually stocked with goldfish to keep the water clean so that it will not clog the spray pumps. The water around the anode is, of course, at high potential, and very long coiled hoses are necessary in order to avoid excessive current passing through the water system to the earthed storage tank. As much as five kilowatts of power may be wasted in water losses on a practical broadcast transmitter whose power output is of the order of 80–100 kilowatts.

Apart from the water-cooling system, the valves are interesting because of the comparison between the voltages and current employed in them and in ordinary receiver valves. With high-powered transmitter valves, the high tension supply may be anything from 10,000–20,000 volts, with anode currents of 1–2 amperes per valve. The low tension or heater voltage may be twenty or more volts, and the filament current is of the order of 20–100 amperes per valve. Corresponding figures for a battery receiving valve are: high-tension voltage 150, anode current up to 10 milli-amps., filament voltage 2, filament current 100 milli-amps. Fig. 18 shows an engineer adjusting the anode potentials of one of the stages of a high power broadcast transmitter.

BROADCASTING AERIAL SYSTEMS

For normal medium-wave broadcasting, as distinct from short-wave broadcasting, which is treated in a separate section, transmitting aerials are usually vertical radiators (Fig. 19). They may take various forms; for example, a short "roof" slung between two tall masts, generally about 500 ft. high. In this type, the main radiation comes from the vertical connector, or "down-lead", and the horizontal roof, which is usually comparatively short, serves chiefly to ensure more uniform current distribution in the system. Another type has the aerial wires arranged like guys around the mast, so that the whole system rather resembles the stick and ribs of an umbrella. For that reason, it is often called an "umbrella" aerial. But the latest types use the mast itself as a radiator—there is no aerial wire at all. An interesting point is that these aerials are usually half-wave aerials—that is to say, their length approximates to half the wavelength of transmission (see Short-wave section). It is found that the half-wave aerial produces less "sky-ray" than a quarter-wave aerial. Since a half-wave aerial must have both ends at high potential, the practice is to feed one end through a high impedance, usually a tuned circuit, one end of which is earthed.

SHORT-WAVE RADIO

SHORT waves are usually understood to be those below 100 metres. For an increasing number of purposes, including television, wavelengths less than 10 metres are employed. These are usually known as ultra-short waves. In the early days of radio, it was believed that wavelengths below 100 metres were of little practical use, and the tendency was to employ ever longer waves for commercial and service purposes. The short waves were given by the Governments of the world, more or less as a plaything, to radio amateurs, who were also very restricted, especially in this country, in the power they could employ. But it soon became apparent that these short waves, far from being useless, were extremely valuable for long distance communication. The main reasons for the great distances that can be covered by short waves are, first, the possibility of transmission by reflection from the conductive layers of the upper atmosphere, much as a schoolboy directs a ray of light from a mirror and, second, that, because of the smaller physical lengths required, aerial systems of great radiation efficiency can be constructed. Whereas, with medium and long waves, radiation takes place in all directions, just as an ordinary lamp throws light in all directions around it, short waves can be "beamed", like an electric torch.

Fig. 19. B.B.C. 500 ft. mast and a part of the aerial system of a high-power broadcasting transmitter. Note the large aerial insulator used.

HEAVISIDE AND APPLETON LAYERS

Above the earth, at distances varying from sixty to three hundred miles high, there are regions or layers which conduct electricity. There are two main layers, namely, the Heaviside Layer, at sixty to eighty miles high, and the Appleton Layer, from one hundred and forty to three hundred miles high (Fig. 20). These layers are formed by the ionisation of the atmospheric gases at great heights by the

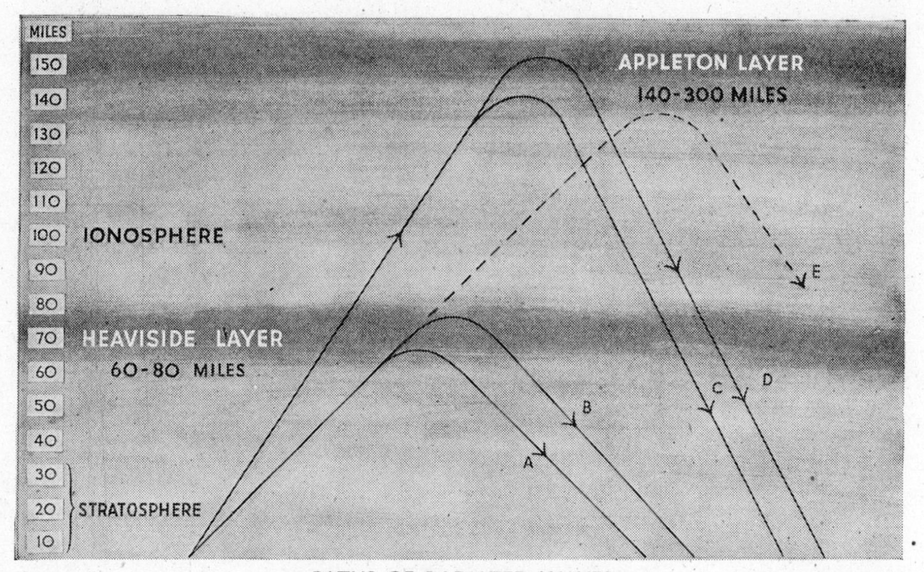

PATHS OF RADIATED WAVES

Fig. 20. A and B show paths taken by two transmissions of different wavelengths ; B is the shorter in daytime, when the Heaviside layer is comparatively low. C and D show the paths taken by the same radiation at night. E illustrates how very high frequencies may pass right through a layer.

action of the sun, and the height will vary with the season and the time of day. Also the layers are not fixed, but are irregular and of varying thickness; in fact, the whole of the atmosphere above fifty miles high is ionised to some extent, and this region is known as the ionosphere.

If a short-wave transmission, radiated from a directive aerial system, strikes one of these layers, the effect is similar to a ray of light striking a mirror at an angle. The angle which the incoming or incident ray, makes with a line at right angles to the mirror, is equal to the angle which the reflected ray makes with the same line. Thus, in the case of short-wave transmission, the transmission will be reflected to another point which may be many thousands of miles distant from the transmitter. Medium and long waves follow the curvature of the earth for the most part, though some part of their radiation is reflected, and part of the wave energy is expended in causing earth currents. The earth is rather a poor conductor, so there is a considerable energy loss due to this cause, and the shorter the wavelength, the greater the loss. The energy which travels in this manner is called the "ground ray", while the energy which strikes the conductive layer, and returns to earth, is known as the "reflected ray". But the reflected ray has no energy loss due to earth currents. Therefore, in the case of short-wave transmission, the ground ray can be received for only short distances from the transmitter, but the reflected ray may reach almost any point on the earth's surface.

From Fig. 20, it is seen that, after the short distance covered by the ground ray is passed, no further signals will be received until the point where the reflected ray strikes the earth. For example, the B.B.C. Empire Short-wave Services are not very well received in this country, although they are perfectly satisfactory in the countries for which they are intended. This phenomenon is known as "skip distance". However, owing to the fact that the layers are irregular and varying in height, reflection and skip distances are often not sharply defined, and signals may be received within the normal skip distance. Also, reflection is not the simple process described above. It is generally accompanied by refraction or bending of the incoming ray.

A common instance of refraction occurs when one looks obliquely at a bowl of water. The water always appears to be shallower than it actually is, owing to the bending of light rays passing from air to water. Different wavelengths penetrate the conductive layers to different depths before reflection occurs, and are refracted at the surface of the layer. Thus the point where the energy returns to earth will vary with different wavelengths. It will also be affected by the season and the time of day. At mid-day the effect of the sun will be at its maximum, and the lower or Heaviside layer will be dense and close to the earth. During the hours of darkness, the ionised atoms will combine with free electrons, and the Heaviside layer will become almost non-conductive. Therefore, reflection will take place chiefly from the Appleton layer, and the point of reflection will be further from the transmitter, with a consequent increase in the skip distance. Similar changes in the layers will occur from summer to winter. Stations operating regular short-wave services make regular changes of wavelength to employ these variations of atmospheric conditions to the best advantage.

It will be seen from Fig. 20 that these conductive regions are not plane surfaces, like mirrors, but are irregular, like the surfaces of pools of water. Although reflection can be obtained from the surface of a clear pond, it will be very distorted, compared with the image that would be obtained from a good mirror, and, as the water will never be quite still, the reflection will be always varying. These conditions are very similar to those which obtain when radio waves are reflected from the Heaviside or Appleton Layers.

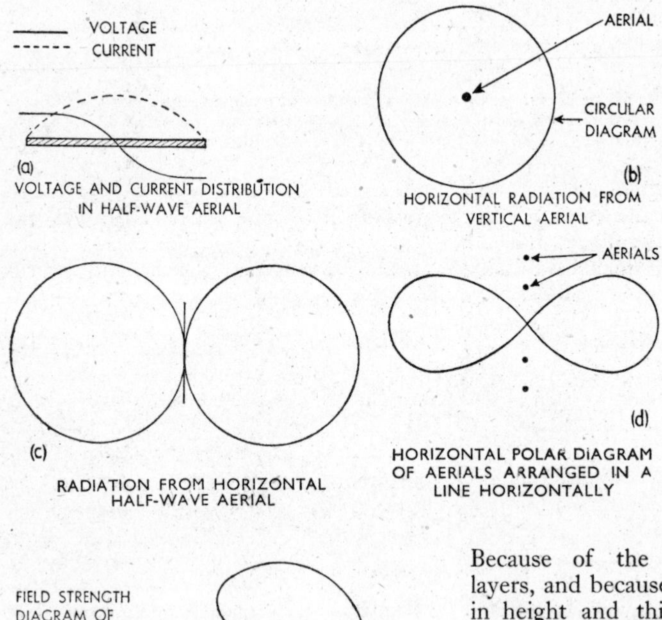

Fig. 21. Polar diagrams of radiation from various types of short-wave aerials. In each case, the distance from the aerial of the line forming the polar diagram shows the amplitude of radiation in that direction. At (d) there is practically no radiation at all along the length of the aerial.

Because of the irregularities of the layers, and because they are not constant in height and thickness, the reflection will be variable, and sometimes will change very quickly. This gives rise to the phenomenon of "fading" which is common on short waves. For reliable short-wave communication, fading must be minimised. The two chief methods are the employment of (1) receivers which have extremely good automatic volume control, so that when the signal fades the amplification increases, and *vice versa*,

SHORT-WAVE AERIAL ARRAY

Fig. 22. B.B.C. modern high-power short-wave directive aerial array. It consists of a number of horizontal half-wave aerials, arranged one above the other, each fed by a transmission line at its centre. The spacing between the elements is half a wavelength to discourage vertical radiation.

and (2) the use of "diversity reception", which means the employment of several receivers situated at different points, and combining their outputs. Fading is often quite local, and a weak period at one of the receivers may easily coincide with a strong signal at another, so that the combined output will be practically free from fading.

SHORT-WAVE AERIAL SYSTEMS

The other great advantage of short waves is that it is possible to devise aerial systems whose physical lengths are directly related to the wavelengths of transmission—Fig. 21 will make this point clear. If the diagram at (a) represents a transmitting aerial, the voltage and current will be distributed as shown in the figure. It will be seen that one end will be a point of high voltage, while the other end will also be at high voltage, but opposite in direction. The point at the centre of the aerial will be a point of zero voltage, but the current will be at maximum there, and zero at either end as shown. Therefore, the aerial has half-a-wavelength of voltage or current on it and the wavelength of transmission of such an aerial will be twice its physical length. This type of aerial is known as a half-wave aerial, and is the basis of almost all short wave aerials. It will be seen that an aerial to work on 20 metres wavelength will be 10 metres long. For reasons of physical length, it is obviously impossible to use

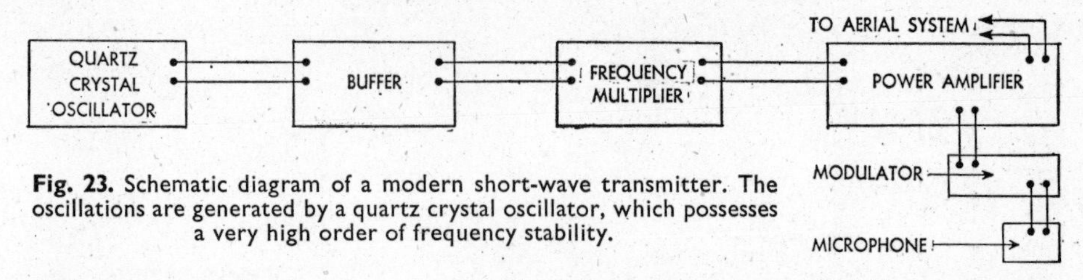

Fig. 23. Schematic diagram of a modern short-wave transmitter. The oscillations are generated by a quartz crystal oscillator, which possesses a very high order of frequency stability.

this type on medium or long waves. In these latter cases, the length of the aerial bears no direct relation to the radiated wavelength, and the radiation will be far less efficient. Half-wave aerials may be used vertically or horizontally—for long distance work, the horizontal form is more common (Fig. 22).

The radiation from a horizontal half-wave aerial will not be equal in all directions, but will be stronger in directions "broadside-on" to the aerial, and at minimum in directions "end-on" to it. If the current in a receiver aerial which can be moved in all directions around the transmitter aerial is measured and plotted as a graph, the result will be the "figure–8" diagram of Fig. 21c. Such an aerial will obviously give a certain amount of directivity, but it can be much improved if one half of the figure–8 can be suppressed. If another half-wave aerial is mounted at a distance of a quarter wavelength from the first, but not connected to it in any way, almost all the radiation will be concentrated in the direction shown by the arrow in Fig. 21e. This arrangement is called a reflector. With slightly different spacing and length, the reflector can be made to concentrate radiation in the opposite direction, so that it is in front of the aerial. The reflector then becomes a director. In practice, aerial systems may be very elaborate. There may be many radiating elements, accompanied by an equal number of reflectors or directors (Figs. 21d and 22).

REPRODUCTION

As the transmitting coils and condensers are, of necessity, smaller than those used in longer waves, the lay-out and general design of short-wave transmitters may often be more simple and compact than on medium and long waves. An interesting point about short waves is that, theoretically, it is possible to obtain improved fidelity of reproduction of speech and music on such wave-lengths. A musical or speech transmission is not made on a single wavelength, but occupies a band of wavelengths equal in width to twice the highest frequency of musical or speech sound. For faithful reproduction, it is essential that the tuned circuits of transmitter and receiver shall give a practically equal response to all frequencies within this band. Now, the longer the wavelength, the lower the radio-frequency to which the circuits are tuned. If the music or speech transmission occupies a band, say, 20,000 cycles wide, it is obvious that this is a greater percentage of the frequency to which the transmitter and receiver circuits are tuned if they are working on medium or long waves, than it would be if the transmission were to be made on short waves. It will clearly be easier to design tuned circuits to give equal response over the whole band of transmission, if this band is a small percentage of the frequency to which the circuits are to be tuned and, therefore, short-wave transmission will give better reproduction. This is true over small distances, within the range of the ground ray, but fading and similar effects cancel most of this advantage if the receiver is a considerable distance from the transmitter. During a short period of experimental television transmissions, some of the normal medium-wave transmissions were also radiated by the ultra-short-wave television sound transmitter at Alexandra Palace. There was a noticeable improvement in reproduction on these transmissions. However, the average broad-

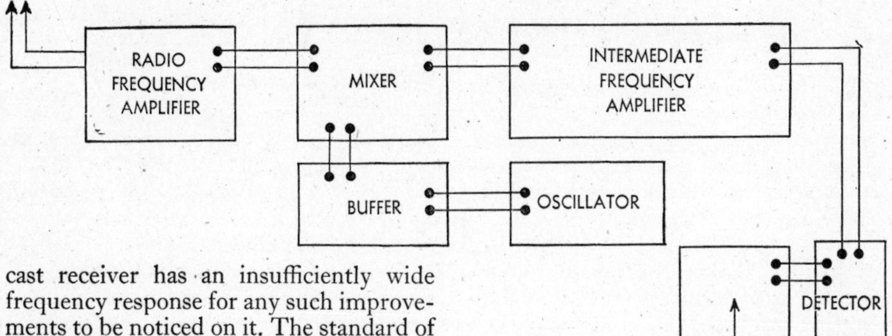

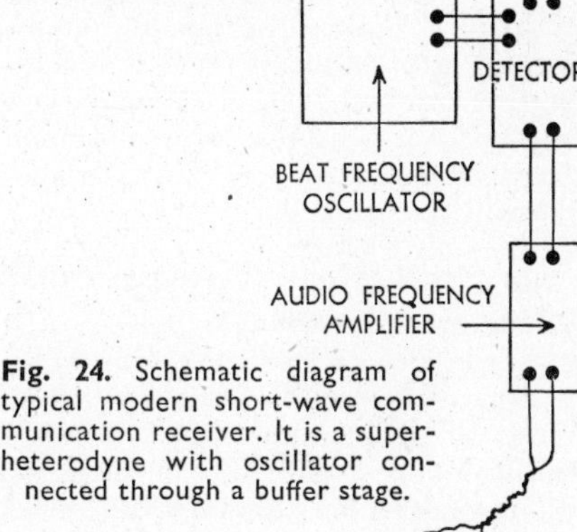

Fig. 24. Schematic diagram of typical modern short-wave communication receiver. It is a superheterodyne with oscillator connected through a buffer stage.

cast receiver has an insufficiently wide frequency response for any such improvements to be noticed on it. The standard of transmission achieved by the B.B.C. on even normal wavelengths is very high.

SHORT-WAVE TRANSMITTERS

Although the general principles of short-wave transmitter design are similar to those on medium and long waves, there is a considerable number of modifications. The most striking difference is the aerial system, which has already been mentioned here. It is very important that short-wave stations maintain a high stability of transmitted wavelength, or reception may be very difficult. Usually, valve oscillators are not stable enough for this purpose, and normal modern practice is to use a quartz crystal as a master-oscillator (Fig. 23). Quartz has the property of producing an electro-motive force when it is subjected to mechanical forces of tension or compression. If a suitable crystal is connected in the grid circuit of a valve, and feed-back arranged from the anode circuit, voltages will be applied to it. These will cause it to vibrate mechanically, which will, in turn, give rise to e.m.fs., which will be amplified by the valve, and fed back to the crystal. The crystal will vibrate at its natural frequency and thus become a source of voltages at this frequency, and owing to the characteristics of the crystal, the frequency stability will be very high; under favourable conditions it may be as good as one part in one million. Although these voltages are of small amplitude they can be amplified and employed to drive a short-wave transmitter. Most of the usual receiver circuits can be adapted for short waves, but, sometimes, components originally intended for medium- or long-wave reception may have excessive losses on short waves. If simple two- or three-valve receivers are employed, good results may be obtained but the reaction control will be very critical. Commercial and service short-wave receivers are almost invariably superheterodynes. Fig. 24 illustrates a schematic arrangement of a typical short-wave communication receiver.

ULTRA-SHORT WAVES

During the last few years, a great deal of work has been done on ultra-short waves, that is, below ten metres. Television was transmitted on between six and seven metres. The special characteristic of these very short waves is their purely local range. So far as is known at present, they are not reflected from the conductive layers of the atmosphere, and so their range is limited by their ground ray, which, owing to the very short wavelength, is usually restricted to an "optical range", though sometimes this can be exceeded.

RADIO DIRECTION FINDING

THIS is among the most useful and interesting branches of radio-engineering. It renders marine and aerial navigation possible in conditions of such poor visibility as to make normal methods useless, and thus contributes largely to the speed and safety of transport. In some parts of the world, notably off the coast of Newfoundland, there is fog for from two hundred to three hundred days out of the year, so the value of a method of navigation independent of visibility will easily be appreciated.

ELECTRO-MAGNETIC WAVES

Radio direction-finding is based on the use of the electro-magnetic wave. This is a combination of two fields of force, namely, an electrostatic field directed vertically, and a horizontal magnetic field. It is possible to design an aerial system which employs either or both of these components, but the aerials in most direction-finding systems are operated by the magnetic field of the electro-magnetic wave. This magnetic field is continually varying and, therefore, when it interlinks with a conductor, such as an aerial, the latter has electromotive forces induced in it.

Loop Aerial. A typical example is shown in Fig. 25a. Suppose this is made in the form of a closed loop or coil of one or more turns. Then the electro-motive forces will be induced in each side of it. But if the aerial is "end-on" to the transmitter (Fig. 25b), the e.m.f. will be induced in side A before it reaches side B, for the wave will have to travel from A to B and will take a certain time (probably less than one millionth of a second). Since the induced e.m.fs. are alternating, it is clear that at any instant the voltages in A and B will not be equal, and, therefore, a current will flow round the loop, which will set up a potential

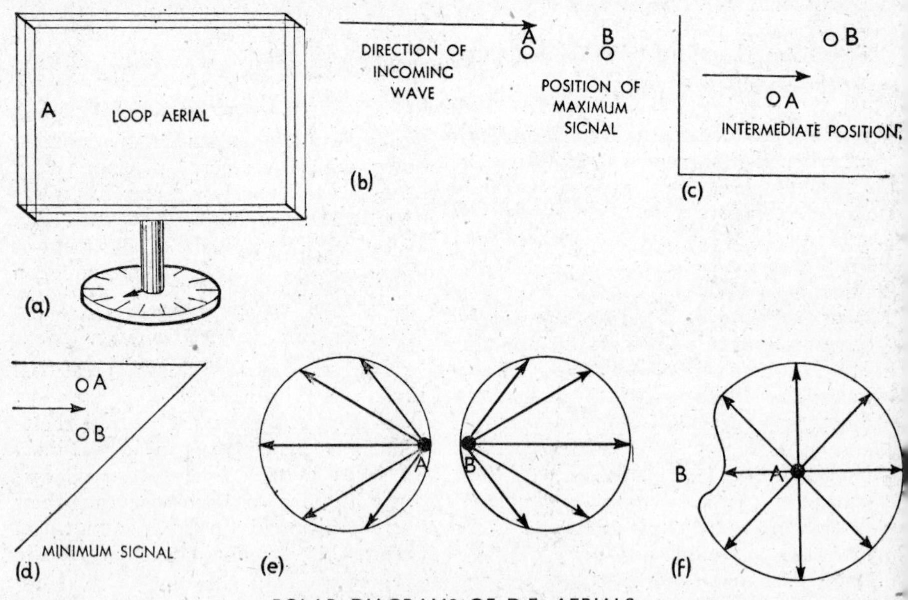

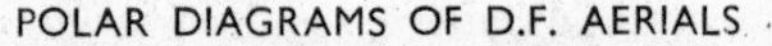

Fig. 25. (a)—General arrangement of unscreened loop. (b)—Maximum signal is received on loop AB when it is end-on to transmitter. (c)—Intermediate position. (d)—Condition of minimum signal when loop AB is broadside-on. (e)—Polar diagram of loop AB and (f)—Effect of using a sense-finder B consisting of a short vertical aerial which is independent of marked directional effects.

difference across the tuning condenser, and thus operate the receiver. Now imagine the loop "broadside on" to the transmitter. For all practical purposes, the sides A and B are equidistant from the transmitter; hence their induced e.m.fs. will be equal and no current will flow in the loop. No signal will be received with the loop in this direction relative to the transmitter. Obviously, intermediate positions will give signal strengths between zero and the maximum obtained when the loop is "end-on" to the transmitter. If the loop is made capable of rotation, it is clear that by turning it to the position of maximum signal strength, the direction of the transmitter can be obtained. In practice, the *minimum* is more sharply defined than the maximum, and direction-finding systems are usually operated on minimum signal, the direction thus obtained being known to be at right angles to the true direction.

SENSE-FINDER

Usually, however, it is found that this simple form of direction finder is not sufficient for navigational work. Reference to Figs. 25 (b and d) shows that there are two maxima and two minima, 180 deg. apart. In some practical cases this is immaterial, as there may be some other means of eliminating the possible error. For example, it is probable in the case of a ship working to a shore D.F. station (Fig. 27), that one possible bearing would come from an inland direction, which is obviously ridiculous. In cases where the ambiguity might cause trouble, a sense-finder is used. This consists of a short vertical aerial which is independent of direction, and whose output is combined with that of the loop and fed to the receiver. In one maximum position of the loop, the vertical aerial voltage will assist the voltage in the loop. In the other maximum position of the loop, the two voltages will be in opposition. If the vertical voltage is adjusted to the same amplitude as the loop voltage, there will not be two maxima, 180 deg. apart, but a maximum and a minimum. Reference to Fig. 25 shows that this

Fig. 26. Typical loop aerial installed in a ship for the purpose of direction-finding by the use of radio waves. There are two loops arranged at right angles and connected to a similar radiogoniometer circuit to that illustrated in Fig. 28.

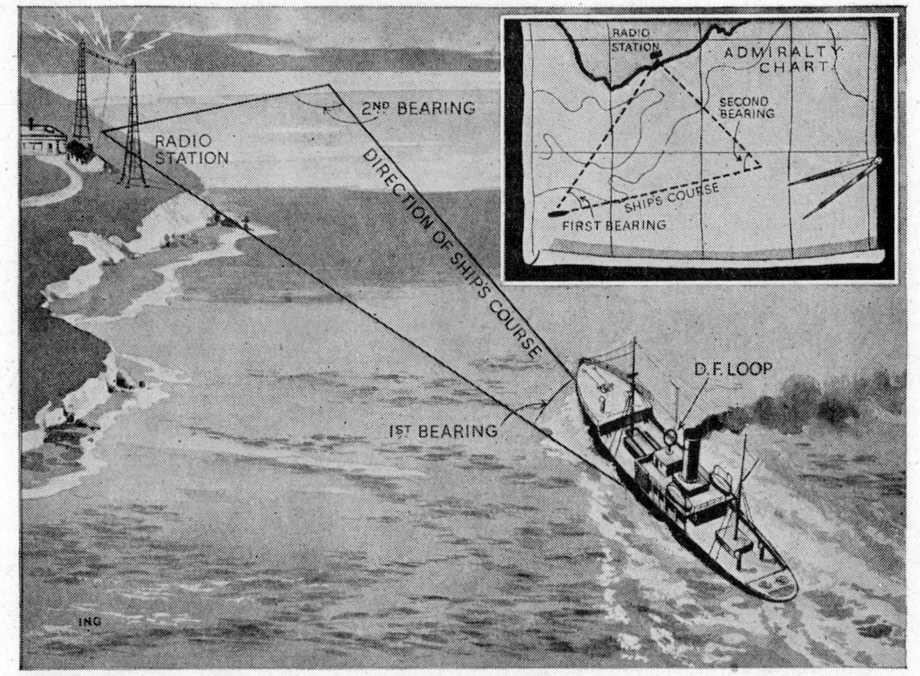

BEARINGS BY RADIO

Fig. 27. Diagram of ship taking bearings by radio from shore transmitting station. Two bearings are taken and a triangle drawn. Thus the ship can establish exactly her distance from the shore.

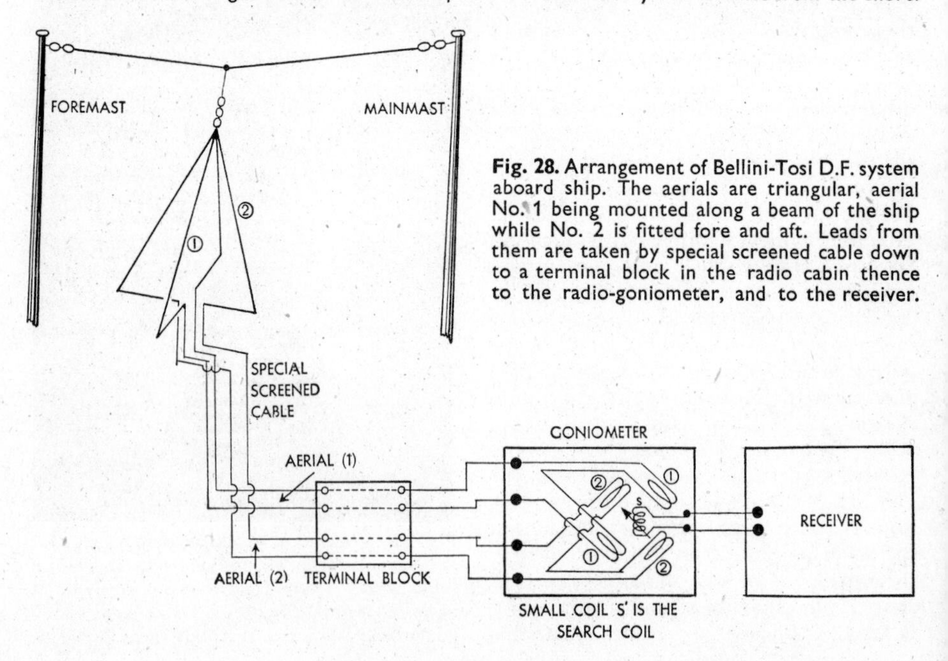

Fig. 28. Arrangement of Bellini-Tosi D.F. system aboard ship. The aerials are triangular, aerial No. 1 being mounted along a beam of the ship while No. 2 is fitted fore and aft. Leads from them are taken by special screened cable down to a terminal block in the radio cabin thence to the radio-goniometer, and to the receiver.

MODERN D.F. INSTALLATION

Fig. 29. Typical modern direction-finding installation (Marconi-type 579) for use aboard ship. The radio officer is in the act of taking a bearing with his hand on the goniometer dial. Principles of the operation of this system are illustrated in Fig. 28. The type of aerial used is shown on page 393.

blurs the real minimum at 90 deg., so bearings should be taken with the loop alone, and the sense-finder then applied to distinguish between the two alternatives.

BELLINI-TOSI AERIAL

The simple loop system described above has certain disadvantages. Perhaps the most important one is mechanical. If the loop is to have a reasonable sensitivity, it must be of a fair size, perhaps three or four feet in diameter. But it will be appreciated that such a loop will have considerable weight, and it may be rather difficult to design a mechanism to rotate it with sufficient accuracy for D.F. work. This is particularly true if the receiving room is some distance below the loop with a long shaft connecting the two points, as is often the case on shipboard. To obviate this difficulty, a modified aerial system known as the Bellini-Tosi system (Fig. 28), was introduced. It consists of single turn aerials, rectangular or triangular in shape, mounted mutually at right angles. These aerials may be of considerable size (perhaps with fifty-feet sides). Leads from them are taken by means of special screened cable to the receiver, where they are connected to two small fixed coils, also mutually at right angles. Inside these coils is a small moving coil, known as the "search coil", the whole arrangement of fixed and moving coils being called a "goniometer", that is, an angle-measurer (see Figs. 29 and 30). The magnetic fields of the fixed coils correspond exactly to those of the aerials, so when the search coil is rotated to give maximum signal strength, it will indicate the direction of the transmitting station. As in the case of the loop the minimum is more sharply defined than the maximum and is, therefore, generally used, and, as with the loop, a sense-finder is used to decide the ambiguity between the two directions indicated by either minimum or maximum signal strength.

SCREENED LOOP AERIAL

The advantage of the Bellini-Tosi system is that only the search coil needs to be rotated, and since it uses large aerials, it is much more sensitive. In fact, the Bellini-Tosi system was originally employed, in the early days, with crystal receivers. But many modern D.F. systems employ modified loops, as receivers of practically any sensitivity are available to-day. In actual fact, amplification of radio signals is limited mainly by the level of atmospherics, etc. As noted at the beginning of this section, an electromagnetic wave consists of an electric and a magnetic field. Now the electric field will set up e.m.fs. in any vertical conductor, which will act like the aerial of an ordinary broadcast receiver and receive, more or less equally, from all directions. The loop will experience these vertical e.m.fs.; in fact, in some systems, the loop is employed as a sense-finder. It will be seen that this "vertical" effect will cause blurred minima.

A modern D.F. loop is of circular section, and enclosed in a tubular non-magnetic metal ring which is just not a complete turn. There will be e.m.f.'s induced in the metallic tube by the electric field, and the loop will be screened from them. But as the screen is not a complete turn, it is not affected by the magnetic field, which induces e.m.f.'s in the loop in the usual manner. To make the aerial weatherproof, the break in the outer tube is completed by a section of strong insulating material. It is obviously more difficult to screen a Bellini-Tosi aerial in this manner and as, with the

DIRECTION-FINDER FOR AERODROMES

Fig. 30. Typical modern direction-finder (Marconi-type 24) as installed at aerodromes. It covers a wave-range of from 15 to 200 metres. A particularly interesting feature is the cathode ray tube on the right which gives a visual indication of direction to supplement the normal audible indications.

DIRECTION FINDING ON AIRCRAFT
Fig. 31. Stream-lined casing on the top of the machine contains an 8 in. screened loop (Marconi type AD 67A/84/50620). Radio direction finding is a vitally important factor in aerial navigation.

gain available in modern receivers, the loop can be made very small, and may be remotely controlled, the Bellini-Tosi system has lost ground of recent years.

RADIO BEACON

There are several other D.F. systems, but it is impossible to deal with them in the scope of a short section. One important point may, however, be mentioned. Direction-finding aerials (a typical one aboard a modern aircraft being shown in Fig. 31) may be used for transmission as well as reception. A large loop aerial may be fed from a transmitter, and arranged to rotate, transmitting for a given time in each of several fixed directions, and radiating the station's call letters or other identifying signal. A ship with an ordinary aerial can receive these signals, note which is the strongest and thus identify the direction of radiation, as the time, duration, and direction of each transmission are issued to ships in Admiralty instructions. Such a station is called a "radio-beacon", and in foggy weather serves the purpose which is normally fulfilled by a lightship or light-house.

RADIO RECEIVERS

A RADIO receiver used for domestic purposes is called upon to "collect" small impulses received by the aerial and to translate them into intelligible and pleasing sound at the loud speaker. The degree to and efficiency with which a receiver performs the functions required of it are conveniently expressed as a combination of certain qualities. In order that a receiver shall possess some or all of these properties in reasonable proportion careful design is entailed as the electrical requirements are often conflicting. This applies particularly to selectivity and quality of reproduction as will be seen.

SELECTIVITY

A receiver must be able to separate a wanted programme from unwanted material on adjacent frequencies. Its degree of ability to do this is called the *selectivity* of the set and is of great importance owing to the congested conditions of the ether.

Effects connected with selectivity depend upon the "band-width" occupied by a transmission and are, therefore, independent of the wavelength used. The behaviour of resonant circuits depends largely upon the ratio between "carrier" frequency (i.e., wavelength) and "modulation" frequency (i.e., band-width) and the selectivity tends to be better on long waves than on short. It is difficult, then, to design a receiver having the same good selectivity on all wave bands, and this, in part, accounts for much of the interference noticed on short-wave reception.

SENSITIVITY

Some receivers can detect relatively weak stations whilst others can only "pick up" the more powerful local transmitters. Their ability in this respect is termed *sensitivity*. Sensitivity is often defined as the input (in micro-volts) to the receiver to produce a given (arbitrary) audio-frequency output at the loudspeaker. An average figure for a typical broadcast receiver would be about 50 micro-volts.

NOISE

One of the most important considerations is the ratio between programme and noise. It is clearly useless to be able to tune in a weak distant station if extraneous noises are of the same level. All highly sensitive sets must therefore have a reasonably quiet "background". Interfering noises may be roughly divided into two classes; those originating outside the receiver and coming in with the wanted programme, and those originating within the receiver itself. External noises are chiefly due to "atmospherics" and electrical plant and machinery and are largely beyond the control of the listener. Their effect can be minimised by careful design and a good aerial. It so happens that the "band-width" occupied by such noises is extremely wide and, therefore, the trouble will be present to a degree on all wavelengths, but, in general, the better the selectivity, the better will be the programme to noise ratio.

Internal noise is partly inevitable and partly avoidable. Its complete elimination is impossible and the consideration of even elementary steps to reduce it is quite beyond the scope of this book.

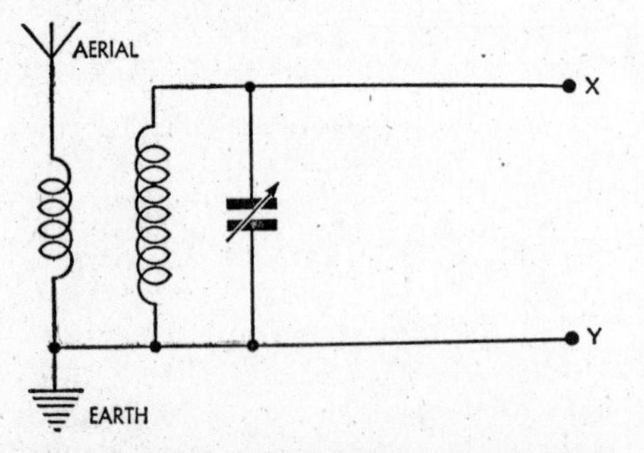

Fig. 32. Simple tuned circuit, frequency selection being by means of a variable condenser.

QUALITY OF REPRODUCTION

In broadcast receivers, the quality of reproduction is a matter of concern. Unfortunately, quite apart from inherent limitations of the loudspeaker and other components in this respect, conditions are largely dictated by permissible band-width in an already crowded ether "spectrum". However, tolerably good and pleasing reproduction can be obtained under conditions laid down by international agreement.

OTHER FEATURES

A receiver must possess electrical and mechanical stability, give consistent results, be easy to handle and, for the popular type, also reasonably inexpensive to run. This last factor includes, of course, both actual cost of electricity consumed and that of replacements as and when necessary. Generally, it must be an ornamental piece of furniture and sometimes it may have to "reproduce" gramophone records. Finally, it must be almost foolproof and electrically safe even if the listener carries out unwarranted investigations from sheer curiosity!

At the receiving aerial, the programme-modulated carrier wave sets up currents which are an exact but weak duplicate of those in the transmitting aerial. By means of a simple tuned circuit as in Fig. 32, voltages corresponding to these impulses are made to appear between X and Y. Now if a pair of head telephones were connected here no sound would be heard because the frequency of the alternations would be too high and the average current driven through the 'phones would be zero. If, however, the voltage across XY could be made unidirectional and not alternating, the telephone diaphragm, whilst not being able to "follow" the individual variations, would rise and fall at a rate determined by their change of amplitude.

To change the alternating current into a unidirectional one, it is necessary only to insert some device which conducts in one direction but not in the other; it is generally called a detector. Various arrangements can be used, but a very simple and effective one is a crystal, or combination of crystals, which possesses this property. The receiver circuit, which, if a crystal, phones and condenser, C, are included, is now complete, Fig. 33.

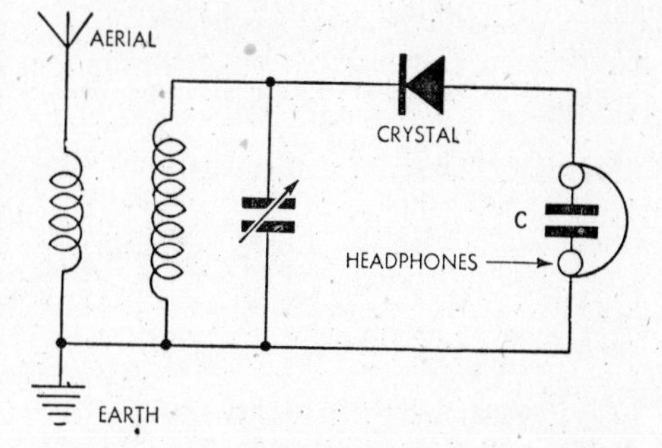

Fig. 33. Receiver circuit employing a crystal detector for demodulating the high frequency current so that headphones can be operated.

Early types of receivers comprised little more than a demodulator (as a crystal or similar detector is now called) and before the introduction of the thermionic valve, the crystal detector was extensively used. The diode, and soon after, the triode, took its place on account of better sensitivity and reliability. The triode is more sensitive than the diode, but the latter is generally chosen because of its relative freedom from distortion.

A simple receiver of this type, whilst suitable for operating headphones when tuned to a fairly powerful local transmitter, is useless for distant reception or for coupling to a loudspeaker. Consequently, some kind of amplification becomes necessary.

Amplification. Amplifying stages may be added either before or after the demodulator, but have distinctly different properties and effects. Post-demodulator amplification, often termed audio-frequency amplification, serves only to increase the strength of the rectified signal and cannot make very weak programmes strong enough to be effectively "detected". One audio-frequency stage is desirable where headphones are used, whilst two or more may be necessary if it is required to operate a loudspeaker at reasonable volume.

Pre-detector amplification, or radio-frequency amplification, serves to increase the strength of oscillations before demodulation. It may not materially increase the loudness of the programme but allows for more effective demodulation (most detectors are more *efficient* with large inputs). It also increases the overall selectivity of the receiver since the selectivity of the amplifying stage is "added to" the selectivity of the demodulator. Finally, it acts as a "buffer" between the aerial and the rest of the set, thus minimising unwanted effects owing to the aerial moving in the wind, etc.

A "STRAIGHT" RECEIVER

Fig. 34 shows a receiver arrangement employing both radio-frequency and audio-frequency amplification. Although only one stage of each is shown, several may be used according to requirements. It should be noted that the loudspeaker requires *power* to operate it and the final valve in the chain is, therefore, so chosen and so worked that the greatest possible amount of power is delivered to the loudspeaker with the minimum of distortion.

A "straight" receiver implies circuit arrangements in which all the radio frequency amplification is carried out at the frequency at which the transmitter is working. It follows that if another programme is selected it will be necessary to retune all the pre-detector circuits. In modern sets, this is accomplished by a single knob and the tuned circuits are said to be "ganged". Such a set is often called a T.R.F. (tuned radio-frequency) receiver.

SUPERHET RECEIVERS

The performance of a straight set leaves much to be desired. Its chief shortcomings are general lack of selectivity, for it cannot separate two powerful stations on adjacent frequencies, and the fact that its selectivity depends upon the wavelength of the station tuned in. Both these drawbacks can, to a limited extent, be overcome by employing a large number of tuned circuits in "cascade", but the difficulty of handling them generally precludes the use of more than four "ganged" circuits, quite apart from the otherwise unnecessary use of several radio frequency stages.

The supersonic heterodyne receiver differs from a T.R.F. set in that after the programme is initially received, its original frequency is changed to another frequency and then amplified before demodulation. This new frequency is known as the *intermediate frequency* and the associated amplifier becomes the "I.F. amplifier". This system offers many advantages. The frequency of any station we wish to hear can be changed to this I.F., and thus all radio frequency amplification may be carried out at a fixed frequency. In such circumstances and since the I.F. amplifiers are fixed-tuned and can be designed to suit requirements, the overall selectivity and amplification will be independent of the frequency of the station received. The only circuits tuned to signal frequency will be those at the "aerial end" of the set and need not exceed two in number. To these must be added the tuned "local oscillator", making only three ganged circuits in all. This comparatively simple arrangement provides all that is necessary for station selection and valves have been produced especially to meet these requirements. All modern domestic type receivers, except the less expensive variety, employ this "super-het" principle. Let us examine in a little more detail the working principle of this arrangement.

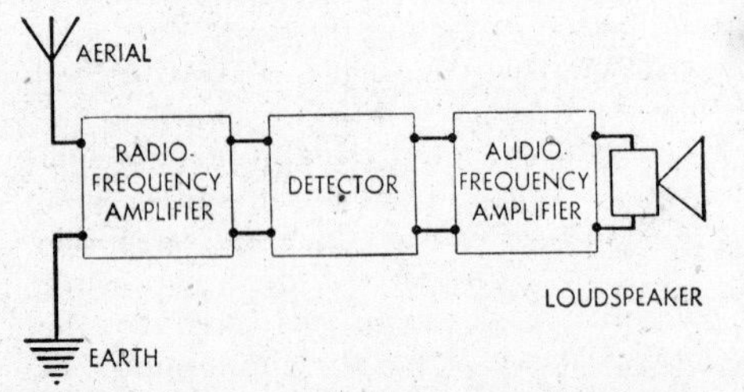

Fig. 34. T.R.F. (tuned radio frequency) receiver circuit using both radio and audio-frequency stages and designed to operate a loudspeaker.

WORKING PRINCIPLE OF SUPER-HETS

Fig. 35 is a schematic diagram showing the various main parts of a super-het receiver. The signal collected from the aerial is put into the *pre-selector*, containing circuits which can be tuned to the desired frequency. In more elaborate sets, the signal undergoes amplification at this stage.

Then the mixer or frequency changer acts on the signal in such a way as to change its frequency. This operation is accomplished by "mixing" a locally generated alternating voltage with the original signal and selecting one of the products of this mixing, namely, a signal whose frequency is the difference between those mixed. It is this new lower frequency which is called the *intermediate* or *supersonic* frequency.

The oscillations, now at intermediate frequency and still carrying the original "intelligence", are amplified to any desired or necessary degree before being passed on to the detector and audio-frequency stages.

If now, in selecting another programme, the signal frequency circuits are altered, i.e., retuned, it will clearly be necessary also to retune the local oscillator in such a way that the difference between the

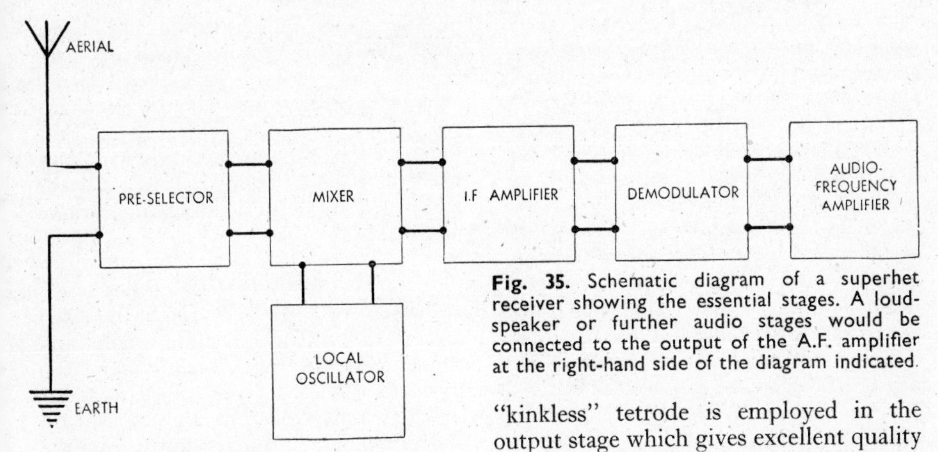

Fig. 35. Schematic diagram of a superhet receiver showing the essential stages. A loudspeaker or further audio stages would be connected to the output of the A.F. amplifier at the right-hand side of the diagram indicated.

resonant frequencies of these circuits shall be equal to the I.F. The tuning condensers concerned are ganged and circuit arrangements are made such that this constant frequency difference exists at all times.

Conflicting requirements influence the choice, which is in the hands of the designer, of the intermediate frequency which is consequently a compromise. "Adjacent-channel" selectivity can be taken care of by the I.F. amplifier if worked at a low frequency. A low I.F., however, calls for sharper tuning of the pre-selector in order to eliminate "second channel" interference. This is only one of the numerous considerations and a complete survey would be very complex.

A typical modern superhet receiver is a "push-button" seven-valve set, and it covers wavelengths of 16·5 to 51 metres, 195 to 560 metres and 750 to 2,000 metres. It has a nominal audio-frequency power output of over 10 watts. Provision is made (in the case of table models) for the use of a gramophone pick-up. Its first stage is a tuned signal-frequency amplifier, and this is followed by a triode-hexode frequency changer with automatic frequency control. The I.F. amplifier incorporates dust-iron-cored radio-frequency transformers and operates at 465 kilocycles per second. A double-diode-triode performs the functions of demodulator, audio-frequency amplifier and automatic volume control. A modern "kinkless" tetrode is employed in the output stage which gives excellent quality owing to a "negative feed-back" arrangement. The loudspeaker has an elliptical cone and is of the "energised" type.

The push-button arrangements involve the inclusion of two small reversible induction motors. Briefly the mode of operation is this. When any particular programme is desired, the appropriate button is pressed, a motor comes into play and drives the ganged condensers to the required position, muting switches silencing the loudspeaker until the station is tuned in. A similar motor is connected to the wave-change switch. The receiver as a whole is a fine example of modern radio engineering and technique.

SUPER-REGENERATIVE RECEIVERS

This type of receiver makes use of a special form of demodulator and is only suitable for operation at very high frequencies (i.e. on short waves). It is well known that a regenerative detector, employing reaction, aids sensitivity.

Now if the reaction feed is increased beyond a certain critical value, oscillation commences and audible beat notes may be produced; in fact, use is made of this for the reception of continuous wave telegraphy. If an increase in sensitivity due to oscillation could be achieved without the production of audible beats, use could be made of this condition for the very effective reception of telephony. For this purpose, an alternating voltage of a frequency above audibility (supersonic) is introduced into the detector circuit in such a manner that oscillation is stopped and started at this new supersonic or "quench" frequency. By this means, audible unwanted beats are not produced and extremely high sensitivity can be obtained. The system has an inherent automatic gain control action and gives excellent results from very simple apparatus. Unfortunately, selectivity is poor, distortion is present and background noise is troublesome. Its use is chiefly confined to amateurs when low cost, weight and size are important, but it is being rapidly superseded by other types of circuit.

COMMUNICATION RECEIVERS

These receivers are designed for and are used by amateurs and others for experimental purposes and should not be confused with commercial equipment for ordinary traffic. They are called upon to deal with all kinds of signals, frequencies and conditions and are, therefore, necessarily elaborate. Generally, they use at least one radio-frequency amplifying stage, a frequency changer, a number of I.F. amplifiers and the usual demodulator and audio arrangements. Normally, band width is variable from a few hundred cycles (using a crystal filter) to tens of kilocycles. Automatic gain control, noise limiters and suppression circuits are incorporated and, for very short waves, double frequency changing is not unusual. Signal strength indicators and beat frequency oscillators are necessary for advanced work and C.W. reception.

To an enthusiast they are a pleasure to handle, but the inevitable number of controls and "gadgets", together with their cost, make them quite unsuitable for domestic purposes.

PORTABLE RECEIVERS

As the name implies, these sets are made to be carried about. They must necessarily contain their own aerial and power supplies and must be neither heavy nor bulky. Modern types are extremely compact, incorporate moving coil loudspeakers and midget valves and derive their power from quite small dry batteries; some, in fact, have provision for "mains" operation where electricity supply is available, thus saving the batteries for occasions when they must be used. The self-contained aerial takes the form of a frame or loop usually wound just inside the case.

CAR-RADIO

Permanent radio sets can be installed (except in war-time) quite easily and conveniently in cars. They differ little from the domestic types except in so far as their power supply and aerials are concerned. The former is drawn from the starter battery, the valve heaters being arranged to suit the voltage. The high tension voltage is provided by a vibratory or rotary converter. The aerial usually consists of a copper mesh or grid slung beneath the chassis or of a vertical rod fixed to the running board. Switch, tuning and volume controls are often attached to the steering column so as to be convenient for their operation.

FUTURE DEVELOPMENTS

Valves. Recent research has produced better and more efficient valves. Cathode heating power and working temperatures have been reduced. Improved structural design has allowed for rigid electrode assemblies, small physical dimensions and uniform characteristics.

Loudspeakers. Domestic-type loudspeakers, although probably still the weakest link in the quality chain, are steadily improving. Twin- and triple-diaphragm models at present in use provide reasonably good reproduction of the available musical register.

Overall Efficiency. A modern mains-operated radio set capable of delivering 5 watts of audio-frequency power to a loudspeaker whose efficiency is well below 50 per cent, requires an input supply of over 70 watts. Thus the overall efficiency is poor. In the years that lie ahead there is certainly much that can be done in the interest of radio receivers in particular and radio engineering in general.

RADIO SERVICE

RADIO service, as the name implies, is that branch of radio engineering dealing with the upkeep and repair of radio equipment. Maintenance of high power transmitters and similar apparatus is a highly-specialised profession and is scarcely within the scope of this chapter.

The repairing of domestic receivers, however, is an important section of the wireless industry, employing thousands of skilled workmen. Modern standards of performance and ever-increasing complexity of design and technique call for a high degree of ability, skill and technical knowledge.

In order to carry out such work, two main conditions must be fulfilled. Firstly, there must be adequate and suitable workshop accommodation and test equipment and, secondly, the engineer must be familiar with electrical and radio technology, have a knowledge of the elements of design and be able to use measuring instruments and various kinds of tools.

A radio service shop, which need not necessarily be large, should be well lighted—naturally, if possible—airy and dry. Good, stout benches, such as the one illustrated in Fig. 36, should be erected in convenient positions, each equipped with a soft covering such as felt and a rack for tools. At least one bench, or perhaps a large shelf, should be reserved for leaving sets on a "time" test or awaiting the arrival of spare parts, and a further "work" bench with a small strong vice should be provided. It is convenient for each working space to be provided with an adjustable inspection lamp, plug points for soldering irons, test gear and instruments. Connections to earth and to an average aerial must also be arranged. Actual lay-out of the shop must, of course, be governed by individual circumstances and requirements, but it cannot be too strongly emphasised that comfortable conditions make the job all the easier. A corner of a typical well-planned radio service shop, with a suitable bench in the background, is illustrated in Fig. 37, whilst Fig. 38 illustrates engineers at work in an E.M.I. service workshop.

TYPICAL SERVICE BENCH

Fig. 36. Typical E.M.I. service bench suitable for two engineers. Note the stout construction and also the conveniently placed rack for tools

SERVICING EQUIPMENT

The diagnosis of faults in a receiver or component cannot, except in a few instances, be carried out unless a certain minimum of test gear is available. Some troubles, such as severed connections or mechanical damage, can sometimes be observed by mere inspection; but as often

WELL PLANNED SERVICE WORKSHOP

Fig. 37. Radio equipment testing and repair are greatly facilitated by the use of oscillators, multi-range meters and other such instruments as are included in this E.M.I. photograph.

SYSTEMATIC FAULT LOCATION

Fig. 38. Engineers at work repairing radio sets in an E.M.I. Service workshop. On the right can be seen the large radiogram assembly, the turntable and receiver units of which are being serviced.

Fig. 39a (above) Universal Avo-Minor. It is less expensive than the Avo-Meter but is, nevertheless, an excellent tester.

Fig. 39b (Right) Model 7, 46-range Universal Avo-Meter having sockets and switches for the selection of ranges. A very comprehensive series of tests is possible with such an instrument.

as not, these occur in inaccessible places and can be readily detected only by electrical test.

The basis of most "universal" testing equipment is a sensitive milliameter. It is essentially a current-measuring device and, by applying Ohm's law, it is simple to determine the voltage across any part of a circuit or the resistance of a component. Milliammeters can be obtained to read currents of the order of a few microamps. upwards but generally one having a full scale deflection of 1 mA is suitable. The range of the instrument, either as an ammeter, voltmeter or ohmmeter, can be extended by the use of shunts, multipliers or external batteries as the case demands. Moving-coil meters are most desirable on account of their accuracy and linearity of scale.

As one is generally concerned with only one reading at a time it is preferable to buy a combined test instrument such as the Universal "Avo-meter" or "Avominor", illustrated in Fig. 39. Each is very simple to use and all the "ranges" are easily selected by means of switches or sockets. In the case of the Avo-meter, it is almost impossible to damage it electrically owing to an ingenious and very efficient overload "trip". This feature automatically disconnects the instrument instantaneously if there is any danger of excessive current burning out the delicate coil. With a modern "universal" test set, it is usually possible to measure accurately direct currents from less than 1mA to about 5 amperes, D.C. voltages from about 2 to 1,000 and resistances from 1 ohm to 0·5 megohm.

A.C. METERS

Unless a good deal of really serious work is to be done A.C. meters need not be considered. However, an A.C. voltmeter, say a two-range type 0–10 and 0–300 volts, will be found very useful both in checking valve heater supplies and mains voltages and possible fluctuations therein. The two "Avo" instruments described above cover these ranges of A.C. voltages.

Another useful instrument is the Megger tester. It consists of a magneto-generator delivering 1,000 volts (sometimes 500), two coils at right angles in a magnetic field, and a scale which is calibrated directly in ohms or megohms. It is used for measuring the resistances or insulations of components under test and is a means of observing their performance under high voltage and often facilitates the detection of a partial breakdown. It is relatively expensive but almost essential for work on large amplifiers and similar gear (see also Chapter 2).

An essential piece of test equipment is the service oscillator or signal generator (Fig. 40). It may be mains or battery driven, the latter type being especially useful for reganging done "on site". No expense should be spared in obtaining a good, reliable instrument. The main features to observe are that it should be thoroughly and efficiently screened; the output should be controllable by a calibrated attenuator and also its scale should be open and easily readable. The calibration charts should be clear and accurate.

To measure the output of a receiver, a "low reading" A.C. voltmeter can be used but it is generally more satisfactory to employ an output meter. Most output meters consist of rectifier-type moving coil meters in conjunction with resistances of specified values. They are, therefore, in effect watt-meters and their scales may be calibrated directly in power units —generally watts or milliwatts; certain "Avo-meters" incorporate this feature. In more elaborate types a matching device is incorporated so that accurate readings can be obtained from the various styles of output circuits in common use, and quite often selector switches are included in order the extend the range of the instrument.

There are two other pieces of apparatus which are very useful but not essential except for more serious or quantitative work. They are a "universal" valve tester and a cathode-ray oscillograph. The former affords a quick and reasonably reliable indication of the state of a valve, the pointer often giving direct reading of mutual conductance. If one is to be purchased, it is desirable that it applies potentials to the valve electrodes approximating to those encountered under usual valve circuit conditions. An adequate supply of representative types of spare valves, however, is just as quick and probably a cheaper solution.

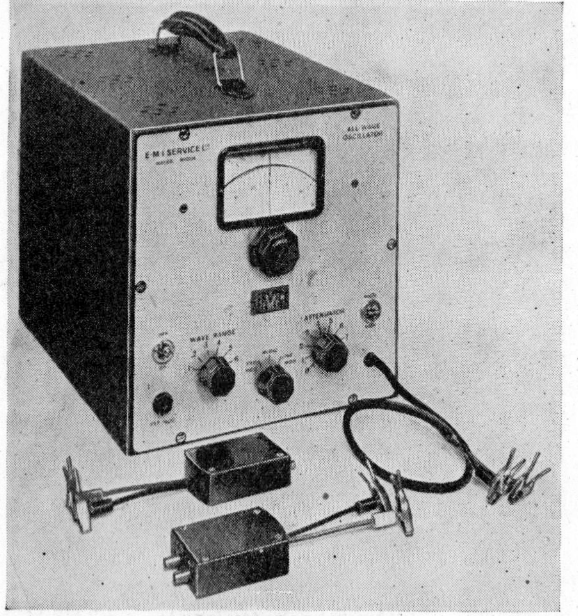

ALL-WAVE OSCILLATOR

Fig. 40. All-wave E.M.I. service oscillator. By generating radio frequency signals it enables R.F. stages of sets to be tested. A "continuous wave" effect is given similar to that of an unmodulated transmission from a broadcasting station.

The cathode-ray oscillograph (Fig. 41) is, strictly speaking, a voltmeter. It has the advantages of a two-dimensional scale and a high-input impedance. It can be used on D.C. or A.C. of almost any frequency and its applications are almost limitless. To mention but a few, it is invaluable in tracing hum, distortion, performance of A.V.C. circuits and for checking or establishing alignment of tuned circuits. For this latter purpose it may be used in conjunction with a frequency-modulated oscillator or "wobbulator". Normally,

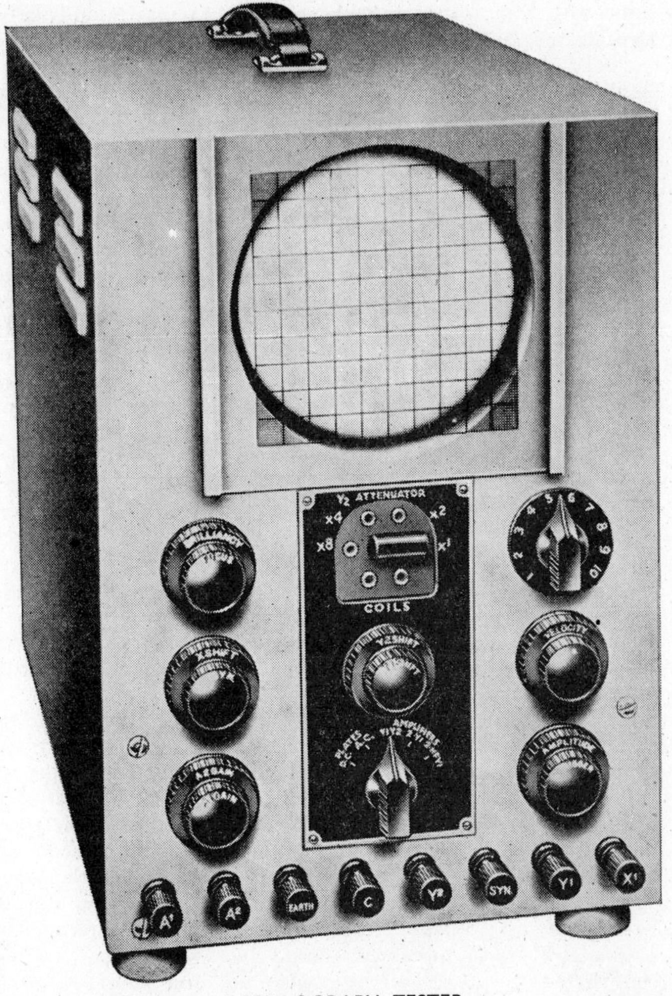

OSCILLOGRAPH TESTER

Fig. 41. Commercial oscillograph using a $4\frac{1}{2}$ in. tube and incorporating a time base suitable for operation up to 225 kilo-cycles per second.

the radio service engineer will require only a few tools but those he must have should be the best obtainable. Two or three screwdrivers (preferably insulated), a pair of "combination" pliers, wire cutter, and a small pair of thin-nosed pliers, are essential. A small adjustable spanner, files, and, of course, a soldering iron must be included. An electric soldering iron is very convenient and should be of the 100-watt type for general work. A non-corrosive flux-cored solder may be used and acid fluxes must have no place in the radio workshop. A supply of reliable mild paste flux and a "heavier" iron are, however, handy for effecting repairs to larger masses of metal which have been exposed to the atmosphere as, for example, aerial wires and for soldering direct to an iron chassis. There are many special spanners, trimming tools and other devices suitable only for certain makes of receivers and their inclusion or otherwise is a matter to be determined by the frequency of their use and whether or not the job can be completed effectively without them.

SPARE PARTS

The most important spare parts to have in stock are a representative range of valves, a good selection of resistors, condensers and potentiometers, tinned copper connecting wire, insulating sleeving, tape, flex, wander-plugs, soldering tags, a tube of adhesive, screws, bolts and washers. A small "mop" type paint brush will also be useful for removing dust.

A receiver, when first handed to the service shop, should be carefully examined to see that it is complete and to make a note of any readily apparent damage. It must be labelled or be provided with some other suitable mark of identification and then passed on to the engineer for fault diagnosis. Generally speaking, the chassis should be removed from the cabinet and again examined for such defects as broken valves and leads and signs of burning or overheating. Its working voltage, if mains-operated, or battery connections if of the latter type, must be carefully checked before switching on. After allowing the set to "warm up" the experienced engineer will apply his first very simple but often extremely informative test—he will listen. The noise that he hears, or the absence of it, together with visible signs, such as brilliance of dial lamps and valve heaters, provide clues as to where to commence routine testing.

The general principle in fault finding is to begin at the end; that is, the power supplies and loud speaker should be checked first, followed by progressive stage-by-stage tests right through the set to the aerial terminal. This method prevents the possibility of one fault being masked by another and ensures that no time is wasted endeavouring to locate a trouble when perhaps there is no power supply reaching the appropriate circuits.

Having made the essential preliminary investigations, systematic examination of the power output stage is the first step. The loudspeaker windings, output valve, electrode potentials and currents should be checked and if a list of typical readings is available, those obtained should be compared with this and ought to agree to within about 10 per cent. Failure to locate a fault here means that it lies "further up" the set and the preceding stage may next come under suspicion.

AUDIO-FREQUENCY SECTION

If the receiver is fitted with gramophone "pick-up" terminals, the whole of the audio-frequency section can easily be tested. The control switch must be set to "gramophone" position, a "pick-up" connected and a record may be played. By this convenient means, not only can the amplification be assessed but also the quality of reproduction can be checked. If no sound be heard, the audio-frequency voltage amplifier (if any) should be examined; if, however, results are satisfactory one may proceed to the "detector" or demodulator stage.

In the absence of local broadcasting, the signal generator may be brought into service. Its modulated output should be connected to the demodulator tuned circuit, care being taken to operate both at the same frequency. Clearly, if now nothing can be heard the detector valve and its associated components may be faulty. On the older types of set it is well worth operating the reaction condenser and listening for the familiar "plop" or whistles.

TESTING R.F. STAGES

If one's patience has not yet been rewarded, attention may be paid to the radio frequency stages. In a T.R.F. receiver, the signal generator may be applied in progressive stages as far as the aerial terminal. In "super-hets", however, the first R.F. stage to be encountered, testing "backwards", will be the intermediate frequency amplifier.

In this case, the generator *must* be employed, since there will be no broadcast signal of the required frequency, but otherwise routine tests can be followed.

In a simple type of set the fault will now have been found, whilst in a "super-het" there remains the examination of the frequency-changing arrangements. Detailed testing of this stage is complicated and except for seasoned experts, the simplest procedure is to test the valve or valves and carefully check each component—by substitution if necessary.

After the repair or replacement has been effected and the set is again working, a final inspection should be carried out before the chassis is replaced in the cabinet. The complete receiver may then be given a "time" test—half an hour is generally sufficient—and left to await re-installation.

Systematic methods and rigorous and exhaustive testing will always ensure a job being well done, and a good service engineer will feel proud and confident when he is able to say "quite O.K. now".

TELEVISION

TELEVISION is the art of seeing at a distance various scenes and happenings at the actual moment of their occurrence.

Unlike the cinema, which only presents a series of photographs of an event, we are enabled by television to see the event and hear the associated sounds without the necessity of first recording and then reproducing them.

Every system of television depends on the conversion of light energy into electrical energy and the re-conversion of electrical energy into light. In addition, television is made possible by that property of the human eye known as "persistence of vision".

The so-called "Photo-electric Effect" or the production of electrical energy by light, was first discovered by Becquerel in 1839, but it was undeveloped and it was not till 1873 that May found that the element selenium possessed the property of varying its electrical resistance when exposed to strong illumination. It was proposed by Ayrton and Perry (1880) to use this property in transmitting an image from one point to another by wires (Fig. 42) and this may be said to be the first television scheme, although, as will be shown later, it had severe limitations.

At the transmitting end the image was focused on a screen composed of numerous small squares of selenium, each square being insulated from its neighbour and connected to the receiver by a wire. At the receiving end a similar screen was erected, composed of electro-magnetically controlled shutters, the movement of which reflected light from a source to the eye of the observer. Each square of selenium was illuminated to a different degree by the light from the image projected on to the screen, and thus each electro-magnet was energised to a degree corresponding to the amount of light falling on the selenium square to which it was connected. The receiving screen then reflected light corresponding to the illumination of the original image, and a reproduction of the image was seen by the observer.

Such an arrangement was crude and remained undeveloped owing to the complexity of the wiring, but it is noteworthy as being the first practical proposal for sending images over a distance. Its main disadvantage lay in the necessity for providing separate wires for each element of the picture, and it was realised

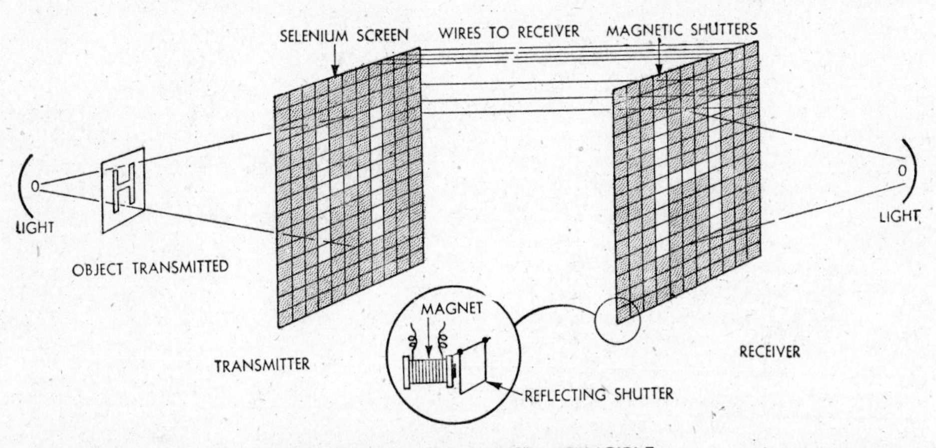

ELEMENTARY TELEVISION PRINCIPLE

Fig. 42. Early proposal for the transmitting of images to a distance using a selenium screen. This was the first practical scheme for sending images over a distance though it had severe limitations.

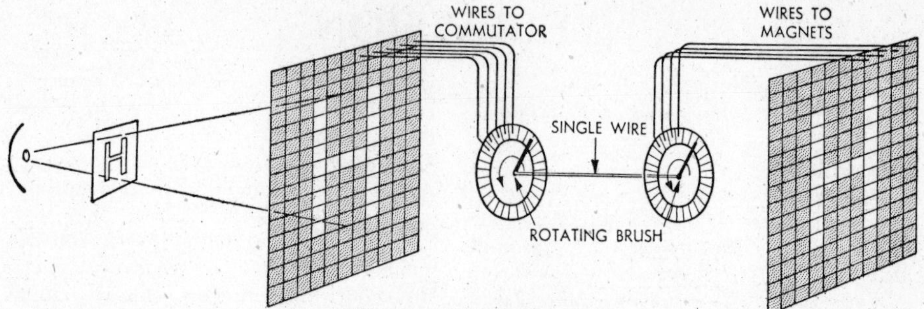

Fig. 43. Modification of the method of Fig. 42 in which the multitude of interconnecting wires is replaced by a single wire and rotating brush contacts working in synchronism.

that any television system to be of use would have to be capable of being transmitted over a single wire or channel.

A step forward was made in the suggestion that the elements composing the picture should be translated into current variations and transmitted in sequence instead of simultaneously, thus enabling a single wire to be used for the link between transmitter and receiver. This could, for example, be done in the Ayrton-Perry scheme by using a rotating brush and commutator, connecting each selenium element in turn to the transmission line. At the receiving end a similar brush rotating in synchronism would connect the appropriate magnet to the line in turn (Fig. 43).

In 1884, however, Nipkow proposed the first really practical system of television using the process known as "scanning", dissecting the scene into a number of small elements which were then transmitted in sequence and re-assembled at the receiver to form the original picture. Fig. 44, which is copied from Nipkow's original patent, shows the proposed arrangement. The image of the scene is focused by the lenses LL on to a selenium plate Se. Interposed in the path of the light is a disc D perforated with a series of holes arranged in a spiral, the pitch of the spiral corresponding to the width of the picture. This disc cut off all light from the selenium plate except that portion of the scene which was opposite the hole at a given instant. The current through the selenium from the battery B was thus proportional to the illumination of the scene at that part, and as the disc rotated the current

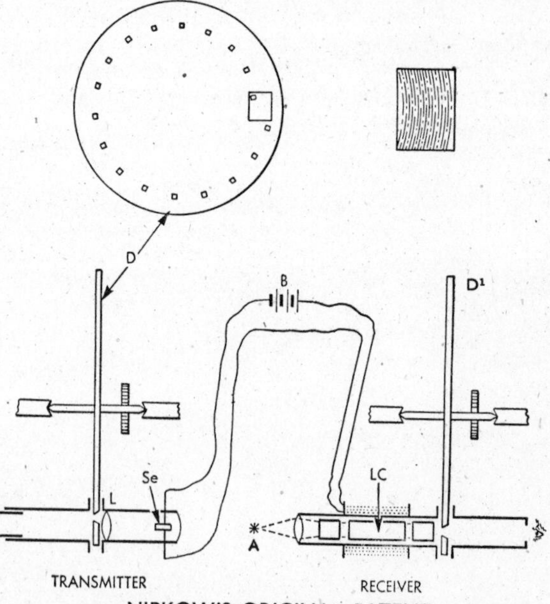

NIPKOW'S ORIGINAL PATENT

Fig. 44. Diagram of Nipkow's television system, taken from his patent specification. This originated the principle of scanning, which is the dissection of a picture into elements.

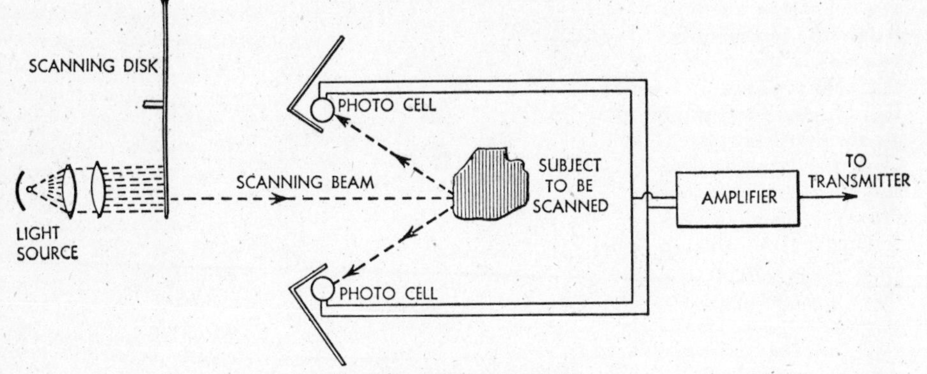

Fig. 46. Diagram showing the layout of a mechanical scanning system, the light from the scanning spot being reflected onto photo-cells placed at each side of the object.

fluctuated with the illumination variations.

Fig. 45 illustrates how the variations in intensity of illumination produce corresponding current fluctuations. At the receiving end the current was caused to vary the light from an arc lamp A through a "light control" LC (the exact nature of which is not important for the moment). A second disc D rotating at the same speed as the first allowed the light to pass to the eye, which then saw the reproduction of the original scene built up by varying intensities of illumination as the disc rotated. An important feature of this particular system is the synchronism of the two discs, as if they rotate at different speeds the reproduced light variations will not appear in their correct space relationship and the result will be chaotic.

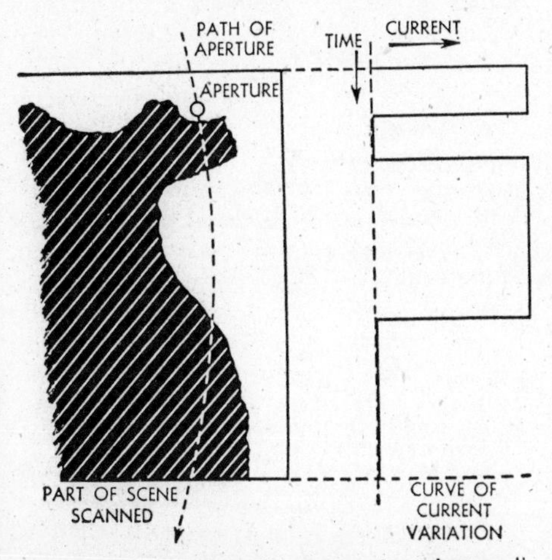

Fig. 45. Showing how the current in a photo-cell varies in accordance with the illumination reflected on it from the scene that is being televised.

Although Nipkow's was the first practical system of television it remained a laboratory curiosity until the invention of the thermionic valve (see page 374) in 1904. This enabled the minute currents to be suitably amplified and transmitted over long distances.

In the beginning of the century Elster and Geitel found that certain metals such as sodium and potassium gave copious emissions of electrons under the action of light falling on them, and produced the first "photo-electric cells" which were far more sensitive than the selenium type of cell.

Meanwhile, the cathode ray tube had been developed as a laboratory instrument and Campbell Swinton saw its possibilities as a reproducer of electrical impulses in the form of light. In a letter to "Nature" (1908) he proposed a television system using cathode ray tubes for both transmission and reception, and it is noteworthy that this proposal was a forecast of practically the whole of modern television transmission and reception. Campbell Swinton did not put his ideas into practical form, but must be given the credit for having originated the present-day television method. Before the revival of his scheme in the modern television system, J. L. Baird had been working on an improved system using the Nipkow disc, and this was demonstrated to various scientific societies in 1923. Following on this, Baird invented a system of television in colour and in steroscopic relief (1928), and his system was finally adopted for public transmission by the B.B.C. in 1929, only to be discontinued in favour of another system in 1936 (see Figs. 49 a and b). Baird's original scanning apparatus can be seen in the Science Museum, Kensington.

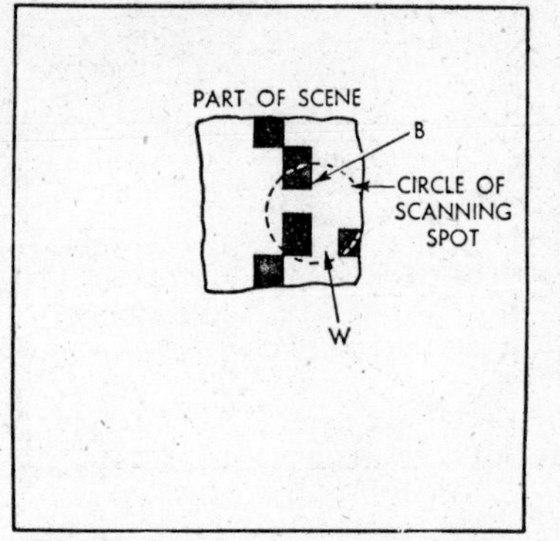

Fig. 48. Showing how reproduction detail depends on the size of the spot of light which is employed for the scanning of the scene at the transmitter.

THE SCANNING PROCESS

The essential part of a practical television system is, as we have seen, the analysis of the scene to be transmitted into a series of elements, the brightness of each individual element being translated into a current value depending upon the degree of that brightness.

This analysis was carried out in Nipkow's system by allowing an aperture to uncover each portion of the picture or scene in turn, but it is also possible to illuminate the scene by a spot of light which is passed across it in a regular manner, the reflected illumination being picked up by a photo-cell placed near the scene (Fig. 46).

In either case, the smallest detail of the scene which can be translated into current impulses is determined by the size of the aperture or scanning spot, as will be seen from Fig. 48.

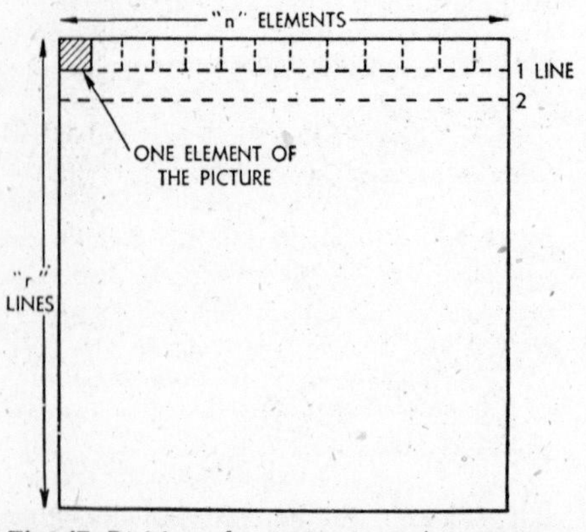

Fig. 47. Division of a picture into elements and lines. This is the fundamental basis of all modern systems of television using cathode ray tubes.

If the circle represents the area covered by the scanning spot, then the light picked up by the photo-cell will be due to the "average" illumination of the area covered by the spot, and the details of black and white marked B and W will be merged into the general light intensity of the background and will appear as a uniform grey shade. For maximum detail reproduction ("definition") the size of the scanning spot should, therefore, be as small as practicable and this size determines the smallest element of the picture which can be faithfully reproduced.

For high definition television the size of spot would be so small and the size of disc so large that its use would be impracticable (although Espley has made a scanning disc for film reproduction at high definition—1940), and the mechanical scanning method has now been superseded by one employing purely electronic means.

The relation between the picture element and the size and shape of the picture is interesting as giving an indication of the needs of the television transmitter and receiver. Referring to Fig. 47, suppose a square picture is scanned by a square aperture which crosses the picture from left to right and top to bottom.

After the spot has scanned one line of the picture, that line is equivalent to, say,

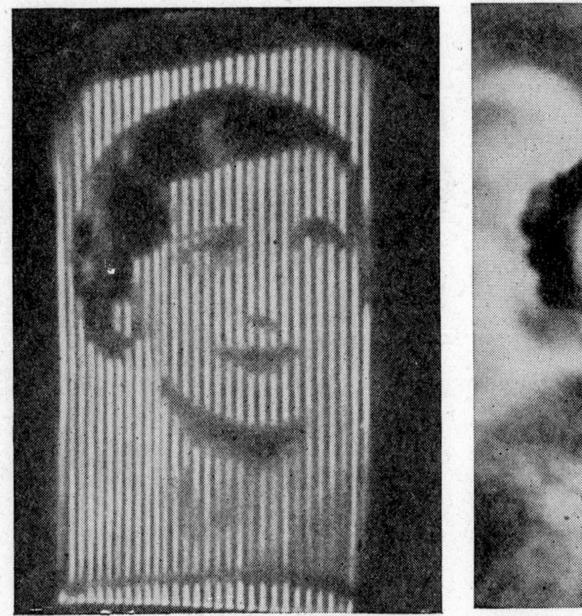

COMPARISON OF DETAIL

Fig. 49a and b. Photograph taken from screen of cathode ray tube showing 30-line B.B.C. television of 1935, and a photograph taken from a television receiver in 1938 (photo. by R. M. Weston, M.A.)

n' elements in a row. At the completion of the line, a second is drawn immediately below the first, and this will also contain 'n' elements.

The total number of elements in the picture is, therefore, 'n^2' if the depth of the element is the same as the width and the picture contains 'n' lines.

It is more usual to refer to the picture by the number of lines into which it is divided, rather than the number of elements; thus we have a 240-line or 405-line picture.

If the picture is rectangular the total number of elements will be multiplied by the ratio of width to height and, if this is denoted by 'k', the total number of elements is 'kn^2'.

PICTURE REPETITION RATE

It is well known from experience at the cinema that if a succession of pictures is presented in sequence an appearance of movement can be given to an object if the sequence follows sufficiently rapidly. To enable television to reproduce moving objects, therefore, the scene must be scanned repeatedly at a sufficiently rapid rate so that persistence of vision will enable the viewer to see the picture as a whole and receive an impression of movement.

CAUSE OF FLICKER

It should be pointed out here that one of the principal differences between television reproduction and cinema film reproduction is that in the latter case the scene is presented as a whole for a short interval of time ($\frac{1}{24}$th sec. approx.) whereas in television only a very small portion of the scene is reproduced at any instant and the effective illumination of the receiving screen is correspondingly less.

It has been found that the minimum repetition rate for producing the effect of motion without jerking is 18 per second, but this gives an objectionable flickering effect and the usually accepted minimum is 24. In practice, this figure is made as high as possible subject to limitations of frequency range (see below).

Each complete scanning sequence must, therefore, take place in $\frac{1}{24}$th second for a 24 per second repetition rate, and if the number of lines per picture is 240, the total number of elements transmitted per second is over a million, and the current waveform corresponding to the smallest details will have a frequency of half this figure. As the lowest frequency which is produced is "zero" frequency it will be seen that the transmitter and receiver have to be designed to pass a much wider range of frequencies than they are called on to do in sound broadcasting. For the same reason, it is not practical to radiate a television signal on the ordinary medium wave band as the frequency coverage would be spread over several hundred broadcasting station frequencies. There is, however, more room on the short-wave bands for a television station to radiate without such a tendency to interfere with neighbouring stations. The signals produced by the scanning of the picture are applied to the transmitter through a chain of amplifiers in a similar manner to that of sound broadcasting. In radiating the signal it is, however, convenient to associate a given amplitude of carrier wave with a given light intensity of scene. This is shown in Fig. 50a, the amplitude of the carrier being a minimum when the black portions of the scene are being transmitted and a maximum when full white is transmitted.

MODULATION

Note that the carrier amplitude does not actually fall to zero on the black signals, for reasons which will be explained later. In America the reverse practice is the case (see Fig. 50b) the "black" signal corresponding to maximum carrier amplitude and white to minimum. This is sometimes called "negative modulation" and the other "positive modulation" or D.C. modulation. The association of carrier amplitude with a definite value of illumination is important as it enables the background lighting to be correctly rendered in addition to the individual variations throughout the picture. The

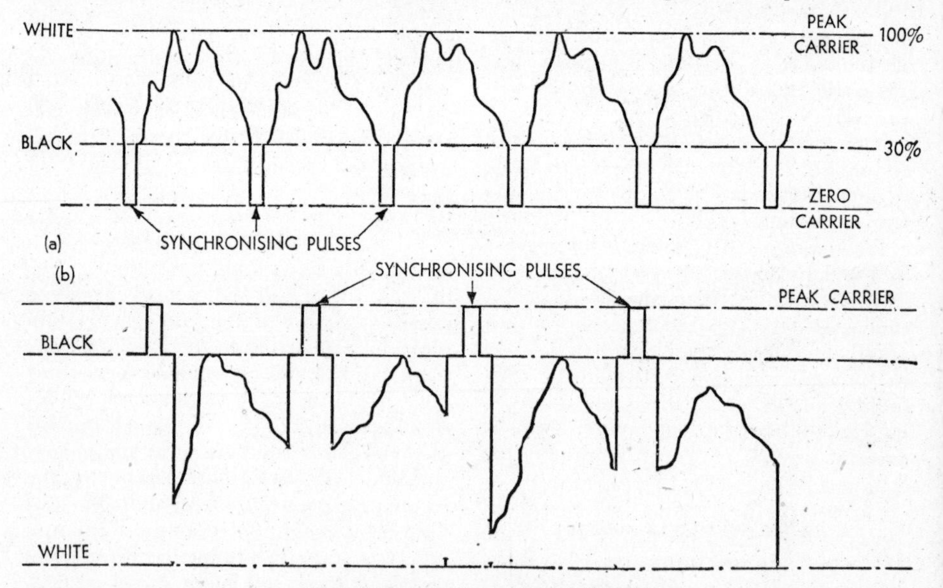

Fig. 50. Outline of two waveforms of the television signal, the peak value corresponding to maximum illumination (a), and the peak corresponding to minimum illumination (b). The latter waveform is used in certain of the American television systems and is sometimes called negative modulation

modulation at the transmitting end is a continuous process while the picture is being scanned similarly to the modulation imported by a microphone with sound. Fig. 51 shows how the illumination of the background affects the transmitted signal, which can be considered as an A.C. component superimposed on a D.C. component, the height of which is proportional to the background illumination.

The introduction of the D.C. component into the signal reproduced by the receiver gives the correct rendering of the overall brightness of the scene which is being viewed.

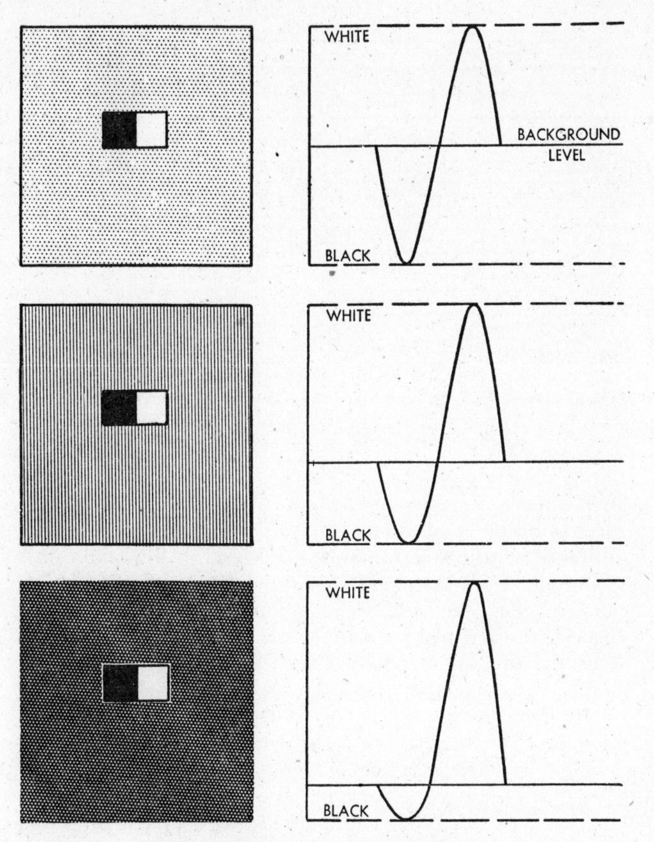

BACKGROUND ILLUMINATION

Fig. 51. How the illumination of background affects television signal. The waveform is that produced by scanning individual black and white squares with a light spot equal in size to one of those squares.

SYNCHRONISING

It was stated in the description of Nipkow's apparatus that it was essential that the scanning spot at the receiver should be moving in exact synchronism with that at the transmitter in order to reproduce the picture correctly. The synchronism of the receiver and transmitter signals in the case of high definition television is all-important and the scanning spot at the receiver is "locked" to that of the transmitter at the commencement of each line scanned and each complete picture scanned. To do this, the signal corresponding to each line is followed by a sharp pulse, the "synchronising pulse", which is radiated by the transmitter and which differs from the picture signals in that it is above or below the level of the black signals. This is marked in Fig. 50, and the complete television signal includes both the picture waveform and the synchronising pulses. Since these are separate from the picture signals they cannot be confused with them and can be filtered out at the receiver and applied to the scanning circuit. At the completion of each one of the pictures a similar synchronising pulse signals the completion of the picture scan and locks the scanning circuit of the receiver in synchronism for the next frame scan.

Although a picture repetition rate of 24 or 25 per second is reasonably satisfactory, it does not completely eliminate flicker. If the picture repetition frequency could be increased to 50 per second, it would be far more satisfactory, but the frequency band required for the transmission would be doubled (see the section

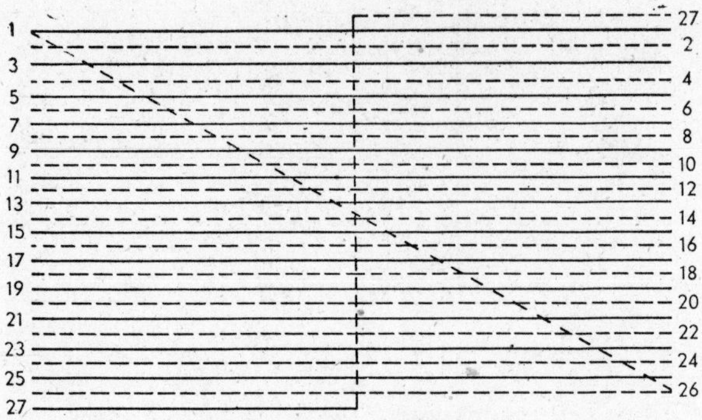

INTERLACED SCANNING

Fig. 52. Lines 1, 3, 5, etc., are first drawn, and then the spot returns to the top of the frame at line 27, filling in the gaps by lines 2, 3, 6, etc., thus doubling the picture repetition rate.

on Picture Repetition Rate), with a corresponding increase in cost and difficulty in transmission and reception.

The effect of a 50-per second repetition can, however, be obtained without increasing the frequency band width if the scanning lines in the picture are "interlaced". To do this, the picture is scanned in alternate lines, a space equal in depth to one line being left between the lines of the scan. When half the number of scanning lines have been drawn the scanning spot moves back to the beginning of the picture and draws the remaining lines of the scan in the spaces between the first set. When the bottom of the picture is reached it has then been scanned twice and the complete number of lines has been drawn. (Fig. 52 shows an interlaced scan of a few lines, the dotted lines corresponding to the second scanning operation.)

The improvement brought about by this arrangement is as follows:—Suppose the total number of lines is 405, and $202\frac{1}{2}$ of these are drawn in $\frac{1}{50}$th sec., which is half the total time taken to scan the whole picture. At the end of $\frac{1}{50}$th sec. the

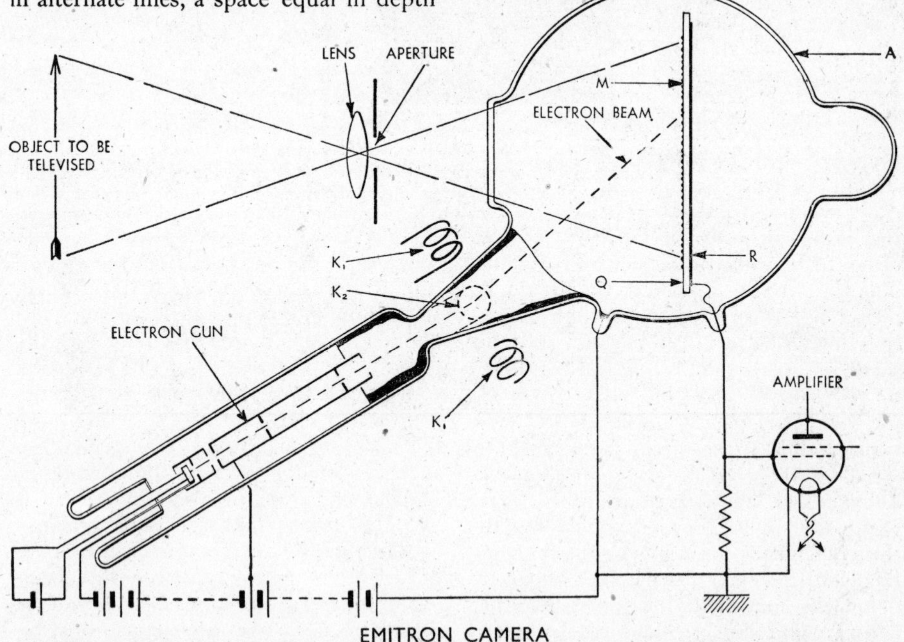

EMITRON CAMERA

Fig. 53. Outline of the Emitron Camera used in the B.B.C. television system. M is the photo-sensitive mosaic screen on which the image is focused by the lens and K_1 and K_2 the magnetic deflecting coils.

scanning spot will return to the top of the picture at a point which is only one line in thickness away from the line drawn at the commencement of the scan. The eye, if sufficiently far away, is unable to distinguish the small displacement of the spot and it appears as though it had returned to its original position.

The apparent rate of scanning is thus 50 per second, although the spot is only covering half the number of lines in this period.

By this method the picture frequency is kept at 25 per second while the flicker is eliminated, except for a slight flicker between adjacent lines of the scan which is unnoticeable in most cases. The picture now consists of two "frames", each containing half the total number of lines.

MODERN TELEVISION

The basis of modern television systems in both translating and reproducing the scene is the cathode ray tube. At the studio end the scene to be televised is picked up by an "electron camera" first devised by Zworykin, and the signals are transmitted on the short-wave band to receivers within a radius of 100 miles or more. The electron camera is shown in Fig. 53 in the form in which it has been developed by E.M.I., Ltd., in this country. It consists of an evacuated glass bulb A containing a mosaic screen M on which the image of the scene is focused by a lens system as in an ordinary camera. This mosaic is composed of a large number of silver globules, each separated from its neighbour and treated so that it is photo-sensitive. When the light from the scene falls on the surface of the mosaic some elements will receive more light than others and will emit electrons in proportion to their illumination. The mosaic is supported on a flat mica plate Q which is covered on the reverse side with a conducting layer R, known as the "signal plate". This layer is connected to the amplifier as shown.

In the neck of the tube attached to the bulb is mounted an electron-producing

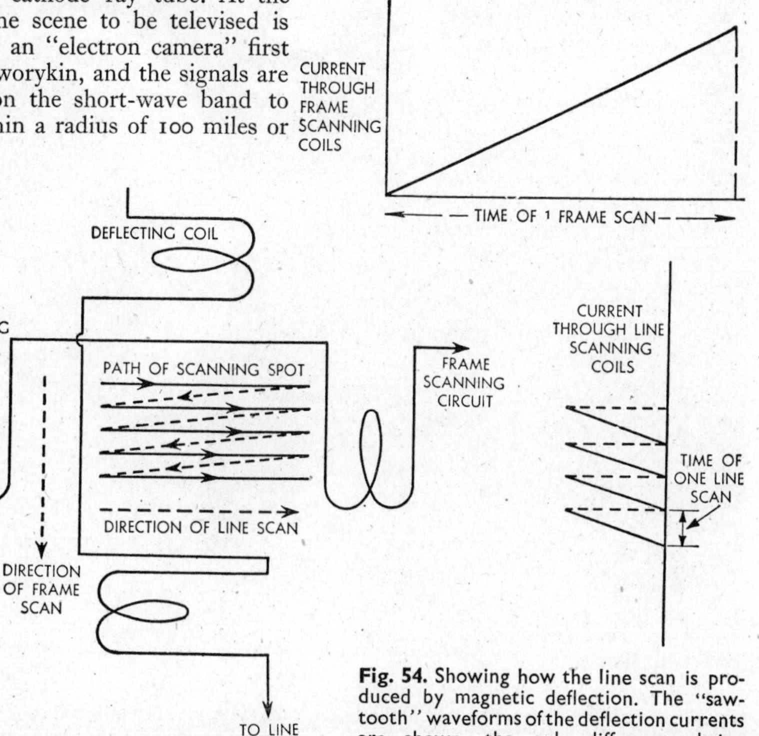

Fig. 54. Showing how the line scan is produced by magnetic deflection. The "sawtooth" waveforms of the deflection currents are shown, the only difference being the rate at which the current increases.

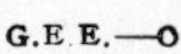

ASSEMBLING CATHODE RAY TUBE

Fig. 55. Preparing a large diameter cathode ray tube bulb for sealing in the electrode structure. Glass work of this type calls for considerable skill and experience. After this sealing air will be exhausted and a high degree of vacuum produced within the bulb, which will be ready for service.

system including an electrically heated cathode similar to that of a cathode ray tube.

The beam of electrons is caused to scan the surface of the mosaic by magnetic deflecting coils K_1K_2 which deflect it in a series of parallel lines across the face of the mosaic. As the beam scans the surface it restores electrons to those globules which have lost them by photo-electric emission and the electron charges are communicated to the signal plate through the intervening dielectric. Hence, as the beam scans the mosaic a train of impulses is sent to the amplifier and transmitter which corresponds in intensity to the illumination of the mosaic and the original scene. There is a metal lining to the bulb which provides the necessary second connection to the external amplifying circuit.

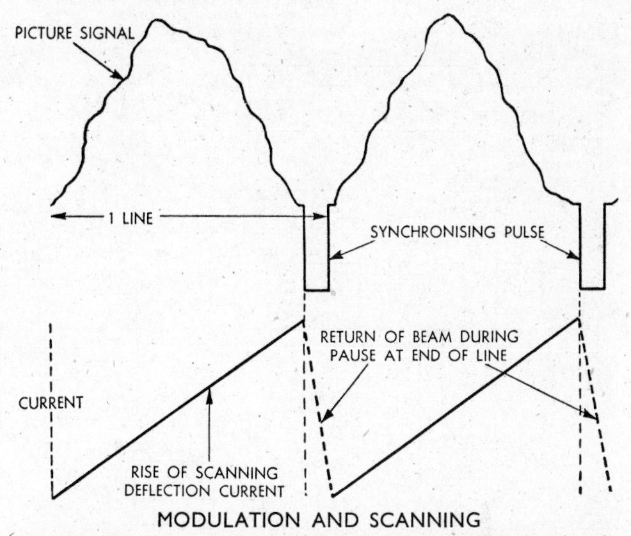

Fig. 56. Relation of picture signal to scanning waveform. The return of the scanning beam takes place at the end of each line and frame. The synchronising signal cuts off the beam during this time in order to prevent it appearing on the screen.

SCANNING CIRCUIT

The circuit for deflecting the beam in the electron camera is of particular interest as it is similar in every respect to that which is used to scan the receiving screen, and the two scanning circuits are locked together by the synchronising impulses previously mentioned.

To produce a uniform movement of the beam across the screen or across the mosaic in the camera tube, a deflecting field is applied to the beam which increases in intensity at a uniform rate and then abruptly decreases to zero as the beam completes its traverse. The action of the field is shown in Fig. 54. While the beam is scanning one line, a similar magnetic field at right angles to the first deflects the beam downwards, but at a slower rate, so that each succeeding line is scanned at the correct distance from the first. When the beam has completed one line it returns to the point from which it started and during this retrace the signal is cut off so that no picture is transmitted. The blank is filled in by the superposition of a synchronising pulse which is applied to the scanning circuit of the receiver and keeps the deflecting system in step with that of the camera (Fig. 56).

The transmitted current impulses are received in a similar manner to ordinary short-wave broadcast signals, except that the frequency response of the receiver circuit has to be made wider in order to accommodate the full range of frequencies used.

SOUND AND VISION

The sound accompaniment to the television scene is transmitted on a slightly different wavelength from that of the vision signals, but is usually received on a common aerial and separated by tuned circuits in the receiver.

The vision impulses after detection are applied to a control shield or modulator which lies in the path of the electron stream of the cathode ray tube and which corresponds to some extent with the grid of a thermionic radio valve. The intensity

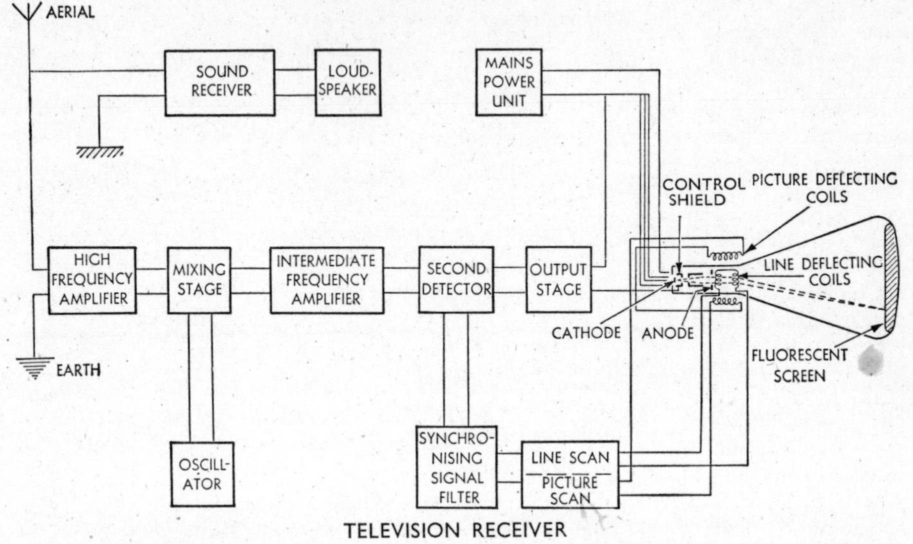

TELEVISION RECEIVER

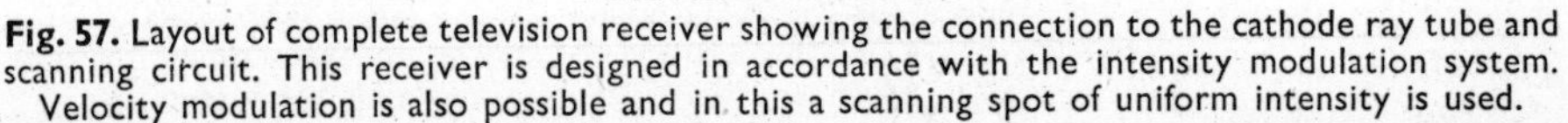

Fig. 57. Layout of complete television receiver showing the connection to the cathode ray tube and scanning circuit. This receiver is designed in accordance with the intensity modulation system. Velocity modulation is also possible and in this a scanning spot of uniform intensity is used.

of the electron beam, and hence the illumination of the screen, is thus varied in proportion to the received signal. The synchronising impulses are applied to the scanning circuit of the tube and as the beam moves over the screen it traces out the light and shade of the picture line by line. Fig. 57 shows a diagrammatic layout of a television receiver circuit.

OTHER TELEVISION SYSTEMS

It was stated above that the modulations of the intensity of the electron beam are obtained at the receiver by a control of the electron beam in a manner similar to the control exercised by the grid of an ordinary valve. There is, however, another system having considerable advantages, known as velocity modulation, in which a scanning electron beam of uniform intensity is used. Modulation is obtained by variations of the velocity of this scanning beam. Yet a further development is a combination of both intensity and velocity modulation.

It should be noted that velocity modulation refers to the velocity of the traverse of the light spot over the screen and not to the velocity of the electrons travelling in that stream as is so often thought by those not fully acquainted with this system.

Although the cathode ray tube has largely displaced systems using a mechanical scanning disk or other apparatus, at least one successful system has been developed for large scale projection of pictures using lenses and mirrors for the projection of a light beam on to a screen. This system which has been developed by Scophony, Ltd., is capable of producing pictures measuring 24″ by 20″ which are not possible by the ordinary type of cathode ray tube. However, special tubes have been developed for the projection onto screens of large pictures and, no doubt, the future will see considerable progress made with this development. Other new developments which hold considerable possibilities include colour television in high definition both in this country (J. L. Baird) and in America (Dr. Goldmark).

The television system of the B.B.C. was the first successful high definition service in the world, and, it has conclusively demonstrated that television in the home can be completely practical.

APPENDIX

Electrical Engineering Drawing. Choice of Instruments. Use of Instruments. Execution of Drawing. Orthographic Projection. Free-Hand Sketching. Units and Standards. Symbols and Formulæ. Definitions of Common Electrical Terms.

THE study of electrical engineering and the practical interpretation of its principles, are greatly facilitated by a knowledge of draughtsmanship. Therefore, in this appendix a brief outline of the subject is given, together with sufficient information to enable the reader to grasp its essential details and apply them as occasion arises. It should also be appreciated that a fundamental basis of sound electrical engineering practice is an exact definition of units and terms. Therefore, this appendix includes these in tabulated form for quick reference. For full explanations of their various purposes and applications the appropriate chapters and sections in the body of the book should be consulted.

ELECTRICAL ENGINEERING DRAWING

IT does not fall to the lot of every electrical engineer to become a professional draughtsman, but it is, however, an essential qualification that he should be able to read a machine drawing intelligently. He may be required to take details of a machine part so that it can be readily manufactured and that necessitates free-hand sketches from which finished drawings can be completed. In this section, it is proposed to outline briefly the principles of this practice with a view of interesting the reader in this important branch of engineering and of encouraging the student to attain such proficiency that will stand him in good stead throughout his whole career.

It may be suggested here that the engineer uses the drawing in exactly the same way as the author uses a language in order to convey to the reader specific ideas. If, for example, the author wishes to describe an electric knife switch he makes use of letters grouped into words arranged into clear explanatory sentences, and the success of the description, which means the ability to convey to the reader the exact appearance of the switch, will depend upon the skill with which the sentences are planned. The engineer makes use of lines instead of letters, of views instead of words, and of arrangements of views in place of sentences, and the intelligent reading of such descriptions is merely a matter of training and practice. Once this preliminary training has been acquired it will be obvious that the drawing will more readily convey to the reader exactly what is in the designer's mind than a written description which can be extremely complicated and lengthy. There can be little doubt that the simplest way to describe the Hampton Court Maze would be to take a pencil and paper and draw an airman's view of it; that is, a "plan view".

In order to standardise drawing office practice so that one set of conventions shall be universally adopted and recognised, the British Standards Institute have issued a useful booklet entitled "British Standard Engineering Drawing Office Practice". This book contains a series of recommended methods to which reference will subsequently be made.

CHOICE OF INSTRUMENTS

All finished drawings of machine parts are executed by scientifically accurate instruments, and in common with all engineering projects these tools should be of good quality. Since the cost of the necessary apparatus is high it is to be strongly recommended that, at the outset, the student should purchase a few "pieces" of first-class quality, which will last him his lifetime. These can be augmented later as requirements dictate. As an absolute minimum to commence with the following articles are suggested:

(1) Pair of spring-bow pencil compasses, approximately 3 inches long, fitted with adjustable needle point and adjustable pencil lead.

(2) Pair of pencil compasses, approximately $5\frac{1}{2}$ inches long, also fitted with adjustable needle and lead points. (Usually the leads supplied by the makers are too soft and the student should extract the lead from an "H" pencil instead.) If the needle point becomes defective an ordinary sewing needle makes an excellent substitute. Large holes bored into the paper by blunt, coarse points ruin the appearance of the paper and the drawing. Fig. 1 shows typical instruments with the correct method of sharpening the leads. The large compasses are usually supplied with additional extension arms.

(3) Transparent set square of 45 degrees angle not less than 8 inches long, and a similar 60—30 degree, one of not less than 10 inches length should be purchased. Those made of wood or tin are absolutely useless. It is an indispensable advantage to see the drawing through the square which covers a considerable area when in use.

(4) Transparent, semicircular protractor of about 6 inches diameter.

(5) (Pencils.) Except for printing and figuring, when an "H" pencil should be used, soft leads are to be avoided because the resulting lines smudge easily as the instruments are moved across the paper, and produce a dirty drawing. A good clean line of uniform thickness can be readily obtained by a "2H" pencil. An "HB" pencil may be employed for free-hand sketching.

The pencil lead should be well exposed for at least $\frac{1}{2}$ an inch and be sharpened to a chisel point as illustrated in Fig. 1. The flat side of the lead is convenient for guiding along the edges of the set square and the tee square; the chisel point gives a line of uniform thickness and remains sharp for a longer period. The pencil points should frequently be touched up on a piece of sandpaper usually supplied in convenient block form or, in an emergency, the edge of a matchbox. For ordinary free-hand drawing the "HB" lead should have the usual

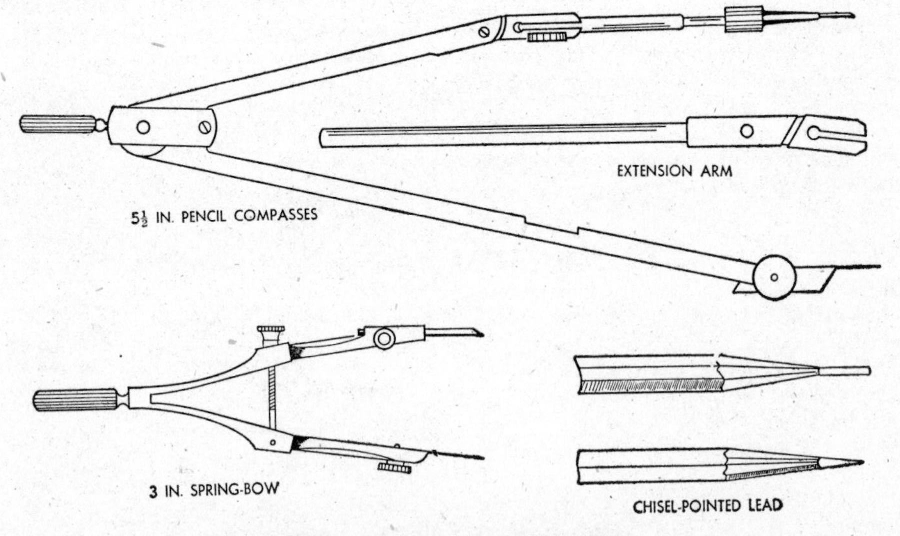

ESSENTIAL DRAWING INSTRUMENTS

Fig. 1. Some instruments for accurate draughtsmanship, including two views of chisel-pointed pencil.

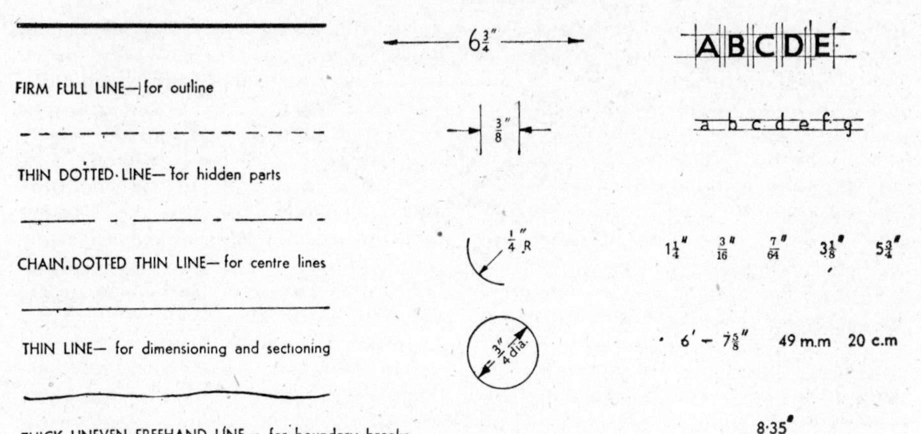

STYLE OF DRAWING

Fig. 2. Typical examples of line, printing and dimensioning as used in machine drawing.

rounded point. Notice that with a short stubby point the wood of the pencil obstructs the view and leads to inaccuracy.

(6) Medium hard rubber for ordinary erasures, and a soft spongy eraser for cleaning should also be supplied.

(7) Drawing board, not smaller than 24 ins. × 18 ins., which accommodates the half-imperial-sized sheet of drawing paper should be of good quality, fitted with stiffeners at the back to prevent the possibility of warping, although, nowadays an excellent and cheap substitute is made of 7 or 9-ply wood without the backing. The paper is secured, normally, at the two upper corners by large flat-headed drawing pins.

(8) Tee square of good quality preferably with an ebonite edging, long enough to span the board comfortably. The cheaper varieties quickly loosen from their stock and develop ragged edges.

(9) Scientific engineer's scale of a double convex type made of either box wood or of the more expensive white ivorine. Here again, an expensive scale is well worth the initial outlay. These scales are variously graduated to suit different classes of work but, as a general rule, they should include full, half, quarter and eighth full-size on one side and three, one-and-one-half, three-quarters, and three-eighths inches to the foot on the reverse. It is frequently an advantage also to have a second scale marked off in tenths and hundredths and the metric system for special work.

GENERAL RULES FOR USING INSTRUMENTS

The drawing board should normally be at a slight slope towards the draughtsman at a convenient height to enable him to stand while working. If the student is using a flat table the board can be raised at the back on two blocks of wood approximately 2 inches high.

All the instruments should be laid out on the left hand side of the board on a clean duster. Much of the dirt that subsequently finds its way on to the paper is picked up from the table when the instruments are carelessly cast aside, and also quite a lot of valuable time is lost in searching for a particular piece.

The following pencil-line conventions are universally adopted and should be memorised:—

In drawing the outline of a machine part, a bold, firm, uniform, thick line is used. Those portions of the machine part which are hidden in any one view appear as thin dotted lines. General centre lines are shown as thin dot-dash chains. Projection and dimension lines are drawn as thin continuous lines, broken in the case of dimensioning approximately at their middle point where the figures are inserted. Arrow heads at the extremities of these lines must be put in carefully and neatly as illustrated in Fig. 2.

The tee-square should be controlled entirely by the left hand, by stroking it into position, making always quite sure that the head, or stock is square against the edge of the board. The set square can be readily guided along the edge of the square by the thumb and forefinger of the same hand. A little practice gives complete control over the two instruments, leaving the right hand free to manipulate the pencil. A constant slight pressure to the right by the left hand will ensure that the tee square keeps true when sliding the instruments up and

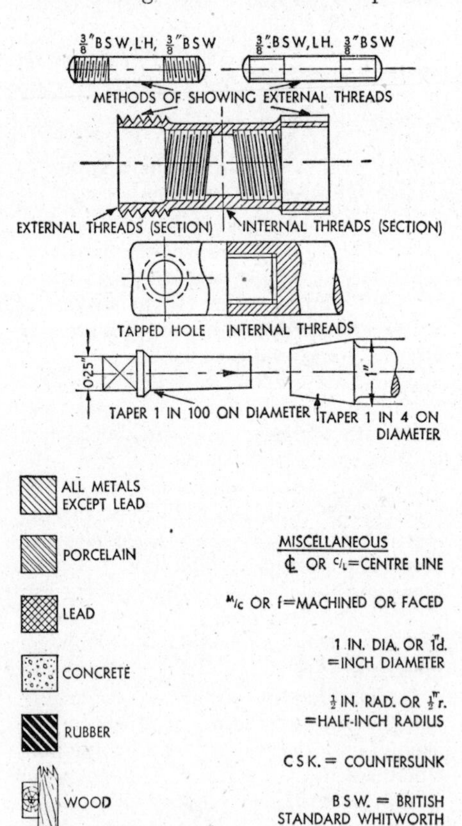

Fig. 3. Miscellaneous conventions employed in electrical drawing, including a selection of some commonly applied lettering abbreviations.

down. In making a line, it is easier and much more accurate to place the pencil point on the exact spot from which a line is to be drawn and then to slide the edge of the tool up to the edge of the pencil. The pencil should lie at an angle away from the square and be dragged firmly and deliberately across the paper rather than pushed. A pushed pencil invariably results in digging grooves and sometimes holes in the paper. When sharp corners are to be made, the pencil point should be placed in turn at each corner and drawn away from the corner. The intermediate space can then be filled in afterwards by a third bold stroke. By this artifice no ragged joins are visible.

The compasses should be handled lightly and carefully, and the needle point inserted just sufficiently deeply into the paper to prevent slipping when scribing a curve. The scale should be held in the left hand with the thumb and little finger below so that it is tipped on to its knife edge. This brings the scale as near to the surface of the paper as possible and, with the pencil held vertically above it, leads to greater accuracy in marking off specific lengths. As a general rule, curves should be drawn in first and the straight lines filled in from the points where the curves finish, adopting the same method as for corners. This method again, obviates bad joins which, of course, spoil the appearance of a finished drawing.

Decide on the number of "views" necessary to describe completely the work in hand, set out the required centre lines so that the work is well spaced within the limits of the paper, and then draw in as much of all the views required as possible with each setting of the squares. Avoid crowding one particular view with dotted lines, indicating hidden parts when an additional view would reveal them more clearly.

Move freely around the board, get well over the work, and choose the best position for every line before making it. An important feature of every drawing is the dimensioning which, if executed badly, disfigures and confuses the result and generally spoils the appearance. As a

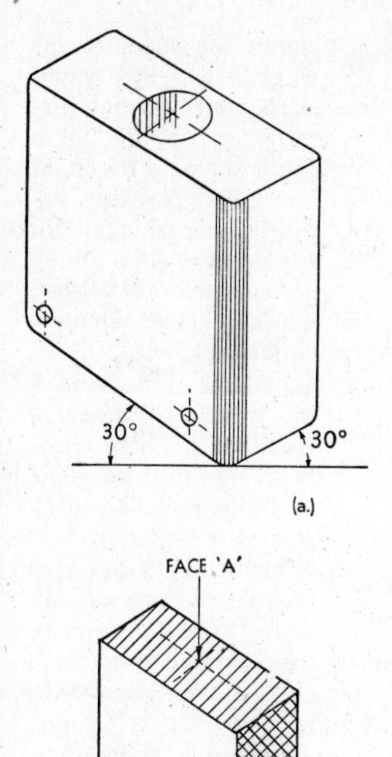

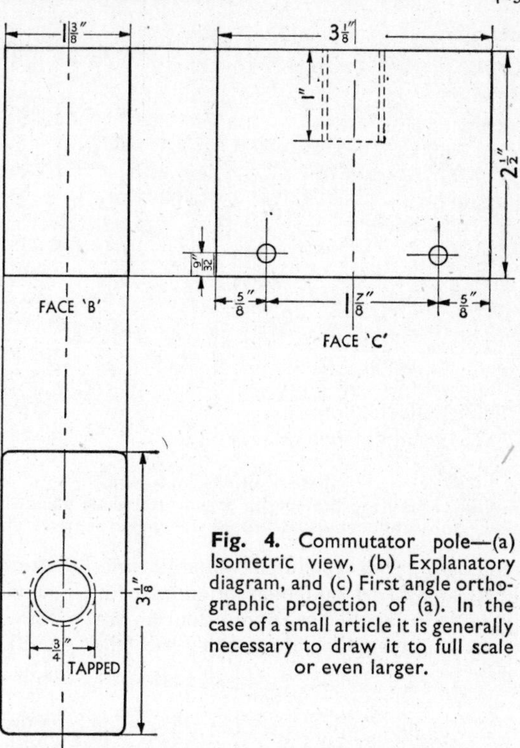

Fig. 4. Commutator pole—(a) Isometric view, (b) Explanatory diagram, and (c) First angle orthographic projection of (a). In the case of a small article it is generally necessary to draw it to full scale or even larger.

rule the figures should appear outside each view and distributed without needless repetition between all the views. All figures must be printed neatly, of uniform proportionate size, and appear, in all cases, at right angles to their respective dimension lines. Vertical dimensions should be placed so that they can be read from one side of the paper only. Fractions are put in about one third higher than the whole numbers with a dividing line parallel to the dimensioning line, and it is important always to add the appropriate units, whether the measurements are in feet, or inches, or millimetres, etc. Typical figuring is shown in Fig. 2.

All notes, instructions and titles must be neatly printed. Block capitals and small script, preferably vertical, are most effective, and fancy sloping characters should be avoided. Numbers of students find great difficulty in producing good-looking printing and are only too painfully aware of the untidy effect of ill-formed characters. For block letter work the easiest and quickest way is to draw lightly two guiding lines to ensure that all the letters shall be of uniform height, and then to divide this parallel space by short vertical lines, drawn in free-hand, to form approximate squares, with the appropriate spacing between so that each square can encase a letter. By this method, a quick estimate of correct spacing of words across the sheet is at once obtained. The letters "M" and "W" it will be found, require a circumscribing rectangle slightly wider than it is high, and correspondingly the letter "I" a narrower rectangle. All other letters fill their respective squares quite neatly and, of course, these guide lines can be erased afterwards.

With a little practice the characters can be executed free-hand, using an "H" pencil with a narrow chisel point. The use of instruments as a help to printing should be avoided as the method is extremely

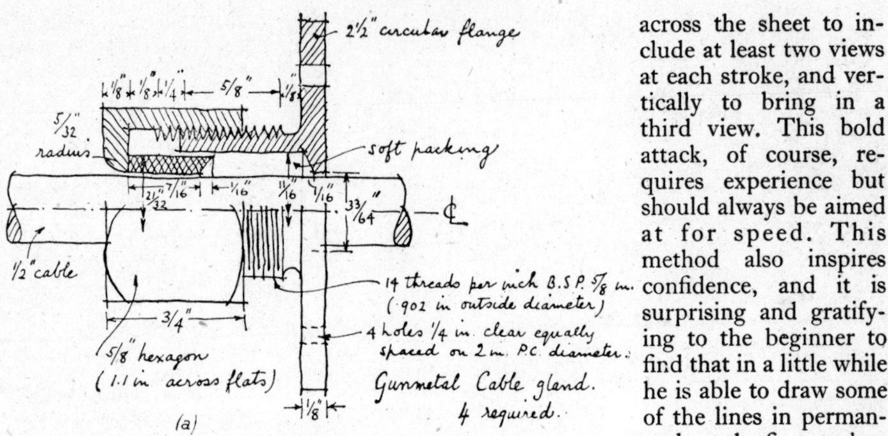

CABLE GLAND (4 reqd.)

Fig. 5a. Free-hand drawing of a gunmetal cable gland in which all dimensions and details for repetition have been carefully noted.

tedious and wastes much valuable time. Professional draughtsmen often provide themselves with a set of stencils for quick uniform results, but for the ordinary engineer these are an expensive luxury.

EXECUTION OF DRAWING

As a general rule geometrical methods are never employed. Parallel horizontal lines are produced by sliding the tee square up and down the paper, and parallel vertical lines, which are also perpendicular to the horizontal ones, are made by the use of the set square. Parallel oblique lines are drawn by sliding the one edge of a set square against the edge of a second set square. When lines are to be divided into equal parts, the trial and error method, using the compasses, is far quicker and quite as accurate with a little practice. The centres of arcs which are to be drawn tangential to given straight lines are again readily found by trial and, as previously explained the arcs are filled in boldly first and the straight lines made to join neatly and accurately afterwards.

Always attack the drawing boldly, that is to say, draw out or, as it is technically expressed, "line out" lightly, with a 2H pencil, the broad outlines of the three views, sweeping the pencil lines right across the sheet to include at least two views at each stroke, and vertically to bring in a third view. This bold attack, of course, requires experience but should always be aimed at for speed. This method also inspires confidence, and it is surprising and gratifying to the beginner to find that in a little while he is able to draw some of the lines in permanently at the first strokes. When the main forms of all the views are thus "thrown down" attention can be concentrated upon each view in turn which it is then possible to "line in" carefully with an "H" pencil used firmly to give uniformly thick lines. The student commencing his studies of machine drawing is always much encouraged by this generous approach. If any further emphasis is required to justify this method it must be obvious that if, say, a side elevation is completed first, then to produce an end elevation which, perhaps, appears on the right hand side, the tee square has to be once more positioned correctly to project further across the paper lines which have previously been drawn and, in consequence, valuable time is lost. Although it isn't particularly desirable to produce quick results, the student loses interest unless he sees the finished product growing fairly rapidly before him and, incidentally, the more times it is necessary to slide the instruments up and down the paper the dirtier the sheet becomes.

ORTHOGRAPHIC PROJECTION

All solids are three dimensional and it is possible in a simple example to make one pictorial view completely to describe it. Fig. 4 shows a simple commutator pole piece giving, in one view, all the required information for its manufacture. In more complicated cases, however, the

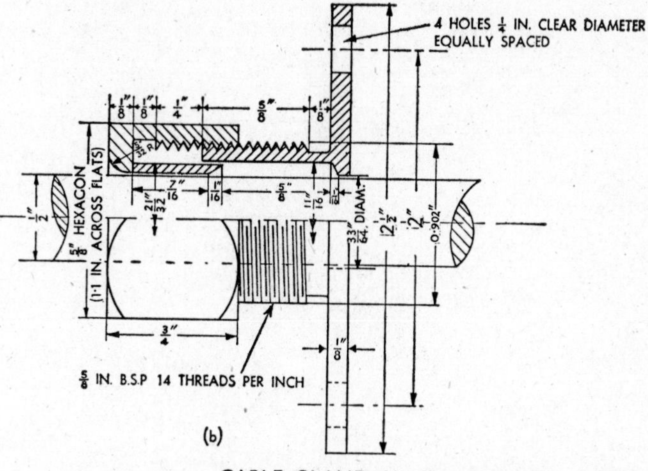

CABLE GLAND (4 off)

Fig. 5b. Finished sectional view of the cable gland that has been drawn from the free-hand drawing which is shown in Fig. 5a. *Note.* The expression 4 off means that four separate glands are to be manufactured from the instructions provided in the plan.

pictorial view becomes very difficult and laborious, and the need for another method is apparent. The conventional alternative is by the method known as the orthographic 1st angle projection.

The simple example in Fig. 4 is also drawn in correct 1st angle projection. Imagine that the commutator pole is placed on the sheet, standing upon the face immediately behind the one marked "b". Looking from immediately above the object, the only visible face is that of "b" (shown double cross hatched) and this constitutes one view or elevation. Now roll the block to the right on one edge, and now the only exposed face visible from above is the one marked "c" (left unshaded). This view gives a second elevation. Return the block to its original position, and now roll it down below the first view, using its front edge as a hinge, and now the only face visible from above is the one marked "a" (shown single cross-hatched) and this constitutes a third view or plan.

These three views are then spaced neatly within the available limits of the paper by the assistance of centre lines, taking care to leave room between the views for the insertion of titles, notes and dimensions. The full significance of this method of projection must be thoroughly understood so that any machine drawing can be immediately and intelligently read, and it is a good idea to practise the three positions with the aid of a match box until the ideas involved are clearly grasped.

Quite frequently, however, these views are insufficient completely to describe the object. Many machine parts have complicated internal arrangements which, of course, remain invisible in the outside views which have already been discussed. It is possible to indicate these internal designs by dotted lines, and often this plan is adopted, but more generally still, the draughtsman imagines that pieces are cut away from the object to reveal what are technically called sections and which clearly expose the internal arrangements. When objects are quite symmetrical about their respective centre lines, it is necessary to cut away only a quarter of the body, thereby producing a view one half of which is external, and the other sectional.

SECTIONS

To denote a section, the part is cross-hatched by thin parallel straight lines at 45 degrees to the axis. These lines should be evenly separated by a narrow space between each line as shown. When two entirely separate pieces of the assembly are in contact, the section lines must be drawn in opposite directions, so that each part is clearly distinguished. In most cases, sections are taken on centre lines, but they may also be taken partly on centre lines and partly on oblique lines radiating from the centre to cut through any interesting detail which occurs off the centre line. When thin supporting

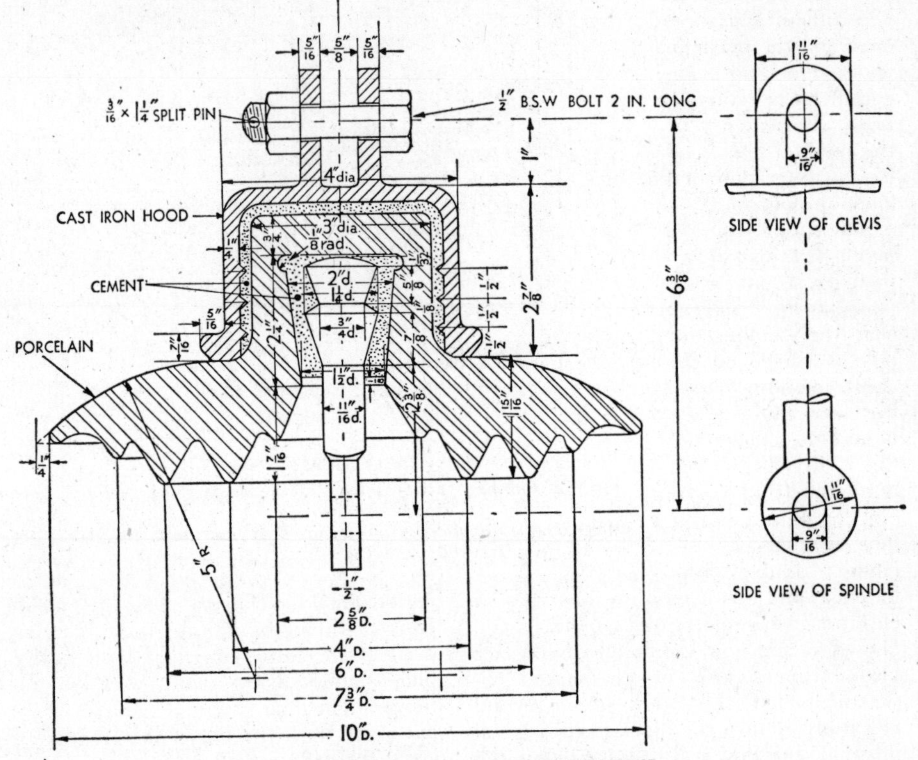

REPRESENTATIVE DRAUGHTSMANSHIP

Fig. 6. Sectional view of high tension insulator with second views of details. If this drawing is carefully examined in reference to Fig. 3 it will be seen that several typical conventions are included.

ribs of castings are cut through these are deliberately left unshaded so that the reader is left in no doubt which of the section is solid metal and which is just thin supporting rib.

FREE-HAND SKETCHING

This part of the draughtsman's training is of great importance and should be studied with the same care as is devoted to that of completing a finished machine drawing. Squared-paper note-books are most useful for this work, and the sketching should be executed with a round pointed H.B. pencil without the assistance of any instrument. The squared paper readily helps the engineer to arrive at approximate proportionate sizes.

Frequently, a single pictorial view is sufficient to describe the object, but in complicated cases rough orthographic projections must be set down, with strict regard to the correct conventional 1st angle projection rules.

The engineer who makes the free-hand sketch may not always be called upon to produce the finished machine drawing from it, and so it is important that every possible detail is included in the rough attempt. It is further worth noting that if the sketch has been made from an object at some great distance from the drawing office, it becomes a waste of valuable time if the draughtsman finds that he has to make a second journey to the spot because of some missing details. Fig. 5a shows an example of a free-hand sketch of a cable gland and Fig 5b an orthographic drawing made from it. It will be noticed that four complete glands are

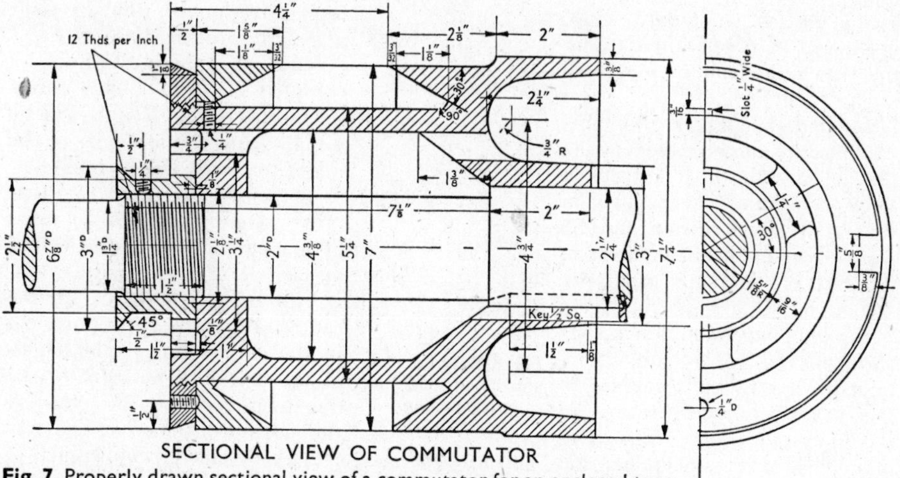

SECTIONAL VIEW OF COMMUTATOR

Fig. 7. Properly drawn sectional view of a commutator for an enclosed type of electric motor assembly (with bars and insulation omitted).

required and that this has been specified by the expression "4 OFF".

Fig. 6 shows a high tension line insulator. Since the insulator is quite symmetrical about its centre lines, there is no object in producing more than one view with the exception of the end fastenings, consequently only these two points require a second view. It should be noted that the different materials involved are sectioned according to the conventional methods set down in Fig. 3.

Fig. 7 is a section through a commutator which includes only a half-outside-end view, an economy of time and space as it is symmetrical about its centre line.

UNITS AND STANDARDS

When the magnitude of a quantity has to be stated it must be given in terms of unit quantity. A road, for example, may be 300 yards or 900 feet long. It is 300 times the length of 1 unit yard or 900 times the length of 1 unit foot. The yard and the foot are units of length. In the same way electrical quantities are measured.

C.G.S. SYSTEM

The three fundamental units, from which are derived the practical electrical and magnetic units, are the centimetre as unit length, the gram as unit mass, and the second as unit time. The system of measurement based on these three units is known as the centimetre-gram-second or C.G.S. system.

One objection to this system is that the units are too small for practical purposes. In the C.G.S. system the unit of velocity, for example, is 1 centimetre per second, the unit of force (dyne) is the force required to produce an acceleration of 1 C.G.S. unit of velocity per second in a body having a mass of 1 gram, and the unit of work (erg) is that done by a force of 1 dyne through a distance of 1 centimetre.

In the same way units of current and electro-motive force can be derived from one or more of the fundamental units of length, mass and time. These derived units also are too small or too large for practical purposes. It is a great advantage to have in addition to a unit, a standard of measurement in which the unit is used as the basis of comparison.

By international agreement it was decided that for all practical purposes the following standards could be taken as giving results sufficiently close to the true values obtained under the C.G.S. system of measurement.

International Ampere. The unvarying current that, when passed through a solution of nitrate of silver consisting of 15 parts in weight of silver nitrate and 85 parts of water, deposits silver at the rate of 0·001118 gram per second.

International Ohm. The resistance offered to an unvarying electric current by a column of mercury, at a temperature of 0° C., 14·4521 grams in weight, of a constant cross-sectional area, and of a length of 106·3 centimetres.

International Volt. That pressure difference which will send a current of one international ampere through a resistance of one international ohm.

It must be noted that the volt is derived from the standards of current and resistance.

The definition of the international ampere, given above, is based on the chemical effect produced under given conditions. In like manner the magnitude of the current may be obtained by the magnetic force produced. For a given current, the magnetic force set up is constant and is independent of time. We can, therefore, define a unit of current in terms of the strength of magnetic force which accompanies it.

It is convenient to consider the magnetic field produced by a current flowing in a conductor bent in the form of a circle, and the point at which the magnetic force is measured to be the centre of the circle.

Unit current is that, which, flowing in an arc of a circle of unit radius and of unit length, produces a magnetic force of unit strength at the centre.

Therefore, referring to Fig. 8 if PQR be a circle of 1 cm. radius and PQ be an arc of 1 cm. length, unit current will produce unit magnetic force at the centre O.

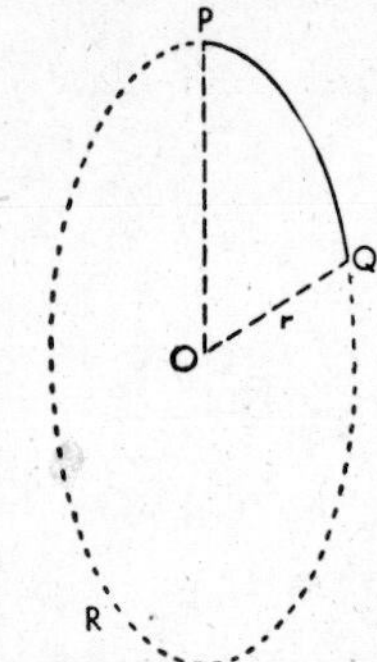

Fig. 8. Diagram illustrating effect of unit current flow.

Now if a wire forming a complete circle of 1 cm. radius is considered, its length will be 2π cms. and the strength of the magnetic force is 2π units.

Therefore, we may say that unit current produces 2π units of magnetic force at the centre of a circle of 1 cm. radius, that is, the magnetic force at the centre of a circle is proportional to the current and to the length of the arc. The strength of the magnetic force is affected by the radius r of the circle and may be shown to be inversely proportional to the square of the radius.

The complete expression for the magnetic force (H) is $H = \frac{li}{r^2}$

For a complete circle $l = 2\pi r$, and if there are n turns of wire, $H = \frac{2\pi rni}{r^2} = \frac{2\pi ni}{r}$, where r is in centimetres and i in units of current. It is obvious, therefore, that in order to measure the current it is necessary to measure the strength of the magnetic force produced.

This force may be measured by an instrument known as the tangent galvanometer, Fig. 9.

This instrument consists of a vertical circular coil AB and when carrying current the magnetic force at the centre will be $2\pi ni/r$ units.

The plane of the circle is placed in the earth's magnetic meridian. A magnetic needle NS suitably supported by pivots and jewels is placed at the centre of the coil.

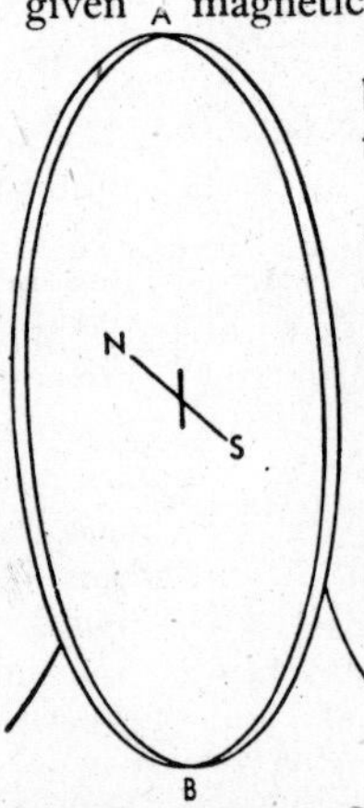

Fig. 9. Diagrammatic representation showing the theory of the operation of the tangent type of galvanometer.

Before the current is switched on the horizontal component of the earth's field will cause the needle to take up a position along the magnetic meridian. Now if current is passed through the coil, the magnet NS will experience a couple which will turn the needle from its original position. The needle will come to rest when the couples due to the earth's field and that due to the current are equal.

If H is the horizontal component of the earth's field and m is the magnetic moment of the needle, the couple due to the earth's field is Hm sin θ. The couple due to the current is $\frac{2\pi nim}{r}\cos\theta$, θ is the angle of deflection from its original position.

When the needle takes up its new position we have $Hm\sin\theta = \frac{2\pi nim}{r}\cos\theta$.

Therefore, i (abs) =

$$\frac{Hm\sin\theta\, r}{2\pi n\, m\cos\theta} = \frac{Hr}{2\pi n}\tan\theta.$$

The magnetic field due to the coil must be uniform over the whole length of the needle and for this reason the needle is made as short as possible.

The deflection of the needle is indicated by a relatively long but light pointer moving over a scale marked in degrees. Before commencing a test the galvanometer is set up so that the pointer comes to rest at the zero point on the scale.

The Ampere. The current i as given above is called the absolute unit of current and one-tenth of its value is called the ampere. Therefore, if I represents the current in amperes, $I = 10\,i$.

POTENTIAL DIFFERENCE

When a current, or rate of flow of electricity exists in a wire, it is due to a difference of electric pressure between the ends of the wire, in just the same way that water flows in a pipe because of the existence of differences of water pressure between any two points along the pipe.

When a current is maintained in a wire, the energy supplied is converted into heat, and the quantity of heat generated in unit time is proportional to the current, and to the potential difference between the ends of the wire.

Unit Potential Difference is defined as that potential difference which causes unit current to flow, and work done at the rate of 1 unit per second. If e and i represent the absolute values of potential difference and current respectively, then quite clearly, the work done in t secs. = e i t ergs.

The Volt. The absolute unit of potential difference is too small for practical purposes, so a larger unit, the volt, is employed, this being equal to 10^8 absolute units. Therefore, if E is the potential difference in volts, $E = \frac{e}{10^8}$

The Ohm is the practical unit of resistance, R. For a circuit to have a resistance of 1 Ohm a potential difference of 1 volt must be maintained to produce a current of 1 Ampere.

We get, therefore, $R = \frac{E}{I}$. Now since $E = \frac{e}{10^8}$ and $I = i \times 10$ and if r, = resistance in absolute units, $r = \frac{e}{i} = \frac{E \times 10^8}{I/10} = \frac{E}{I} \times 10^9 = R \times 10^9$.

Therefore, the ohm is equal to 10^9 absolute units.

THE WATT AND THE JOULE

When using the absolute units of current i and pressure difference e, the product ei gives the rate of working in ergs per second.

When using the practical units of current, I amperes, and pressure, E volts, the rate of working is given by the product IE joules per second.

Therefore, the joule is a unit of work, and unit rate of work, i.e., one joule per second, is called the Watt.

Therefore, Watts

$$= E \times I$$

$$= \frac{e}{10^8} \times i \times 10$$

$$= \frac{ei}{10^7} = \text{ergs per second} \times 10^{-7}$$

The C.G.S. unit of power is one erg

per second. The erg is the C.G.S. unit of work, and is the work done by a force of 1 dyne acting through a distance of 1 cm.

The British unit of power is 33,000 ft. lbs. per minute and is called the horse power.

$$\text{Taking 1 cm.} = \frac{1}{30 \cdot 6} \text{ ft.,}$$

$$\text{1 dyne} = \frac{1}{981} \text{ grams,}$$

$$\text{1 gram} = \frac{1}{453 \cdot 6} \text{ lbs.}$$

We get 1 ft. lb. $= 30 \cdot 6 \times 981 \times 453 \cdot 6$ ergs.

1 horse power = 33,000 ft. lbs. per min.

$$= \frac{30 \cdot 6 \times 981 \times 453 \cdot 6 \times 33{,}000}{60} \text{ ergs}$$

per second

$$= \frac{30 \cdot 6 \times 981 \times 453 \cdot 6 \times 33{,}000}{60 \times 10^7} \text{ Watts}$$

= 746 Watts.

KILOWATT HOUR (BOARD OF TRADE UNIT)

The unit of electrical energy which is generally used in the supply of electricity is a rate of working of 1,000 Watts maintained for one hour. This is the Kilowatt Hour.

Therefore, the Kilowatt Hour is 1,000 Watts for 1 hour, and since the joule is 1 Watt for 1 sec. it follows that:—

$$\text{Kilowatt-hours} = \frac{\text{joules}}{1{,}000 \times 60 \times 60}$$

$$= \frac{\text{joules}}{3 \cdot 6 \times 10^6}$$

$$= \frac{\text{Ergs}}{3 \cdot 6 \times 10^6 \times 10^7}$$

Therefore, 1 Kilowatt Hour
= 1,000 Watt Hours
= $3 \cdot 6 \times 10^6$ Joules.
= $3 \cdot 6 \times 10^{13}$ Ergs.

FARAD

The unit of capacitance. A condenser has unit capacitance when 1 coulomb of electricity raises the potential difference across its plates by 1 volt.

$$\text{Farads} = \frac{\text{coulombs}}{\text{volts}}$$

The farad is too large for practical purposes, and so one millionth of this, that is, the microfarad (μF) is generally employed as the unit.

In radio frequency work the micro-microfarad is sometimes used.

1 Farad = 10^6 microfarads.
1 Farad = 10^{12} micro-microfarads.

HENRY

The unit of inductance. A circuit has unit inductance if, when the current varies at the rate of 1 ampere per second, an e.m.f. of 1 volt is induced. The millihenry and microhenry are also employed.

VOLTAGE

The standard of voltage used in this country is a special form of voltaic cell. Two reliable standards are available. The Latimer Clark and the Weston cells. The Weston which possesses certain advantages over the Clark cell will be the one considered here.

In a standard cell the materials used must be as pure as possible in order to avoid any local action, and in cells for standardising purposes, it is necessary for the metals used to have a high degree of purity.

THE WESTON CELL

This cell, named after the inventor, consists of the H shape glass container, Fig. 10, in which mercury forms the positive electrode and cadmium amalgam the negative. The electrolyte is a solution of cadmium sulphate. Saturation of the electrolyte is necessary, this being provided for by including some cadmium sulphate crystals. The terminals of the cell are pieces of platinum wire sealed into the glass container.

The voltage of the cell is given by $E = 1 \cdot 0183 - 0 \cdot 0000406 (t - 20)$ volts where t = temperature in degrees centigrade. Since the cell is a standard of voltage, it is not required to supply more than a small fraction of one milli-ampere and, therefore, to guard against possible damage owing to short circuit, a high resistance of several thousand ohms is permanently connected in series with the cell.

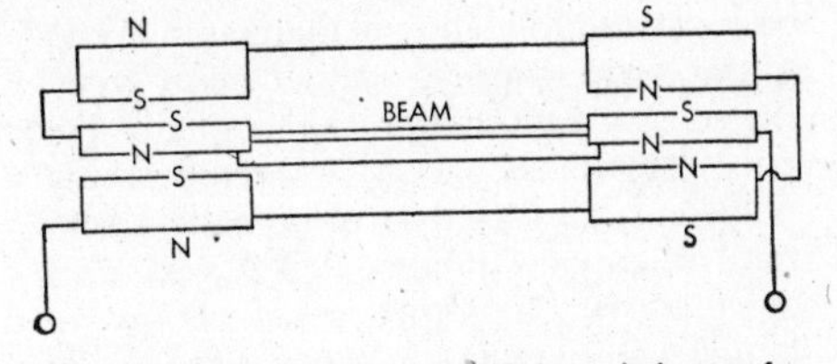

Fig. 11. Principle of the Kelvin balance for making precise measurements of current.

CURRENT

Current standards cannot be produced so directly as those of voltage and resistance. Some effect of the current must be measured and relationship between cause and effect established.

An instrument called a current balance is used as a current standard. The principle of the balance is that if two current-carrying coils are placed parallel with each other and their axes are coincident, a force will be set up between them. The force which will tend either to bring the coils together or move them apart, is proportional to the product of the currents in the two coils. Now one of the coils is free to move and, therefore, the force can be measured by making the free coil form one arm of a balance.

KELVIN BALANCE

The current balance designed by Lord Kelvin utilises the principle given above. The instrument consists of two moving coils and four fixed coils. The moving coils are fixed to a beam, one at each end, and the beam is suspended by a number of thin copper wires.

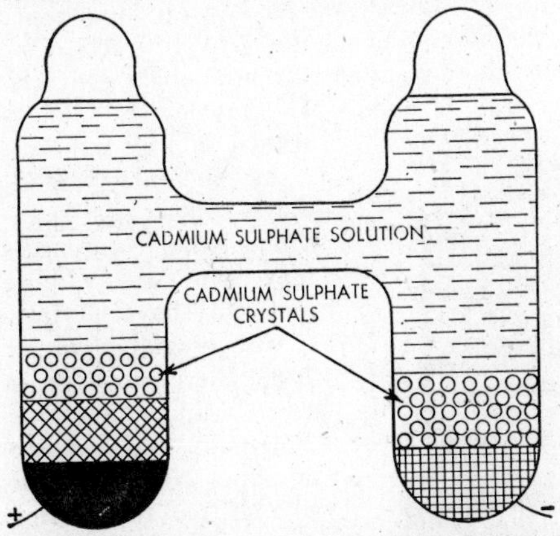

Fig. 10. Diagram showing principle of the Weston standard cell which enables very accurate laboratory measurements to be made.

These wires also carry the current to and from the moving coils. The six coils are connected in series and are so wound that when carrying current, poles are formed as shown in Fig. 11. The left hand moving coil will be forced downwards and the other upwards. A scale which is attached to the beam also carries a movable weight. The weight is moved to such a position that the beam is brought back to the horizontal position.

The instrument is calibrated so that the position of the weight gives directly the current in amperes.

Since the deflecting couple, due to the current, is proportional to I^2 and the restoring couple is proportional to the displacement of the weight, it follows that the scale markings are not uniformly spaced for given current increments.

RESISTANCE

Reference to the mercury standard of 1 International Ohm has been made already.

Standard resistances, for use in the laboratory, are much more convenient in setting up, if made of wire or sheet metal. These laboratory standards may be compared, from time to time, with the international standard. The correct term to apply to them is really substandard resistances. However, much use is made of them in the testing, and standardising, of electrical apparatus.

They must be sound mechanically, the resistance must not vary with time, the effect of temperature variation must be negligible, and thermo-electric effects small. To satisfy the above requirements alloys are generally employed. Probably the most suitable alloy is manganin. With 84 per cent. copper, 12 per cent. manganese, 3·5 per cent. nickel and 0·5 per cent. iron, it has a very low temperature coefficient, and as it is quite satisfactory from other view points, it is a very useful material for the construction of standard resistances. The resistivity of manganin is approximately 50 microhms per centimetre cube and its temperature coefficient is 0·0004 per cent. per degree centigrade at 20 C.

Certain other alloys are also used.

STANDARD INDUCTANCES AND CONDENSERS

The values of these standards depend on the dimensions of the coils, and formulæ are available by which the inductance can be calculated. The dimensions of the coils must not vary, otherwise the inductance will not be constant. For this reason also, the material of the formers, on which the wire is wound, must be non-magnetic. It is desirable, therefore, that the coils should be wound on non-metallic formers so that eddy currents are not set up.

A marble cylinder is generally used as the former, since this material possesses characteristics which make it eminently suited to the purpose. Its electrical resistance is high, the coefficient of expansion is extremely small and it is unaffected by moisture. The coils are usually of the single layer type, and for the mutual inductance standards a secondary coil also is wound and placed at the centre of the longer primary coil.

The primary coil is ong axially compared with its diameter and the flux density at the centre of the coil is $\frac{4\pi \times IT}{10\, l} \cos\theta$, where I is the primary current in amperes, T the number of primary turns, and θ the angle between the axis of the coil and a line drawn from the centre of the axis to a point on the end turn. The value of the mutual inductance, in henries, is given by $\frac{\Phi T_1}{10^8 I} \cos\theta$, where Φ is the flux linking the secondary coil and T_1 is the number of turns on the secondary.

Φ is obtained from a knowledge of the flux density and the cross-sectional area of the secondary coil.

The capacitance of standard condensers can be obtained from their dimensions. It is of the utmost importance, therefore, that once fixed, the dimensions shall not vary. A rigid mechanical assembly is necessary. The dielectric is air, since its dielectric constant is known and its dielectric loss is zero. In condensers with solid dielectrics, the plates are held in position, generally, by the dielectric itself, but in an air condenser they must be supported and kept apart by solid insulators.

There are, of course, very few materials which are suitable for this purpose. Fuzed quartz and amberite have been used with success and it appears that only these two possess the characteristics which ensure permanence of calibration. As a dielectric, air is superior to solids and liquids, for reasons given above, but its dielectric strength and permittivity are lower. Therefore, for a given capacitance an air condenser is relatively bulky. One form of standard air condenser (Messrs. H. Tinsley & Co.) is shown in Fig. 12.

Fig. 12. Standard air condenser.

As secondary standards mica and paraffined paper condensers may be used. These materials have permittivities greater than air and, therefore, for a given capacitance the dimensions of a mica or paper condenser are smaller than those using air as the dielectric. The dielectric strength of these materials is higher than that of air.

SYMBOLS AND FORMULÆ

The employment of symbols and formulæ in technical literature is undertaken for convenience in expressing the relationship of various quantities to one another. They form a kind of shorthand enabling ideas, which might otherwise be cloudy and diffuse, to be presented in a clear and concise manner.

In order to measure a quantity, units are required, and in the majority of cases these units are named. For example, the units of length, mass and time are called the foot, pound and second in the British system of units. When larger or smaller quantities are involved additional units are adopted, such as the mile and the inch, the ton and the ounce, the hour and the minute.

In the measurement of time, we have no common unit smaller than the second. The relationship between these various units representing the same kind of quantity is very irregular. For example, the mile is equal to 5,280 feet and the foot is equal to 12 inches; the ton is equal to 2,240 pounds and the pound is equal to 16 ounces. In time measurements we have different multipliers, the hour being equal to 60 minutes and the minute to 60 seconds. All this is very cumbersome and has led to the introduction of another system of units, called the metric system, where all the multipliers are 10 or multiples of 10.

METRIC SYSTEM

In view of the great simplification brought about by the metric system, it has been adopted entirely for scientific work and is very largely used in engineering, especially electrical engineering. The multipliers, both large and small, are known by names. The ones giving rise to the larger units are :—

deka = 10.
hecto = 100
kilo = 1,000.
meg(a) = 1,000,000.

Of these, the two most commonly met with in practice are the kilo and meg (or mega). For example, a kilovolt is a short way of writing 1,000 volts; a megohm is 1,000,000 ohms; a megawatt is 1,000,000 watts.

Another series of prefixes is used to denote quantities that are smaller than the normal unit. These prefixes are as follows:—

$$\text{deci} = \frac{1}{10}$$

$$\text{centi} = \frac{1}{100}$$

$$\text{milli} = \frac{1}{1{,}000}$$

$$\text{micro} = \frac{1}{1{,}000{,}000}$$

Examples of the use of these prefixes are to be found in the centimetre which is $\frac{1}{100}$th of a metre, milliampere which is $\frac{1}{1{,}000}$th ampere, and microhenry which is $\frac{1}{1{,}000{,}000}$th henry. Occasionally, still smaller units have to be used; for example, the micro-microfarad which is $\frac{1}{1{,}000{,}000}$th of $\frac{1}{1{,}000{,}000}$th farad. In working out actual examples it is essential that the various quantities should be expressed in the correct unit.

Compound units are also used such as a foot-pound, which is the work done in raising a weight of one pound through a distance of one foot. Another example of a compound unit is the watt-hour, which is the energy expended when a power of one watt is maintained for a duration of one hour. From this unit is derived the kilowatt-hour, which is simply 1,000 watt-hours.

STANDARDISATION OF SYMBOLS

Engineering quantities that are capable of measurement are denoted by letters as symbols (sometimes Greek letters are used) and these have now been standardised so that the same quantity is symbolised by the same letter wherever it may be encountered in technical literature. This applies not only to technical matter written in the English language, but also to that written in the language of any other country subscribing to this international agreement.

Consider the case of electric current, the general symbol for which is I. When a current of a certain number of amperes is to be indicated, the practice is to write the number this being followed by the symbol A. Thus I = 4A means that the current is 4 amperes. It is obviously a short way of expressing this fact. Similarly, I = 4 mA states that the current is 4 milliamperes.

The use of the small letter m followed by the capital letter A is here of importance. It is the practice to indicate all the metric prefixes by small letters, in spite of the fact that the symbol immediately following it is a capital letter. Thus kV (and not KV) represents kilovolts. Again, it is the practice to use hr. for hour, so that killowatt-hours becomes kWhr.

Temperature measurements are worthy of a special note. On the Fahrenheit scale they are denominated °F. and on the Centigrade scale °C. In certain classes of work, temperatures are measured from the absolute zero of space. On this scale they are denominated °K (Kelvin).

MATHEMATICS IN ENGINEERING

A knowledge of mathematics is utilised by the engineer in making necessary calculations, so that mathematics is to him just as much a tool as a screwdriver or a pair of pliers. It enables him to perform certain operations, and facility with the one is just as important, even more important, than dexterity with the other. It is, therefore, urged that any mathematical development in this book should not be skipped.

If a little thought and commonsense be applied to these sections, it will be found that for the most part they are quite simple. Many terms are used merely for purposes of economy in words; they also present a clearer picture of the values to be obtained. As an example, 10^7 has no obscure mathematical significance, it merely represents a large number, in this case 10,000,000 or one followed by seven noughts. The form, 10^7, is used for compactness; in words it is called the seventh power of ten. Sometimes negative powers are encountered, these representing reciprocals, or one divided by the number concerned. Thus 10^{-7} means one divided by 10^7, or $\frac{1}{10,000,000}$, that is one ten-millionth.

The symbol $\sqrt{}$ is called the square root sign, the square root being that number which when multiplied by itself gives the number mentioned. Thus $\sqrt{64} = 8$. Another way of representing this is $64^{\frac{1}{2}} = 8$. Sometimes square roots can be evaluated exactly; in the case in question $\sqrt{64} = 8$. In many cases, however, square roots cannot be evaluated exactly, in which case they are evaluated as closely as possible; for example, $\sqrt{2} = 1{\cdot}41$. This is called three figure accuracy. If a more accurate determination is required, it is written $\sqrt{2} = 1{\cdot}414$. This is called four figure accuracy, and so on. The greater the number of digits in the evaluation, the more nearly accurate is the result.

Another mathematical symbol that is constantly recurring in electrical engineering is the symbol π (Greek letter pronounced pi). It is well known that the circumference of a circle is rather more than three times its diameter. It is also known that the ratio of the circumference to the diameter is a constant for all circles. This ratio cannot be expressed exactly, and the symbol π is used to denote it. The value of π to three figure accuracy is $3{\cdot}14$. If greater accuracy is desired, its value to five figures is $3{\cdot}1416$.

A working knowledge of logarithms and of elementary trigonometry is of great value to the engineer, and the serious student is referred to any text-book on elementary mathematics.

A further symbol that is being used by electrical engineers to a greater and greater extent is the symbol "j", usually called the "j" operator. As used by electrical engineers this is really quite simple in its application. In drawing vector diagrams, lines are drawn at various angles to the horizontal and vertical. All such lines, representing vectors, can be resolved into horizontal and vertical components. Mathematicians call the horizontal component of any vector its real component and the vertical component its imaginary component. In point of fact, the vertical component is just as real as the horizontal, but these terms need not worry the engineer.

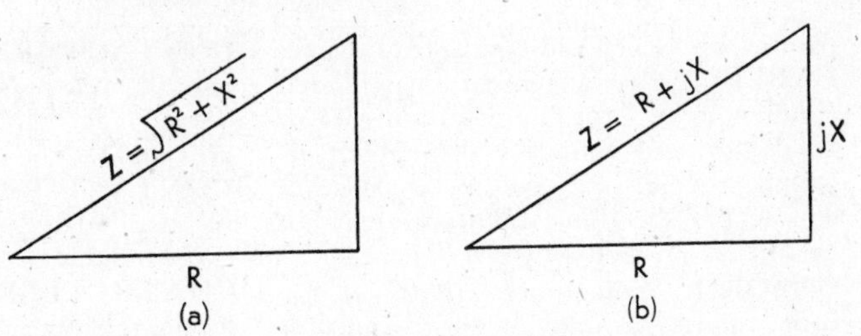

SIMPLIFIED METHOD OF CALCULATION

Fig. 13. Diagram illustrating (a) normal impedance triangle, (b) one using the "j" operator; "j" precedes all quantities drawn vertically.

The use of this notation is very simply illustrated by the impedance triangle (see Fig. 13). At (a) the impedance triangle is drawn in the normal way. The resistance line, R, and the reactance line, $X = 2\pi fL$, are drawn at right angles. The numerical value of the impedance is obviously equal to $Z = \sqrt{R^2 + X^2}$, from a knowledge of the properties of right-angled triangles. With the "j" notation, the resistance line is called R the same as before, but because the reactance line is drawn in the vertical direction it is called jX, the letter j simply denoting the fact that it is drawn in the vertical direction. The impedance is now expressed as $R + jX$. This means that it consists of two components, the first representing the resistance, drawn horizontally, and the second representing the reactance, drawn vertically. The actual numerical value of the impedance must be obtained by evaluating $Z = \sqrt{R^2+X^2}$, the same as before.

This method of calculation is becoming more and more popular, familiarity with it proving in the long run to be a great simplification.

Finally, all engineering students are urged to acquire and make themselves familiar with the use of a slide rule. It will prove itself to be a labour-saving device of great value in electrical work.

ELECTRICAL TERMS

EVERY branch of engineering has its own particular terms of reference to various apparatus, and the object of this section is to define some of the more important ones encountered in electrical engineering.

ACTIVE COMPONENT. An alternating current or voltage has active and reactive components. For instance, the active component of current is in phase with the voltage.

AERIAL. A conductor or arrangement of conductors used for radiating or collecting electromagnetic energy.

AMPERE is the practical unit of current and is defined electrolytically. It is also known as the international ampere and defined as follows. The international ampere is that current which when passed through a solution of silver nitrate in water (A_gNO_3) deposits silver at the rate of 0·001118 gram per second.

AMPERE-HOUR. A unit of quantity equal to a current of one ampere flowing for one hour.

BACK ELECTRO-MOTIVE FORCE. An electro-motive force acting in an opposite direction to the main electromotive force in a circuit, and which causes a reduction in current.

BOND. Usually refers to an earthing bond by which the lead sheath and armour of one or more cables, or the casing or framework of electrical apparatus, are electrically connected to earth.

CABLE. An arrangement of stranded conductors to form one common core or conductor and insulated throughout its length. Several cores may be enclosed in a protective sheathing and may or may not be further protected by armour.

CALORIE. Sometimes known as the little calorie; a unit of heat used for scientific purposes. Is the amount of heat required to raise the temperature of one gram of water at 15° C. by 1° C.

CAPACITANCE. The property of a conducting body which, if it has a quantity of electricity imparted to it, will produce a potential difference between that conductor and surrounding bodies.

CATHODE is the point of exit when a D.C. is passed through an electrolyte. Also the source of electrons in a gas discharge or thermionic tube.

CELL. A source of electrical energy depending upon chemical reaction, types being primary and secondary cells. Cells may be joined together to form a battery.

C.G.S. SYSTEM OF UNITS has the centimetre, gram and second as its fundamental units.

CHOKING COIL. A coil which possesses inductance and gives rise in a circuit to a resistive effect to a changing current.

CIRCUIT. An arrangement of conductors connected together to carry a current.

CIRCUIT BREAKER. An automatic switch for making and breaking a circuit under normal or fault conditions.

COERCIVE FORCE. The magnetomotive force required to coerce the residual magnetism out of a magnetised body after removal or reversal of the magnetising force.

CONDUCTANCE is that property of a circuit which may be regarded as the opposite of resistance. The unit is the Mho, and the symbol, G.

CONDUCTOR. A substance which offers low resistance to a flow of electricity.

CONDUIT. A pipe or trough for accommodating and protecting electric cables.

CONTACTOR. A switch used for frequently making and breaking an electric circuit. It is usually automatic in operation.

CONTACT RESISTANCE. The resistance between the contact surfaces of two conductors.

CONTROLLER. A piece of apparatus for altering the speed of an electric motor at will.

CONVERTER. A machine for converting power from A.C. to D.C. and vice versa.

CORE TYPE TRANSFORMER. A type of transformer in which the windings surround the greater part of the magnetic circuit.

COULOMB. Unit quantity of electricity; and is represented by one ampere flowing for one second. Symbol, Q.

CURRENT. The rate of flow of electricity round a circuit, and unit current is equivalent to 1 coulomb per second. Unit, ampere, Symbol, I.

CURRENT DENSITY. The current flowing in a conductor per square inch or per square centimeter.

DAMPING. In a circuit, that property of the circuit which tends to eliminate oscillations. Of an instrument, reduction of vibration.

DEAD BEAT. A measuring instrument is said to be dead beat when, by means of damping, the pointer comes to rest at the particular reading with a minimum of oscillation.

DELTA OR MESH CONNECTION. A form of connection employed in three-phase circuits where the finish of one winding is connected to the start of the next. It is represented by a triangle.

DIELECTRIC. The name given to insulating material.

DISTRIBUTION BOX. The box from which branch circuits are fed, either by links, switches or fuses.

DISTRIBUTOR MAIN. The main which is laid down a road and to which consumers' service cables are connected.

EARTHED CIRCUIT. A circuit in which one or more points are connected to earth.

EDDY CURRENT. A local current that is induced in a conductor as a result of a changing magnetic field.

EFFICIENCY. The ratio of energy output to energy input; usually expressed as a percentage.

ELECTRICITY METER. An instrument which sums up energy supplied over a given time.

ELECTRIC STRENGTH. The property of an insulating material to withstand electric pressures. Frequently referred to as the dielectric strength. Expressed in kV per mm. thickness.

ELECTRODE. A conducting body used to pass an electric current into and out of an electrolyte or gas or vacuum tube.

ELECTROLYSIS. The process of decomposing an electrolyte.

ELECTROLYTE. A solution through which the passage of an electric current will cause chemical decomposition.

ELECTRO-MAGNETIC INDUCTION. The production of electro-motive forces by varying magnetic fields.

ELECTROSTATIC FIELD. The space round a charged body where lines of electric force may be detected.

E.M.F. Electro-motive force. The sum of the potential differences existing in the various parts of an electric circuit. Unit, volt. Symbol, E.

ERG. The C.G.S. unit of energy. The energy expended by a force of one dyne in moving a mass of one gram through a distance of one centimetre.

EXCITER. A generator used to supply magnetising current, usually to the field winding of an alternator.

FARAD. The unit of capacitance. Symbol, F.

FEEDER PILLAR. An outdoor pillar fitted with links, switches or fuses for connecting local circuits to main feeders.

FOOT-CANDLE. The unit of illumination. If a point source of 1 candlepower be placed at the centre of a sphere of radius 1 foot, an illumination of 1 foot-candle will be produced per square-foot of surface area.

FREQUENCY. The number of times a second that a recurring quantity goes through a complete cycle of changes.

FORM FACTOR. The ratio of the R.M.S. value to the average value of a periodic function taken over one half-cycle from 0 to 180°. For a sine wave is equal to 1·11.

FUSE. A piece of apparatus designed to give protection to a circuit or circuits against excessive current.

GENERATOR. A machine that converts mechanical energy to electrical energy. A D.C. generator is one that supplies direct current to an external load, an A.C. generator or alternator is one that supplies alternating current to an external load.

GREAT CALORIE is equal to the amount of heat required to raise 1,000 grams of water 1° C., and equal to 1,000 calories.

HARMONIC. An oscillation having a frequency which is a multiple of the fundamental frequency. The frequency of a second harmonic is twice that of the fundamental frequency.

HENRY. The unit of self- or mutual-inductance. Symbol, H.

HORSE-POWER. Unit of mechanical power. Is equal to 33,000 foot-pounds per minute, 550 foot-pounds per second or 746 watts.

IMPEDANCE. The ratio of R.M.S. voltage applied to a circuit to R.M.S. current flowing in that circuit. Symbol, Z.

INDICATOR. A signalling device which is usually operated electro-magnetically and shows whether a current is flowing or has flowed in a circuit.

INDUCTANCE. That property of a circuit which results in induced e.m.f.'s when there are certain changes in the conditions in the circuit.

INPUT to a piece of apparatus, is the total power supplied.

INSTALLATION. Either the operation of installing electrical equipment, or the complete electrical equipment for a definite process.

INSULATION RESISTANCE. The resistance between a conductor and earth or between two conductors when they are separated only by an insulating material.

INSULATOR. A substance which offers

a high resistance to an electric current. To insulate is to surround a conductor with insulating material and restrict the current to a definite path.

JOINT. A means of connecting conductors, and is usually either a straight-through or tee-joint.

JOULE. Unit of energy, is equal to 1 watt-second, or 1 ampere × 1 volt × 1 second.

KILOVOLT (kV). 1,000 volts.

KILOVOLT AMPERE (kVA). 1,000 volt-amperes.

KILOWATT (kW). Large unit of power, 1,000 watts.

KILOWATT-HOUR (kWhr). Large unit of energy, equal to 1,000 watt-hours, or 3,600,000 joules.

LEAKAGE. The flow of current in an undesired path due to poor insulation.

LENZ'S LAW. The e.m.f.'s induced either by the movement of a magnet and a circuit, or two circuits, produce currents active in such direction as to oppose the movements which produced them.

LINE VOLTAGE. In A.C. circuits; single-phase, the voltage between the opposite ends of a winding; two-phase, the voltage between the two ends of the same winding; three-phase, the voltage between any two lines.

LOAD. The power carried by a circuit or taken from a generator or other apparatus.

LOAD FACTOR. The ratio—expressed as a percentage, of the average load to the maximum load during some interval of time.

MAGNETIC FIELD. The space round a magnetic or current-carrying conductor where magnetic lines of force may be detected.

MAGNETIC FLUX. The number of magnetic lines of force passing through a given cross-section. Unit, Maxwell. Symbol, Φ.

MAGNETIC FLUX DENSITY. The number of magnetic lines of force per unit area. Unit, Gauss. Symbol, B.

MAGNETO-MOTIVE FORCE (M.M.F.). The magnetic potential existing between the ends of a line of magnetic force. Symbol, F.

MAXWELL. Unit of magnetic flux.

MEASURING INSTRUMENT. A device for measuring standard units, such as units of current, electro-motive force, power, etc.

MUTUAL INDUCTANCE. That property which exists between two circuits when a change of flux in one causes an e.m.f. to be induced in the other. Unit-Henry. Symbol, M.

NATURAL FREQUENCY. The frequency of oscillations in a system determined by the constants of the system.

OUTPUT. The power given out by a piece of apparatus in a specified form for a specified purpose.

OHM. Unit of resistance. The international ohm is the resistance offered to an unvarying current by a column of mercury 106·3 centimetres in length, of constant cross-section, 14·4521 grams in mass, and at the temperature of melting ice.

OHM'S LAW. The law governing the flow of a steady current in an electric circuit. It can be expressed by the equation; Current (amperes) = Voltage divided by Resistance (ohms).

OSCILLATING CURRENT. The same as alternating current except that it is usually applied to currents which reverse their directions to the extent of having frequencies of the order of thousands of cycles per second and higher.

OSCILLOGRAPH. A device for producing the graph of a rapidly recurring electrical quantity to a base of time.

PARALLEL CONNECTION. Conductors or circuits are said to be in parallel when they are so connected that the sum of the currents in the individual conductors or circuits is equal to the total current supplied.

PERIODIC TIME. The time taken to go through one complete cycle of changes.

PHASE. One of the windings or circuits of an electrical system or of a piece of polyphase electrical apparatus.

PHASE DIFFERENCE. The difference, expressed as a fraction of a cycle or period, between the occurrence of corresponding instantaneous values of two periodic functions of the same frequency.

POTENTIAL. The potential difference between some point in a circuit and a common reference point.

POTENTIAL DIFFERENCE in an electrical circuit, is the voltage measured between any two points when current is flowing. Unit, volt. Symbol, V.

POWER. The rate at which energy is expended. Units, watt, kW, H.P. Symbol, P.

QUANTITY OF ELECTRICITY is given by the product of the rate at which current is flowing and the time for which it flows, i.e., amperes × time.
Units, coulomb and ampere-hour. Symbol, Q.

RATING of a piece of apparatus, refers to limitations of performance under definite conditions. "Rated output" is output assigned by makers to apparatus under specified operating conditions.

RECTIFIER. A device used for converting alternating current into unidirectional current.

REGULATION of a D.C. generator, the increase in voltage when the rated load at rated voltage is reduced to zero, without any alteration being made to the exciting circuit. Usually expressed as a percentage of the voltage at rated load. Of an A.C. generator, is the increase in voltage when the rated load (at rated voltage and specified power factor) is reduced to zero, no alteration being made to the exciting circuit. Usually expressed as a percentage of the voltage at rated output. Of a transformer, is the increase in voltage when rated load (at rated voltage and specified power factor) is reduced to zero, the primary applied voltage remaining constant. Usually expressed as a percentage of the open circuit voltage of the secondary winding.

RELAY. An automatic switch to control the circuit in which it is placed or another circuit.

RELUCTANCE. The ratio of the magneto-motive force to the flux in a magnetic circuit. It may be regarded as analogous to resistance in an electric circuit. Unit, Oersted. Symbol, S.

RESIDUAL MAGNETISM. The magnetism remaining in a magnetised body after the magnetising force which produced it has been removed.

RESONANCE. The condition of a system in which the natural period of oscillation is the same as that of the impulses to which it is subjected.

RESONANT FREQUENCY. The frequency of a circuit at which the resultant of the reactive components is zero. Symbol, Fr.

RHEOSTAT. A resistor provided with means of varying the amount of resistance in a circuit.

R.M.S. VALUE. The effective or virtual value of a periodic function taken over one complete cycle.

ROTOR usually refers to the rotating part of A.C. machines.

SCOTT CONNECTION. A transformer connection used to effect a three-phase to two-phase transformation or vice versa.

SERIES CONNECTION. Conductors or circuits are said to be in series when they are connected so that the same current flows in each conductor or circuit.

SERVICE LINE. An arrangement of conductors, usually a multicore cable, for connecting a consumer's installation to a distributor.

SERVING. A protective covering of jute-yarn, or tape applied over armour or sheath of a cable. The serving is treated with a compound for preservation.

SHELL TYPE TRANSFORMER. A type of transformer in which the magnetic circuit surrounds the windings.

SHORT CIRCUIT. A point of very low resistance in a circuit; usually if accidental it results from failure of insulation.

SLIP RING. A metal ring on which a brush bears to maintain contact between a stationary and moving conductor.

SOLENOID. A coil used to produce a magnetic field due to the flow of an electric current.

SQUIRREL CAGE ROTOR. The rotor of an induction motor having a winding of metal bars which are connected to end rings.

STAR CONNECTION. A method of connection used in polyphase systems in which one end of each winding is connected to a common point.

STAR-DELTA STARTER. A type of starter used in connection with three-phase induction motors. In the starting position the stator windings are connected in star, and in delta in the running position.

STARTER. A device for starting and running an electric motor up to normal speed.

STATOR usually refers to that part of an A.C. machine which contains the stationary magnetic and electric circuits.

SUB-STATION. A point in a supply area at which electricity is supplied in bulk, and is there converted or transformed to suit the system of supply to the particular area.

SWITCH. A device for making or breaking an electric circuit.

SYNCHRONISM. The condition which exists when two machines or two systems have the same frequency and are in phase.

SYNCHROSCOPE. An instrument employed to determine the phase relationship between two alternating voltages of the same frequency.

TAP CHANGER. An arrangement of tappings taken from either primary or secondary windings of a transformer whereby the turns ratio may be altered. The tap changing may be effected by one of the following methods depending on design:—(a) when the transformer is in circuit, i.e., on-load tap changing. (b) when the transformer is out of circuit, i.e., off-circuit tap changing.

TAPPING. An intermediate connection between the main connections of either a circuit or a component.

TEMPERATURE COEFFICIENT as referred to resistance, is the increase or decrease in resistance for a rise in temperature of 1° C. Is expressed as a fraction of unit resistance at a definite temperature.

TEMPERATURE RISE as referred to with apparatus, is the difference between the temperature under operating conditions and the initial temperature.

THERMOSTAT. A device which functions due to changes in temperature. Often used to control the opening and closing of electric circuits.

TIME CONSTANT is the time taken for a function which follows a logarithmic law to rise from zero to 63·4 per cent. of its final value, or decrease from a maximum value to 34·6 per cent. of that value.

TRANSFORMER. A device which transforms, by electromagnetic induction, alternating power in one winding to alternating power in another winding, usually at different values of current and pressure.

TRANSIENT. The results which arise in a circuit due to a sudden change in the conditions in the circuit.

VOLT. Unit of electromotive force or potential difference.

VOLTAGE DROP. The potential difference between any two points on a conductor or in a circuit. For D.C. circuits is the product of current and resistance. For A.C. circuits is the product of current and impedance.

VOLTAMETER. An electrolytic cell used for the measurement of quantity of electricity.

WATT. Unit of power. Watts = volts × amperes.

WATT-HOUR. Unit of energy. The energy expended in one hour when the power is one watt. Symbol, Wh.

WAVE-FORM. The graph representing a periodic quantity plotted against time.

WAVE LENGTH. The distance between corresponding points in two consecutive waves in the direction of propagation. Symbol, λ.

WHEATSTONE BRIDGE. A piece of apparatus used for measuring resistance. Consists of network of resistances, galvanometer and a source of e.m.f.

WINDING. An arrangement of conductors in a piece of apparatus which either produces or is acted on by a magnetic field.

YOKE. That part of a machine which supports the main poles and is part of the magnetic circuit. Alternatively, the connecting-part joining the limbs of a transformer.

INDEX

(FIGURES IN ITALICS REFER TO ILLUSTRATIONS)

D

E

F

Reprinted 1947
Made and Printed in Great Britain by Ben Johnson & Co. Ltd., York and London.